Contents

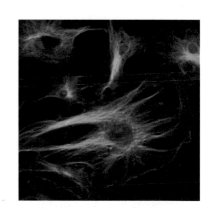

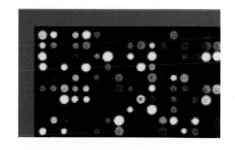

CHAPTER 4. VARIATIONS   44

CHAPTER 5. NATURE VERSUS NURTURE   58

CHAPTER 6. SEX   72

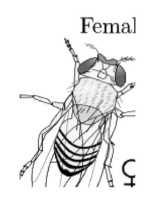

Universe 2005 Composite Image

delegates   All - 81 delegates   Eur

delegates   Finalists - 15 delegates   Amer

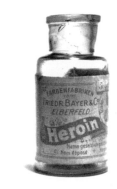

CHAPTER **19.** DIVERSITY   **254**

CHAPTER **20.** ARMS RACE **268**

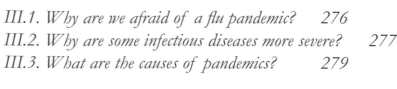

PREFACE

I have spent over 12 years thinking about what should be included in this book. I have decided that I will teach you the aspects of biology that I think are interesting and intriguing from a non-biologist standpoint. There are many things that biologists find interesting, but these topics are often not of interest to the general public. However, there are certain topics in biology that interest everyone, and they are important to our daily life. Some of this information affects how we view ourselves and others, and some have deep philosophical significance. Much of biology can be told as wonderful stories of discoveries that have had profound impacts on the modern world.

This book represents the evolution of my personal growth as a teacher. I have learned more through this book project than from my many years of formal education. Each semester I have discovered that there are new ways to make the information more interesting, relevant, and applicable. Even after teaching the course for 12 years, I still look forward to the first lecture of every new semester. I hope to make a difference in your life by showing you aspects of the world that you might not have realized before. I firmly believe that education is the only way to improve both our individual lives and our society.

At the end of the semester, you can judge whether or not this book and course has achieved my objective to expand your intellectual horizon. I want to show you that discoveries in biology have changed the world, affecting our daily life and social interactions. The information in this course is less important than the overall messages, and my effort would be considered successful if I can convince you to turn to science when you need to solve both personal and social problems. Furthermore, I will be successful if I can teach you to understand the nature of scientific discoveries and how science is a way of acquiring knowledge.

I have taught the material in this book in various combinations during the past several years, but this is the first time that I have put the material together as a complete textbook. I welcome your comments and suggestions to help me to make the book more interesting, effective, and readable. We all lead busy lives in this modern world, and I hope that you will find it worthwhile to read this book.

ACKNOWLEDGEMENT

This book project would not have been started without the students in BSC 101, *Fundamental Concepts in Biology*. Over the past twelve years, there have been over 20,000 students who have taken this course, and the development of this textbook has been largely based on their input and feedback.

There are two campus units that have provided me assistance in various ways: Center for Teaching, Learning, and Technology and Lab of Integrated Learning and Technology. Individuals from these units have provided me with support in the pedagogical and technological development of the course and its book. The General Education Program at Illinois State University is the impetus for this project, and the College of Arts and Sciences has provided me with the necessary time to further the development of this course. This project would not have been possible without their commitment to the General Education Program.

Finding time to develop this project and to teach the course amidst my administrative duties would not have been possible without the support from the departmental staff. In particular, I have received strong support and encouragement from Nancy Doss, my administrative assistant. I also would not have been able to pursue this project if I have not received the support from Anne Bettendorf, the course coordinator of BSC 101. Her efforts in managing the laboratory portion of the course have been invaluable.

Finally, this book would not have met the printer's deadline without the efforts of Joni St. John, Emily Wittrig and Sally Little. Their effort in editing, proofreading, and correcting the final draft within a very short time frame is greatly appreciated

Chapter 1

General Education

Your place in the universe as a unique intelligent organism

Blue Marble
This is the famous photograph of Earth, taken from Apollo 17.
(Public Domain)

CHAPTER 1. GENERAL EDUCATION

I. GENERAL EDUCATION

I.1. *What is general education?*

Students are generally less interested in general education courses than in their major courses, and their behavior in lecture often reflects their lack of interest. For example, during lectures, students converse with each other, text message, read newspapers, and occasionally leave in the middle of class. On one occasion, a student watched a movie on her computer during the entire class. During a different semester, a student fell asleep in less than five minutes after each class began and only awakened at the end of each class. One wonders why he did not stay in his room and have a more comfortable sleeping arrangement.

To improve the learning environment of the class, many different approaches have been employed, but most of them have failed to make any improvement. One approach that works well is to convince students that general education is a vital part of their college educational experience that will extend to the rest of their lives. Once students accept the importance and benefits of general education, the learning environment improves. This chapter will discuss what general education is, why it is important, how it is relevant, and how this course achieves the goals of general education.

General education is a significant part of any college education. At Illinois State University, each undergraduate takes 14 courses in general education for a total of 42 credit hours. In other words, one third of the courses taken in an undergraduate degree program are general education courses. Most students take these courses during their freshman and sophomore years. Often, 75% of a freshman's curriculum is composed of general education courses. Why are the majority of general education courses taken during the first two years of college?

One of the main purposes of general education is to reinforce the basic academic skills that students have learned in high school. These include writing and speaking

Can general education be fun?
General education is an important part of college education in enhancing your academic experiences and promoting your success in life. *(Cheung)*

General Education Program at Illinois State University
Take a few minutes to explore the ISU General Education website to find out more about the General Education program.
(Education Fair Use)

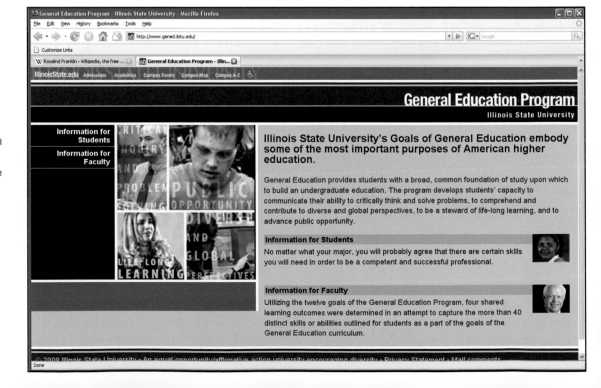

skills, critical reading skills, basic mathematical skills, and an understanding of the natural sciences. In the first-year general education curriculum, students learn how to conduct research projects, write papers, analyze data, and give oral presentations. These are basic skills that are essential for all students regardless of their majors.

The Inner Core at Illinois State University includes two courses which integrate composition, communication, critical thinking, and information literacy. Information literacy is the ability to know, evaluate, use, and remember information. The Inner Core also includes a course in mathematics and two courses in the natural sciences. Taking this course fulfills one of the requirements for natural science in the Inner Core of the General Education program.

The general education courses in the Inner Core are designed to provide every student at Illinois State University with a common set of skills and a common core of knowledge. The choices of courses in the Inner Core are limited in order to provide students with a shared learning experience. There are four courses to choose from in the natural sciences: biology, chemistry, physics, and geology. Students are required to take two of these courses and are free to choose them based on their personal interests. Even though the courses are in different scientific disciplines, each course is designed to help students understand the scientific process and the impact of science on society.

Clovis point
This projectile point was made by Native Americans 13,500 years ago. It represents the most sophisticated technology of the time. *(Public Domain)*

The next two levels of the General Education program at Illinois State University consist of the Middle Core and the Outer Core. Students need to take nine courses in areas such as language, economics, politics, humanities, social sciences, natural sciences, and technology. Students are given a much greater choice in selecting these courses. The Inner and Middle Core courses are intended to promote opportunities for students from different disciplines to collaborate. At its best, the General Education program creates a vibrant intellectual environment, encourages interdisciplinary collaboration, and promotes creative thinking.

Someone once said that in today's society "The only constancy is change." The current rate of change for human society is unprecedented. The primary driving force of this change is science and technology. For example, the entire world has been changed by the Internet. Medical advances, communication technologies, and manufacturing technologies have created and eliminated job opportunities. It is possible that scientific and technological advances may create jobs that could not be imagined today. What students learn today in their undergraduate majors will most likely become obsolete within ten years. Their future job security relies on their ability to learn and adapt. General education is designed to prepare students for changes by emphasizing the skills of learning, communicating, and solving problems..

Space technology
By the mid-20th century, human technology had led to space exploration. Space colonization is most likely by the end of the 21st century. *(Public Domain, NASA)*

On average, college students change their majors three times before they graduate. Furthermore, on average, American workers change their jobs ten times, and they change their careers two to three times within their lifetimes. The purpose of general education is to help students see new possibilities by exposing them to various disciplines. Students will have the ability to quickly sense new opportunities because of these varied courses. Through general education, students develop the skills to think critically and to solve problems. Therefore, general education is the best education that prepares students for a rapidly changing world.

I.2. How is general education relevant?

In addition to equipping students with basic skills in writing, communicating, and mathematics, general education is also relevant at three different levels. First, general education courses have academic relevance, particularly to the students' majors. Second, general education courses have social relevance, which results in students being able to apply what they have learned to current political and societal issues.

Third, general education courses are relevant at an individual level because students are able to apply the information they have learned when making personal choices and decisions.

In general education courses, students are taught about the relationships between different majors. For example, the relationship between psychology and biology is one that is emphasized in this course. Biological research into the mechanisms of how neurons communicate with each other is related to the psychological studies of mental disorders and behavioral abnormalities. Similarly, the studies on the biochemical mechanisms of neurotransmitters have led to a better understanding of mental diseases. This link between biology and psychology is just one example of how different majors are linked in general education. One important goal of general education is to demonstrate these relationships and to stress the relevance of one major to others.

Understanding the connections between majors enhances the collaboration between students of different majors. In general education courses, group projects are set up to promote joint activities. In these activities, students from different majors contribute their disciplinary expertise to solve common problems. Working together across disciplines is a crucial skill; such collaboration is essential in the modern world. For example, the human genome project required the collaboration of biologists, mathematicians, engineers, chemists, and artists. Through general education, students are likely to have a greater appreciation of the connections between their majors and other fields.

General education provides opportunities for exploring the social issues of the past, present, and future. Students can explore social issues from many different perspectives because of the integrative nature of general education. For example, the development of oral contraceptives can be addressed from biological, social, cultural, economical, and political perspectives. Similarly, the biological and cultural significance of the germ theory can be discussed from a historical perspective. Today's society would be very different without the use of oral contraceptives and the application of the germ theory. General education courses synthesize information across disciplinary boundaries to demonstrate its social relevancy in modern society.

The rapid change in modern technologies has had many social consequences. For example, the development of industrial farming has affected the diet and nutrition of modern society. Economic and political factors have shaped these changes, not all of which have been in the best interest of consumers. Through general education, students are engaged across disciplines to discuss the social relevance of industrial farming from historical, sociological, biological, political, and economic perspectives. These types of conversations break through the barriers that exist between majors and help students to become more aware of different viewpoints.

General education courses are also relevant to students' personal lives. For example, through general education courses, students address issues such as cigarette and alcohol usage from many different perspectives. After receiving this information, students can make informed decisions about their cigarette usage and alcohol consumption. Similar personal issues, such as the use of abuse substances and sexual behavior, are addressed from an interdisciplinary approach, which would not be possible within a single major. Through general education courses, students gain background information from different disciplines which they then use for making critical inquiries and for drawing conclusions.

Many current social issues, such as stem cell research, teaching intelligent design in American high school science classes, and global warming, involve a personal decision as a voter, consumer, and tax payer. Understanding these issues is multi-dimensional and involves many disciplines. Furthermore, different interest groups

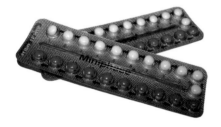

Oral contraceptives
Power of technology in controlling human reproduction.

Obesity in mice
Technology and change in life style have created serious health issues in humans. These mice have been valuable in the studies of human obesity. *(Public Domain)*

often provide the general public with views biased by their own political and social agendas. This situation can make issues confusing. Through general education, these issues are discussed from an interdisciplinary approach, and students learn how to think about an issue by researching and analyzing information through the methods and procedures of critical inquiry.

In summary, general education is more than just learning how to write, read, research, and analyze. Through general education courses, students learn to apply these skills when addressing issues regarding their disciplines, the society, and their personal decisions. General education courses allow students to expand their knowledge and create a worldview that will enhance their future career success.

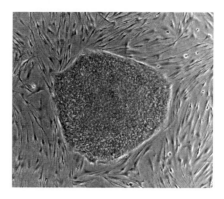

Embryo stem cells
Your understanding of basic biology will help you to participate in the public debate over stem cell research. *(Public Domain)*

II. BIOLOGICAL KNOWLEDGE IN GENERAL EDUCATION

This course is different from the biology courses commonly offered in junior high school or high school. This course is also different from the introductory biology courses taken by biology majors. This is a general education biology course which has been designed to accomplish the goals of general education. The content information in this course is designed to transcend disciplinary boundaries so that students can apply biological concepts and principles to their majors. Through this approach, information in a student's major will take on a new perspective and become more relevant.

II.1. How does this course provide an interdisciplinary perspective?

Most disciplines have distinct boundaries separating them from each other. The complexity and large body of knowledge make this separation a necessity so that students can focus on their disciplines. Some disciplines have an almost impenetrable boundary. For example, visual arts and biology seem to have nothing in common. Other disciplines, however, such as biology and psychology, are closely related. For some issues, information from several disciplines is needed before a basic understanding can be achieved. The following examples are used to illustrate the relationships between disciplines and explain why the general education approach is a vital educational approach.

One example of the interdisciplinary link between biology and art was surprisingly discovered because of a small statuette. The Venus of Willendorf, which is a Paleolithic statuette standing 4 3/8 in tall, was discovered near Willendorf, a small village in the hills of Lower Austria. The statuette was carved from limestone and was dated to be over 25,000 years old. The Venus is an idealization of female fertility, and her vulva, breasts, and abdomen are heavily exaggerated. However, her arms and face are obscured, suggesting that they were not important to the carver. For over nearly 15,000 years, this form of female depiction was prevalent across most of Europe and Asia. Experts in Paleolithic art were puzzled by the appearance of the Venus Willendorf and by similar statuettes. It was not until recently that neurobiology provided an acceptable explanation.

An understanding of the appearance of the Venus Willendorf came from a biological principle known as sign stimulus. This principle suggests that biological organisms can focus on the most important signal and ignore the rest. If this signal is vital for successful reproduction, then it will pass on to future generations. A large vulva, breasts, and abdomen are clear signs of a fertile female, and the preference for these external physical characteristics was valuable to the survival of the hunter-gatherers in pre historical times. Does this preference apply to female sex appeal in modern times? Using the general education approach, this biology course will

Venus of Willendorf
Stone age sex symbol. *(GNU Free Documentation License)*

answer such questions and in doing so, will bring two separate disciplines together to address a common issue.

Even though some disciplines are closely related, they often fail to cooperatively address common issues. For example, biology and psychology are closely related disciplines, but the two curricula are very different and have few overlaps. However, there have been instances when the interconnection between the two disciplines has led to a greater understanding. One such instance includes a mysterious psychological disorder known as Capgras syndrome, which was first reported in 1923. One particular sufferer from this syndrome was a man who suffered a head injury in an automobile accident and was in a coma for several weeks. Upon recovery, he behaved normally, except for the unusual symptom of thinking that his parents were impostors. This unusual mental disorder baffled psychologists for decades until the study of the neurobiology of the brain provided an acceptable explanation.

Studies in neurobiology have established that discrete parts of the brain carry out different functions. The temporal lobes are parts of the brain in the cerebral cortex that are responsible for the memory of faces. The temporal lobe is connected to the amygdala, a part of the brain that is responsible for emotion. When someone sees a face, the temporal lobe recalls the facial structure and the amygdala adds the emotional quality for that particular face. For example, the face of a loved one will receive strong emotional input from the amygdala. In Capgras syndrome, the connection between the temporal lobe and the amygdala is damaged. Without feeling the appropriate emotion, the significance of a particular face is misinterpreted. A person may look like a loved one, but they will not feel like a loved one. In this course, other similar examples will be used to illustrate the importance of interdisciplinary collaboration for solving common problems.

Some topics in biology also involve many other disciplines. One of these topics is the origin of different forms of life. This topic involves philosophy, religion, and history. In fact, determining life's origin began as a philosophical issue and was first written about extensively by the Greek philosopher, Aristotle. He proposed the immutability of life forms and suggested that all life came into being in the forms that we know today. His idea had a significant influence for over 2,000 years, and many religious doctrines adopted this viewpoint, including Judeo-Christian creationism.

By the 18th century, there was irrefutable evidence that biological organisms had evolved through time. However, no good explanation for the mechanism of this change was known until the 19th century when Charles Darwin proposed the theory of natural selection to explain the process of evolution. This theory created conflicts between the religious and scientific communities. The recent court battles regarding the teaching of intelligent design/creationism and the theory of natural selection in high school science classes is a continuation of this debate. This course will address this and other biological issues that involve other disciplines.

In summary, it is important to view biology from an interdisciplinary angle, because no discipline can exist in isolation. Unfortunately, most majors are too restricted in their curricula to use an interdisciplinary approach. Through general education, students are given an opportunity to examine topics that involve multiple disciplines. Recognizing this potential will help students adapt to a changing world.

II.2. How will this course integrate with your major?

Biology is connected to other majors in two different ways. In one way, the foundation of the biological connection is in majors such as physics, chemistry, and geology. These disciplines make direct contributions to biological understanding. In the second way, biological knowledge, mostly through technology, has changed the practice and basic assumptions of other disciplines. By having this understanding,

Aristotle

He was the first philosopher who also wrote extensively on biology.
(Lysippos)

Charles Darwin

He offered the first comprehensive theory on the diversity of the biological world.
(Public Domain)

students can view their majors from a slightly different perspective and gain an appreciation of the integration of knowledge. The following examples demonstrate how this course integrates with other majors.

The connection between biology and chemistry is well known, as chemistry provides the foundation for biochemistry, molecular biology, and genetics. Linking the clinical symptoms of diabetes to energy metabolism, for example, provides students with an insight into the close connection between these two disciplines. Chemistry majors can benefit from learning how chemical knowledge is applied to biological systems through the explanation of the clinical manifestations of a deadly disease.

Physics majors can also learn from this course certain topics that directly relate to their discipline. Astronomical events, such as a supernova explosion, contribute to the formation of elements such as calcium, iron, and potassium that are essential for life. Geology majors can learn how tectonic plate movement of the earth's crust has led to biological mass extinctions due to the change of habitats and disruption of ecosystems. Mathematics majors will discover that the human genome project would not have been possible without the development of mathematical models to analyze the vast amount of DNA sequence data.

The connection between biology and psychology is well documented. Biology has affected psychology in many different ways by demonstrating that all behaviors have a biological basis. This understanding has led to the formulation of psychiatric medications. Psychology majors can benefit from the biological research that studies how neurons in the brain communicate with each other to create consciousness.

Petrified wood
Biology, geology, chemistry, and physics come together in the study of fossils. *(Public Domain)*

The connection between biology and other social sciences, such as sociology and anthropology, is also strong. Many social issues, such as substance abuse, domestic violence, and child abuse, can be addressed through biological perspectives. Understanding the biological origins of these disruptive social behaviors can help us understand how to prevent and manage these social issues. Through this course, students will recognize that knowledge from a different major can help prepare them for their majors.

Aesthetic experience in the arts and music is based on the biological senses of sight, sound, hearing, smell, and touch. This information must also be processed by the brain to realize the aesthetic values. Therefore, biology is fundamental to the human perception of beauty and the sublime. Human creativity is also based on the neurological activities of the brain that results in having visions. Biology has demonstrated that these visions can be achieved by chemicals that induce hallucinations. Consequently, understanding biology can enhance artistic appreciation and creativity.

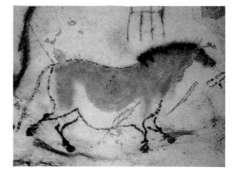

Lascaux painting
These famous cave paintings were painted 13,500 years ago in Europe.
(Public Domain)

The relationship between biology and the humanities is well known, as many topics in philosophy, history, and language have deep biological roots. The rise of the scientific process as a way to seek knowledge of the natural world is an important chapter in human history. Similarly, the philosophical distinction of scientific knowledge from other forms of knowledge is an important topic of study for philosophers. In this course, many examples will be discussed that highlight the relationship between science and other forms of knowledge.

The education of children must take into account their biological development. This includes the development and maturation of the brain from birth until early adulthood. In the past, education has often been an exercise in trial and error because the complexity of the brain has made it hard to understand how people learn. With 100 billion neurons that make over 100 quadrillion connections with each other, the working of the brain has been a complete mystery. However, biology has made great progress in the study of the brain over the past several decades. With the development of new brain imaging technology, researchers can now study the workings of the brain.

In the last ten years, researchers have located various parts of the brain that are involved in language, logical reasoning, planning, forming long-term memory, and executing complex procedures. Working with neurobiologists, developmental psychologists have tracked the developing brain in children to reveal how they learn and utilize complex information. Increasingly, educational strategies are becoming based on biology rather than on anecdotal accounts of teaching and learning successes. The role of biology in education will be discussed in this course to demonstrate the benefits of the general education approach.

In summary, examples will be used in this course to demonstrate how the understanding of biological principles can prepare students to be more successful in their majors.

II.3. How will this course prepare you for making moral and ethical judgments?

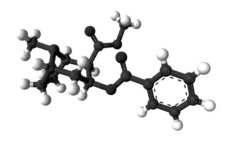

Cocaine

A simple molecule with profound psychological effects.

Every discipline contributes to a student's capacity for making moral and ethical judgments. The interconnectivity of disciplines suggests that moral and ethical judgments are best made only after examining an issue from different angles. For example, all societal issues have many different perspectives including economic, political, and biological. A suitable solution only comes from taking into consideration every aspect. A general education course is designed to help students recognize the importance of taking an interdisciplinary perspective. Three examples are given below in order to demonstrate how the biological perspective affects moral and ethical judgments of important societal issues.

Substance abuse is a major social problem of modern society, and the disruptive power of this problem can be measured in social and economic costs. Society often views substance abuse using moral and ethical standards, with the users and distributors of addictive drugs being perceived as deviant and socially unfit. In the United States, using and selling certain addictive drugs leads to stiff prison terms. However, there are discrepancies in the moral and ethical perspectives on types of abuse substances. For example, the use of alcohol and tobacco are condoned and even encouraged by society. However, the use of cannabis, which is less dangerous and harmful than both alcohol and tobacco, is criminalized.

Understanding the social consequences of substance abuse requires an understanding of the biological mechanisms of addiction. In this course, the neurological process of addiction will be discussed to demonstrate that the biological basis for chemical addiction is identical to the neurological mechanism for love and for other pleasurable human activities. Through this understanding, students will gain a new perspective on the power of addictive drugs on the human brain and will be able to make their moral and ethical judgments with greater circumspection.

Does race exist?

Why do people from different parts of the world look different?
(Public Domain)

Racism has been a divisive force at both the community and global levels. Throughout history, racial discrimination and prejudice have created divisive social structures, allowing one group of individuals to oppress and even enslave other groups. It has left deep cultural scars that many modern societies, including the United States, have yet to heal completely. Many of the modern anti-racism policies are based on moral and ethical considerations that are philosophical and/or religious in nature. Most of them lack the scientific understanding that humans are too similar to each other to be divided into different racial groups.

In this course, it is emphasized that racism has no scientific support because, from a biological standpoint, the distinctions among groups of individuals around the world are cultural rather than biological. The physical distinctions of individuals from various geographical regions of the world are caused by minor adaptations to local climatic environments. Using physical traits, such as skin color, facial features, and body types, to derive racial classifications is scientifically untenable. The scientific knowledge on human variations has provided new perspectives on the issue of racism.

Sex is one of the most important biological processes of life. The human species would cease to exist if sexual reproduction came to an end. However, sex has been one of the most complex and difficult issues in human history. Society has a traditional definition of what are acceptable and unacceptable sexual relationships. Any deviation from this standard perception of acceptable sexual behavior often receives harsh and unforgiving moral and ethical judgments. Most individuals of modern society receive mixed signals on what sexual behaviors are appropriate, and this confusion often leads to moral and ethical dilemmas.

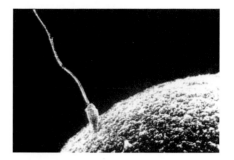

Sperm fertilizes an egg
What is the purpose of sex? *(Public Domain)*

From the biological standpoint, human sexual behaviors are instinctual, and human sexual attraction has evolved over millions of years. Furthermore, there are wide individual variations of what is considered sexually attractive. The understanding of the biological basis of sexual attraction has led to the creation of more circumspective approaches in perceiving the variations in sexual orientation. In a more pluralistic society that promotes personal freedom, incorporating the biological perspectives on this vital aspect of human existence is both necessary and critical to reframe our moral and ethical judgments of sexual orientation.

Male and female pheasants
Why do they look so different?
(GNU, Chris O)

In summary, biological information has provided the foundation for making moral and ethical judgments in modern society. This knowledge provides an understanding of social issues that have powerful consequences. Society has struggled with these issues for thousands of years based on knowledge that was arbitrary and non evidential. For the first time, the moral and ethical consideration of these issues can be viewed from a biological perspective that is based on scientific evidence.

II.4. How will this course prepare you for civic engagement?

Biology is important in a modern democracy, and many social issues are tightly linked to our biological understanding of human individuals, social interactions, and the global environment. This course will use biology as an example to demonstrate how scientific knowledge is important to modern society in promoting civic engagement. There are many issues both at the local and global levels that affect our present lives and the lives of future generations. This knowledge has convinced many individuals to become engaged at the political and social levels. A thorough understanding of the scientific basis of these issues has enriched the debates on some of the most important social and environmental issues. The following examples demonstrate the role of biological knowledge in eliciting civic engagement in modern times.

Biology can be both a solution and a problem. During the Green Revolution in the 1950s and 1960s, biologists provided a solution to world population growth by increasing agricultural production through the use of chemical fertilizers, herbicides, and pesticides. The crop yields were increased worldwide and potential famine in many parts of the world was prevented. However, the applications of agricultural chemicals in such a large scale created other problems. These chemicals pose serious health hazards to humans and are destructive to the environment.

Rachel Carson
The first environmentalist.

In the late 1950s, the use of synthetic pesticides, such as DDT, became a serious threat to both humans and the environment. In 1962, Rachel Carson, an American marine biologist and nature writer, published *Silent Spring*, which was a pivotal book in initiating environmental movements around the world against the indiscriminative use of agricultural chemicals. Her book represents one of the most significant examples of how a civic engagement started because of biological knowledge. The goal of general education is to encourage students to acquire a broad perspective of different disciplines so that they can fully participate in the democratic process of our society.

Civic engagement can take on different forms and address different issues. One of the common civic engagement efforts is to raise money for research for treating particular diseases. Some of the common fund raising efforts are the annual Labor Day telethon for muscular dystrophy, American Cancer Society fund raising, and many others. One of the most well-known civic engagement efforts is the March of Dimes, which was founded in 1938 by the National Foundation for Infantile Paralysis to find a treatment for polio and how to prevent it.

Civic engagement
Fighting a deadly disease through civic engagement. *(Public Domain)*

Through numerous volunteers, millions of dollars were raised for scientific research to develop a vaccine against polio. The effort began with a radio appeal, asking everyone in the nation to contribute a dime to fight polio. For its first 17 years, the March of Dimes supported many virologists in their efforts to discover a vaccine against the disease. The effort paid off in 1955, when Dr. Jonas Salk developed a safe vaccine that could successfully prevent polio. Through large scale civic engagement, the largest clinical trial in U.S. history was carried out, involving 1.8 million school children. The consequence was momentous because it almost completely wiped out paralytic polio in children. Today's childhood immunization policies were derived from this type of biological perspective.

Scientific research is directed by societal needs and political forces. Prior to the modern era, scientific research was often tightly controlled by the state. For example, Galileo was prohibited from carrying out his astronomical research by the ruling of the Roman Catholic Church because of philosophical differences on the nature of the universe. Today, most scientific research is supported by tax dollars. Consequently, the direction of research is often dictated by political processes. Therefore, through civic engagement in the political process, individuals can change the research agenda of the nation.

A recent example of the impact of civic engagement on scientific research concerns research in cloning and stem cell development. Based on moral and ethical grounds, human cloning for reproductive purposes was ruled unethical and morally wrong, and it is now against the law to conduct this type of work. However, research in human cloning for the development of embryonic stem cells has been debated over the past years among the politicians and the general public. Individual civic engagement efforts, despite the opposition of the federal government, has resulted in many states allocating tax dollars to support research for the development of embryonic stem cells for therapeutic purposes. This is an example of how biological knowledge in a specific area is crucial for civic engagement.

In summary, there are many social issues that require a good understanding of their biological perspectives. To publicly engage in these issues, citizens must develop the ability to examine various angles of the issues. Through this course, students will acquire the skills to conduct research on the issues and to evaluate the pros and cons of the arguments. Their ability to play a part in shaping the future of our society relies on acquiring and making use of these skills.

II.5. How will this course help you develop critical thinking skills?

Critical inquiry is one of the most important skills that students will learn through the General Education program at Illinois State University. Critical inquiry combines critical thinking, collecting information, analyzing data, and drawing inferences. Critical inquiry is the first step in solving personal, professional, and societal problems. This course will demonstrate critical inquiry and problem solving through biological examples that are relevant at the societal and personal levels. Students will learn the important differences between evidential inquiry and other forms of knowledge acquisition, such as those used in the arts and humanities. Furthermore, this course will demonstrate the differences between situation and universal knowledge, and how they are used differently.

Throughout history there have been different methods of inquiry. All human beings carry out personal inquiries for food, shelter, and mates as a part of our need to survive and reproduce. This forms personal knowledge, and we use it every single moment of our lives. If an individual lived alone on a remote island, his or her knowledge would consist of his or her own personal experiences. However, as social organisms we share our knowledge with each other. In most cases, we inform each other of the locations of food and water, how to avoid danger, and where to seek shelter. This type of inquiry is known as evidential inquiry, because the knowledge can be confirmed by physical evidence of food or the presence of predators.

However, there is another type of inquiry that occurs in the abstraction of the mind. This includes the perception of supernatural forces or spiritual revelations that cannot be confirmed by other people. This type of inquiry is used in the realms of religious experience, artistic creation, and philosophical contemplation. It is vital for students to distinguish this type of inquiry from evidential inquiry. Evidential inquiry is often referred to as scientific inquiry, because the conclusions of the investigations rely on evidence that can be confirmed by all observers in similar situations. On the other hand, non-evidential inquiry does not have this requirement. Biology is a discipline based on evidential inquiry, and this course will provide examples of this important way of gaining knowledge.

Galileo
The earliest applications of the scientific method to study physics and astronomy. *(Public Domain)*

The purpose of all inquiries is to generate knowledge that has predictive power, which is the ability to foresee future events. To maximize the chances of our individual survival, we create this knowledge at a personal level in order to predict the outcome of our actions. There are two types of knowledge that we encounter in our everyday life. The first type of knowledge is known as situation knowledge which is knowledge that we can experience ourselves. For example, gravity is a form of situation knowledge because we can experience it directly when we fall out of tree. Our personal experiences confirm the existence of gravity.

However, there are aspects of gravity we cannot experience, and our acceptance of this form of knowledge is based on evidence that we cannot directly observe. The idea that the same gravitation force is responsible for maintaining the orbit of the moon around Earth as well as the orbits of the planets around the sun will seem unbelievable to a person who is not educated in physics. This form of knowledge is known as universal knowledge, because it cannot be easily experienced at the individual level, but is nevertheless universally true. In this course, examples will be discussed to demonstrate the relationship between these two different forms of knowledge.

An important part of the critical inquiry process is to understand the nature of knowledge and how it relates to truth and belief. The study of the nature of knowledge is a philosophical discipline known as epistemology. This discipline addresses questions such as what is knowledge?, how is knowledge acquired?, and what do people know? Epistemology also considers the meaning of truths or what it means when someone considers something to be true or false. What is the role of truths in the formation of knowledge? Another important consideration is the meaning of beliefs. What is the relationship between beliefs and knowledge?

The nature of knowledge is important in the study of biology. For example, what is the nature of the idea that all life forms on Earth are descendents of a common ancestor? Is it a truth, a belief, or knowledge? In this course, biological examples will be used to demonstrate the differences, similarities, and relationships between truths, beliefs, and knowledge. This discussion will further highlight the importance of the interdisciplinary approach in general education.

In summary, through the general education approach, this course will demonstrate the application of the scientific process or evidential inquiry as a way to seek biological knowledge. Through these examples, students will learn the reasons why education is the only vehicle for acquiring knowledge that cannot be gained through direct experience. Using examples from biological principles and concepts, this course will demonstrate the nature and application of knowledge.

II.6. *How will this course promote lifelong learning?*

Scientific journals

They play a critical role in promoting communication among scientists. *(Fair use magazine covers)*

Helping students to become lifelong learners is one of the most important goals of general education. Lifelong learning results from curiosity and the need to resolve problems. People are curious about matters that they find relevant in practical ways, such as how to maintain a healthy diet, how to become more successful in their jobs, and how to raise better children. People are also curious about intellectual matters, such as the origin of life on Earth, the existence of extraterrestrial intelligence, and how our minds function. This course will demonstrate that biology has both practical and intellectual significance in our lives. Also, by acquiring a basic knowledge of biology, students can continue to pursue knowledge in areas of biology that interest them.

We are motivated to learn when we find the information relevant for solving problems or for answering questions that we have regarding ourselves and the world around us. We are interested in various aspects of our life, factors that affect our society, and how the world functions. In this course, examples of how biology has changed our daily lives will be used to demonstrate the importance of biological knowledge in the shaping of the modern world. For example, the discovery of immunization has saved billions of lives from childhood infectious diseases. Similarly, applications of the germ theory have impacted every aspect of modern lives, and the discovery of the structure of DNA has resulted in the development of genetic engineering.

Biology is relevant in our daily lives, and it will become even more relevant in the future. The progress of biology is extraordinary, with new discoveries occurring almost daily. These discoveries have both personal and societal implications. With new medical advances, human life expectancy has dramatically increased in the past 100 years. New drugs and therapies have been developed to treat diseases that were untreatable in the past. Furthermore, with the advent of genetic engineering, it has become possible to alter the traits of future generations. Modern biology has ushered in a new world that is full of promises and perils.

There are many different levels in lifelong learning, ranging from casual to serious. However, no matter how little or how much a person chooses to learn in a discipline other than his or her major, an understanding of the general principles and concepts of the discipline is essential. This course will teach students the most important and fundamental concepts in biology that they can then use for future independent learning.

These fundamental biological concepts will be illustrated by relevant examples and will draw upon historical significance as well as implications on modern life. These examples are interdisciplinary in approach and will demonstrate relationships to other disciplines. The examples will come from personal, societal, political, and environmental perspectives and will emphasize the importance of biological concepts and their influences on various aspects of the modern world. Using different examples to illustrate the relevance of these fundamental biological concepts will reinforce the students' understanding and will help them to apply those concepts in different circumstances. This approach will also help students to identify other fundamental biological concepts on their own as their knowledge grows.

This course will use two strategies to help students become lifelong learners. First, learners must enjoy the learning process. To learn beyond the working environment, the subject must be interesting, and the learning process must be rewarding. One of the best ways to learn in the age of mass communication is through edutainment, which is a form of entertainment designed to educate as well as to amuse. This includes television programs, computer and video games, films, music, websites, and multimedia software. Public Broadcasting Service has produced television programs, such as *NOVA*, *Nature*, and *Cosmos*, to educate and entertain simultaneously. Commercial channels, such as the Discovery Channel, History Channel, and Animal Planet have utilized the same format. In this course, examples of this type of television program will be introduced to encourage students to develop a habit of watching these programs.

The second approach is to encourage students to become regular readers of science news on the Internet. News Internet sites such as *The New York Times* online, *New Yorker magazine*, *Scientific American*, and others offer a wide range of high quality articles on science and science-related issues. Another approach for lifelong learning in biology is to read non-fiction books on biology and other natural sciences. These books provide more in-depth knowledge on a scientific topic. In this course, students will be encouraged to develop a self-initiating learning strategy and a regular reading habit.

Gorilla
One of humans' closest relative.
(Kabir Bakie, 2005)

In summary, this course will use several different strategies to help students develop lifelong learning habits in biology and its related topics. These include an emphasis on the importance and relevance of biology at the individual and societal levels. Students will also learn the fundamental concepts in biology that will allow them to appreciate new developments in biology, medicine, and biotechnology. Thirdly, students will be introduced to various tools for further learning in biology.

III. WHAT IS THE THEME OF THIS COURSE?

A successful general education course will help students develop a new perspective of the world around them and give them a fresh view of how they fit into the world. An effective general education course also provides students with information that they can apply to their everyday lives as well as to the larger societal issues that affect them. This course intends to bring together information from many disciplines to achieve these goals. When students complete this course, they will be glad that they have this new knowledge because it will improve their lives both in the next several years as college students and in the rest of their lives as citizens of this ever-changing society.

This course is designed to help you understand yourself better. We will bring together all the knowledge that humanity has acquired in the past to give you a better understanding of yourself. Biological discoveries in the past 150 years have completely revolutionized the way individuals see themselves. For thousands of years, humans were puzzled by individual uniqueness, and the only explanation for this was based on philosophy and religion. However, in the past 100 years, the biological basis of individual uniqueness has become completely understood. Understanding biological uniqueness has a profound impact on modern society and in personal relationships.

This course will also address the biological basis of intelligence and how human intelligence differs from the intelligence of other biological organisms. Understanding the working of the mind is an intriguing aspect of biological investigation. In the past several decades, remarkable progress has been made in this area because of

Chimpanzee
Chimps and humans share the same intelligence. *(Steve, 2007)*

sophisticated techniques that analyze the human thought process, emotion, and creativity. This knowledge has affected society in many ways, including education, treatment for mental disorders, and improving quality of life. This information also allows us to see our relationships to other living organisms, including the great apes,

Spiral galaxy
This galaxy is one of 40 billion galaxies that are known to exist in the universe. *(Public Domain)*

our closest relatives.

The understanding of your uniqueness and your intelligence will allow you to appreciate your place in the human world as a member of society and in the biological world as a living organism. This course will examine the cycle of life at the human level as well as at the biological level. Our individual existence in the context of the biological world offers a unique perspective of our relationship to other living organisms. This knowledge will allow you to have a greater philosophical understanding of your place in the biological world as well as in the universe.

Another purpose of this course is to help you understand your physical existence in terms of atoms and molecules. It is an extraordinary intellectual achievement for humans to contemplate the origin of life and the origin of the universe. Knowing that the atoms in the molecules around you and in your very cells originated from supernova explosions brings a new perspective to our existence. With the general education approach, it is possible for this course to bring all the discrete information together to provide you with insights that will impact the rest of your life.

At the completion of this course, you should be able to reflect upon the following statement and provide an explanation of this statement to yourself and others:

"Your place in the universe as a unique, intelligent organism"

This statement embodies the goals and spirit of general education by helping you develop a better understanding of yourself and the world around you. The major goal of this course is to continue your intellectual journey and increase the knowledge that will help you to lead a successful and productive life. This course is a vehicle for reaching this outcome, and biology is one of many disciplinary examples that can be used. If this course can raise your interest and desire to learn about biology then I have succeeded. I hope that I have convinced you that your attention and effort in this course will be well rewarded.

Chapter 2

Biological Traits

The Role of protein and DNA in your biological existence

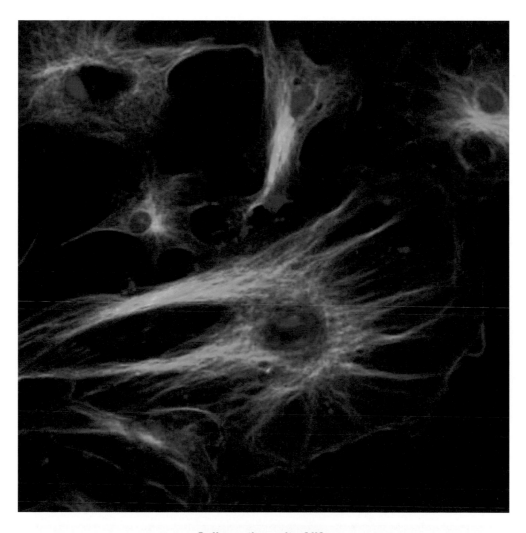

Cells as the unit of life

These cells are stained to demonstrate their internal structure known as cytoskeleton. The human body contains 100 trillion cells. *(Public Domain)*

CHAPTER 2. BIOLOGICAL TRAITS

When you look into a mirror what do you see? You see your external appearance such as the color of your skin, eyes, and hair, and the shapes of your eyes, nose, and mouth, and the build of your body. You have learned enough biology from grade school and high school to know that all these traits are determined by your genes. You have also learned that these traits are passed down from your parents, and that you inherit traits from each parent. However, do you know why you have a unique set of traits that makes you different from any other humans that have ever lived or will ever live? Until 150 years ago, one of the greatest mysteries was the understanding of how living organisms are similar to each other and unique at the same time. This chapter will demonstrate to you why this knowledge is vital.

I. WHY ARE PROTEINS LIFE'S WORK FORCE?

In the movie *Indiana Jones and the Last Crusade*, the bad guy took a drink from the wrong Grail, and his flesh and bone instantly turned into ashes. This type of scene has been portrayed many times in horror movies. In other movies, gangland murder victims have been subjected to acid treatment, and their hair and skin literally dissolved. Could this happen in real life? What is our body made of? What are basic building materials of different parts of our body? How are they built? How does the body know what, where, and when to build? The answers to these questions lie in the understanding of proteins.

I.1. *How do proteins make a living organism?*

What do you see when you look at your hand? You might be surprised to learn that your hand, including your skin, hair, fingernails, and everything else beneath the skin, is constructed entirely from proteins. In fact, your entire body, from the exterior to all the bones, muscle, and internal organs, is constructed from proteins. Your body is constantly making new proteins to replenish those that have worn out. Proteins are the most important molecules in our life, and there are over 100,000 different proteins working together to make a human being. Therefore, you should know something about the working of proteins.

When you look at dietary information on food labels, you will find that many processed foods have amino acid supplements. The reason for this is that the human body synthesizes proteins from amino acids, which are simple chemical molecules that are only found in living organisms. They are known as organic molecules because of their biological origins. There are 20 different amino acids found in proteins, and they all share a basic chemical structure with slight differences in a region of the molecule known as the functional groups. There are over several hundred different amino acids, but living organisms use only 20 of them for making proteins. From this standpoint, all living organisms speak the same chemical language.

Proteins are similar to balls of yarn, coiling and wrapping into different shapes. Proteins are long chains of amino acids linked to each other. Some of the proteins can have as many as several hundred thousand amino acids, making them extremely complex. If you imagine each type of amino acid as different colored balls, the variation of the sequences is infinite. The functional groups on the amino acids behave like sticky arms that grasp any other functional groups in the neighborhood. The amino acid sequence of proteins determines the protein shapes and structures, which are critical for their functions.

Proteins are made inside cells by linking different amino acids together, in the same way a jeweler makes a necklace by joining different kinds of beads together. This is a process known as protein synthesis or translation, and it takes place in

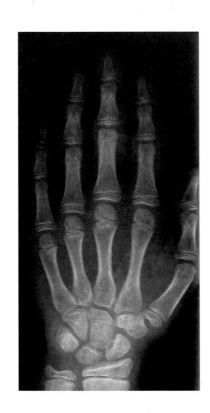

X-ray of a boy's hand
Except for the calcium in the bones, proteins are the main ingredients of the hand. *(Public Domain)*

a special part of a cell using highly sophisticated molecular machines. They are frequently referred to as biological nano machines. The speed of protein synthesis is astounding; a cell can synthesize thousands of proteins every second.

The raw materials of proteins are amino acids, which contain four elements: hydrogen, oxygen, carbon, and nitrogen. Plants can make all 20 amino acids from water, carbon dioxide, and ammonia. Animals have lost the ability to make some of the amino acids, and they must get those from their diets. For example, human cells can produce 11 of the 20 amino acids, and they obtain the remaining 9 amino acids, known as essential amino acids, from their diet. Without this commonality of the amino acid "language" in the biological world, predator-prey relationships would not exist, and the nature of food would be very different.

Proteins, the basic building blocks of the human body, can be compared to the nuts and bolts that make up a complex machine such as a Boeing 747 jumbo jet. However, even the simplest living organisms are more complicated than most manmade objects. Proteins are more than nuts and bolts because most of the proteins in a living organism behave like self-programmed robots, going about their business without any obvious instructions and supervision. With over 100,000 different proteins in the human body, the harmony and perfection in their execution is astounding.

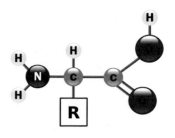

Basic structure of amino acids

All 20 amino acids are based on the same structure with R being different in each amino acid. *(Public Domain)*

There are five major groups of proteins, arranged according to their functions. The first group is structural, forming the skin and bones that provide structural support; they are the most abundant proteins in the body. The second group is mechanical, providing for motility at the cellular as well as the organismal level; muscle proteins are the best known members of this group. The third group is enzymatic; they are responsible for catalyzing chemical reactions. The fourth group is for transportation; hemoglobin is the most notable example for transporting oxygen. The fifth group is for communication between cells; hormones are important examples.

In summary, your existence is based on proteins, with their extraordinary diversity and amazing integration. It is hard to imagine that there are a quadrillion proteins working together to create you, and billions of new proteins are produced each day. Understanding the complexity of protein function and structure has been one of the most important scientific discoveries of the past 200 years.

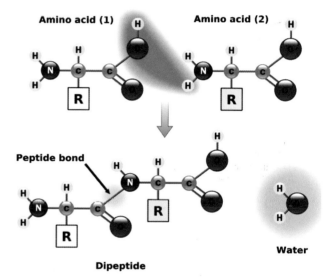

Peptide bond formation

The amino acids are joined together by peptide bonds by removing a molecule of water. *(Public Domain)*

I.2. How do proteins impart physical traits?

Our individual identities are based largely on our physical traits. For thousands of years, human skin color has been one of the most important physical traits in racial classification. Even in modern America, skin color serves as one of the most important traits for social considerations. Over history, skin color has often created insurmountable barriers for many social groups. In the past 50 years, the biological basis of skin color has become understood at the biochemical, molecular, and genetic levels. This knowledge is essential for everyone to know in a pluralistic society to dispel misconceptions that have been associated with this biological trait.

Skin color is a biological trait based on pigmentation of the skin. Pigmentation is a biological property found in all living organisms, from dogs to flowers. Proteins become pigments when their three-dimensional structures alter their light reflecting properties. In the visible light, the different colors of an object are based on its ability to absorb light. An object that can absorb light in all visible wavelengths appears black. A green object absorbs light in all other wavelengths but a green wavelength and appears green. A biological pigment uses the same principle to display its color. Nearly all biological pigments in the natural world are proteins.

An albino child

Even though he was born from a African mother, a genetic mutation in pigmentation caused his albino condition. *(Creative Commons Attribution)*

Skin color and light absorption

Light contains a spectrum of colors. Skin color is the result of light absorption by the skin pigments. *(Public Domain)*

One of the most common biological pigments in the animal world is the protein eumelanin. This protein absorbs light at all wavelengths and consequently appears black. Eumelanin causes the skin to appear black when it is incorporated into the epidermis layer of the skin. It causes the hair to be black when it is incorporated into the hair shafts. There is another pigment protein known as pheomelanin, which gives a red color due to its absorption wavelength. The varying amounts of these two pigment proteins give the entire range of human skin and hair color. These two proteins also provide the range of fur color in dogs and other mammals.

The amino acid sequences determine the three-dimensional structures of the pigment proteins. A slight alteration of the amino acid sequences can make profound changes in the pigment protein structure. For example, in some of the conditions of albinism, the structure of the pigment protein is significantly altered so that its light absorption capacity is abolished. The change in the light absorption capacity of the pigment proteins is continuous; there is a gradual transition of the pigment proteins from high light absorption to no light absorption.

As you have learned in your previous biological classes, the amino acid sequences of proteins are determined by genes. Through long time periods, genes of the pigment proteins undergo gradual changes, leading to changes in the structure of the protein pigments and their light absorption capacity. This leads to variations of skin color in the population. However, there are other biological mechanisms that can cause changes in skin color.

Human skin color can also be changed by controlling the production of the pigment proteins in the skin. The human body can respond to the external environment by regulating the production of skin pigment proteins. In response to strong ultraviolet wavelengths in sunlight, a hormone, known as melanocortin, is produced to stimulate the skin cells to synthesize pigment proteins. The hormone binds to a cell surface protein known as a melanocortin receptor which serves as a communicator between the external signal and internal cellular activities. This is the biological basis of tanning.

However, dark and light skin colors can become permanent biological traits as a result in the change of the melanocortin receptors. Some receptors have slightly different structures making them highly sensitive to the hormone. This will lead to dark skin color, because the skin cells continue to produce pigments. In some cases, changes in the structure of the receptors make them insensitive to the hormone, leading to light skin color. In some individuals, the receptors are non-functional. These individuals cannot develop a tan which makes them highly susceptible to the damaging effect of UV light.

In summary, human skin color is determined by the production of the skin pigments eumelanin and pheomelanin. The variations in these proteins are one of the factors that contribute to skin color. Another contributing factor to skin color is the ability of the cells to respond to regulatory hormones. The biological understanding of skin color demonstrates the fallacies in using skin color for racial classifications and discrimination. Now we realize that it is not only morally and ethically wrong but also scientifically unsound to apply racial criteria to human populations based on skin color.

I.3. How do proteins impart behavioral traits?

Proteins affect our behavior as well, and most of us are not aware of it. If you were unable to tell the differences between various colors, the world would be quite different. Consequently, you would behave differently than someone who can perceive different colors. We often take our vision for granted, and we only notice the remarkable process of discerning color when we are unable to detect it. Most of us do not understand the biological process of seeing color and the implications of color blindness. In this section, we will examine how proteins are crucial in the perception of color.

Human vision is a remarkable biological process with two major components. The first component is the eye, which acquires visual information from the environment in the form of light. The second component is the brain, which integrates the visual information and creates visual images. The first part of the process can be compared to a digital camera taking a picture. The second part of the process is extremely complex, as it involves as many as several hundred million neurons in different regions of the brain interpreting the information and constructing visual images for the mind. Despite the differences in these two components, proteins are central in carrying out both functions.

The acquisition of visual images is relatively simple compared to the integration of information. Even the simplest animals use a similar mechanism for gathering visual information. The first animal eye evolved in the simple flatworm about 550 million years ago. The basic structure remains the same for both the primitive flatworm eye and complex human eyes. However, the human brain that is involved in processing the images is light years ahead of the first animal brain which did just a little more than detecting the intensity and direction of the light source.

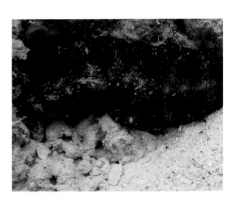

Evolution of the eye
Flatworms are the simplest animals with eyes. *(Public Domain)*

Light is a source of energy which can affect proteins by changing their structures. The earliest form of the eye contained a depression near the head of an animal. The surface of this concave area was lined with special proteins that could undergo a slight structural change when they were hit by light. Through a series of intermediate proteins, this light-induced structural change was converted into a very weak electrical signal. This signal activated the neurons connected to the light sensing cells. In early primitive animal brains, this protein allowed animals to sense light. Also, the placement of these proteins in a depression made it possible for the animals to detect light from different directions. Human eyes have retained a spherical shape for this reason.

Animal vision has demonstrated that proteins can play a variety of roles in sensing the environment. Proteins are amazingly versatile due to the infinite number of three-dimensional structures that they can assume by varying their amino acid sequences. As animals have become more complex, the structure of the eye has evolved to acquire more information. The brain has expanded with more neurons for processing the incoming data, but the basic detecting mechanisms have remained unchanged. In the case of color blindness, the defect is associated with the light collecting proteins rather than the brain.

To understand color blindness, we need to briefly address the four proteins that are involved in light detection. The region inside the human eye, known as the retina, is lined with a layer of light sensing cells known as rods and cones. Inside the rod cells, there are proteins for detecting light sensitivity. This is a pigment protein known as rhodopsin, which can be activated by light to alter its structure. There are three types of cone cells, with each one containing different pigments for red, green, and blue. Our entire visual system is based on these four protein pigments that capture the necessary information for creating complex images in our brain.

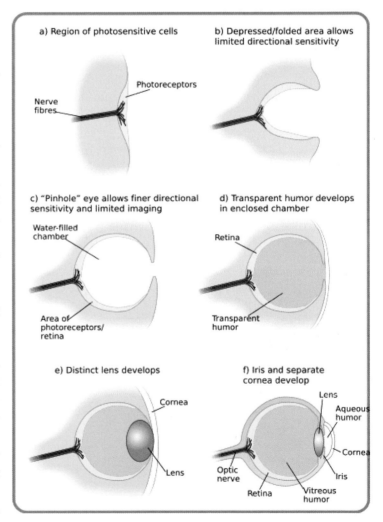

a) Region of photosensitive cells

b) Depressed/folded area allows limited directional sensitivity

Nerve fibres

Photoreceptors

c) "Pinhole" eye allows finer directional sensitivity and limited imaging

Water-filled chamber

Area of photoreceptors/ retina

d) Transparent humor develops in enclosed chamber

Retina

Transparent humor

e) Distinct lens develops

Cornea

Lens

f) Iris and separate cornea develop

Lens

Aqueous humor

Cornea

Iris

Optic nerve

Retina

Vitreous humor

Evolution of the eye
Human eyes evolved from simple flatworm eyes. *(GNU Free Documentation License)*

Color blindness is when one or all of the cone pigment proteins are defective. The reasons for their defects are due to changes in their three-dimensional structures resulting in the change of the amino acid sequences. Even a single amino acid change in a critical site of several hundred amino acids can alter the structure in such a way that the function of the protein is completely negated.

In summary, proteins have remarkable properties through their three-dimensional structures, and our ability to perceive the visual world is based on the visual pigments that collect light. The example of color blindness demonstrates the importance of the amino acid sequences in determining the structures of proteins. Our next logical questions are: What determines the amino acid sequences of proteins, and why do changes in amino acid sequences occur?

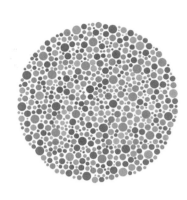

Ishihara chart
This is used for testing certain types of color blindness. *(Public Domain)*

II. Why is DNA the secret of life?

On February 28, 1953, two young biologists walked into The Eagle, a local pub for scientists, from the nearby Cavendish Laboratory of Cambridge University, England. They were James Watson, a 23-year-old American biologist from Chicago on a post-doctoral fellowship, and Francis Crick, a 35-year-old British graduate student working on his Ph.D. They were working together on finding the structure of DNA. Francis Crick interrupted the patrons' lunch to announce that he and Watson had "discovered the secret of life" after they had came up with the structure of DNA early that morning. This story was described in Watson's book *The Double Helix*, and a plaque was installed at the entrance of The Eagle in 2003 to commemorate the event. The structure of DNA is certainly one of the most important scientific discoveries in the 20th century. We will discuss its significance and impact on human society from the general education perspective.

II.1. What is DNA?

It is important for you to know about DNA and its relationship to proteins. DNA is found in all living organisms, and it is known as the secret of life. Since the discovery of its structure merely 55 years ago, the world has been changed beyond recognition by this knowledge. Today, almost every aspect of society is affected by applications derived from this knowledge, and the pace of change has accelerated.

I will use the step ladder analogy to help you envision the structure of DNA. DNA molecules are built by repeating units similar to a ladder, and all DNA molecules have basically the same structure as all ladders have. However, there are three major differences between the ladder image and the structure of the DNA. First, the DNA molecule is twisted on regular intervals, whereas the ladder is not. Second, the DNA molecule is very long with millions of rungs, whereas most ladders rarely have more than 50 rungs. Third, the DNA molecules can be untwisted and the two halves of the ladder can be separated from each other.

The basic unit of DNA molecules is a nucleotide, which is made up of three smaller chemical structures. The key chemical structure is a simple sugar known as deoxyribose, which connects to the other two chemical structures: a phosphate group and a base. The ribose and the phosphate form the sides of the ladder, and the base forms the rungs of the ladder. When the two halves of the ladder join together, the bases from each side link up to form the complete rungs. There are four different bases: adenine, thymine, guanine, and cytosine (A, T, G, and C). In order to form the rungs of the ladder, A must pair with T, and G must pair with C. This is a phenomenon known as base pairing.

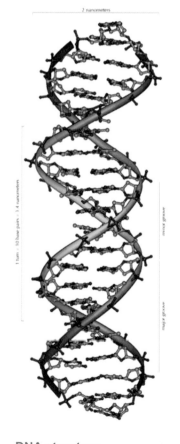

DNA structure
It resembles a twisted step ladder.
(Creative Commons Attribution)

Shortly after World War II, biologists realized that the chromosomes inside the cell nucleus are responsible for transmitting genetic information. They had learned that the instructions for the synthesis of all the proteins reside within the chromosomes. Therefore, understanding how the chromosomes carry this information and pass it from generation to generation would reveal the secret of life. Chemical analyses demonstrated that the chromosomes contained protein and DNA, but scientists at the time were skeptical that DNA was the material for genetic information because it seemed too simple.

By the late 1940s, experiments had provided strong evidence that biological traits could only be passed from one organism to another through DNA, not proteins. The question was how a simple molecule like DNA could be the carrier of complex molecular information. Watson and Crick in Cambridge University and another group of scientists (Rosalind Franklin and Maurice Wilkins) at King's College in London were in a race to reveal the structure of DNA. The King's College group used X-ray to examine the structure of DNA. In early 1953, Franklin took the now famous X-ray photo that revealed that DNA is a double helix. This photo was the key to unlocking the secret of life.

James Watson
(Public Domain)

Watson saw the photo when he visited King's College before it was published. He immediately recognized its significance and rushed back to Cambridge to discuss it with Crick. Based on this information, they proposed the DNA double helix model. There are two important aspects of the model that convinced them that this was the correct model, because it met all the requirements for carrying genetic information for biological organisms. The first aspect is the nearly identical dimension of the nucleotides, allowing them to stack on each other to form a stable and large DNA molecule with millions of nucleotides. This provides a very efficient way to organize and package DNA molecules in a minimum amount of space.

The second aspect is the double helix that is formed by complementary base pairing of AT and GC. This structure provides an ingenious mechanism for replicating the DNA molecule. All it takes is untwisting the DNA molecule and separating the two halves. The exposed halves now become the templates for the synthesis of the other halves. The building of the new half will be guided by the exposed bases on the existing half, with A only pairing with T, and G pairing with C. The final double helix molecules contain one original strand and one newly synthesized strand. The two new daughter DNA double helices are now identical to the original DNA molecule and to each other. In less than five years the molecular mechanism for DNA replication was discovered, confirming the DNA structure model.

Francis Crick
(Creative Commons Attribution)

In summary, the discovery of the structure of DNA has been a culmination of research over the first half of the 20th century. Watson and Crick were at the right time and the right place to put the information together. If they had not done so, it was quite likely that Rosalind Franklin and her colleagues at King's College would have made the same discovery in less than a year. This is an example of how science is shared knowledge that can be built upon by previous observations, principles, and theories to reach a better and fuller understanding.

II.2. How does DNA carry genetic information?

The structure of DNA discovered by Watson and Crick formed the foundation of molecular genetics. From that point on, biologists knew where to look for the biological answers of inheritance, and the progress in this area came in a fast and furious pace. Almost immediately after the structure of DNA was revealed, the A, T, G, and C that make up the rungs of the ladder were recognized to represent some type of code that could be translated into the amino acid sequences of proteins. Within ten years from the discovery of the structure of DNA, the genetic code was discovered. Since so much of the modern world relies on this knowledge, it is very important for you to have at least a general understanding of the workings of the genetic code.

Rosalind Franklin
(Public Domain)

Watson and Crick knew that bases must join together to form a code to represent the sequence of the amino acids in proteins. A coding system with two bases (4^2)

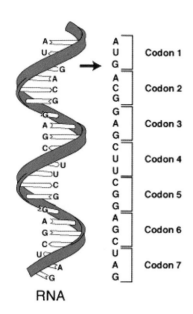

RNA

Ribonucleic acid

Genetic Code

Each triplet nucleotide are codes for an amino acid. *(Public Domain)*

gives 16 codes, which would not be sufficient because there are 20 amino acids. A coding system with three bases (4^3) has 64 codes, more than enough for the 20 amino acids. By the early 1960s, the genetic codes were broken, and the three-base code was discovered to be the correct code. Since there are more codes than amino acids, it was revealed that all amino acids are represented by more than two codes. There are additional codes serving as punctuation marks. For example, there are codes known as stop codons, signifying the end of the protein, and codes known as start codons, denoting the beginning of a protein.

When the genetic codes of different living organisms were compared, researchers discovered that the genetic code is universal. The same code is used by all living organisms on Earth, from simple bacteria to highly complex mammals. Furthermore, viruses use the same genetic code. This universality of the genetic code makes it possible to carry out genetic engineering. DNA from individuals of one species can be introduced into individuals of another species. This DNA will be used to synthesize proteins from another organism. This type of DNA manipulation is how human insulin is produced in bacterial cells.

DNA indirectly controls protein synthesis by directing the synthesis of RNA, a process known as transcription. RNA is almost identical to DNA with these five exceptions. First, instead of having deoxyribose, RNA has ribose. Second, in RNA the base thymine is replaced by uracil. Third, RNA is a single strand rather than a double helix. Fourth, RNA is much smaller than DNA molecules, and lastly, RNA is very unstable and turns over rapidly. The most important type of RNA is the messenger RNA (mRNA). Imagine the messenger RNA as copies of a page from the master plan that is given to the contractors to use on the job.

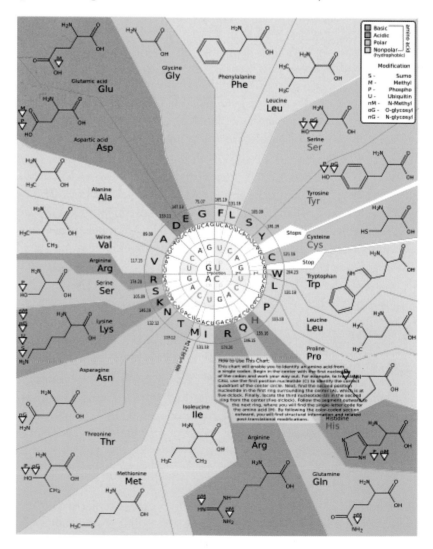

Genetic Code

The letters on the outer ring represent the amino acids. More than one genetic code is used for each amino acid. *(Public Domain)*

With the use of the mRNA, the cell can have precise control of what proteins need to be made at any one time by transcribing specific regions of the DNA molecules. Furthermore, the cells can control the production of the amount of protein by controlling the number of RNA copies transcribed. Finally, cells can terminate the synthesis of a particular protein by stopping transcription and by destroying any existing copies. Therefore, the mRNA system provides the cells with precise regulation of protein synthesis.

Protein synthesis involves components that are found in the cytoplasm outside the nucleus. The process of protein synthesis is also known as translation and requires the following components: mRNA, ribosomes, transfer RNA (tRNA), and free amino acids. The ribosomes are complex biological molecules that can be considered to be biological nano machines. They capture mRNA as soon as they leave the nucleus. The tRNAs are small RNA molecules that deliver the amino acids to the ribosomes. The tRNA has two important regions: one for binding to amino acids and the other for binding to the mRNA through base pairing. They serve as molecular taxis for the amino acids.

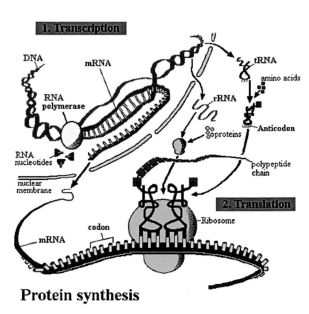

Protein synthesis

Protein synthesis
Cells utilize a two-step process to produce proteins. *(Public Domain)*

During translation, the tRNA supplies amino acids to the ribosomes, which then join them together to form proteins. The amino acid sequence of the protein is determined by the mRNA. As the protein is being synthesized, it gradually emerges from the ribosome. The protein will fold to its proper shape as the functional groups of the amino acids begin to interact with each other. The entire process occurs spontaneously and at a very high speed. A cell can synthesize over several thousand different proteins each second.

In summary, through the process of transcription, small segments of the DNA can be copied into mRNA, which then in turn directs the synthesis of proteins according to the genetic code. This is a system with extraordinary simplicity and elegance. This knowledge has transformed the understanding of life. In addition to its biological significance, it also has philosophical implications.

II.3. Can DNA Change?

The transmission of genetic information from DNA to RNA to protein has become the tenet of modern biology. In the late 1950s, Francis Crick coined the phrase Central Dogma to describe this path of biological communication. The information flow is unidirectional, suggesting that the changes in amino acid sequences of proteins in living organisms cannot lead to change in DNA sequences. This Central Dogma will hold as long as no counter evidence is found. Thus far, no exception to the Central Dogma has been discovered. This example further illustrates the falsifiability of scientific knowledge because of its evidential nature. As long as there is no evidence violating the prediction of a scientific theory, it will remain as truth. In the case of the Central Dogma, it has survived all the tests in the past 50 years.

A human cell has six billion bases (or base pairs) of DNA in its 46 chromosomes located in the cell nucleus. Each time a cell divides, the entire 46 chromosomes must be replicated. Throughout the lifetime of a human individual, a quadrillion cell divisions take place, and the number of DNA bases that are replicated is astronomical. However, DNA replication is amazingly accurate, and researchers have estimated that the error rate is one in every one billion base pairs replicated. Therefore, there are only six errors made when replicating six billion bases during each cell division which is a truly remarkable fidelity. The double helix property of the DNA evolved to ensure such accuracy.

Now we have learned that the DNA replicating machineries have additional features to ensure the accuracy of the replication process. This includes a proofreading mechanism. After the replication of each segment of the DNA, a protein machine goes through the newly replicated bases to ensure proper base pairing between the new strand and the old strand of the double helix. If an error is detected, another protein will excise the incorrect base in the new strand and replace it with the correct base. To ensure that the replication is accurate, there is more than one level of proofreading mechanisms.

Despite the accuracy in DNA replication and proofreading mechanisms, errors in DNA replication are inevitable. The resulting change in DNA sequences is known as mutation. Most mutations only affect the individuals during their lifetime. These mutations are partially responsible for aging, leading to the decline in cellular functions. Some of these mutations cause cancer, as the mutated cells fail to respond to the regulatory control on cell growth and cell division. These types of mutation are known as somatic mutations, because they affect somatic cells. However, there are other types of mutation that can be passed onto the future generations.

If the mutations take place in the cells of the reproductive system, the resulting errors in the DNA sequences will be incorporated into the sperm and eggs. These changes will be passed to the next generation, and all future generations will be affected. These types of mutation that can affect future generations are known as gametic mutations. The consequences of gametic mutation can be detrimental as well as beneficial. In some cases, fetal development fails completely. Most of the mutations appear to be inconsequential, whereas some mutations are beneficial and provide survival advantages.

All mutations take place during DNA replication, as the mutating agents (also known as mutagens) cause the DNA replicating machinery to make mistakes. Most of the mutagens cause chemical modifications of the bases on the original strand. If these chemical modifications are not corrected, a base of A could be misconstrued as the base G. Therefore, instead of inserting a T, a C is incorporated into the new strand. Consequently, during the next round of replication, the opposing strand will get a G instead of an A. It is now known that the base T can undergo a spontaneous shift into a structure resembling the base C. The likelihood of this occuring is one in 100 million; this type of mutation is known as spontaneous mutation.

However, mutation rates can be elevated by as much as 10 to 1,000 times in the presence of mutagens. The most common mutagens are UV light, X-ray, and ionizing radiations. Due to their high energy content, all these agents can lead to the activation of the bases, causing them to become temporarily or permanently modified to resemble other bases. Another major group of mutagens is chemical mutagens, which chemically modify the bases. During DNA replication, the modified bases are read incorrectly by the DNA replicating machinery. This type of mutation is known as induced mutation.

In summary, DNA replication has evolved exceptional accuracy, with an extremely low error rate. However, the bases can be changed spontaneously or chemically, causing them to be misread. These changes are essentially random, affecting any part of the DNA molecule. If the mutation occurs in somatic cells, it will not be passed to the next generation. If the mutation occurs in the gametes, it will affect the future generations.

Nagasaki atomic bomb
Many of the citizens suffered from radiation damage to their DNA years later. *(Public Domain)*

III. WHAT ARE THE CONSEQUENCES OF GENETIC CHANGES?

Throughout the life of a biological organism, mutation takes place constantly. These genetic changes can occur at any point in the human DNA. The location of the mutation is unpredictable, and the effects of the mutation are also unpredictable. However, exposure to mutagens can lead to increased incidents of cancer during the lifetime of the individual. Survivors of the Hiroshima and Nagasaki atomic blasts had cancer rates many times higher than normal. However, the greatest impact of mutation is on the future generation when the targets of change are the gametes. Once these changes in DNA occur, they will be passed down from generation to generation. The effects of these changes have shaped the biological world since life first appeared on Earth.

III.1. What are the effects of genetic changes?

The study of mutation was first conducted by using X-ray to alter biological traits in fruit flies nearly 30 years before the discovery of the structure of the DNA. The effect of the X-ray was entirely random, causing many common morphological changes, such as eye color, wing markings, and length of the antennae. However, some of the changes were profound, such as inappropriate embryonic development, severe muscle defects, inappropriate appendage development, and other physiological disturbances. Interestingly, many of these disorders are similar to genetic disorders found in humans. The short generation time of the fruit flies has made them ideal experimental organisms for studying genetic changes and genetic disorders.

Mutation can affect the DNA sequences in several different ways, and the resulting changes to the amino acid sequences of the protein could be minor or severe. The most common form of mutation is known as base substitution, in which a single base is replaced. Base substitution can be unnoticeable or can be severe for the individuals depending on how they alter the structure and function of the proteins. Researchers have discovered that the DNA sequences of many genes within the population are full of DNA substitutions. These base substitution mutations arise randomly, and if they do not affect the survival and reproductive success of the offspring, they are passed from one generation to the next.

The protein hemoglobin provides an example of the significance of base substitution. Hemoglobin is a protein involved in the transportation of oxygen. It has 143 amino acid residues, which is determined by its DNA sequences. Together this DNA sequence is known as a gene. Since each amino acid is encoded by three nucleotide bases, the entire gene has 429 bases (three bases for each amino acid). The human disease sickle cell anemia is caused by a single base substitution. How this base substitution came about is unknown, but it is probably caused by replication errors. The result of this base substitution is a single amino acid change in the protein.

Sickle cell anemia was first recognized by a Chicago cardiologist and professor of medicine in 1904 when he observed the elongated and sickle shape red blood cells in a 20-year-old dental student, Walter Noel, from Grenada. He was admitted to the hospital after suffering from anemia, a condition of low red blood cell count. He also suffered from periodic severe muscle pain and joint disorders. He died eight years later from pneumonia in association with his anemic condition. Further studies demonstrated that the anemic condition is associated with the abnormal rigid, sickle shape of the red blood cells, restricting their normal movement through blood vessels. Consequently, they are easily damaged and destroyed, leading to the anemic condition.

The sickle shape of the red blood cells is caused by the unusual behavior of hemoglobin, which is the main protein inside the red blood cells. Hemoglobin is responsible for binding and transporting oxygen to different parts of the body. In normal individuals, the hemoglobin molecules assume a globular shape due to their amino acid sequences. As discussed earlier, the shape of a protein is based on the folding of the molecule. The amino acid sequences are critical in determining how the proteins fold into a specific shape. Furthermore, the shape of a protein also

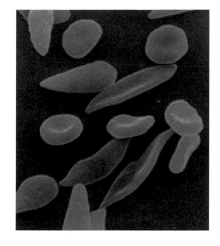

Sickle cell anemia
The red blood cells assume irregular shapes and are easily damaged. *(Public Domain)*

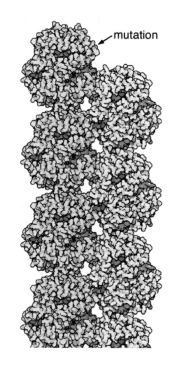

←mutation

Hemoglobin polymerization
Mutation causes the hemoglobin to stick together. *(Public Domain)*

governs how it will interact with other proteins in the environment. Each protein is a part of a complex machine, and their shapes determine how they function as a whole. If a protein folds improperly, it can affect the function of the entire "machine."

Sickle cell anemia is one of the best examples to demonstrate how a single base change in the gene of one protein can lead to a serious and fatal medical condition. This is a further demonstration that the human body is a complex and highly integrated system with multiple parts. Some of the parts are critical for the function of the entire system, and any defects in these components, no matter how small, are fatal. The defect in the sickle cell hemoglobin is due to a single base change in the genetic code of the 6th amino acid in the amino acid sequence of the protein. This amino acid is crucial in how the protein folds to assume its three-dimensional shape.

This tiny base change has severe consequences because it affects how the sickle cell hemoglobin behaves under low oxygen tension, which can be created by strenuous exercise, flying, and mountain climbing. The shape change of the sickle cell hemoglobin caused by the single amino acid substitution makes the proteins aggregate to form a rigid, rod-like structure when oxygen concentration is low. The cells are stretched into the characteristic sickle shape as a result. Researchers have discovered that similar changes in protein shapes are due to the changes in DNA sequences caused by mutation. The results of these changes can be detrimental as in the case of sickle cell anemia. If they do not affect the structure and function of the proteins, they have no effect. They can even be beneficial if they improve the function of the proteins.

III.2. What are other types of genetic changes?

In order to understand how mutation affects the structure and function of proteins, it is important to know the definition of a gene. The definition of a gene is more complex than what can be fully explained in this course, and we will address the most relevant aspects to derive a better understanding of the significance of genetic changes.

DNA sequences are continuing strings of nucleotides of ATGC with no space to separate one gene from the others. Researchers have discovered that there are internal structures that serve as punctuation marks to separate the genes. Among the 64 codons, there is one start codon, which signifies the beginning of a gene. There are three stop codons, which signify the end of a gene. Between the start and the stop codons are the DNA sequences representing the amino acids according to the triplet genetic codes. These sequences are known as the coding DNA regions. There are other DNA sequences that do not encode for any amino acids. These are known as the noncoding DNA regions.

The start and stop codons form the basic demarcation of a gene, and they serve as the beginning and termination points of the transcription of mRNA. Base substitutions can change the start and stop codons and can cause problems in the synthesis of mRNA and subsequently protein synthesis. For example, if a base substitution converts one of the codons in the middle of the gene into a stop codon, mRNA transcription will be terminated prematurely. A short mRNA makes a short protein, which folds improperly resulting in improper function. Similarly, a base substitution of the start codon will result in the mRNA not being transcribed at all, and the proteins of this gene will be absent. Therefore, understanding the structure of genes is important in order to appreciate the consequences of base substitution.

In addition to base substitutions, base insertions and deletions are the most common forms of mutation. They are normally caused by chemical mutagens, which lead to the base insertion and deletion during DNA replication by slightly altering the structure of DNA. The number of base insertions or deletions can range from one base to several thousand bases. Depending on the number of bases that are

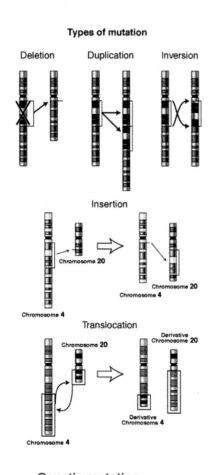

Types of mutation

Deletion   Duplication   Inversion

Insertion

Chromosome 20

Chromosome 20
Chromosome 4

Chromosome 4

Translocation

Chromosome 20

Derivative
Chromosome 20

Derivative
Chromosome 4

Chromosome 4

Genetic mutation

These types of mutations are caused by chromosome rearrangement. *(Public Domain)*

inserted or deleted from the DNA sequence, the results range from minor to severe consequences.

The most severe effect of either base insertion or deletion is the disruption of the sequence of the triplet codes. Since there is no punctuation mark within the DNA sequence of a gene, removing or adding one base will alter the reading frame up or down, respectively, from the point of mutation. The result is catastrophic, as the amino acid sequence of this mutated gene is completely different from the normal gene. This type of mutation is known as frame shift mutation, because the reading frame is shifted as a result. The only time that the reading frame remains intact is when the deletion and insertion is in the multiple of three bases.

Mutation can also occur in scales larger than base substitution, deletion, and insertion. The human genome, the total DNA of a human cell, consists of 6 billion nucleotide base pairs, forming 23 pair of chromosomes. Human chromosomes are like chapters of a book, and they are numbered based on their size, with chromosome one being the largest and chromosome 22 being the smallest. The last pair consists of the sex chromosomes, the X and Y chromosomes. During each cell division, the chromosomes are replicated and divided equally between two daughter cells. However, mistakes sometime occur resulting in large scale chromosomal abnormalities.

The most well-known chromosomal disorder is Down syndrome, which is a genetic condition with an extra chromosome 21. During the formation of the gametes, the two chromosomes 21 fail to enter into two separate gametes. The extra chromosome 21 is responsible for the physical characteristics and mental disabilities associated with Down syndrome. This phenomenon of inappropriate chromosome separation is known as chromosomal nondisjunction. There are other types of large scale mutation. In some cases, a segment of chromosome can be moved from one chromosome to another in a process known as translocation. In other cases, a segment of chromosome is turned upside down in a process known as inversion. There are genetic disorders associated with each of these large scale mutations.

In summary, genetic changes in the form of mutation occur in almost every conceivable way. These genetic changes are completely random, and the outcomes for the individuals are mostly either detrimental or neutral. Occasionally, these changes provide benefits for the survival and reproductive success of the individuals.

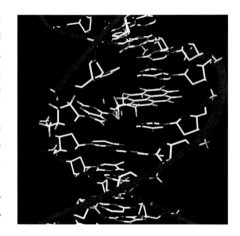

Cigarette smoke
Compound in cigarette smoke distorted the structure of DNA, leading to replication errors and mutation. *(Public Domain)*

III.3. How do genes cause different traits?

Genes have an interesting dichotomy; they are both static and changeable at the same time. Genes are the foundation of biological inheritance, and through the fidelity of DNA replication, biological traits are passed from one generation to the next. As we have learned earlier, genes can be altered by mistakes during DNA replication, and these mistakes occur spontaneously or are induced by environmental factors, ranging from radiation to chemicals. As we progress through the course, you will discover that these two properties of genes are responsible for every aspect of the biological world. These two aspects of the genes are also the foundation of human traits. To understand individual variations and uniqueness, we will further explore how genes cause different traits.

There are some traits, such as sickle cell anemia and other genetic disorders, that are caused by a single gene. Most of these traits are linked to the mutation of a critical gene, such as the hemoglobin gene in sickle cell anemia. It is easy to identify a gene that is responsible for a particular trait when the trait is a matter of life and death. There are many other examples of traits that can be grouped in this classification, because they often lead to highly specific symptoms.

Another example includes hemophilia. The clinical symptom of hemophilia is the inability of the blood to clot. The gene in question encodes for a protein that is critical in the clotting process. Another well-known example is cystic fibrosis, and the gene responsible for this disorder is a membrane protein that controls the flow of ions through the cell membrane. Cystic fibrosis is the result of a deletion in the gene, leading to a nonfunctional protein. This affects the ion transport in many cells in the body, with the most severe consequences affecting respiration. However, for most other traits, the genetic pictures are more complex.

The skin color trait has a more complex genetic pattern, which is responsible for wide variations in skin color. The two genes that encode for the pigment proteins are eumelanin and pheomelanin. The various amounts of these two proteins play a role in determining skin color. Mutations in these two genes also affect the pigment quality of these two proteins, being darker or lighter. These result in complex interactions between various mutations of the pigments genes leading to a wide range of color combinations.

Another factor that affects the skin color trait is based on how much pigments are produced by the pigment producing cells, the melanocytes. Environmental factors regulate skin color as in the case of tanning by inducing the secretion of a hormone, which then stimulates the melanocytes to synthesize the pigment proteins. Researchers have identified genes that encode proteins that are involved in the regulatory pathways. Mutation of these genes causes an indirect effect on skin color via the effectiveness of these proteins in carrying out their regulatory functions. Therefore, in the case of the skin color, about four to ten genes form an interactive network in controlling the full range of skin colors.

The interactions between genes and the environment exist over a broad range. In some traits, such as sickle cell anemia, the environment has little or no impact on the outcome. Having the sickle cell anemia mutation inevitably leads to the development of the sickle cell trait. This is also true for cystic fibrosis and hemophilia. However, the majority of human traits are more complicated because many genes interact with each other to determine observable traits such as hair color, height, and body weight.

Understanding the impact of environment is of particular importance with complex diseases such as cancer, heart disease, diabetes, and mental disorders. Environmental factors are known to play an important role in the formation of these diseases in addition to genes. With a better understanding of the functions of genes involved in these diseases, making predictions of their occurrences has become possible. This knowledge is obviously important in both their treatment and prevention. Many of these diseases occur late in life, suggesting that the interactions between genes and environmental factors are crucial in the formation of these diseases. By knowing their genetic dispositions, people can avoid certain diseases through pursuing certain lifestyles.

In summary, biologists have come a long way in understanding biological traits since the discovery of the DNA structure by Watson and Crick merely 55 years ago. The future of genetics is almost impossible to imagine, as the applications of this knowledge has led to the development of remarkable technology.

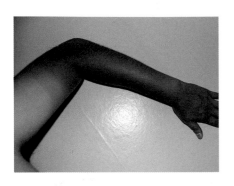

Sun tanning

UV light as an environmental factor in the stimulation of melanin production in serving as a protection against damage to dermal cells.
(Public Domain)

Chapter 3

Genetic Disorders

How perfect is your genetic heritage?

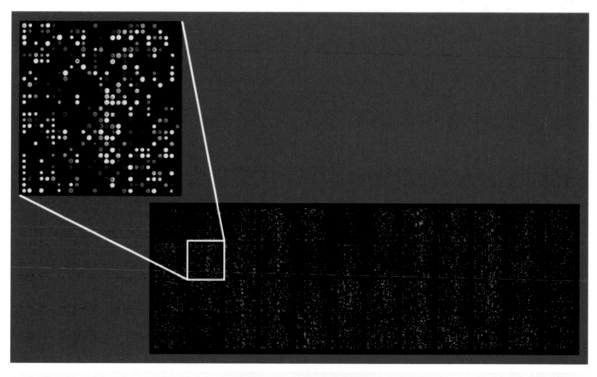

Future of genetic testing

A genetic technique known as microarray (also known as gene chip) can be used to test the genetic activities of thousands of genes simultaneously. *(Public Domain)*

CHAPTER 3. GENETIC DISORDERS

Future of genetics

A science fiction movie about human genetic testing and genetic engineering. *(Fair use poster)*

In the science fiction film *GATTACA*, the protagonist of the story was tested at birth and was found to have a 60% probability for developing a neurological condition, a 42% probability for developing manic depression, a 89% probability for developing an attention deficit disorder, a 99% probability for developing a heart disorder, and a life expectancy of 30.2 years. Will this technology become a reality? If so, how long will it take before this type of genetic testing becomes widely available? How will this knowledge be used to avoid genetic disorders, to carry out gene therapy, or even to enhance individual genetic potential? What would be the impact of genetic testing on society and on the human species?

I. WHAT ARE EARLY-ONSET GENETIC DISORDERS?

Some genetic disorders appear early in life, sometimes even in the first several months. In most cases, however, symptoms of the disease first become noticeable to parents when their child fails to meet certain developmental milestones. These conditions are collectively known as early-onset genetic disorders. There are many different types of early-onset genetic disorders, and most of the children affected by these disorders die in their infancy. In some of these genetic disorders, medical intervention can extend life expectancy into early adulthood. With a few exceptions, however, the early-onset genetic disorders are not curable.

I.1. *What is an example of an early-onset genetic disorder?*

There is a rare, early-onset genetic disorder known as Tay-Sachs disease. There is presently no cure for this disease. When it occurs, a family faces devastating effects. One sad story about this disease concerns a little boy named Hayden. Hayden was a healthy infant boy, and he grew and developed normally in the first eight months of his life. He was his parents' first child, and they adored his easy going and happy temperament. He and his father loved to make each other laugh, and they bonded immediately. But, by about one year, Hayden started to miss developmental milestones, and his parents became alarmed by his increased passivity.

Hayden was examined by a pediatrician, who at first, thought Hayden had only a slight delay in his development. As the weeks went by, however, Hayden's condition worsened, and he started having difficulty moving his arms and legs. Eventually, Hayden was diagnosed with Tay-Sachs disease, a genetic disorder that causes cumulative brain damage. After Hayden was diagnosed with the disease, his condition deteriorated rapidly. Within six months, Hayden could not move, had great difficulties swallowing, and experienced over 100 seizures each day. Hayden died shortly after his fourth birthday.

After Hayden was diagnosed with Tay-Sachs disease, his father's identical twin brother Charlie came to stay with the family to provide emotional support. The night after Charlie arrived in their home, he called his wife Blythe to tell her about Hayden's condition. To learn more about Tay-Sachs disease, Blythe went on the Tay-Sachs web site. She read the symptoms of Tay-Sachs and learned that one of the early warning signs is an exaggerated startle response in babies between six and eight months of age. Blythe and Charlie had two daughters, 3-year-old Taylor and 8-month-old Cameron. Blythe had always noticed that Cameron had a more exaggerated startle response than her sister.

Blythe took her daughters to the pediatrician and had both of them tested for Tay-Sachs disease. Sadly, it was discovered that Cameron had Tay-Sachs disease and that Blythe was a carrier for the Tay-Sachs gene. Tay-Sachs is a rare disease, and in order for a child to have Tay-Sachs, both parents must be carriers. Both Charlie and his twin brother Tim were carriers. Blythe and Hayden's mother Allison are not related, but they were best friends and college roommates. All four parents were carriers; for them, it was a bad roll of the genetic dice.

Tay-Sachs is a relentless disease; it starts gradually and causes damage to a baby's brain at about six months of age. The actual pathological process seems benign, but the consequences are devastating. In Tay-Sachs babies, the brain lacks an enzyme that is required to breakdown excessive fatty tissues that are produced by neurons in the brain. Without this enzyme, the fatty metabolites accumulate and slowly kill the neurons. The absence of the enzyme is caused by a mutation of the gene that encodes the enzyme. A single base substitution changes the DNA sequence, resulting in a change of the amino acid sequences. With this change, the appropriate three-dimensional structure of the protein is gone, and the enzymatic function of the protein is lost.

I.2. What are autosomal recessive disorders?

There are many other early-onset genetic disorders. One characteristic that these disorders share is their inheritance pattern which is autosomal recessive. In autosomal recessive disorders the child must receive a copy of the defective gene from both parents, even though the parents have no symptoms of the disease. This mode of inheritance makes autosomal recessive disorders nearly impossible to predict. In Hayden's case, neither of his parents realized that they had passed the defective gene to him. Therefore, autosomal recessive disorders can remain hidden for generations until chance puts two carriers together. Even then, not all their offspring will have the disease.

The cause of an autosomal recessive disorder is a mutation that results in a gene losing its function. This is known as a loss-of-function mutation. Imagine that you have two cell phones in your possession, and both of them are in working condition. If one breaks, you still have the other one to use. If both of them are broken, however, you are out of luck. This is how autosomal recessive disorders work. In each of your cells, you have two copies of the same gene. If one copy is mutated and becomes non-functional, the other copy still produces enough product to keep a cell functioning. In this situation, the person who carries only one copy of a mutated gene is known as a carrier.

Carriers are asymptomatic, and in Hayden's story, his parents, uncle, and his aunt were all asymptomatic carriers. When Hayden's parents reproduced, there was a 25% chance for their offspring to receive two copies of the defective gene. In Hayden's case, without functional enzymes to remove the fatty acid metabolites, his brain underwent a slow and inevitable deterioration. From this example, there are four important genetic terms: dominant, recessive, homozygous, and heterozygous.

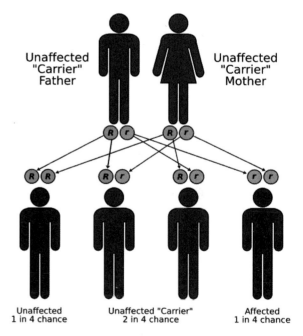

Autosomal recessive disorders

If both parents are carriers of the mutation, their offspring has a 1 in 4 chance of developing Tay-Sachs disease. *(Public Domain)*

Hayden was homozygous recessive for the defective gene, which means that he had two copies of the mutant gene. Homozygous means the same, and recessive means that the gene is defective. Hayden's parents had one copy of the normal gene and one copy of the mutant gene, making them heterozygous. The normal gene is referred to as dominant because it can compensate for the mutant gene. Another useful genetic term is allele. All versions of the same gene are referred to as alleles. For example, all different colors or models of the Volkswagen Beetle are alleles in the automobile world.

Autosome refers to all the chromosomes in a human cell other than the sex chromosomes. In reproductive cells, such as the sperm and the eggs, there are 22 distinct autosomes and one sex chromosome, which is either an X or a Y chromosome. In a normal body cell, also known as a somatic cell, there are 44 autosomes (one set from the father and one set from the mother) and two sex chromosomes (XX or XY) for sex determination. In an autosomal recessive disorder, the gene in question is located on one of the autosomes.

The majority of genetic disorders are autosomal recessive disorders. The most common genetic disorder in the United States is cystic fibrosis, which affects one baby in every 2,000 live births. Recent genetic studies have showed that as many as 1 in every 20 Caucasians is a carrier for cystic fibrosis. Other common autosomal recessive disorders include sickle cell anemia and phenylketonuria. The genetic and biochemical mechanisms of all autosomal recessive disorders are due to a loss of gene function. Until the advent of genetic testing, autosomal recessive disorders had been difficult to predict because they often "skip" generations.

I.3. What are sex-linked recessive disorders?

During the 19th and early 20th centuries, a mysterious disease swept through the European royal families and became known as the royal disease. The disease was a genetic disorder in which the afflicted individuals were unable to stop bleeding after an external or internal injury. However, the disease occurred mainly in male children and only rarely in female children. The disease was hemophilia. In this condition, a defect occurs in the blood clotting system, which consists of a complex set of interacting proteins that form a physical barrier to seal off injury sites of blood vessels. Researchers have discovered that hemophilia is a group of recessive genetic disorders that are caused by a mutation in any one of the proteins in the clotting system.

The most common form of hemophilia is hemophilia A. In this condition, a clotting factor, known as factor VIII, is mutated and non-functional. Without factor VIII, blood does not clot, and patients can bleed to death. Hemophilia A occurs in about 1 in 5,000-10,000 male births, making it one of the most common genetic disorders in the U.S. The source of the European royal disease was traced to Queen Victoria. The disease was then passed on by two of her daughters (Princess Alice and

The young Queen Victoria

A mutation in the blood clotting system was passed from her.
(Public Domain)

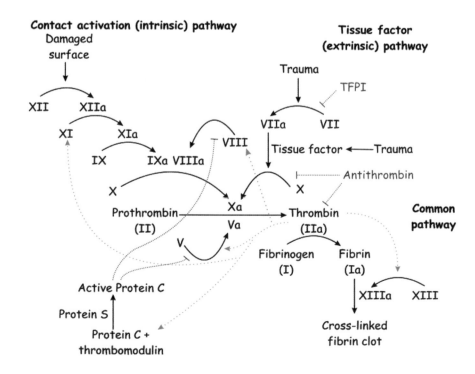

The blood clotting pathways

Many components are involved in the blood clotting cascade. Each component acts on another component. If one of the components is defective, the cascade comes to a stop. *(GNU Free Documentation Licence)*

Princess Beatrice) to their children. The disease was spread to the royal families of Spain, Germany, and Russia through intermarriages between the European families.

The most intriguing aspect of the European royal disease was that none of the female descendents of Queen Victoria were affected. However, it was clear from analyses of the royal family tree that the female descendents were carriers. From subsequent genetic studies in the early 20th century, hemophilia became a prime example of a sex-linked recessive genetic disorder. The mutant hemophilia allele was considered recessive, because the mutation changed the DNA sequences of the normal allele, leading to the production of a non-functional factor VIII protein. In

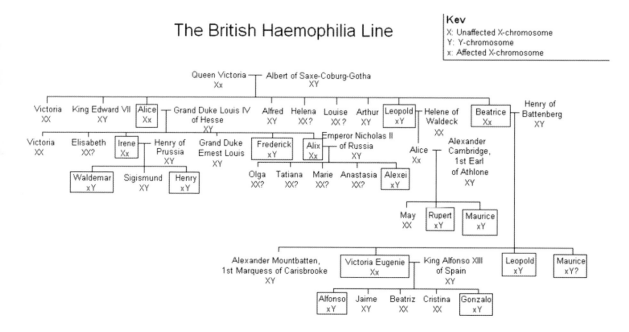

a heterozygous state, in which there is a copy of the normal gene, there is an adequate production of the factor VIII protein, and the individual is normal.

The male-bias occurrence of hemophilia results because the factor VIII gene is located on the X chromosome. In human sex determination, two X chromosomes are female, and one X and one Y chromosomes are male. The X and Y chromosomes contain genes for sex determination. However, the X chromosome is much larger than the Y chromosome and contains other genes, including the factor VIII gene. Since females have two X chromosomes, they also have two factor VIII genes. Therefore, females can become carriers for hemophilia A when they carry one copy of the normal factor VIII gene and one copy of the mutated factor VIII gene.

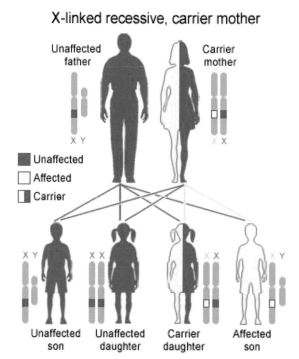

The Royal Disease

With intermarriage between members of the European royal families, hemophilia had a profound impact on 19th century European history. *(GNU Free Documentation License))*

X-linked recessive traits

Sons are more likely to acquire the traits than daughters. *(Public Domain)*

If a male inherits the X chromosome that carries the mutated factor VIII gene, he will surely get the disease. Since there is no factor VIII gene on the Y chromosome, there is no mechanism for compensation. Since hemophilia could not be treated in Victorian England, all affected children died before reaching reproductive age. Consequently, it is unlikely for a female to receive two copies of mutated factor VIII genes from her parents. This is why sex-linked recessive disorders are rarely found in female offspring. This is not only true for hemophilia but also for almost all other sex-linked recessive disorders.

Today, most individuals with hemophilia A can live beyond childhood and have children. Even though hemophilia A cannot be cured, it can be treated by factor VIII that is isolated from donated blood and plasma. The treatment is highly effective. However, until 1992, blood products were not routinely screened for pathogens. This resulted in many hemophiliacs being infected with HIV and hepatitis C. It has been estimated that as much as 50% of the U.S. hemophilia population (greater than 100,000 people) was infected with AIDS from the contaminated blood supply. Today, the blood supply around the world is closely scrutinized.

The discovery of sex-link recessive genetic disorders allowed for a new understanding of the nature of genetic disorders. Genetic counseling has become important for advising potential parents of the chances of their children developing these genetic diseases. How all this information will be used, however, is still unknown.

II. WHAT ARE LATE-ONSET GENETIC DISORDERS?

Until the 1960s, most researchers only considered the genetic disorders that affected the early life stages. Until then, environment factors were considered more important in determining the health of older individuals. Personal health, such as obesity, diabetes, and mental disability, was considered to be the consequence of life styles, behavior, and personal choices. Alcohol, drugs, excessive consumption, and lack of exercise were thought to be the main factors involved in health problems and mental incapacitation. However, these notions have been unsubstantiated by recent research, and increasingly, it has become clear that the interplay between genes and environment is critical in the development of many different types of diseases.

II.1. What is an example of a late-onset genetic disorder?

Woody Guthrie was a legendary American songwriter and folk singer. He wrote over 1,000 songs, and his best known song is "This Land is Your Land." As a musician constantly traveling on the road, Woody Guthrie lived a frantic life. By the late 1940s, his health declined, and his behavior became increasingly unpredictable. He received various diagnoses, including alcoholism and schizophrenia. During the next ten years, his condition worsened, and he developed jerky, random, and uncontrollable movements called chorea. Difficulties in eating, continence, and mobility led to a further decline in his health. Woody Guthrie died in 1967 at the age of 55.

Toward the end of his condition, Woody Guthrie was diagnosed with Huntington's disease. George Huntington first described this genetic neurological disorder in 1872. It was the first late-onset genetic disorder discovered. Huntington's disease occupies an important place in the research of genetic diseases. It was intensely studied in the 1980s and 1990s, because a cluster of Huntington's disease cases was discovered in a small isolated fishing village in Venezuela. Many of the families had multiple family members who were afflicted by the disease. This allowed geneticists to trace the inheritance pattern and to eventually determine the gene that is responsible for the disease.

From the studies, Huntington's disease was determined to be an autosomal dominant disorder. The term, autosomal, indicates that the mutant gene

Woody Guthrie
The lengendary folk singer and songwriter died from Huntington's disease at the age of 55. *(Public Domain)*

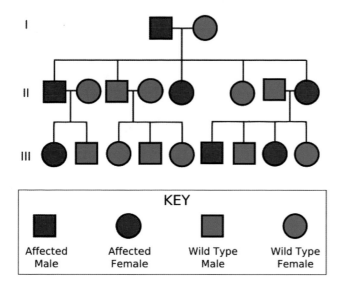

KEY

Affected Male | Affected Female | Wild Type Male | Wild Type Female

Autosomal dominant disorders
The chance for the children of parents with the disease to have the disease is 50%.
(Public Domain)

responsible for the disease is located on an autosome. In fact, it is located on chromosome 4. The disease is referred to as dominant because a single mutant gene is sufficient to cause the disease. In contrast, an autosomal recessive disorder requires two mutant genes for the disease to occur. A recessive mutant gene commonly leads to a loss-of-function, such as a loss in the function of an enzyme. The dominant mutant gene works differently.

With a dominant mutant gene, the mutation of some DNA results in a protein that causes havoc in the cell. For example, in Huntington's the mutant gene encodes for a protein that, instead of carrying out its normal function, induces the death of neurons in the brain. This type of mutation is called a gain-of-function mutation, but the function is often detrimental to the cell. In summary, in a recessive mutant gene, the function of the protein is lost, and the lack of function causes problems for the cells. In a dominant mutant gene, its protein product causes damage to the cells.

Why is Huntington's disease a late-onset genetic disorder? The answer to this question concerns the pathology of the disease. With this disease, the neurological damage in the brain does not fully develop until the third decade of life. It is possible that the damaging effect of the mutant gene accrues through time, because either the mutant proteins act slowly, or they are not very toxic to the cells. Because of the late onset of the disease symptoms, the afflicted individuals often have children and, therefore, pass the genetic disorder to the next generation. The children of someone with an autosomal dominant disorder, such as Huntington's disease, are at a 50% risk of developing that disease. It was later found that Woody Guthrie died from Huntington's disease, and two of Woody Guthrie's five children also died from Huntington's disease.

By the early 1990s, the mutant gene for Huntington's disease was discovered, and genetic testing for the disease became available. It was one of the first genetic diseases that allowed high risk individuals to be tested in order to determine their potential for developing the disease. Some of the individuals who have worked hard and have supported the research in identifying the Huntington's disease gene also had a family history of the disease. Interestingly, some of these individuals have chosen not to be tested. Initially, Arlo Guthrie, son of Woody, chose not to take the test, based on the argument that there was no cure for the disease. Knowing that he had the mutant gene would only complicate his life. Several years later, he changed his mind and took the test, because he felt a responsibility to have this information available for his children. It was a deep relief for him when his test was negative.

First Alzheimer's patient

The disease was first described in 1901 by Alois Alzheimer. *(Public Domain)*

II.2. How complex are late-onset genetic disorders?

As the world demographic shifts towards an older population, many age-related diseases, such as cardiovascular diseases, cancer, and stroke, have become more prevalent. Caring for the elderly has become a social and economic challenge. Of all the age-related conditions, however, the most difficult one to deal with is dementia. People with dementia suffer memory loss, confusion, and eventually, total mental incapacitation and loss of motor function. The most common cause of dementia is Alzheimer's disease, which is quickly becoming the greatest health threat to the well being of modern society. Finding a cure for this terrible disease is of the highest priority, because the social and economic cost of the disease is devastating.

There are two types of Alzheimer's disease based on their patterns of occurrence. The most common form is known as the sporadic form, which occurs in individuals over 65 years old. The risk of the disease increases dramatically as an individual gets older. The risk at 65 years is about three percent, but the risk at 85 years of age is between 35 to 50 percent. Until the appearance of the first symptoms, no diagnostic test is currently available to predict the development of Alzheimer's disease. The duration of the disease is estimated to be between 5 and 20 years. The only confirmative diagnosis of the disease is an autopsy.

The second type of Alzheimer's disease is characterized by the development of the disease earlier in life, usually between the ages of 30 and 50. Julia, a mother of eight children, first started to show symptoms of forgetfulness. One of her younger daughters recalled that she was left at her kindergarten because Julia forgot to pick her up after school. The other children recalled that she would get up in the middle of the night, dress, and prepare to go shopping. At first, they thought she suffered from severe depression, and she even received shock therapy to treat depression. Her young family was unable to understand the nature of their mother's illness until she was diagnosed with Alzheimer's disease.

After Julia died from pneumonia when she was 45 years old, the family thought their ordeal was over. Then, at the age of 37, one of the daughters, Fran, started to show symptoms of Alzheimer's disease, first with the loss of memory followed by mental confusion. Several years later, her younger brother Butch also developed Alzheimer's disease. At this point, three of the eight siblings have been afflicted with Alzheimer's disease. This form of Alzheimer's disease is known as familial Alzheimer's. Although this form of Alzheimer's disease accounts for less than 5% of the total cases of Alzheimer's disease, it serves as a model for studying the sporadic form of Alzheimer's disease.

Brain with Alzheimer's

Extensive loss of brain tissues in patients with Alzheimer's disease is seen with the MRI brain imaging on the left in comparison to the normal brain on the right. *(Public Domain)*

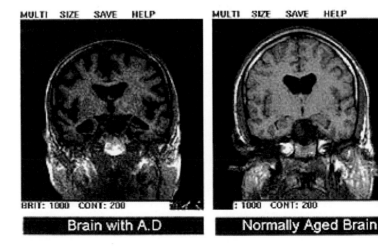

Brain with A.D   Normally Aged Brain

The familial form of Alzheimer's disease is an autosomal dominant disorder, and it follows the same pattern of inheritance as Huntingon's disease. Julia's children had a 50% chance of inheriting the disease. However, the genes that are responsible for the disease are more complex, and it appears that multiple genes are involved in the development of the disease. There are at least three known genes that are involved in Alzheimer's disease; a mutation in any one of these genes is sufficient to cause the familial form of Alzheimer's disease. These mutant genes produce proteins that affect the structure of the neurons in the brain and cause them to die. Researchers are currently working to understand how these proteins affect the brain.

Even though the two forms of Alzheimer's disease share many pathological similarities, researchers remain uncertain if the causative mechanisms are the same for the two types. Alzheimer's disease also demonstrates the interactions between genes and environment. In the familial form of the disease, genes are responsible for triggering the disease, whereas in the sporadic form, the environment is primarily responsible for initiating the disease. The ultimate disease process is the same for both, but the inducing process is different. Many genetic disorders follow a similar path. The next example demonstrates the importance of this knowledge in preventing the development of this type of genetic disorder.

II.3. *What are the genetics of cancer?*

Cancer is the second leading cause of death in the United States. Cancer is defined as a group of cells in the body that grow out of control and form large clusters of cells known as tumors. Occasionally, some of the cells detach from the tumor and spread to other parts of the body to form new tumors in a process known as metastasis. Researchers discovered that through mutations in genes that normally regulate cell division and growth, normal cells become tumor cells. For many years, it was believed that these mutations occurred in somatic cells during the lifetime of an individual and that they were not passed onto the next generation.

However, in the early 1970s, a researcher discovered that some cancers occur more frequently in families and demonstrate a pattern of genetic inheritance. One such cancer is breast cancer. Similar to Alzheimer's disease, there are two forms of breast cancer in genetic terms. The sporadic form occurs later in life with no clear pattern of inheritance, and the familial form occurs early in life and has a clear pattern of inheritance. The familial form accounts for 5% of all cases. The remaining incidents of breast cancer are the sporadic form. Together, breast cancer is the second most common cause of cancer, after lung cancer, in the U.S. In 2007, there were 41,000 breast cancer deaths, accounting for 7% of all cancer deaths in the U.S.

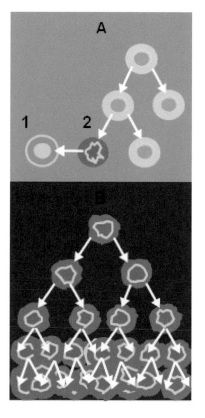

Progression of cancer
A mutation in a normal cell caused it to grow out of control. This single cell grows and develops into cancer. *(Public Domain)*

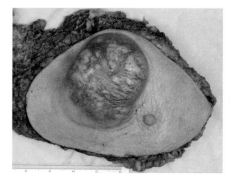

A large tumor in the breast
Some breat tumors can be highly aggressive and grow rapidly as in this case. *(Public Domain)*

Colon cancer

A tumor has erupted from the wall of the colon leading to ulceration and bleeding. *(Public Domain)*

Deborah Linder, a 30-year-old medical resident, was affected by the familial form of breast cancer. Linder's mother is a breast cancer survivor, and her first cousin also had breast cancer at the age of 33. Her cousin was treated, but the cancer had returned, and she was losing her fight. Another first cousin had died from breast cancer at the age of 40. Her daughter, who is 33, just recently learned that she also has breast cancer. This is not unusual for the familial form of breast cancer. Female members of such families harbor deep fears that they might one day also develop breast cancer.

In the 1970s, Mary Claire King, a geneticist, decided to search for the genetic cause of the familial form of breast cancer. She assembled several hundred breast cancer families, and by looking through their family trees, she identified the gene that is responsible for causing this form of breast cancer. The identification of this breast cancer gene in the 1990s made headline news around the world, because this was the first demonstration that cancer can be inherited and "run" in the family. This gene became known as the BRCA1 gene. Its normal function is to prevent cells from multiplying, and it belongs to the group of genes that are known as tumor suppressor genes. The mutant BRCA1 gene produces a protein that signals the cells to grow rather than suppress their growth.

The impact of BRCA1 on developing breast cancer is clear. Those who carry the mutant form of the BRCA1 gene have a risk as high as 80% of developing breast cancer. Since 2004, commercial testing for BRCA1 and BRCA2 (another gene that is also involved in breast cancer) has become available. Linder decided to be tested for the BRCA1 and BRCA2 mutations. When the test results came back, Linder discovered that she was positive for the BRCA1 mutation, suggesting that she has an 80% chance of developing breast cancer before her 40th birthday.

Since breast cancer affects both the breasts and the ovaries, removing these organs can reduce the risks in the individuals with the BRCA mutations by up to 90%. Linder's sister, at the age of 37, had her breasts and ovaries removed before the genetic test for BRCA mutations were available. She took the tests later on for the sake of her children. Only then did she know that she had not received the mutant gene from her mother. After much consideration, Linder decided that she was going to have her breasts and ovaries surgically removed. This case provides a scenario of what the future may bring. It is increasingly probable that many human diseases are based on genetic inheritance, but environment also plays an important role. Genetic testing will become increasingly common as portrayed in the science fiction movie *GATTACA*. This information will no doubt shape our lives.

II.4. *What is the future of genetic testing?*

John considers himself lucky, because other than watching his diet carefully, he has lived a full life. However, he has a genetic disorder that could have killed him before he reached his 10th birthday. John has an autosomal recessive genetic disorder known as phenylketonuria (PKU), which is a condition that, if left untreated, causes problems with brain development, severe seizures, progressive mental retardation, and eventually, death. John was fortunate, because his family doctor recognized the disorder when he was less than a year old. He put John on a special diet, which effectively treated his condition. Many others, however, were not as fortunate at the time.

PKU is an autosomal recessive disorder similar to other recessive disorders. The condition is caused by a mutation in a gene that encodes a protein that metabolizes the amino acid, phenylalanine, to another amino acid, tyrosine. The mutant gene fails to produce a functional protein, leading to the accumulation of the amino acid, phenylalanine. Excessive amounts of this amino acid affect brain development, leading to neurological symptoms. The discovery of the cause of this disease was important in the development of genetic testing. In 1934, a Norwegian physician noticed the high concentration of phenylalanine in the urine of these patients. He developed a simple test to identify the disorder.

Once he identified these patients, he placed them on a diet with low phenylalanine and high tyrosine. The result was remarkable. The patients recovered almost immediately. They lived normal lives as long as they maintained this diet. This development was the first application of a simple test to determine a genetic condition. Based on this information, patients can be identified and treated. Today, every newborn in the United States and in most countries around the world is tested for excessive amounts of phenylalanine in their blood to screen for PKU. This genetic test has saved many lives.

When Aaron and Mary were contemplating getting married, they were advised by their rabbi to be tested for the Tay-Sachs gene. Even though they lived in New York, both of their parents were descendents of Ashkenazi Jews who had emigrated from Eastern Europe. In the United States, approximately 1 in 30 Ashkenazi Jews is a recessive carrier for the Tay-Sachs mutant gene. In addition to testing for Tay-Sachs, testing for the carrier state for sickle cell anemia is also routinely done. This disease is more common in those individuals who have an ethnic background in sub-Saharan Africa. Genetic testing has become routine for individuals of certain ethnic groups.

Other genetic tests for predicting diseases such as Huntington's disease, Alzheimer's disease, breast cancer, and many others, have become increasingly common. Before the use of DNA to test for mutant genes, tests for biochemical products (in the case of PKU) or abnormal cell shape (in the case of sickle cell disease) were the only available tests. However, they were often inaccurate and gave false results. Genetic testing has provided more accurate results. Furthermore, genetic testing can be conducted on a large scale using small pieces of DNA embedded in a matrix. This allows for the testing of up to several thousand genes at the same time. This type of testing device is often referred to as gene chips.

It is predicted that in the next decade, genetic testing technology may reach a level in which as many as 10,000 genes could be tested on a single gene chip. How this information is used poses a serious moral and ethical challenge for parents and society. What will be the decision of parents if they discover that their child will suffer from a serious genetic disorder that has neither cure nor treatment? How will the medical community react to this information? How will the health insurance industry respond to the possibility of providing long-term care for the child? These types of issues are not far away. The human genome has already been decoded, and the routine decoding of our individual genomes will most likely be available in the coming decade.

III. WHAT IS THE HUMAN GENOME?

It was less than 22 years from the time when Watson and Crick discovered the structure of DNA in 1953 to the determination of the DNA sequence of a bacterial virus known as φX174 in 1975. When you put this in the context of human history, the progress in genetics and molecular biology is astounding. The genome of φX174 is only 5386 bases. It took Fred Sanger, the biochemist who invented the method of DNA sequencing, two years to complete the sequence of this simple virus. In 2000, 25 years after the sequencing of the first biological organism, the entire human genome, three billion bases in all, was determined.

Fred Sanger
He invented the method for sequencing DNA and was the first person to sequence a viral genome in 1975. *(Public Domain)*

III.1. What is the significance of the human genome?

The significance of the human genome can best be illustrated by the following story. Doug is a father of five children, and he has suffered from clinical depression since he was a child. He recalled when he was seven years old visiting his uncle's farm. There were animals, tractors, barns, and everything that a little kid should be excited about. However, when he arrived at the farm, he was inexplicably sad and depressed. For the next 35 years, he had repeated episodes of severe depression, suicide attempts, and hospitalizations. Of his five children, four of them also suffer from depression.

Similar to Alzheimer's disease and breast cancer, clinical depression also has a sporadic and a familial form. The diagnosis of the familial form of clinical depression is the first step toward its effective treatment. There are many other human diseases where genes and environment interact in their development and progression. Thus far, over 4,000 genetic disorders have been identified, with various degrees of severity, time of onset, and prevalence. Many of them are rare, and very little is known about them. However, it is clear that every human individual is affected by a genetic disorder to some degree. To understand how these diseases develop will improve quality of life and extend longevity.

In the early 1980s, shortly after the development of DNA sequencing technology, James Watson and several other scientists convened a meeting to discuss the possibility of sequencing the entire human genome. Their argument was that the mapping of all the genes in the human genome would provide a starting point for determining how these genes assemble a human being. Some scientists believed that this was not the best use of research funding and scientific talent, because a list of all the genes would not provide information on how they work together. Some suggested the analogy that having a list of all the parts that make up a Boeing 747 does not indicate how the jumbo jet flies.

After a long debate among the scientists, the decision was to proceed with the project of sequencing the human genome. The consensus was that with the sequence of every gene available, it would be easier for researchers to pinpoint mutant genes that are responsible for genetic disorders. This would allow for the development of genetic tests that could make more precise diagnoses of the 4,000 known genetic diseases. Furthermore, by having the sequences of the genes, researchers could deduce the amino acid sequences and hence, have an idea of the structure and function of certain proteins. In other words, by having the knowledge of all the human genes, it would be possible to carry out reverse engineering.

Francis Collins

He replaced James Watson as the head of the Human Genome Project in 1993. *(Public Domain)*

James Watson was elected to represent the scientific community to lobby the U.S. Congress to appropriate three billion dollars for the project. In 1986, the U.S. Congress approved the funding, and the Human Genome Project officially began in 1990 under the auspices of the United States Department of Energy and the United States National Institutes of Health. The project also received international support from China, France, Germany, Japan, and the United Kingdom. James Watson was appointed as the head of the newly formed National Center for Human Genome Research. However, he was eventually fired because of a disagreement with the head of the National Institutes of Health and was replaced by Francis Collins in 1993.

The Human Genome Project was the biggest publicly funded project since the Apollo Project that resulted in the moon landings. The entire project was to be completed over 15 years by 2005. However, the sequencing technology in the beginning was slow and tedious, and it appeared that the completion date would be beyond 2005. In 1992, Craig Venter, one of the team members, left to start a commercial company to take advantage of new sequencing technology. His company was in competition with the public project. This led to a fierce competition between the rival groups, resulting in an acceleration of effort put forth by both groups. In 2000, President Clinton brought the rival groups together and later announced that the two groups had independently decoded the human genome. With this announcement, a new chapter was opened in human history. We can now read our own parts manual.

III.2. What is in the human genome?

Just before President Clinton was going to make the announcement at the White House on the completion of the human genome, the public and private genome teams were scrambling to determine how many genes were in the human genome. Both teams were shocked by the number they found. They even called each other to verify their results. Both teams used a software program that picked up the start and stop codons that mark each gene. Using this method, they counted the number of genes in the human genome. They were very surprised by what they found.

Even though the Human Genome Project was originally touted to provide information for the detection, treatment, and cure of genetic disorders, the benefits of the project will take many years to be realized. However, one of the greatest benefits of the human genome project is to understand the evolution of the human species. One of the first big surprises was the number of genes in the human genome. The human genome is huge, with over three billion bases for every one set (23) of chromosomes. If the entire human genome encodes for amino acids, the human genome would encode for one billion amino acids, which would be equivalent to at least five million genes. However, researchers already know that human cells only have about several hundred different proteins. Therefore, a conservative estimation is approximately 100,000 genes in the human genome.

However, the gene counters from both teams could only find 30,000 genes, much smaller than the predicted 100,000 genes. As more accurate methods became available to pick out genes, the current estimate has dropped to as low as 20,000 genes. Despite the apparent complexity of our anatomy and physiology, humans have the same number of genes as a microscopic roundworm that lives in the soil. However, the roundworm has only 100 million bases in a genome that is 30 times smaller than the human genome. The analyses of the human genome sequences offer some intriguing insights into the evolution of the human genome.

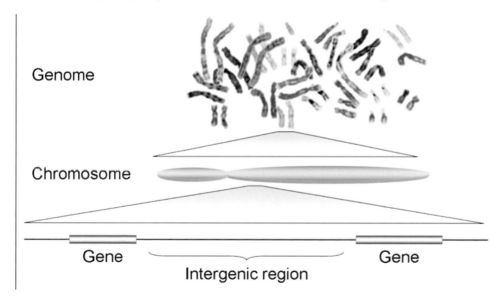

The human genome

The human genome is organized into chromosomes, which contain regions of genes that are separated by intergenic regions of DNA. *(Public Domain)*

The most surprising finding is that 98.5% of the human genome does not encode for any genes. Only 1.5% of the human genome is used for making proteins. The rest appears to have no function. This seems to be an extraordinary waste and an extreme inefficiency. The most interesting part of this non-coding portion of the human genome is the vast stretches of sequences, ranging from two to three bases to several hundred bases, that are repeated from 5 to 20 times to several thousand times. The number of repetitions vary among individuals, and the patterns are passed from one generation to the next. These sequences are useful in a technique known as DNA fingerprinting for determining paternity and individual identification.

Nearly 50% of the human genome is packed with a type of DNA sequence known as transposons. These are short stretches of DNA ranging from several hundred bases to several thousand bases. They have special DNA sequences that allow them to loop out from the DNA and move to another region of the DNA in a process called transposition. Transposons were first discovered in maize, and they are often also referred to as mobile genetic elements or jumping genes. If a transposon jumps into the middle of a gene, it causes a mutation and inactivates the gene. Researchers believe that transposons are the ultimate parasites; they are DNA hitchhikers. They most likely have originated from ancient viruses. At this point, many parts of the human genome remain a mystery. The human genome is the ultimate Rosetta Stone that will help to decode the biological history of the human species.

The impact of the human genome on medicine, technology, society, and culture is inconceivable. There is nothing more useful than having a map for solving a difficult problem. The human genome has lifted the mystery that surrounds the making of a human being. The DNA sequences have become a digital code that can be manipulated in the same way as a computer program. What can be done with this information is only being gradually realized. In a decade, it is possible that all of us will carry with us our personal genetic code recorded on a plastic card. Perhaps your future can be predicated as portrayed in the movie *GATTACA*.

Gene chips

With the knowledge of the human genome, gene chips have been designed to contain up to 10,000 genes for diagnostic testing. *(GNU Free Documentation License)*

Chapter 4

Variations

Why are you unique?

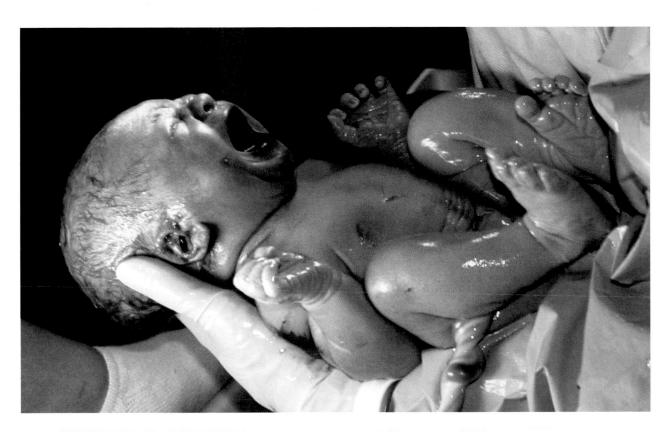

Everyone is unique.

There are four babies born around the world every second, and each one is unique in their genetic makeup. What is the biological process in creating this uniqueness? *(GNU Free Documentation License)*

CHAPTER 4. VARIATIONS

Sometime in 2010, a special baby will be born. This baby will be the one that tips Earth's population to seven billion. This baby could be a boy or a girl; he or she could be born in a modern hospital equipped with the latest technology, or he or she could be born in a poverty-stricken place somewhere in Africa. This baby could be born to a mother in excellent health or to an HIV-infected mother. He or she could be born with pearly skin and blue eyes or with brown eyes and dark skin. We do not know what this baby is going to be like, but there is one certainty about this baby: He or she will be unique, different from all humans who have ever lived and who will ever live. Like this baby, our biological uniqueness is also guaranteed. What shapes our individual uniqueness? What is its biological significance?

I. WHAT IS THE ORIGIN OF GENETIC VARIATIONS?

The Human Genome Project proved that variations exist between all humans. It is well-known that every human is unique; even identical twins are not truly identical. Before the availability of the DNA sequence information, the actual degree of differences that exist between different individuals was not known. When comparisons in DNA sequences were made between different individuals, it was discovered that, despite the geographical distributions of different human populations, the differences between humans are consistent. On average, the difference in DNA sequences between human individuals is 1 out of 1,000 bases. In other words, we are 99.9% identical in regards to our DNA sequences. What is the origin of the 0.1% difference? What is the biological significance of this difference?

I.1. How do random mutations occur in cystic fibrosis?

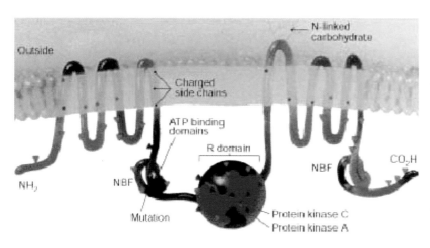

NBF = Nucleotide binding fold

CFTR protein

This protein plays a critical role in controlling movements of ions, such as sodium and chloride. (Public Domain)

To understand how random mutations generate genetic differences, we will use cystic fibrosis (CF) as an example. Cystic fibrosis is one of the most common genetic diseases in the United States. It affects mainly the respiratory function of the lungs by producing an excessive amount of mucus, which then leads to a functional impairment and frequent respiratory infections. The disease is caused by a lack of, or a functional defect in, a protein known as CFTR, which normally regulates the ion concentrations between the inside and the outside of the cells lining the surface of the lung. Without a proper balance of ions, the cells produce an excessive amount of mucus.

The genetic basis of CF was discovered in 1988. Researchers discovered that the CFTR protein is a large protein consisting of 1,480 amino acids, and it is encoded by a gene consisting of 170,000 bases. Changes in the DNA sequence resulting from a mutation alter the amino acid sequence, which then changes the shape of the protein and affects its function. Shortly after the discovery of the CFTR gene, the mutation that is responsible for CF was discovered. The CFTR mutant gene has lost three bases out of the 170,000 bases that encode the gene. This mutation was given the name ΔF508, because the deletion occurs in the amino acid position, number 508.

The ΔF508 mutation results in the deletion of one amino acid out of the 1,480 amino acids in the CFTR protein. Nevertheless, the loss of this one amino acid is sufficient enough to alter the CFTR protein. The protein can no longer interact with other proteins, which then causes the cell membrane to fail in its functions. Interestingly, researchers have discovered that there are over 1,400 different mutations of the CFTR gene that can cause CF. However, the ΔF508 is the most common mutation that causes CF; it is responsible for 90% of cases in the United States and 70% of cases worldwide.

The studies on CF have revealed some interesting aspects of genetic disorders. First, genetic disorders are caused by random mutations resulting from base substitution, insertion, deletion, and other mechanisms. The mutation can occur anywhere in the gene, and the process is random and unpredictable. Therefore, in the general population there are many mutations within the same gene. All these versions result from a mutation that occurs during the formation of the reproductive cells. These mutations pass onto the next generation and are maintained in the population, especially if they do not affect the survival and reproductive success of the offspring.

Before modern medical advances, CF patients rarely lived beyond their early teens because of fatal respiratory complications. Today, with the use of antibiotics to control respiratory tract infections, CF patients have an average life expectancy of 36 years. One puzzling aspect of this disorder, however, is the high prevalence of CF in the population. In the United States, CF occurs in 1out of 3,900 births. Furthermore, the carrier rate in people of European decent is 5% in the general population. Why is CF so common, whereas other genetic disorders, which have a similar mortality, are very rare?

Another interesting aspect of CF is the inheritance of the ΔF508 mutant gene. Of the 1,400 mutant genes that can cause CF, why does ΔF508 dominate? Why can over 90% of the cases in the United States be traced to ΔF508, whereas it causes only 70% of CF cases in the world at large? These are important questions that will help to address the patterns of inheritance not just for CF but for the inheritance of other genetic disorders in different parts of the world.

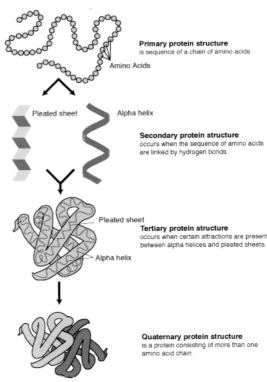

Primary protein structure
is sequence of a chain of amino acids

Amino Acids

Pleated sheet   Alpha helix

Secondary protein structure
occurs when the sequence of amino acids
are linked by hydrogen bonds

Pleated sheet

Tertiary protein structure
occurs when certain attractions are present
between alpha helices and pleated sheets

Alpha helix

Quaternary protein structure
is a protein consisting of more than one
amino acid chain.

Protein structure

Based on their amino acid sequences, proteins fold into a specific 3-D structure. *(Public Domain)*

I.2. What is the inheritance pattern of sickle cell disease?

Fatu is a six-year-old girl living in Senegal, which is along the tropical coast of West Africa. She has difficulties keeping up with her cousins and friends. She gets tired easily and has a difficult time doing the things that children love to do. Periodically, she experiences debilitating muscle and joint pains that confine her to bed for weeks. Fatu suffers from an autosomal recessive genetic disorder known as sickle cell disease (also called sickle cell anemia). Under certain conditions, the red blood cells in this disease assume an elongated, rigid shape, resembling a sickle. The oddly-shaped red blood cells rupture easily as they try to squeeze through blood capillaries. This large-scale rupture quickly leads to anemia.

This autosomal recessive disorder is due to a single base substitution in the hemoglobin gene. The resulting change is a substitution in the amino acid position number 6 from glutamine to valine. This substitution, however, does not significantly alter the structure and function of the protein. The protein still functions in binding and transporting oxygen. However, this single amino acid change creates an unusual property of the protein. When the oxygen tension in the body is low, a condition that commonly results from high levels of physical activity, the mutant hemoglobin proteins start to stack on top of each other and form long, rod-shaped polymers. These polymers then cause the red blood cells to form an elongated, rigid shape.

Sickle cell disease is a recessive trait, because in the presence of a normal copy of the hemoglobin gene, the normal hemoglobin molecule maintains an adequate concentration of oxygen to prevent the polymerization of the mutant hemoglobin proteins. Through this compensatory mechanism, heterozygous individuals for the sickle cell disease gene display no clinical symptoms of the disease. In contrast, individuals who have two copies of the mutant gene suffer from the disorder and have a reduced life expectancy. Various complications, including bacterial and viral infections, lead to death often before a patient reaches reproductive age. Because of this, it would be logical to assume that the mutant hemoglobin gene should have disappeared from the population. However, this is not the case, and sickle cell disease remains one of the most common genetic disorders.

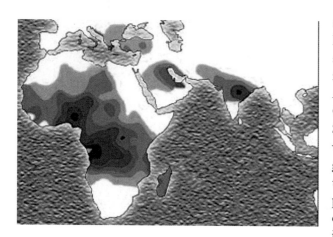

Distribution of the sickle cell trait

Mainly in Africa and parts of Asia. *(Public Domain)*

In the United States, the rate of sickle cell disease is highest among Americans of African descent. The prevalence is the highest among those from sub-Saharan Africa. The disease occurs as frequently as 1 in every 400 births, and the carrier rate for the mutant hemoglobin gene is nearly 12% (one in every eight African Americans). The frequency, however, is less than 0.01% among Caucasian Americans. When the carrier rates were examined in sub-Saharan Africa, the carrier rate in some countries, such as Senegal, was as high as 30% (one in every three of the local residents). These geographical differences suggest that there must be some factors that maintain this harmful mutant hemoglobin gene in the local population. The answer to this question derives from the protective effect of the mutant hemoglobin gene against one of the deadliest infectious diseases in human history.

When Europeans first traveled to sub-Saharan Africa in the 17th and 18th centuries, they succumbed to a mysterious disease that the local inhabitants were resistant to. The symptoms of the disease included alternating episodes of fever and chills with flu-like symptoms, and in severe cases, convulsions and death. The disease was malaria, an infectious disease which is caused by microbial parasites known as plasmodium. The parasites are transmitted by mosquito bites, and after gaining entry into the blood stream, they infect the red blood cells. Once inside the red blood

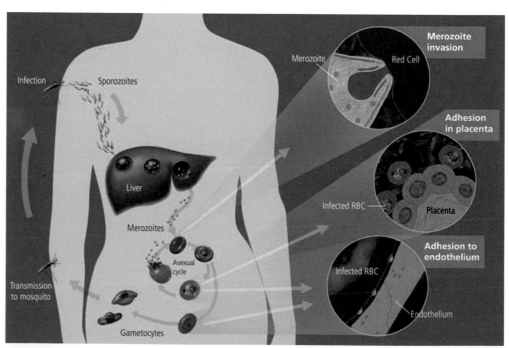

The life cycle of malaria parasites

The parasites exist in both humans and mosquitoes. *(Public Domain)*

cells, they multiply and form large numbers before bursting open the cells and being released into the blood stream. The episodes of chills and fevers coincide with the infectious cycle in the red blood cells.

Curiously, individuals who are heterozygous for the sickle cell gene are protected against malaria. In these individuals, the malaria parasites cannot complete their life cycles, and because of this, cannot cause the serious symptoms of malaria. These individuals are protected because their red blood cells cannot support the growth of the malaria parasites. During their growth in the red blood cells, malaria parasites require a high and constant demand for oxygen. Once in the red blood cells, these parasites quickly lower the oxygen tension in the cells. However, in those individuals who have one copy of the sickle cell hemoglobin gene, the mutant hemoglobin protein polymerizes under low oxygen concentration. For these individuals, their malaria-infected red blood cells rupture before the parasites are ready to reproduce. Therefore, it is an advantage for individuals who live in areas where malaria is pervasive to have one copy of the mutant hemoglobin gene. This interaction between malaria and the sickle cell hemoglobin protein explains the high carrier rates of the mutant gene in regions of the world where malaria is a serious health threat.

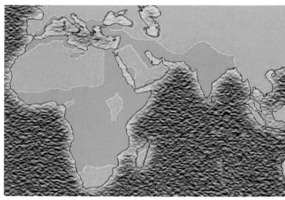

Distribution of malaria
It coincides with the distribution of the sickle cell trait. *(Public Domain)*

I.3. How did human skin color evolve?

The studies on the interaction between sickle cell disease and malaria have provided evidence that mutations and environmental factors interact to form the genetic makeup of a population. The high carrier rate of the sickle cell gene results because of its protective value against malaria. Having one normal and one mutated copy protects an individual against malaria; this phenomenon is known as the heterozygous advantage. In contrast, possessing two copies of the mutated gene leads to sickle cell disease. This interaction between malaria and the sickle gene demonstrates how an environment can affect the genetic makeup of a population.

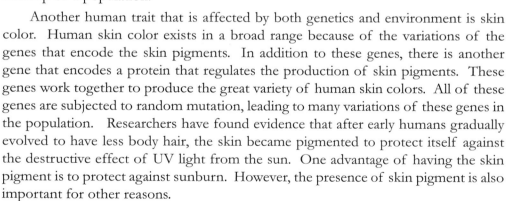

Skin complexion
Humans have a wide range of skin complexion. *(Public Domain)*

Another human trait that is affected by both genetics and environment is skin color. Human skin color exists in a broad range because of the variations of the genes that encode the skin pigments. In addition to these genes, there is another gene that encodes a protein that regulates the production of skin pigments. These genes work together to produce the great variety of human skin colors. All of these genes are subjected to random mutation, leading to many variations of these genes in the population. Researchers have found evidence that after early humans gradually evolved to have less body hair, the skin became pigmented to protect itself against the destructive effect of UV light from the sun. One advantage of having the skin pigment is to protect against sunburn. However, the presence of skin pigment is also important for other reasons.

Underneath the skin, there are cells that produce and store an important vitamin known as folic acid. Folic acid is vital for many cellular functions, such as DNA replication. In adults, folic acid deficiency causes anemia because the lack of it causes an insufficient production of red blood cells. Also, folic acid is vital to support the rapid cell growth and division that occurs during fetal development. Maternal folic acid deficiency leads to serious birth defects, such as spinal bifida, which is a malformation of the spinal cord. Other disorders include the improper development of the central nervous system resulting in anencephaly, which is a malformation of the brain and skull. Today, many of these conditions are prevented because prenatal care includes dietary supplements of folic acid. The connection between folic acid

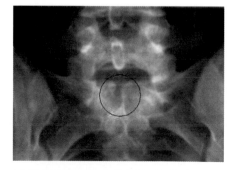

Spinal cord defect
Due to folic acid deficiency during pregnancy. *(Public Domain)*

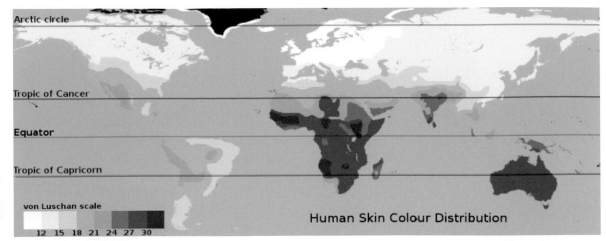

Skin color distribution

It coincides with UV light intensity. *(Public Domain)*

and skin color derives from the location of folic acid near the skin surface. Because of its proximity to the surface, it is susceptible to destruction by the sun's UV light. Dark pigments prevent the penetration of this light and therefore protects the integrity of the folic acid.

The genetic selection for humans with dark skin began with early humans living under the intense sun of the African savanna. Individuals who had dark skin could better protect their folic acid and therefore produced healthier offspring than individuals who had light-colored skin. With time, the entire population living in this environment had a dark skin color. Researchers have estimated that early humans first evolved to have black skin after they lost their body hair at about 1.2 to 4 million years ago. Prior to that time, their skin was white beneath their black hair, a condition that still exists today in modern chimpanzees.

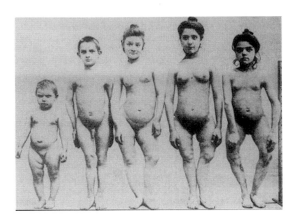

Children suffering from rickets

French children in the 1900s with bone deformities due to vitamin D deficiency. *(Public Domain)*

At about 40,000 years ago, humans left Africa and began to inhabit other parts of the world. Because the intensity of the sun's UV light gradually declines in locations away from the equator, the protective skin pigments were not as important to those humans living away from the equator. It would be logical to assume that humans became lighter skinned because they no longer needed to shield their folic acid from destruction. However, the human skin did not become lighter for this reason. Instead, the lighter skin color evolved because of a need to synthesize vitamin D. Vitamin D is a steroid hormone that is essential for calcium absorption for bone formation. Humans obtain the precursor of vitamin D from their diets, but the conversion to vitamin D occurs in the skin. Vitamin D deficiency in children causes rickets, a bone-softening disease. Deficiencies of vitamin D in pregnant women leads to a fractured pelvis and possible death during childbirth.

Inuit diet

Their diet is rich in vitamin D, and their skin remains dark. *(Public Domain)*

As humans moved away from the equator, the production of skin pigment lessened so that more UV light could pass into the skin and result in vitamin D synthesis. Researchers have discovered that human skin color correlates strongly with the UV light intensity in different parts of the world. In other words, in areas that have less UV light intensity, the population of that area has lighter skin. One interesting exception to this is the dark skin color of the Inuit and Yupik, who live in northern habitats with low UV light intensity. Their skin has remained dark because they have received a sufficient amount of vitamin D from their traditional animal-rich diet. Therefore, it was unnecessary for them to lose their skin pigments. The evolution of human skin color is another example of how the variation of traits, which are created by random mutation, provides some members of the populations with the ability to adapt to new environments.

I.4. Origin of human traits

Throughout history, different physical appearances have often posed an insurmountable divide between groups of people. From slavery in ancient Egypt to slavery in the United States, racism continues to cast a long, dark shadow. Even though the American Civil War was fought in part to abolish slavery, the South resisted the change because of their moral and religious beliefs. Racial segregation continued in the United States for another 100 years after the Civil War. Many states created laws to mandate the segregation of American blacks and whites in public places, schools, and residential areas. The continuing use of skin color as a standard for racial classification is a failure of biological education to demonstrate the unscientific nature of race.

Racial segregation

Alabama Governor George Wallace blocked African American students to attend an all white college. *(Public Domain)*

Human skin color is controlled by only four to six genes out of the 22,000 genes that construct a human being. With this knowledge, it is difficult to conceive that a person with white skin is intellectually or morally superior to a person with black skin. Biological studies have proven that differences in skin color are an adaptation to the intensity of UV light and have no bearing in intelligence or temperament. Unfortunately, throughout history, human society has used physical appearance as a way to separate groups of people. In all cases, this is a pretext to address social, ethnic, and religious differences rather than biological differences.

One of the most hideous episodes of racism occurred in 1935. Germany under the Nazi Party formulated the Nuremberg Laws for the Protection of German Blood and German Honor. Under these laws, an individual of "German blood" was defined as having four German grandparents. In a similar manner, a Jew was someone who had four Jewish grandparents. Individuals who had one or two Jewish grandparents were referred to as a crossbreed or "mixed blood." It was during this period that the German leadership placed all the blame of their political and economic woes on the Jews, who together with the Eastern Europeans, were deemed as racially inferior. This form of politically-motivated racism led to the Holocaust.

In 1942, Adolf Hitler sought "a solution to the Jewish question in Europe." After the infamous Wannsee Conference of the high ranking Nazis, Germany launched the Final Solution. This became the worst mass murder in the history of mankind ever undertaken by a society of culture and sophistication. By the end of World War II in 1945, over six million people had been systematically murdered. At the infamous Auschwitz concentration camp, 1.1 million men, women, and children were killed by forced labor, systematic starvation, execution in gas chambers, or medical experiments. It was one of the darkest chapters of modern human history.

The Nazis adored blonde hair, blue eyes, high cheek bones, and stocky bodies. They described these features as characterizing the master race. However, based on the data from the Human Genome Project, researchers have estimated that for all the humans alive today, there are only approximately 20 genes that determine facial characteristics, such as eye color, the shapes and sizes of the eyes, nose, and ears, and facial configuration. Therefore, facial features have no reflection on a person's character, personality, and intelligence. Using facial features is as erroneous as using skin color to make racial classifications.

Race identify card

Citizens checked such a card to indentify their race in Nazi Germany. *(Public Domain)*

The different facial features that are characteristic of populations living in different geographical regions result from adaptations to the environment. For example, the variations in human nose shapes are an adaptation to air temperature. In climates with hot, humid air, the nose shape is broad and flat, allowing the air to cool before inhaling. However, in climates with frigid air, the narrow and long nasal cavity warms the air before it enters the lung.

The differences in human body types that are found in different parts of the world also result from adaptations to local climatic conditions. Native inhabitants in regions with long and cold winters possess a high body mass and a stout physique. These characteristics are favorable for heat preservation; the Inuits living near the Arctic Circle exemplify this body type. However, for native inhabitants in areas of the world with hot and humid climates, a body type of low mass is preferable for efficient heat dissipation. For example, native inhabitants living in Southeast Asia possess a small body frame with low body mass.

I.5. Does race exist?

What is race? What is racism? This dreaded word possesses a clear and unmistakable implication that one group of humans is considered intrinsically superior to other groups. Racism is an ideology suggesting that inherited differences in characteristics or abilities exist between groups of humans and that these differences give the right for one group to dominate other groups. During the Age of Colonization, Europeans established colonies around the world and ruled over the native inhabitants based on their perceived racial superiority on political, economic, and religious issues. The European colonizers used racism to justify the cruel and unjust manner in which they treated the local populations.

In the 19th and early part of the 20th centuries, the study of racial differences led to the formation of a pseudoscientific discipline known as scientific racism. Sir Francis Galton, who was a half cousin to Charles Darwin, proposed that humans can be classified into racial groups based on their physical appearance. For example, he suggested that Europeans had an oval face, which distinguished them from Africans. He also measured the size and shape of the skull, claiming that the Europeans had a perfect skull dimension. He and others formed a new branch of human biology, known as craniometry. A similar pseudoscientific field, known as physiognomy, used human facial features as a means for racial classification and assessments of personality.

The assumptions of the early, pseudoscientific racist theories were that physical characteristics could be used to determine intelligence, personality, and behavioral traits. These racist theories were formed during the time when any understanding of the formation and inheritance of biological traits was completely lacking. However, these pseudoscientific racist theories continued to influence societal views on human populations. Unfortunately, a lack of understanding of human genetics by the general population continues to perpetuate racism. This misconception prevents any appreciation of both the similarities and differences between groups of humans who are separated by geographical regions. The pseudoscientific racist theories are difficult to overcome even in light of new evidence.

From a scientific standpoint, race does not exist. The genetic differences that exist between two human groups, such as Caucasians and Africans, are nearly the same as that between two individual Caucasians. The Human Genome Project has revealed that the difference in DNA sequences between all humans is approximately 0.1%. This minute difference is the same whether it is between two inhabitants living in the same area or between two persons living on opposite sides of the world. The two people who live in the same area might have similar physical traits, but they might also have genetic differences that are not apparent at the morphological level. Similarly, a Caucasian and an Asian might have obvious physical differences, but their "unseen" biological traits could be nearly identical. For example, minor differences in DNA sequences in six genes produce the entire range of human skin color.

Another important discovery from the Human Genome Project was the low degree of variation within the human species as compared to other species. Two human inhabitants who live on the opposite sides of the world are more genetically similar to

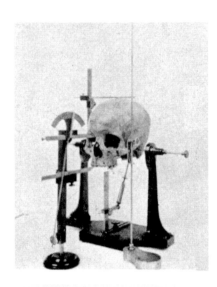

Craniometry
Scientific racism in the late 19th and early 20th centuries. *(Public Domain)*

each other than are two chimpanzees living in different parts of the same forest. Researchers have proposed that the low genetic variation of the human population resulted from an environmental disaster, such as a drought, that nearly caused the extinction of the human species about 100,000 years ago in East Africa. Only several thousand of these early humans survived, and all modern day humans are their descendents. This type of population change is known as a population bottleneck. About 40,000 years ago, these early humans emigrated from Africa and populated the world.

The human genome has approximately 22,000 genes, and it can generate infinite variations through mutation within these genes. These variations help populations adapt to local environments. The variations in skin color, facial features, and body build are examples of these adaptations. Studies on human genetic changes and information from the Human Genome Project have shown that only minor changes in very few genes can generate these different morphological features. To use these morphological features to classify humans into different racial groups and to judge their intellectual potential and behavioral characteristics is to ignore human genetics. Therefore, it is vital that we understand this information and use it to dispel the misconception of race that remains prevalent in our society.

The *first* of these figures represents a Negro head, elongated, and narrow in front, with expanded zygomatic arches, projecting cheek bones, and protruded upper jaw. The *second* is a Caucasian skull, in which those parts are nearly concealed in the more symmetrical outline of the whole head, and especially by the full development of the frontal region. The *third* figure is taken from a Mongol head, in which the orbits and cheek bones are exposed, as in the Negro, and the zygomæ arched and expanded; but the forehead is much broader, the face more retracted, and the whole cranium larger. Having been at much pains to give the *norma verticalis* of the skulls figured in this work, the reader will have ample opportunity to compare for himself. He will see that the American head approaches nearest to the Mongol, yet is not so long, is narrower in front, with a more prominent face and much more contracted zygomæ.

Shape of skulls
This pseudoscientific method was used to define the "perfect" race.
(Public Domain)

II. WHAT IS INDIVIDUAL UNIQUENESS?

One of the most important biological questions concerns the origin of individual uniqueness. The answer to this question has many biological implications. It can explain how differences between various geographically separated populations arise. It also addresses an important philosophical question of our individual uniqueness. Are biological processes responsible for individual uniqueness? If they are, how do they work? What is the significance of biological uniqueness?

II.1. What is biological uniqueness?

We take our uniqueness for granted and rarely think much about it. However, once we look closer at our individual uniqueness, we will inevitably be impressed by how extraordinary it is. In fact, our uniqueness is guaranteed in the universe and in the entire history of time. Each of us is unique among the 6.67 billion people alive on Earth today, and we are unique among the approximately 110 billion humans that have ever been born during the 250,000 year history of humans. Furthermore, each of us will remain unique, and unless scientists find the existence of a parallel universe, our physical uniqueness is all but guaranteed. Also, biological uniqueness is not exclusive for the human species. Even an insect flying across a room is as unique as any one of us.

Biologists have been asking questions about individual uniqueness for several hundred years. The answer to these questions came from studying the phenomenon of sexual reproduction, which is the opposite of asexual reproduction. During the growth of the human body, all cells reproduce by asexual reproduction. Asexual reproduction results in two daughter cells that are identical to each other and to the mother cell. Many simple organisms, such as bacteria and yeast, use asexual reproduction, which allows them to grow rapidly in number. However, almost all complex multi-cellular organisms use sexual reproduction to create their offspring.

For sexual reproduction to occur, two members of the same species are needed. Prior to sexual reproduction, a multi-cellular organism creates specialized cells, known as gametes. A male gamete is a sperm, and a female gamete is an egg. The sperm must find and fertilize an egg, and together they pool their genetic material and form a fertilized egg or a zygote. The general principle of sexual reproduction is straight forward, but the outcome has puzzled biologists for centuries. If all the offspring receive the same genetic information from their parents, why are the offspring different from each other? What is the biological mechanism for two individuals to generate an infinite number of different offspring?

Sexual reproduction is the preferred reproductive strategy for many living organisms, such as plants, animals, and fungi. Even bacteria use some type of sexual reproductive strategy during their life cycles. More than 99% of complex multi-cellular organisms reproduce sexually. The chief advantage of sexual reproduction is to generate individual variations within the next generation. By having a large pool of individual variations within a group, the chances of survival for that group are enhanced. This occurs because some individuals are likely to have the appropriate biological traits that allow them to adapt to a new environment. This is why sexual reproduction has become important for many biological organisms.

The basic biological mechanism that is used to generate variation is genetic mutation. Any gene that has become mutated can be passed onto the next generation. With asexual reproduction, individuals of all generations will be exactly the same and possess the same mutant genes. However, through sexual reproduction, all mutants are not necessarily passed onto all future generations. In other words, different individuals receive unique combinations of the mutant genes. This biological process of mixing different mutant genes was discovered by Gregor Mendel in 1865, and it is among the greatest scientific discoveries in human history.

Gregor Mendel
The father of modern genetics.
(Public Domain)

II.2. *What are Mendel's Laws?*

The principle of genetic inheritance described by Mendel's laws is a very important biological principle to understand. These laws describe and predict the process of genetic inheritance that affects all biological organisms on Earth. Even the structure of DNA was discovered partly because of Mendel's laws because the laws provided the theoretical basis to search for genes. Despite their importance, Mendel's laws were not immediately accepted, and their significance was not recognized for 35 years. Mendel died 18 years before his findings were independently "rediscovered" by three scientists in 1900. It is likely that Mendel would have been shocked to discover that his famous experiments with garden peas are currently described in biology textbooks.

Mendel's Abbey
The Augustinian Abbey of St. Thomas, Brno. *(Public Domain)*

Mendel's discovery is tightly linked to the process of sexual reproduction. He and other scientists recognized that after sexual reproduction, the fertilized egg has a normal amount of DNA, even though it was formed by the fusion of two cells. If both cells had a normal amount of DNA, why did the fertilized egg not have double the normal amount of DNA? To prevent an abnormal doubling of DNA after each cycle of sexual reproduction, the organism must have a way to reduce the amount of DNA in its gametes by half. Before Mendel, no one really had a good idea how this may work. Mendel came up with an ingenious idea based on experiments he conducted with pea plants. He suggested that in an adult organism there are two types of cell division. In the first type of cell division, all the genetic material is replicated and the offspring get an identical set of genes. This type of cell division is known as mitosis.

In a brilliant interpretation of his experimental data, Mendel concluded that there are two copies of the same gene; one copy from the mother and one copy from the father. He proposed that during gamete formation, the gametes receive only one copy of every gene. This is Mendel's first law, known as Mendel's Law of Segregation. Segregation refers to the separation of the two sets of genetic material, with each half going to a separate gamete. This is important, because it provides a biological mechanism for the reduction of the amount of genetic material at each reproductive cycle.

Based on Mendel's theory, genes from the father and mother are apportioned into each gamete during their formation. The particular gene that a gamete receives can come from either the mother or the father. Mendel also recognized that, through mutation, different versions of the same gene are present in the mother and in the father. This is particularly true if the father and mother are not related through kinship. Based on his experimental evidence, Mendel also hypothesized that the particular combination of genes (maternal or paternal) that each gamete receives is totally random. In other words, each gene is sorted into the gametes independently of each other. This process became known as the Law of Independent Assortment, Mendel's second law. Mendel's laws are taught in almost every biology class. They are important because they provide the ultimate explanation of uniqueness in humans and in all other biological organisms.

II.3. How is your individual uniqueness generated?

All life is based on cells, the microscopic units of life. Humans and many other biological organisms are multi-cellular organisms that are composed of millions to trillions of cells. For example, the human body is made up of 100 trillion cells. However, humans start with one cell. This cell is the zygote or fertilized egg, which is formed by the union of a sperm and an egg. This cell grows and divides into two identical cells using a process known as mitosis. The most significant event that occurs during mitosis is the condensation of vast amounts of DNA (six billion bases in total) into chromosomes. These chromosomes line up in the middle of the cells before separating into two sets of 46 chromosomes. The two new daughter cells are identical to each other.

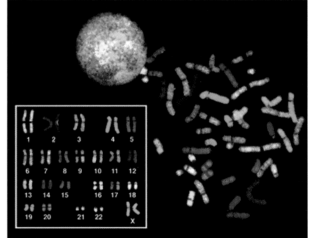

Human chromosomes
Human chromosomes (23 pairs) arranged according to size. *(Public Domain)*

Gametes are reproductive cells that are formed in the testes of males and in the ovaries of females. They are formed from precursor cells that have 46 chromosomes or 23 pairs of chromosomes (one set from each parent). This genetic condition is known as diploid. To prevent the doubling in chromosome number after each reproductive cycle, the number of chromosomes in the gametes is reduced to 23 (one set). This is a genetic condition known as haploid. Gamete formation occurs through a cell division process known as meiosis. In meiosis, the resulting gamete has 23 instead of 46 chromosomes.

Meiosis occurs in two cell division cycles. The first division is similar to mitosis in that the chromosomes replicate and form two new daughter cells, each with 46 chromosomes. These daughter cells divide again, but during this division, the chromosomes do not replicate before cell division, and the resulting daughter cells have only 23 chromosomes (haploid). The most important difference between mitosis and meiosis is how the chromosomes are distributed between the daughter cells.

During their formation, each gamete receives a different assortment of paternal and maternal chromosomes. For example, a particular gamete can receive maternal chromosome 1, paternal chromosome 2, and maternal chromosome 3. The process is completely random; receiving one chromosome has no influence on receiving other chromosomes (Mendel's Law of Independent Assortment). Consequently, an individual can generate many different gametes based on the independent assortment of maternal and paternal chromosomes. The number of possible chromosomal assortments can be calculated by the equation:

$$x = 2^n \quad \text{(x is the chromosomal assortments and n is the number of chromosomes)}$$

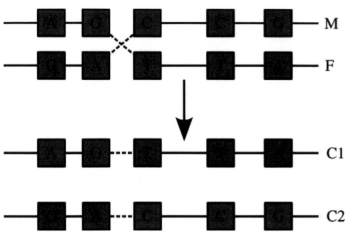

Chromosome crossover

Crossover can lead to further diversity in the formation of gametes. *(Public Domain)*

Based on this calculation, with 23 chromosomes, each human being can produce 8.6 million different gametes. To determine the number of different zygotes that two individuals could possibly form, a different formula is used: the square of 8.6 million or 70 trillion. In other words, there are up to 70 trillion different zygotes that could possibly be formed during each episode of fertilization.

In addition to meiosis, there is another process that can further increase the amount of genetic variation between each gamete. This process occurs during the first meiotic cell division after the chromosomes have been replicated. During this brief period, the maternal and paternal chromosomes of each pair align next to each other. Breaks can occur at the same regions of the maternal and paternal chromosomes, and small chromosome pieces are exchanged with each other. This phenomenon is known as chromosome crossover.

With chromosome crossover, three different kinds of chromosomes can result: maternal chromosomes, paternal chromosomes, and hybrid maternal-paternal chromosomes. This process increases the possible number of different gametes. The number of chromosome crossover events can range from 5 to 50. If, for example, the number of chromosome crossover events within a certain gamete is five, then the possible gamete combinations will increase from 8.6 million to 268 million. Furthermore, the possible zygote combinations will increase from 70 trillion to 72 quadrillion. This is the biological basis of our uniqueness.

II.4. *What is the significance of individual variations?*

Variations in the human population through mutation and sexual reproduction have created diversity and individual uniqueness. Such variations have important survival values for the human population as demonstrated for sickle cell disease and for human skin color. Even infectious diseases that occurred centuries apart can demonstrate the importance of our genetic variation for our survival. We now have evidence demonstrating that an infectious disease, which occurred in the 14th century, has provided protection against another disease in the 20th century. This is a remarkable example of how genetic variations within a population serve as insurance against unexpected environmental factors, from climatic changes to the emergence of new infectious diseases.

In 1981, the world was shocked by the emergence of a new disease, acquired immune deficiency syndrome (AIDS). AIDS is caused by the human immune deficiency virus (HIV), a previously unknown virus. Since then, AIDS has killed more than 25 million people. In 2005, an estimated three million lives were claimed by AIDS, with more than a half million being children. In the United States and Western Europe, the incidence of AIDS has been significantly reduced due to better treatment and effective preventive measures. People in sub-Saharan Africa, however, continue to suffer from AIDS. Each year, over two million deaths from AIDS occur in this area, accounting for 71% of the world's death toll. If the current trend does not reverse, the total death toll resulting from AIDS in Africa may reach 90-100 million by 2050.

For years, researchers were puzzled by the ferocity of AIDS in Africa. The disease was spreading at a rate that was much faster than expected. On average, the progression of the disease from the onset of symptoms to death was taking two years instead of the eight to ten years in other parts of the world. One answer

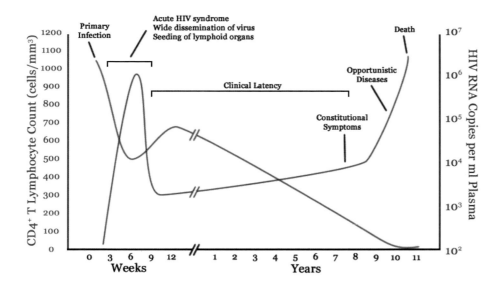

HIV infection

Time from infection to development of AIDS varies among individuals. *(Public Domain)*

to this question came from studies in 1993, when researchers in the United States discovered different rates of disease progression in individuals who were infected with HIV. They discovered that some individuals survived as long as 30 years without exhibiting any clinical symptoms. These individuals came to be known as long-term nonprogressors. They also found individuals, also known as elite controllers, who were infected but who had almost non-detectable levels of HIV antibodies in their blood.

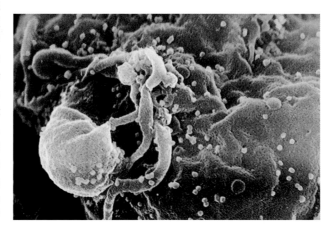

HIV viruses

Viruses emerge from infected lymphocytes. *(Public Domain)*

HIV attacks their target cells, the T lymphocytes, by first attaching to a set of cell surface proteins. These proteins serve as receptors for the viruses to gain entry into the cells. One of the receptors is known as CCR5, and it is the mutation of the CCR5 gene that protects both the long-term nonprogressors and the elite controllers from developing AIDS. These individuals carry a mutation of the CCR5 gene, known as CCR5-Δ32, which encodes for a protein that no longer binds to the HIV viruses. The long-term nonprogressors are heterozygous, carrying one copy of the CCR5-Δ32 gene, whereas the elite controllers are homozygous, harboring two copies of the CCR5-Δ32 gene.

The prevalence of the CCR5-Δ32 mutation is the highest among individuals of Western European descent and is almost completely absent in the sub-Saharan populations. The reason for this observation was understood when researchers linked the CCR5-Δ32 mutation to survivors of the bubonic plague, a disease that had devastated the European population in the 14th century. The Black Death that occurred during the 1340s killed nearly 75 million people in Europe and in other

Black Death

Showing the dying with lesions on their bodies. *(Public Domain)*

Barack Obama

His mother is Caucasian American.
(Public Domain)

Tiger Woods

His mother is Thai American.
(Creative Commons Attribution)

parts of the world. However, sub-Saharan Africa was spared from the epidemic. Furthermore, historical accounts verified that in almost every town or city, someone would survive and recover from the disease. These survivors assumed the role of taking care of the sick and of burying the dead. Evidence thus far strongly supports the observation that the CCR5-Δ32 mutation arose during the time of the Black Death because it also prevented the bubonic plague bacteria from attacking an individual's lymphocytes.

In summary, genetic variations created by mutation and sexual reproduction are critical for the survival of a species. It is important for us to value our individual uniqueness and accept the uniqueness of other people. It is unfortunate that the general public remains entrenched in racial classifications that are based on non-scientific perceptions. It is unfortunate that an American with moderately dark skin and a slight hint of African features is labeled as African American. Barack Obama and Tiger Woods are both reported in the news media as African Americans, even though their mothers are Caucasian American and Thai American, respectively. Racial ideology is unscientific and poses a serious threat to human societies because it serves as a powerful trigger of human xenophobic instinct. Education is the only way to overcome ignorance and dispel this irrationality.

Chapter 5

Nature versus Nurture

Your genes versus the environment

What are different kinds of twins?
A pair of fraternal twins (a boy and a girl) taking a nap.
(Dustin M. Ramsey)

CHAPTER 5. NATURE VERSUS NURTURE

Identical triplets

These identical sisters might be similar in appearance, but they are different in personality. *(Creative Commons Attribution)*

Our individual uniqueness results from the combination of our genes that we have inherited from our parents. We are unique because our species uses sexual reproduction and meiosis. Through these processes, each child receives a unique combination of genes from his or her parents. However, genes are not the only factor that determines what a person will become. A person's environment is also important, because environment can influence the functioning of one's genes. Throughout our history, our genes have constantly interacted with our environments. This interaction has resulted in us becoming what we are today.

I. WHY ARE SOME INDIVIDUALS GENETICALLY IDENTICAL?

How environment affects human development has long been debated. Recently, studies on identical twins have revealed some interesting findings on the interaction between genes and the environment. In one study, a pair of identical twins was separated at birth and adopted by two different families living in two different states. During their early years, they never had any contact with each other. Only when they were in their 40s were they reunited. They were shocked by their many similarities. Not only did they resemble each other, but they also had many behavioral similarities. They both loved motorcycles and beer, and both were captains in their volunteer fire departments. They even held their beer cans alike with their pinkies on the bottom to prevent the can from slipping. Neither was married. Also, one installed burglar alarms, whereas the other installed fire alarms for a living. Do these remarkable similarities suggest that genes are more powerful than the environment?

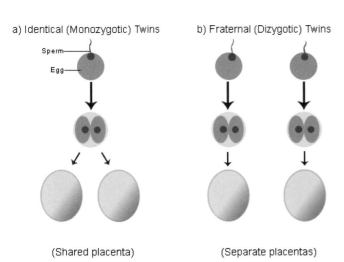

Twin formation

Different biological processes in forming identical and fraternal twins. *(Public Domain)*

I.1. Why are identical twins identical?

The human uterus was designed for single births. There is only enough space to support one fetus, but multiple births do occur on occasion. Twins are the most common type of multiple births; nonidentical twins occur in 1 out of 80 live births, and identical twins occur in 1 out of 250 live births. Twin pregnancies generally do not reach the full term of 40 weeks because the uterus is too small. Delivery of twins typically occurs about three weeks early. Nonidentical twins are known as dizygotic twins, because they result when two separate eggs are fertilized by different sperm. Therefore, dizygotic twins can consist of different sexes, and the odds for a pair of dizygotic twins to be genetically identical are the same as those for normal siblings, about 1 in 70 trillion.

Monozygotic twins are genetically identical because they are derived from the same zygote or fertilized egg. During the early stages of embryonic development, the zygote forms a small cell cluster. If this cluster splits into two, both develop into complete and identical human beings. Researchers have been successful in creating identical embryos in mice by physically dividing one cell cluster into two cell clusters. The forming of monozygotic twins is nature's way of cloning or creating two genetically identical individuals. Because the process is akin to asexual reproduction, identical twins share the same genes.

In addition to twins, there are other types of multiple births ranging from triplets to quintuplets. The likelihood for nonidentical triplets is 1 in 6,400 live births, and the odds for identical triplets are 1 in 500,000. The gestation for triplets is even shorter than the gestation for twins. The occurrence of quadruplets is rare, and the odds for naturally-conceived, nonidentical quadruplets are 1 in 512,000. For identical quadruplets, the odds are 1 in 1.13 million. As expected, the gestation periods decrease as the number of fetuses increase. Therefore, infants from multiple births are premature and often need care in neonatal intensive care units.

There are more than several hundred sets of identical quadruplets alive today. Identical quintuplets are extremely rare, and the odds for an identical quintuplet birth are 1 in 57 million. Most quintuplets fail to survive, because they are born severely immature. Usually, only two or three babies out of the five survive into adulthood. All types of multiple births are formed through the same processes as those that form the monozygotic and dizygotic twins. For identical triplets, quadruplets, or quintuplets to occur, the early embryo must split into multiple clusters of cells. The likelihood for these cell clusters to survive decreases as the number of fetuses increase.

One of the most famous multiple births were the Dionne quintuplets, born on May 26, 1934 in Ontario, Canada. They were born two months premature and were the first set of quintuplets that survived beyond infancy. They were born into a poor family. To earn some extra income, their father exhibited them at the World's Fair in Chicago. As a result, the Canadian government took them away from their parents and placed them in the care of their family doctor. They lived in a specially built house, which was near their family home. This house was unusual in that it had an observation gallery, which was used to display the quintuplets. In time, over 6,000 daily visitors paid to view the quintuplets. In fact, the quintuplets surpassed Niagara Falls as the biggest tourist attraction of the era. In 1943, the quintuplet's father won back the custody of the children, and at age nine, they returned to their family. Two of the quintuplets are still alive today.

Dionne quintuplets
They were the first set of quintuplets that survived beyond infancy. *(Public Domain)*

The human uterus was not designed to accommodate multiple births. The health of each fetus is increasingly threatened with each additional fetus in the uterus. In the past two decades, the number of nonidentical multiple births has increased due to the use of fertility drugs and in vitro fertilization. Normally, only one egg is released for each cycle of ovulation. However, the use of fertility drugs increases the number of eggs released during ovulation. Furthermore, to ensure the success of in vitro fertilization, several fertilized eggs are implanted in the uterus.

I.2. How identical are identical twins?

Every year in August, the largest gathering of twins and multiple births takes place in Twinsburg, Ohio. Over several thousand twins attend the Twins Days festival. There is also a large contingency of biologists, medical researchers, psychologists, and sociologists who attend the festival. This festival presents a good opportunity for researchers to ask questions concerning the balance between nature and nurture in determining a person's physical and behavioral characteristics. These studies allow researchers to examine the interactions between biology, nutrition, education, culture, and society.

The studies of genes and environment are divided into three major categories. The first category is to examine the impact of environment on physical traits such as weight, height, facial features, and body build. Researchers can examine the correlation of these parameters between twins who grew up together as well as those

Identical twin girls
They become more different as
they become older. *(Public Domain)*

who lived separately. For many physical traits, researchers have discovered that twins remain alike regardless of whether they grow up together or not. The heights of twins, for example, were discovered to have a correlation of 0.92 (a correlation of 1.0 would indicate the exact same height). Therefore, this high correlation indicates that twins' heights are almost the same. The results from this and similar types of studies concluded that physical traits of twins are under a strong genetic control and that their environments have little or no impact.

The second category of study is to examine the impact of environment on behavioral characteristics. Studies were conducted on twins by psychologists using individual interviews, personality inventories, and other psychological surveys. Researchers also examined academic backgrounds, career preferences, hobbies, spiritual experiences, and philosophical outlooks. The overall correlation of these parameters between identical twins raised in the same household was 0.49. In comparison, the correlation for nonidentical twins was 0.22. Even though the correlation for behavioral traits was significantly lower than for physical traits, it was, nevertheless, much higher for identical twins than for nonidentical twins. When similar tests were administered to identical twins raised apart since birth, the correlation was 0.51. This correlation was nearly the same for the identical twins who had grown up together in the same environment.

These results indicate that genes have different effects on physical traits and behavioral traits. Physical traits, for example, are strongly governed by an individual's genetic makeup. Also, since most of the structural features that are observed in adults are first established during fetal development and infancy, the impact of environment is likely to be insignificant. Some exceptions to this are malnutrition or famine in a mother during her pregnancy and fetal exposure to toxic chemicals. Both of these events can permanently affect the growth and development of a child. Chemicals, such as pollutants and abuse substances, can profoundly impact early fetal development and result in permanent damage to vital organs. Fetal alcohol syndrome is a well-known developmental disorder of the brain that occurs when a fetus is exposed to alcohol during the first trimester of pregnancy.

Prior to the studies on identical twins and their behavior, most researchers considered intelligence, social behavior, emotional behavior, outlook, and other behavioral traits to be the result of the environment. Until recently, the mind was considered nothing more than a blank slate, or *tabula rasa*, that needed to be shaped entirely by experience. Therefore, researchers were surprised to discover that the behavioral correlations of the identical twins who were raised together and of those who were raised apart are nearly the same. These results suggest that genes are important for shaping our behavioral traits. However, researchers have also found that environment has a stronger impact on behavioral traits than it does on physical traits. Identical twins may look exactly alike (because of their genes), but they often have separate personalities (because of their environments). Furthermore, certain diseases, such as alcoholism and depression, are often more closely correlated in identical twins than in nonidentical twins. These findings provide strong support for the genetic components of these disorders.

The third category is the study of disease frequencies in identical twins. The results of these studies are similar to those on the physical and behavioral traits. For some diseases, particularly the early childhood genetic diseases, genes are important. In genetic disorders such as Tay-Sachs disease, cystic fibrosis, and sickle cell disease, the development of the disorders is completely determined by the presence of a mutant gene. For other diseases, however, such as heart disease, diabetes, Alzheimer's disease, and breast cancer, genetics have less of an impact. In summary, genes are important for determining those traits that are vital for the survival of the organisms. These traits are often not affected by the environment. However, when a biological trait is determined by many different genes, the environment becomes more important.

1.3. Identical twins and organ transplants

In the early 1950s, patients suffering from kidney failure faced a certain death because of the toxic waste products that accumulated in their bodies. The development of kidney dialysis machines prolonged their lives, but did not provide a cure. To find a cure, a group of surgeons in Boston had started experimenting with kidney transplantation. They discovered that the transplanted kidneys would work for several days but then fail when the recipient's immune system recognized the kidney as foreign and destroyed it. The surgeons tried every conceivable method to save the transplanted kidney from rejection. They even tried to wrap the kidney in plastic. After multiple attempts, the surgeons were ready to give up because they could not overcome the kidneys' repeated rejections.

In 1954, a man, who was dying from kidney failure, came to the Boston surgeons for help. He had with him his identical twin brother. The surgeons discussed the possibility of transplanting one of the healthy kidneys from his twin brother to him. All parties agreed, and the operation was performed. This surgery was first time that an operation was performed on a healthy individual to save another individual. The patient accepted his brother's kidney without a sign of rejection, and the kidney functioned perfectly. This surgery was a medical triumph, and for the first time, unequivocal evidence was provided indicating that the human body is a machine. Parts of the machine can be replaced with other parts, as long as the immune system does not recognize the replacement parts as foreign.

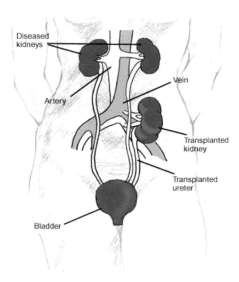

Kidney transplant
The transplanted kidney is often placed below the original kidney. *(Public Domain)*

Genetic barriers make organ transplantation difficult. Studies with identical twins and with animal models discovered that the surface of all body cells, except the red blood cells, exhibits a group of proteins, known as transplantation antigens. These proteins are encoded by a group of genes that are important in the normal function of the immune system, particularly in the defense against viral infections. There are many alleles (different versions) for each of these genes in the human population. Therefore, it is unlikely that two individuals will share identical alleles for all these genes. These alleles most likely evolved to create enough diversity in the human population to insure that a few humans survive the emergence of every new viral disease.

Until the 1970s, organ transplantation was rare because of the difficulties of finding matching individuals. The actual surgical procedures for most major organ transplants were well-developed, but the low availability of suitable organ donors prevented any additional developments in this field. Then, in the late 1970s, a new drug, known as cyclosporine, was discovered. This drug suppresses the immune system, and when it is given to the organ transplant recipients, they no longer reject their transplants. Because of this drug, organ transplantation entered a new golden age, and many patients, who had been previously diagnosed with incurable diseases, could be treated.

Prior to the first successful kidney transplant, which was performed in 1954, a cornea transplant had been successfully conducted in 1905. Cornea transplants were successful early on because the immune system ignored the corneas and left the transplanted corneas unscathed. The next major advance in organ transplantation was the first successful heart transplantation, which was performed by Christian Barnard in 1967. In addition to major organ transplants, the following transplantations have been performed: the first hand transplant in 1998; the first successful partial face transplant in 2005; and the first successful penis transplant in 2005.

Christian Barnard
He performed the first heart transplant in 1967. *(Public Domain)*

Organ and tissue transplantation has saved many lives and has improved the quality of life for many others. However, organ donors are scarce, and the availability of organs remains low. Further complicating organ transplantation is the difficulties of transporting organs from where they are harvested to where they are needed. Consequently, the waiting lists for organ donations are long, and many people

Dolly

Dolly's remains are exhibited at the Royal Museum of Scotland. *(Public Domain)*

Scottish Blackface
(Cytoplasmic Donor)

Finn-Dorset
(Nuclear Donor)

Enucleation

Mammary Cells

Direct Current Pulse

Blastocyst

Surrogate
ewe

Dolly

Reproductive cloning

The cloning process that produced Dolly. *(Public Domain)*

have been on these lists for many years. Recently, however, the development of embryonic stem cells may offer a new solution to the organ donation problem. This technology may someday provide treatments for many chronic diseases.

II. CLONING AND ITS CONTROVERSIES

Human uniqueness poses a difficult challenge when treating diseases and disorders with tissue and organ replacements. The barriers caused by transplantation antigens remains a major obstacle in the treatment of strokes, neurological damages, and heart damages. For these conditions, transplantation may not provide the answers. Instead, scientists have been working on a different technology to treat certain conditions: therapeutic cloning. Therapeutic cloning, however, is controversial for several reasons. One reason is its similarity to reproductive cloning. Reproductive cloning results in individuals who are genetically identical to each other. Many ethical considerations of reproductive cloning need to be considered before this technology could ever be developed in humans. In animals, however, cloning has already been achieved. The cloning of the sheep Dolly in 1996 by a group of scientists in Scotland opened this new chapter in biology. Another problem with therapeutic cloning is the use of human embryos. Cells from these embryos are needed to provide the cells that are used in therapeutic cloning. This has elicited one of the most significant public debates on a new technology since in vitro fertilization (IVF). Interestingly, cloning is based on IVF technology, even though IVF has become widely accepted around the world.

II.1. What is IVF?

Amid intense controversy over the safety and morality of IVF, the first test tube baby, Louise Brown, was born in England in 1978. The procedure was highly controversial, because the baby was conceived outside the mother's body. Eggs were retrieved from the mother and placed in a Petri dish. Sperm from the father were then added to the dish. After the sperm fertilized the eggs, the zygotes were cultured for several days and were allowed to form into a tiny embryo. A catheter was then used to transfer the embryo into the uterus. From this point, the pregnancy followed a normal course. IVF was originally developed to help women who, like Louise's mother, have defective Fallopian tubes.

The Fallopian tubes connect the ovaries to the uterus. Each month, the ovaries release a single egg into the Fallopian tubes. If intercourse occurs within about two days after the egg's release, it will be fertilized within the Fallopian tubes. After fertilization, the egg travels from the Fallopian tubes into the uterus. Once the egg has successfully implanted in the uterine wall, pregnancy begins. Judy Carr, the mother of the first American test tube baby, was unable to naturally conceive because her Fallopian tubes had been removed. This occurred because of a prior, and inappropriate, implantation (ectopic pregnancy) within her Fallopian tube. With ectopic pregnancies, the Fallopian tubes need to be removed because they will eventually rupture as a result from the implantation. For her and women like her, the only chance to have a baby is by using IVF. In 1981, her daughter, Elizabeth Carr, was the first IVF baby born in the United States.

IVF is commonly used in the United States and in the world. IVF is the only chance for many couples to have a biological child. In the United States, 1% of all births are through IVF, and over 115,000 IVF babies have been born. Today, IVF is also an important treatment for male infertility, which is often caused by a low sperm count, a defect in sperm motility, and an inability to penetrate the egg. In a procedure known as intracytoplasmic sperm injection (ICSI), a sperm cell is injected directly into the egg using a fine glass needle.

IVF has many social implications because it changes the traditional role of motherhood. One of the consequences of IVF is surrogacy. In surrogacy, the genetic mother is different from the gestational mother. Commercial surrogacy occurs when childless couples "hire" surrogate mothers who "carry" the babies for a fee. Another consequence of IVF is that it allows for women who are beyond their reproductive age to become gestational mothers. Through IVF, a woman in Spain gave birth to a baby shortly before her 67th birthday.

Another social consequence of IVF is the surplus of embryos that are currently kept in frozen storage. During an IVF cycle, a woman produces multiple eggs after using fertility drugs. As many as 15 eggs can be retrieved to be fertilized by sperm. Normally, no more than three eggs are implanted, and the rest are kept in storage for future use. Occasionally, the frozen eggs are used for a subsequent implantation. One woman gave birth to a son through IVF, and 21 months later, she gave birth to twin daughters using the frozen embryos. This makes her the first women in the United States to give birth to a set of triplets who were born 21 months apart. However, most of the frozen embryos are not used. Determining the future of these embryos has become a moral issue.

IVF also creates another moral dilemma because of a diagnostic procedure known as preimplantation genetic diagnosis (PGD), also known as embryo screening. For example, if parents are concerned with the possibility of their child having cystic fibrosis, IVF can first be used to generate a number of embryos. The embryos can then be tested before implantation to determine the presence or absence of the CF gene. Any embryo that possesses two CF genes could be discarded. This method can also be used to eliminate the carrier state as well. In the case of autosomal dominant disorders, such as Huntington's disease, PGD is the only way to assure that future offspring will be unaffected by the disease. Critics of PGD point out that it could be used to select embryos on factors other than disease states. For example, PGD could be used to select the sex of the embryo. PGD also has the potential to screen for genetic traits which are unrelated to medical necessity, leading to the prospect of creating a "designer baby."

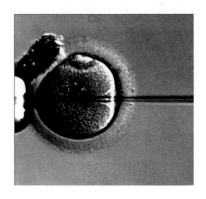

Intracytoplasmic sperm injection (ICSI)
Sperm is injected into an egg with a hollow needle. *(Public Domain)*

INTERESTED IN ADOPTING MULTI-ETHNIC EMBRYOS? CLICK HERE

Adoption of frozen embryos
They are called snowflake children.

II.2. *What is reproductive cloning?*

All through history, there has been a fascination with the cloning of both animals and humans. Farmers dream of cloning a herd of super cattle that could produce milk and meat of the highest quality. Kings and emperors would have liked to have had armies of cloned soldiers who were strong, fast, and powerful. Scientists are also interested in cloning to produce clones of identical animals or plants for experimentation. Cloning is asexual reproduction, and it has both costs and benefits. Its main benefit is the elimination of the need to find another member of the same species to reproduce. Another benefit is that each member can reproduce, eliminating the "two-fold" cost of sexual reproduction. Its cost is the elimination of variations, making the species unable to adapt to environmental changes.

Asexual reproduction is found in simple unicellular organisms, such as bacteria. The rapid generation time of bacteria can generate sufficient genetic variations through spontaneous mutation alone. Still, most bacteria species have evolved some form of sexual reproduction to exchange DNA between them. In one method, known as conjugation, two bacteria are joined by a narrow tube-like structure, known as a sex pilus, through which DNA transfer occurs. For billions of years in Earth's biological history, asexual reproduction was the only mode of reproduction. Sexual reproduction did not evolve until organisms became more complex and their generation time lengthened.

Asexual reproduction is rare among higher organisms because of the advantage of maintaining genetic variations. However, there are a few plant and animal species that reproduce asexually through a process known as parthenogenesis. In this form of asexual reproduction, the females produce zygotes without fertilization. Some lower plants reproduce through parthenogenesis. Water fleas, aphids, and some species of bees, scorpions, reptiles, and fish also reproduce through parthenogenesis. Among the whiptails (a type of lizard), there is one asexual type that reproduces via parthenogenesis and two that reproduce sexually. Interestingly, when the two sexually reproduced species hybridize, the resulting offspring is of the asexual species. The biological significance of this process remains unclear.

During the 1950s, researchers discovered that the vast majority of cells in the bodies of higher animals are differentiated cells. These cells assume specialized characteristics and form organs and tissues that have different morphological features and biological functions. Cell differentiation is unidirectional, and it was first thought that differentiated cells lost some of their genetic potential as a result of their differentiation. In other words, it appeared that cells lose some of their DNA when they differentiate. However, the scientific community was surprised when one researcher in 1960 demonstrated that the nuclei from differentiated cells of a tadpole were capable of producing an entire frog. His results demonstrated that a differentiated cell still retains its entire set of genetic information.

The method the scientist used is now known as somatic cell nuclear transfer (SCNT). In his experiments, egg cells were harvested from female frogs. Using a micromanipulation procedure, the nuclei of the eggs were removed. The nuclei from cells located in the tails of the tadpoles were then removed using a similar procedure. The nuclei of the tadpole tail cells were finally injected into the egg cells. Some of these eggs hatched and developed into frogs. These frogs were genetically identical to each other and to the tadpole that provided the nuclei from the tail cells. These were the earliest experiments to demonstrate that cloning is possible in higher animals.

However, after repeated attempts by scientists all over the world, SCNT failed to produce clones of mammals. Many researchers believed that mammals were too complicated for SCNT to work. Then, in 1997, the world was shocked by the announcement of a sheep named Dolly. Using cells from the mammary gland of a donor, a Scottish team of researchers used SCNT to create a zygote, and with the

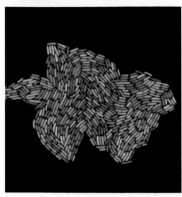

Asexual reproduction

A growing colony of *E. coli.*
(Public Domain)

Parthenogenesis

The asexual species is in the middle of its sisters species. *(Public Domain)*

technique of IVF, they implanted the embryo into a surrogate ewe. This success began a new era of creating mammalian clones. Since then, many mammals have been cloned, including cats, cattle, deer, dogs, ferrets, goats, horses, mice, mules, pigs, rabbits, rats, wolves, water buffaloes, and rhesus monkeys. With all this success, it is now clear that humans may someday be successfully cloned.

II.3. *What is therapeutic cloning?*

The cloning of animals is reproductive cloning; it results in an exact genetic copy of another animal. This type of cloning has found applications in the study of animal development. However, this cloning is performed on a small scale and mainly for research purposes. In a more controversial application, reproductive cloning has been used in the breeding and in the raising of domesticated animals. With this procedure, breeds of cattle, goats, or pigs that are genetically identical can be created. This is done to assure that every member of the breed possesses desirable traits. Furthermore, through genetic engineering, traits can be introduced and manipulated within the breeds. However, concerns have been raised about the creation of "Frankenstein" animals.

Two outcomes of cloning
Reproductive and therapeutic cloning use the same process for different outcomes. *(Public Domain)*

From the beginning, human reproductive cloning has been considered to be ethically and morally unacceptable. Almost immediately after the announcement of the creation of Dolly, governments around the world began passing laws to ban human reproductive cloning. From a biological standpoint, human reproductive cloning is devoid of biological purpose. Cloning is asexual reproduction, and living organisms have evolved sexual reproduction to replace asexual reproduction. Sexual reproduction generates genetic diversity, which is essential for the survival of the species. Therefore, creating humans through cloning is against biological "logic." From the moral and ethical standpoints, human reproductive cloning deprives us of the genetic uniqueness of every individual.

However, in the past ten years, researchers, who have been looking for ways to treat genetic disorders and other diseases, have seen that human cloning could provide a method for curing many conditions. There are diseases and conditions that currently have no treatment or cure available. These include many conditions that result from neuronal damage of the peripheral and central nervous systems. Such problems often occur in accidents, such as in automobile accidents or falls. One well-known example is Christopher Reeve, the star of *Superman*, who fell off his horse during training. When his head struck the ground, his first and second vertebrae were shattered, and his spinal cord was severed. From that point on, Reeve was paralyzed from his neck-down. There was no hope for his recovery, because adult neurons cannot regenerate. In time, it is hopeful that therapeutic cloning can be used to form new neurons that can then be used to treat spinal cord injuries.

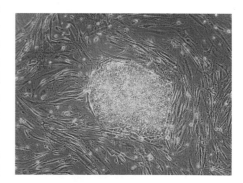

Human stem cells
They are obtained through therapeutic cloning. *(Public Domain)*

Another example is type I diabetes, also known as juvenile diabetes. In this disease, the pancreatic cells that are responsible for producing insulin are destroyed by the body's immune system. The exact cause is unknown, but researchers have suggested that episodes of viral infections trigger a case of misidentification of these cells by the immune system. Without insulin, the cells in the body cannot absorb glucose from the blood. This leads to a state of starvation and to many other physiological complications. Unfortunately, the destroyed pancreatic cells cannot regenerate. Currently, the treatment of diabetes is through a lifetime administration of insulin.

Research on animals has recently found that cells from embryos can repair damages in the adult nervous system and in other tissues, such as the pancreas. The embryonic cells have retained their growth and differentiation potential. Also, animal studies have demonstrated that embryonic cells that have been injected into the site of a severed spinal cord can result in the animal regaining mobility within a few weeks. In this case, the embryonic cells have repaired the damage and have rejoined the severed spinal cord. However, there is one problem with this technique. Unless the embryonic cells share the same transplantation antigens as the recipient's, they will be rejected by the recipient's immune system. This poses the same transplantation barrier as that faced by the transplant organs and tissues.

One way to overcome the transplantation barrier is to create embryonic cells from the recipients. How can embryonic cells be created from an adult? Human cloning offers a solution to this problem. Instead of cloning an entire person, human cloning can proceed and stop at the embryonic stage. The cells from the embryo can be harvested to treat the donor. This form of human cloning is known as therapeutic cloning, which was designed as a means of therapy. Therapeutic cloning is strongly supported by medical researchers and practitioners because it offers treatment strategies that were unavailable before. However, its opponents characterize it as "destroying life in order to save life," and they consider it ethically and morally wrong.

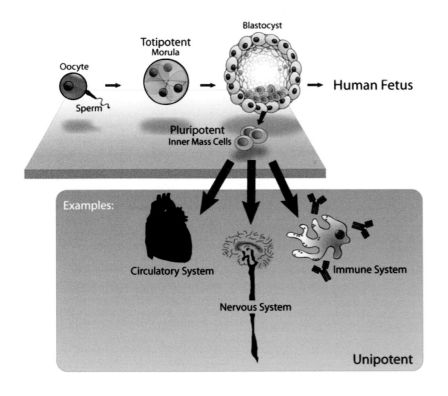

Pluripotent stem cell

These cells are capable of being any cell type in the body.
(Public Domain)

II.4. What are embryonic stem cells?

Therapeutic cloning is based on the discovery of how a fertilized egg develops first into an embryo and then into an adult that possesses tissues and organs that are made up of 200 different cell types. Even though all cells in a human body are genetically identical, they are different structurally and functionally. They are known as differentiated cells. For example, muscle cells are different from neurons and skin cells. Their differences are remarkable when considering that they share the same genetic information. Cell differentiation results from the synthesis of different proteins. For example, muscle proteins are synthesized in muscle cells but not in liver cells. Since all body cells possess identical genetic information, liver cells also possess the genes for muscle proteins.

The reason that liver cells do not make muscle proteins is due to a phenomenon known as differential gene expression. In the liver cells, the genes for muscle proteins are shut off, and they are not expressed. However, the genes for making liver cells are expressed. During embryonic development, genes are selectively turned on and off in order to create specialized cells for the formation of tissues and organs. Through a set of tightly regulated steps, the zygote is first transformed into an embryo, which then undergoes further development in forming the foundation of tissues and organs. By the end of the first trimester of human pregnancy, the embryo becomes a fetus, which by this time possesses the basic structure of the human body plan. The remainder of the pregnancy is for growth and expansion.

The first stage of human embryo development involves the most critical steps, which interestingly, can take place outside a mother's body. This also makes IVF possible. Immediately after fertilization, the zygote divides rapidly, from one cell to two, two to four, four to eight, and so on. When the ball of cells reaches about 128 cells, the cells rearrange themselves to form a hollow ball. At this stage, it is known as a blastocyst or blastula. During IVF, the development from the zygote to the blastocyst takes place in a Petri dish. The next step in IVF is to implant the blastocyst in the uterine wall.

In the center of the blastocyst is a group of cells known as the inner cell mass. These cells are the precursors for all the differentiated cells. In addition to their differentiation capacity, these cells are self-renewable. Through an unknown mechanism, these cells can set aside a portion of the cells at their undifferentiated state. These cells are referred to as pluripotent stem cells. Pluripotent refers to their ability to differentiate into any cell type; stem cell refers to their renewal capability. As the blastocyst enters the next stage of development, the pluripotent stem cells gradually disappear. They are apparently absent in the adult body.

Researchers have discovered the processes by which the pluripotent stem cells differentiate into specialized cells. They found that as the embryo develops, cells produce chemical signals in the form of small chemical compounds or protein molecules. These chemical signals regulate gene expression, shutting off some genes and inducing other genes. The combination of the genes that are turned on and off is believed to be responsible for cell differentiation. In animal studies, these chemical signals are responsible for switching on the differentiation pathways for different tissues cells, including muscle, immune cells, neurons, and hormone producing cells.

Cell differentiation is also known as cell programming, and thus far, it appears that the programming is unidirectional. Once a pluripotent stem cell is programmed to become a particular type of cell, it is not easily reprogrammed. However, it also appears that reprogramming is not impossible. In SNCT, the differentiated adult cells, such as the mammary gland cells used to clone Dolly, can be reprogrammed. It appears that once the nucleus is inserted into the cytoplasm of an egg, genes are reprogrammed to assume the role of a zygote and to undergo development into an embryo. It is important to understand how genes are turned on and off and to understand the environmental factors that affect these activities.

III. GENE EXPRESSION

From the studies of identical twins and from the development of embryonic stem cells, genes and the impact of the environment on them are now understood to be closely intertwined. Genes are the instructions for building biological organisms. Over a long period of time, genes change due to environmental pressures that favor the genetic variations that are best suited for survival and reproductive success. These genetic variations will pass onto future generations. If the environment stays stable, they will become the most prominent versions in the population. However, our traits can undergo subtle changes at the individual level. The examples of the differences among individuals of multiple births offer clear evidence that such subtle changes occur. The examples of cell differentiation during embryonic development further strengthen the idea that the same set of genes can have different biological outcomes. This is known as genetic plasticity.

III.1. What is genetic plasticity?

One surprising and devastating demonstration of genetic plasticity is the separate mental development of one particular pair of identical twins. When they were born, they looked identical to each other as do all identical twins. During their first year, they reached their developmental milestones in synchrony. They started to hold

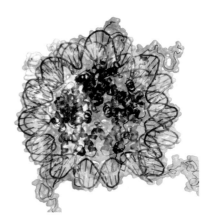

Nucleosome

Nuclear proteins surround the DNA and regulate transcription.
(Public Domain)

their heads up and to crawl on nearly the same days. However, their mother noticed something very different at their first birthday party. One of the twins behaved excitedly as most normal one year olds would, but the other twin wandered back and forth in the room as if no one was present. Their behavioral differences continued to grow, and before their 9th birthday, one of the twins was diagnosed with severe autism. Their parents were baffled by this development.

This extreme example represents how the same set of genes can unfold in such different ways because genes are not as simple as computer programs. At the level of individual genes, the protein products are always the same, because their amino acid sequences are controlled by the DNA sequences of the genes. However, the timing of the expression of each gene and the quantity of the proteins synthesized are not fixed. Cells receive cues from the environment, mostly in the form of chemicals, to regulate when and how much to produce these proteins. Most of these signals control the synthesis of messenger RNA from the DNA. These signals come in the form of hormones and protein molecules that bind to regions of the DNA that are not involved in coding.

This type of molecule is known as a transcriptional regulator. The positive transcriptional regulators activate RNA transcription, and negative transcriptional regulators inhibit RNA transcription. One example is tanning, where transcriptional regulation is responsible for the production of skin pigment proteins. In this case, the UV light causes damage to the skin cells and stimulates the nerve endings embedded in the skin. Nerve signals travel to the brain and activate a region (the pituitary gland) in the brain to produce the hormone melanocortin. This hormone is transported to the skin via the blood circulation. At the region where sunburn has occurred, the melancortin activates the melanocytes to transcribe the skin pigment genes. The transcription of the messenger RNA leads to the production of the skin pigment proteins.

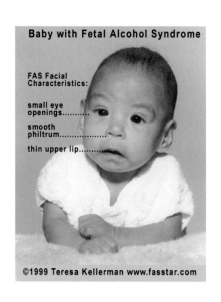

Baby with Fetal Alcohol Syndrome

FAS Facial Characteristics:

small eye openings..........

smooth philtrum.................

thin upper lip.........

©1999 Teresa Kellerman www.fasstar.com

Fetal alcohol syndrome
This FAS baby has distinctive facial features. *(Public Domain)*

Genes continuously interact with the environment through physical, chemical, and other means. In some cases, if the environmental factors occur at a critical stage of development, the effect is long lasting and often permanent. One example is the drug thalidomide that was prescribed between the late 1950s and early 1960s to pregnant women as an antiemetic to combat morning sickness and as an aid to help them sleep. Unknowingly, this drug was a powerful transcriptional regulator that affected the expression of critical genes during development. From 1956 to 1962, approximately 10,000 children were born with severe malformations, including very short or absent long bones and a flipper-like appearance of the hands and feet.

Another well-documented interaction between genes and environment is fetal alcohol syndrome (FAS), a disorder of permanent birth defects that occurs in the offspring of women who consume alcohol during pregnancy. Alcohol crosses the placental barrier and affects either directly or indirectly the transcription of critical genes during the early stages of embryonic development. The main result of FAS is permanent central nervous system damage due to the underdevelopment of certain regions of the brain. The consequences are cognitive disabilities including poor memory, attention deficits, impulsive behavior, and emotional instability. FAS is the leading known cause of mental retardation in the Western World. Thus, the current recommendation by the U.S. Surgeon General is not to drink at all during pregnancy.

Genetic plasticity occurs less in physiological and biochemical traits that are required for basic survival. Genes coding for critical enzymes have no room for errors because the malfunction of these genes prevents survival. Genetic plasticity occurs more in cognitive functions and in behavioral traits. These genes continue to interact with the environment, and these genes also form a complex network of multiple genes. Consequently, these complex interactions create many alternative pathways and flexibilities. This interaction of genes with their environment is both inevitable and necessary, as organisms must continue to make adjustments to a changing environment.

III.2. What is epigenetics?

During the past ten years, researchers have discovered a way in which the environment affects gene expression without changing the sequences of DNA. Normally, environmental factors that do not cause a change in DNA sequences only affect one generation. The future generations will not be affected if the DNA sequences are not changed. This is the fundamental principle of molecular genetics. Unexpectedly, researchers discovered that certain traits can be passed from one generation to the next, even though the DNA sequences remain unchanged. For example, if certain environmental conditions, such as the lack of food or the presence of environmental pollutants, cause a particular disease in a person, those traits may be passed on. When these adverse environmental conditions were amended, the disease condition went away. However, this person's offspring can show symptoms of the disease one or two generations later. Furthermore, no mutation has occurred in the DNA.

This type of inheritance is known as epigenetics, which means beyond genetics. In other words, there are some other factors that affect inheritance other than genes. One example that demonstrates the impact of epigenetics is how two seemingly-unrelated genetic disorders can be caused by the same genetic mutation. The first genetic disorder is known as Angelman's syndrome (AS). It is a rare genetic disorder that is characterized by intellectual and developmental delays, speech impediments, seizures, and a jerky gait. However, these patients maintain an unusually happy demeanor, which was described by the older term, Happy puppet syndrome. AS is related to another genetic disorder known as the Prader-Willi syndrome (PWS), which is characterized by small stature, mild learning difficulties, food preoccupations, and obesity.

Even though AS and PWS appear to be two entirely different genetic disorders based on their clinical presentation, they are linked in an unusual way. Both disorders have the exact same segment of DNA deleted in chromosome number 15. The manifestation of AS and PWS depends on the inheritance of chromosome 15. If the child inherited the mutant chromosome 15 from the father, he or she develops PWS. If the child inherited the mutation chromosome 15 from the mother, he or she develops AS. When this was first discovered, researchers were puzzled and could not understand how the same DNA sequences could cause entirely different genetic disorders.

Further research discovered a phenomenon known as DNA imprinting, which is caused by the chemical modification of DNA bases by the attachment of methyl groups (the chemical structure is $-CH_3$), a process known as DNA methylation. This modification does not change the DNA sequences, but it can alter gene expression and can be passed from one generation to the next. Even

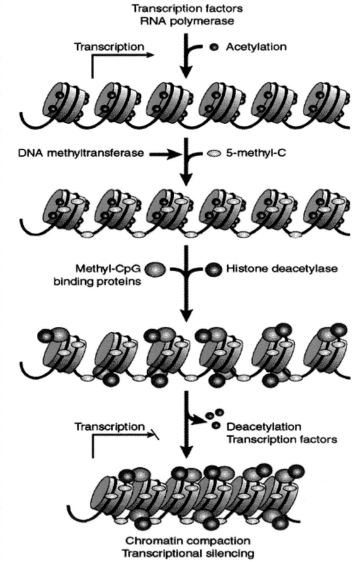

DNA methylation
Methylation of DNA regulates its transcription. *(Public Domain)*

though the DNA sequences between the mutant maternal and paternal chromosome 15 are identical, their patterns of DNA methylation are distinct. These differences are known as DNA imprinting.

Interestingly, DNA methylation can be passed from one generation to the next. The exact mechanism remains unclear, but it appears that after DNA replication, the methylation patterns are also copied. In a recent study that was designed to find the origin of DNA methylation, researchers discovered that long term stress in the form of famine, malnutrition, toxic chemical exposure, and psychological stress can cause DNA methylation. This appears to be a response of organisms preparing for long-term genetic changes without changing the DNA sequences. These changes can be passed down to the next generation.

In one recent study, researchers discovered that the grandchildren of a man who experienced famine during his teenage years were four times more likely to suffer from chronic diseases, such as diabetes, and to experience a reduction in life expectancy. A similar phenomenon occurred in a woman whose grandmother also experienced famine. Researchers hypothesized that the nutritional stress of famine had led to DNA imprinting through DNA methylation. This DNA imprinting is transmitted to the gametes and passed onto the future generations. Researchers now have evidence that many other environmental stressors (such as alcohol, cigarettes, farm chemicals, and environmental pollutants) can lead to DNA imprinting.

In summary, nature and nurture are analogous to the music and lyrics of a song. Both are important in the formation of biological traits, like music and lyrics are both important in a song. Understanding the biological principles involved in the interactions between genes and the environment is important to us, both at the personal level and the societal level.

Chapter 6

Sex

Do you know your sex?

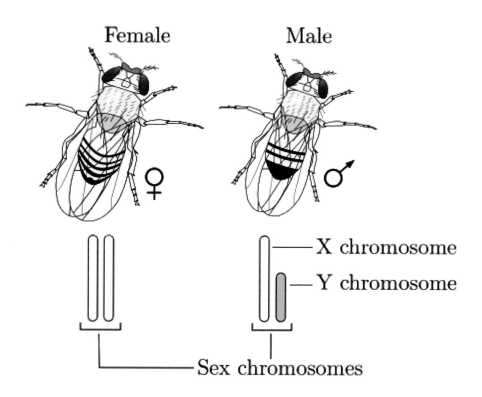

What can the flies tell us about sex?

The studies of the fruit flies have led to new understandings of the biological processes of sex. Their sex determination is similar to human and has X and Y sex chromosomes. *(Public Domain)*

CHAPTER 6. SEX

In multicellular organisms, differential gene expression allows for the production of specialized cells, which are used for the formation of tissues and organs. However, differential gene expression is also important in another area: the formation of different sexes. Even though males and females that come from the same species appear different from each other, they have nearly the same genetic information. In humans, the differences between the sexes reside in the sex chromosomes, the X and Y chromosomes. XX and XY are the chromosomal compositions for females and males, respectively. The reason that males and females are genetically very similar is because the Y chromosome contains only a few genes. Furthermore, in some species that do not use sex chromosomes, the males and females have exactly the same genetic information. For many years, researchers were puzzled by the way in which male and female characteristics are determined even though both sexes have the same genetic information. In the past 30 years, studies on sex determination have revealed that differential gene expression is responsible for determining the different sexes.

I. WHAT IS SEX?

Sex has many biological, social, and cultural implications in human society. Without sex, humans would not exist. However, the biological basis of human sexuality has only recently become understood. This knowledge is vital for our understanding of sexual issues. It is also important for those individuals who suffer from abnormal sexual development. The causes for these cases are varied and include such problems as chromosomal abnormalities, insensitivity to sex hormones, and enzyme deficiencies.

In one case, a young woman's problem with her sexual development was only discovered after she was hospitalized because of a diving accident in the early 1950s. While she was recovering from her surgery, her physicians made a surprising discovery. Even though she appeared female in every aspect, they discovered that she lacked both a uterus and ovaries. In the 1950s, human sex chromosomes were used as the primary criteria for determining sex. To the physicians' surprise, instead of having XX chromosomes as expected, she was XY, the male sex chromosome complement.

The physicians were both surprised and alarmed by this unusual finding. They informed her father, but they could not provide him with an explanation. Her father explained to both her and her future husband what he had been told. However, her family failed to fully understand her condition. As a result, she lived in fear and shame for most of her life, and her husband treated her as a freak. It was not until the 1980s when she responded to an announcement by a group of researchers who were looking for subjects like her to participate in a research project that she began to understand the cause of her condition, and her life was changed. She came to accept who she was and to understand herself from a biological standpoint. She and others, who have sexual development disorders, can now live their lives without guilt and shame. But, the question remains: why do such individuals exist?

I.1. Why does sex exist?

Sex is the most important aspect of biological organisms; it maintains the species. In contrast to asexual reproduction, sexual reproduction requires two members of the same species to pool their genetic information together. In the biological world, nearly 99% of higher organisms use sexual reproduction for both maintaining and expanding their species. Not only do animals use sexual reproduction, but plants,

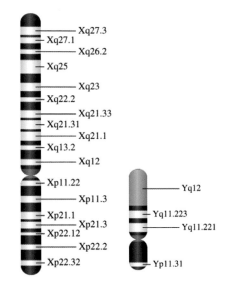

Human sex chromosomes

The Y chromosome is smaller and has only a few genes.
(Public Domain)

Xq27.3
Xq27.1
Xq26.2
Xq25
Xq23
Xq22.2
Xq21.33
Xq21.31
Xq21.1
Xq13.2
Xq12
Xp11.22
Xp11.3
Xp21.1
Xp21.3
Xp22.12
Xp22.2
Xp22.32

Yq12
Yq11.223
Yq11.221
Yp11.31

fungi, and even unicellular organisms also use this type of reproduction. Through sexual reproduction, biological organisms can create the necessary genetic diversity that is crucial for adapting to changing environments.

The importance of genetic diversity was studied by a group of researchers who studied a small fish that lives in pools of water along mountain streams. This fish species has an unusual reproductive characteristic; it can reproduce either sexually or asexually by parthenogenesis. In parthenogenesis, the females can reproduce without the need for males to fertilize their eggs. This occurs when the fish are infected by a certain type of parasite. When this occurs, the male fish die, and the females start to reproduce through parthenogenesis. Interestingly, this situation results in the fish population experiencing a dramatic increase.

In any population, the growth rate of asexual reproduction always exceeds the rate of sexual reproduction. This observation leads to the biological concept of the two-fold cost of sex. In asexual reproduction, every member of the species can contribute to the production of the young. However, in sexual reproduction, only the females can bear the young. Even though the males make genetic contributions, they cannot bear the young. This creates the two-fold cost of sexual reproduction. Furthermore, in sexual reproduction, the two different sexes must meet in order to procreate. This situation further increases the amount of energy that must be invested in the reproductive process. In asexual reproduction, however, a single organism can create many offspring without the need to find a mating partner.

Parthenogenesis

The Komodo Dragon can reproduce by parthenogenesis. *(GNU Free Documentation License)*

For many years, researchers hypothesized about the importance of genetic diversity in offsetting the two-fold cost of sex in sexual reproduction. The studies on the fish species that can reproduce both sexually and asexually offer a clear demonstration of the value of genetic diversity. Initially, the fish that could reproduce asexually overtook the population of the fish that reproduced sexually. After the first few seasons, almost all the fish in the ponds were those that reproduced asexually. However, the situation gradually changed, and the asexually reproduced fish started to die from infectious diseases and from other genetic disorders. Eventually, the numbers of the sexually reproduced fish increased, and they reclaimed their place in the ponds.

This research provides clear evidence of the importance of genetic diversity in a species. Without genetic diversity, a species can become highly vulnerable to attacks by infectious microorganisms. Even though the fish had an effective defense mechanism to fight off the invading microorganisms, many eventually died because the microorganisms evolved rapidly and found ways to overcome the host defense system. One way for a species to counter the ever-evolving microorganisms is to reproduce through sexual reproduction. Sexual reproduction generates individual variations. It is these variations that allows some members of the species to survive.

Arms race

Through sexual reproduction, the cheetahs and gazelles undergo constant change as predators and prey. *(GNU Free Documentation License)*

Another example that demonstrates the importance of sexual reproduction is the predator-prey relationship between the cheetahs and the gazelles. The cheetahs are the fastest animals on land, making them master gazelle hunters. The gazelles are master cheetah evaders, making them the second fastest animal. Cheetahs excel in short bursts of speed, whereas the gazelles have greater stamina and are better in making turns. With each generation, the cheetahs continue to create faster offspring. However, they will never be fast enough, because the gazelles are also changing and are getting better at evading the cheetahs. These variations are created through sexual reproduction. If the gazelles would reproduce asexually, the faster cheetahs could eliminate them within a single generation.

I.2. How did sex evolve?

Primitive forms of sex are found in bacteria, the simplest form of biological organisms. All bacteria belong to a group of organisms known as the prokaryotic cells. As described by their name (pro = before and karyo = nucleus), these cells do not have nuclei. The other major group of cells is the eukaryotes, which are cells with nuclei. The prokaryotes normally reproduce asexually using a cell division process known as binary fission. Prokaryotes grow rapidly and have a cell cycle of less than 30 minutes. Because of this rapid cell growth, spontaneous mutations occur often, which gives rise to individual variations. Consequently, prokaryotes do not require sexual reproduction. Their short cell cycle allows them to create sufficient genetic variations to respond to environmental changes.

However, under certain environmental conditions, some bacteria use sexual reproduction. One such environmental change is the use of antibiotics. The first antibiotic to be widely used was penicillin in 1945. At first it was highly effective in treating many bacterial diseases, but within two years, antibiotic-resistant bacteria began to emerge. These penicillin-resistant bacteria contain mutations, which allow them to be resistant against penicillin. To battle the penicillin-resistant bacteria, other antibiotics were developed. Within a few years, resistant bacteria to the new antibiotics emerged. A race quickly developed between developing new antibiotics and the emergence of resistance.

In the beginning, bacteria that were resistant to one antibiotic were usually sensitive to the other antibiotics. Within a few years, however, some bacteria became resistant to multiple antibiotics. In subsequent studies, it was discovered that these bacteria had acquired resistance to the multiple antibiotics because of a gene transfer mechanism that was similar to the sexual reproduction used by eukaryotic cells. This observation suggests that a primitive form of sexual reproduction evolved very early in the history of life.

The sexual reproduction that is used by bacteria is known as conjugation. This process involves both a donor and a recipient bacterium, and DNA is transferred from one bacterium to the other. Antibiotic resistant genes can be transferred through this mechanism. If different bacteria that harbor different antibiotic resistant genes are placed in the same environment, some bacteria could receive multiple antibiotic resistant genes. In the past several years, such multi-antibiotic resistant bacteria have been found in hospital patients. The use of a wide variety of antibiotics in hospitals has created a suitable environment for the development of multi-drug resistant bacteria. It was only through a primitive form of sexual reproduction that these bacteria adapted to their new environment and became multi-antibiotic resistant.

The evolution of eukaryotic cells led to the development of true sexual reproduction. Instead of the occasional use of conjugation, eukaryotic cells use only sexual reproduction. To solve the problem of doubling the amount of DNA each time when two cells pool their genetic materials together, eukaryotic cells evolved the diploid-haploid cycle. The normal (somatic) cells are diploid, with two sets of chromosomes, whereas the reproductive cells (gametes) are haploid, with one set of chromosomes. Meiosis reduces the DNA content by half but also creates gametes that have different genetic makeups. Sexual

Binary fission

Bacteria can grow rapidly and generate variations through mutation. *(Public Domain)*

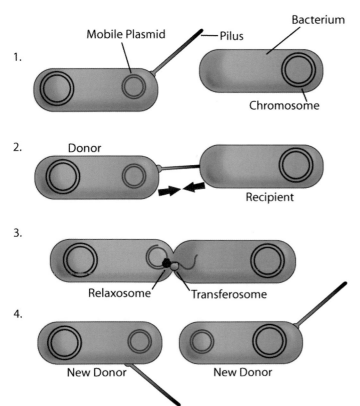

Conjugation

The microbial form of sexual reproduction. *(Public Domain)*

reproduction was so successful when it first evolved about 1.2 billion years ago that it has become the preferred reproductive strategy.

The first form of sexual reproduction that evolved consisted of simple unicellular organisms, such as amoeba and paramecium, simply fusing with each other. In these organisms, there was no distinction between the male and female gametes. With the evolution of multicellular organisms, however, the gametes started to appear and function differently. Some gametes were small and highly motile; these eventually became sperm. In contrast, some gametes were large and immotile; they became eggs. This specialization of the sperm and eggs was the first step toward the formation of the different sexes. These cells evolved because the organisms needed a more efficient way for the gametes to find each other. Also, the fertilized eggs needed a source of nutrients for their development. As organisms became more complex, more elaborate ways were evolved to deliver the sperm to the eggs. However, the basic roles of the sperm and the egg remained unchanged.

I.3. Why are there males and females?

Why do males and females exist? They exist because of the differences between male and female gametes. Why are there differences between male and female gametes? This difference has not always existed; there are a few primitive organisms that have nearly identical male and female gametes. This is a reproductive strategy known as isogamy. However, nearly all other sexually-reproduced organisms use a different strategy, the anisogamy strategy. They have gametes with very different properties. In all the species that use the anisogamy strategy, the male and female gametes are very different in morphology, behavior, and cellular properties. Despite these differences, both gametes make the same genetic contribution to the offspring. They are different but equal.

The human gametes are typical examples of the differences between male and female gametes. The human female gamete is nearly 30 times larger than the human male gamete. The human egg is 145 μm in diameter, making it the largest cell in the human body. The human sperm is only 5 μm in diameter, making it one of the smallest cells. It is difficult to recognize that eggs and sperm are basically the same type of cell when they are so different in size. This size difference evolved very early in the biological history of sexual evolution. It occurred during a time when most organisms lived in the ocean.

For many aquatic organisms, the size difference between the egg and sperm is vital for sexual reproduction. Corals are one of the most primitive living organisms. The size difference between their egg and sperm, however, is similar to that of humans. For a few days each year, all individuals of the same coral species reproduce in synchrony. They release a large number of eggs and sperm into the ocean water. The number of sperm released far exceeds the number of eggs released. The sperm are small, and they swim through the water with a long tail, known as a flagellum. The eggs are many times larger, and they are nonmotile. The sperm's role is to search for the eggs. Since there are many more sperm than eggs, this is an effective strategy for the sperm to fertilize the eggs.

Researchers believe that the evolution of the sperm and egg is critical for the success of sexual reproduction. In isogamy, the identical features of the gametes preclude specialization. In an aquatic environment, sexual reproduction is more likely to be successful if some of the gametes (sperm) are highly motile. Their motility increases their chance of finding other gametes. However, a fast swimming gamete needs to be small and is therefore unable to pack its cell with the nutrients that are needed for embryonic development. This situation is balanced by the use of another gamete (egg) which is large, immotile, and packed with adequate nutrients to support embryonic development.

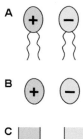

Isogamy
Early male and female gametes have identical appearance.
(Public Domain)

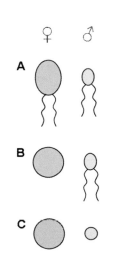

Anisogamy
Male and female gametes become specialized. *(Public Domain)*

Human egg
Large and highly specialized.
(Public Domain)

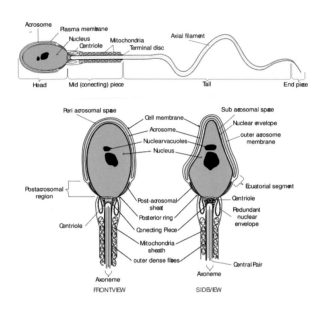

Human sperm

They are specialized to search. *(Public Domain)*

What has resulted through evolution is the specialization of the gametes for different roles during sexual reproduction. The sperm is specialized to take on the role of the searcher. It is designed to be highly motile, and other than its package of genetic material, it carries only the amount of nutrients that it needs for swimming and fertilizing an egg. Because of its small size and minimum investment of energy, sperm are manufactured in large numbers. In contrast, the egg is specialized to be the nurturer. It is much larger than the sperm, sometimes as much as several thousand times larger. The main content of the egg is the nutrients that are required for the development of the embryo. Because of the heavy cost in producing each egg, a much smaller number of eggs can be produced.

In summary, the specialization of the gametes is vital for the success of sexual reproduction. In the ocean, it is not easy for the gametes to find each other. Therefore, sperm are produced by the billions by each individual, since the investment in producing them is low. On the contrary, eggs are produced in limited numbers, because of the high cost in producing them. The sperm play the role of the searchers, and the eggs await the sperm. When the sperm finds the egg, they pass their genetic materials into the egg. The newly-formed individual resides inside the egg, drawing on the nutrients which are there for their embryonic development.

II. WHAT ARE MALES?

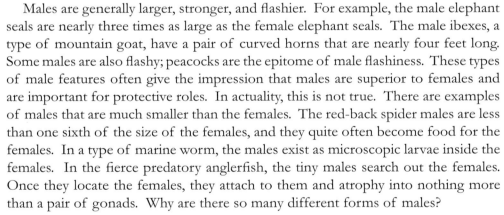

Peacock

Extraordinary color and texture.
(Creative Commons Attribution, Stuart Seeger)

Males are generally larger, stronger, and flashier. For example, the male elephant seals are nearly three times as large as the female elephant seals. The male ibexes, a type of mountain goat, have a pair of curved horns that are nearly four feet long. Some males are also flashy; peacocks are the epitome of male flashiness. These types of male features often give the impression that males are superior to females and are important for protective roles. In actuality, this is not true. There are examples of males that are much smaller than the females. The red-back spider males are less than one sixth of the size of the females, and they quite often become food for the females. In a type of marine worm, the males exist as microscopic larvae inside the females. In the fierce predatory anglerfish, the tiny males search out the females. Once they locate the females, they attach to them and atrophy into nothing more than a pair of gonads. Why are there so many different forms of males?

II.1. Why males?

The structural and functional characteristics of male organisms can be traced back to their gametes. The definition of maleness is to search for the female gametes and to deliver the genetic information. This role for the male gametes is the same for nearly all living organisms that reproduce sexually. For organisms living in aquatic environments, for example, the function of the sperm is to swim and search for the eggs. This search, however, is not aimless, because the eggs produce chemical signals that attract the sperm. This situation also applies to human sperm. During in vitro fertilization, the sperm are attracted by chemical signals and swim toward the eggs. The reason that IVF is technically feasible is because of this innate property of sperm.

In the ocean, aquatic organisms produce an astronomical number of sperm. In one species of giant clams that live in the coral reef, 100 billion sperm are released. In the same species, only several million eggs are released. Despite this huge production of both sperm and eggs, only a tiny fraction of the eggs are fertilized. In humans, the males release approximately 300 million sperm at each ejaculation and over several trillion sperm throughout their lifetime. Human females, on the contrary, release only one egg each month and less than a thousand eggs over their entire reproductive age.

This discrepancy creates a situation of supply and demand, with the sperm in an abundant supply and the egg in demand. In circumstances where the eggs are surrounded by an over abundance of sperm, competition between the sperm becomes inevitable. If all sperm are equal, the first sperm that reaches the egg will fertilize the egg. However, not all sperm are equal, because through meiosis, sperm have different genetic combinations. Some sperm are faster swimmers, some are more efficient in penetrating the outer lining of the eggs, and some are better in sensing the chemical signals produced by the eggs. These traits cause an intense competition between the sperm as they try to fertilize the small number of eggs.

During human fertilization, only 1 out of the 300 million sperm that enters the vagina will fertilize the egg. Why it is necessary for human males to produce such large numbers of sperm if only one is needed for successful reproduction? Also, why does an ejaculate that contains less than 150 million sperm result in infertility? It seems inexplicable why large numbers of sperm are produced for human mating, especially when considering that the sperm does not need to swim in open water in search of the egg. Human sexual intercourse delivers the sperm directly to the egg. One possible explanation is that the large sperm number is simply a vestige of the evolution of sexual reproduction.

In human reproduction, 300 million sperm compete fiercely to reach the egg. Human ovaries are placed deep in the abdomen, and each month one egg is released into the Fallopian tube. This region is nearly 8 in away from the opening of the cervix, which is a muscular structure located just beyond the vagina. After entering the vagina, the sperm must swim to the Fallopian tubes to fertilize the egg. There are many barriers along this journey, and only a small fraction of the sperm reach the openings to the Fallopian tubes. Only the strongest and luckiest sperm survive. Generally, less than a few million sperm enter the Fallopian tubes, and only a few hundred reach the egg. Less than 100 sperm pass through a layer of protective cells that surrounds the egg. The sperm that eventually reaches the egg sends a molecular signal to the egg. If the signal is accepted, the egg takes in the nucleus of the sperm and discards the rest of the sperm cell. Immediately, the outer layer of the egg turns into an impenetrable barrier, and no other sperm can enter.

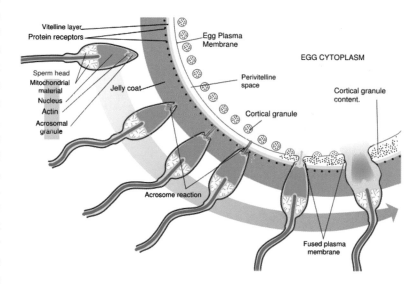

Fertilization

Only a single sperm can fertilize an egg in a highly coordinated process. *(Public Domain)*

In some ways, human reproduction is no different from that of the aquatic organisms. The different roles for male and female gametes apply to every living organism that uses sexual reproduction. However, organisms have evolved many different strategies to facilitate this process. When life conquered land, terrestrial organisms had to find different ways to deliver the sperm to the egg. The process of human reproduction is the result of such adaptation.

Hermaphroditism

They produce sperm and eggs at separate times to prevent self-fertilization. *(Public Domain)*

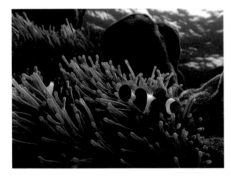

Protandry

Clownfish start life as males and become females later in life. *(GNU Free Documentation License)*

Protogyny

Wrasses begin as females and become males later in life. *(Creative Commons Attribution)*

II.2. What makes a male?

The chief criterion for maleness is the production of sperm. The sexual organs responsible for producing sperm are the testes. In most animals, the male and female sexual organs are found in different individuals. However, in plants, such as flowers, the male and female organs often reside in the same individual. Most flowers contain stamen, which produce pollen (the equivalent of sperm). The center portion of the flower is the stigma, which through the style, is linked to the ovary, which produces ovules (the equivalent of eggs). Flowering plants are hermaphrodites (also known as heterosporangiate), which means that they can produce both male and female gametes (also known as spores in plants). Only few animal species are hermaphrodites.

Corals are among the simplest animals and are hermaphrodites. They live in the ocean in colonies, and their calcium carbonate skeleton is the foundation of the coral reefs. Each year, during a certain night, corals of the same species will release their sperm and eggs in synchrony. However, to prevent self-fertilization, either the sperm or the egg will be released first. Through chemical signals, the mass release of eggs and sperm are carefully orchestrated to maximize cross-fertilization. Hermaphroditism is disadvantageous because of the risk of self-fertilization. Therefore, in more complex organisms, the male and female reproductive organs are found in different individuals.

For most aquatic organisms, the testes and a simple delivery system are all it takes to function as a male. Similarly, the ovaries and a system for releasing the eggs are sufficient for functioning as a female. For most animals, these systems are separate, but for some, the systems are interchangeable. There are species of fish living in the coral reef that can change their sex. This type of sexual system is known as sequential hermaphroditism. An individual fish can begin life as either a female or a male. Then, when the environment changes, it can transform into the opposite sex. One example of this is the clownfish (as in *Finding Nemo*). All clownfish start life as males, and if the breeding female in the colony dies, one of the males will transform into a female. This form of sexual transformation is known as sequential protandry hermaphroditism. There are other species that start out as females and later become males. This type of transformation is known as protogyny.

Sex transformation is not possible for land organisms because of the complexity of the reproductive system. In addition to the testes for sperm production, all terrestrial organisms possess an elaborate delivery system that transfers the sperm directly to the female reproductive tract. This is essential because fertilization does not occur in an aquatic environment. The males of all terrestrial animals have a specialized device, the penis, which is used to facilitate sperm delivery.

The overall design and basic components of the human male reproductive system are similar to those of other mammalian species. The human sperm delivery system contains three basic parts. First, it contains a storage system that is located outside the body to store the sperm after production. For unknown reasons, human sperm production and storage are most effective when conducted at one to two degrees below body temperature. The second part is a system that produces fluids to suspend and protect the sperm after they enter into the female reproductive tract. The third system is for the delivery of the sperm.

The human male reproductive system is ready to deliver sperm at any moment. Human males are actively searching for opportunities to deliver their sperm from the time of sexual maturity until death. This is the biological imperative of maleness, in the same way as the sperm takes every opportunity to fertilize eggs. The basic drive for reproduction is the same for the sperm as it is for the entire organism. However, unlike simple animals, humans have complex social interactions, and the desire for reproduction is tempered by social and cultural factors. Therefore, understanding human male behavior also requires an understanding of these factors.

II.3. How do males develop?

Human males appear entirely different from females. However, both sexes use the same genes for the formation of their reproductive systems. The studies on the fish that can change sex provide a clear indication that there is no genetic difference between males and females. Therefore, other factors must be responsible for forming the different sexes. Finding these factors has been one of the major goals of biological research.

One of the most interesting systems that are used for sex determination is found in reptiles, such as turtles, alligators, and crocodiles. Their sex determination is based entirely on the incubation temperature of their eggs. Crocodiles, for example, bury their eggs in the ground with decaying vegetation. The decaying process releases heat and helps to incubate the eggs. However, the incubating temperatures can vary depending on how deep the eggs are buried. If, for example, the temperature is 30°C, then the sex ratio of the offspring is 50:50. However, if the temperature is 31°C, then 75% of the offspring becomes male, and if the temperature is 29°C, then 75% becomes female. In this case, it is the incubation temperature of the eggs, and not genetic differences, that determine the formation of the sexes.

What is the trigger for sex differentiation in humans? The first evidence that human sex is partly determined by genetic factors was the discovery of the sex chromosomes (X and Y chromosomes) in the early 1900s. By the 1950s, it was widely accepted that the presence of the Y chromosome determined maleness, but how the Y chromosome caused maleness was unknown. Then, in 1960, researchers discovered that there are females who are XY and males who are XX. This discovery suggested that the entire Y chromosome is not solely responsible for maleness. Instead, it suggested that there is a trigger on the Y chromosome that is responsible for directing male sex development.

After an intense search, the sex "trigger" gene, the SRY gene, was discovered in the 1980s. It is located on the Y chromosome and produces a protein, known as the SRY protein, which is a transcriptional factor. It causes the activation of a cascade of genes that turns the primitive gonads into testes. The testes then start to produce testosterone, a powerful male hormone. Testosterone can transform all the primitive reproductive tissues and organs into the male reproductive system. One of the most important systems is a primitive ductile system, known as the Wolffian ducts. In the absence of testosterone, this duct system degenerates. In the presence of testosterone, the Wolffian ducts develop into the epididymis and vas deferens of the male reproductive system. The testosterone has another important effect in shaping the male reproductive system. It converts a primitive group of tissue cells, known as the cloaca, into male external genitalia. As the fetus continues to grow, the testosterone causes the cloaca to form the bladder, the urinary tract, and the glans penis.

Transsexual

An XY woman at a protest in France to raise awareness of transsexualism. *(GNU Free Documentation License)*

This entire developmental process results from a single gene, the SRY gene, which is located on the Y chromosome. The protein of this gene triggers human sex development in the same way as temperature triggers sex development in reptiles. An understanding of the SRY gene and its location allows for the explanation of XY females and XX males. In the case of the XY females, a mutation of the SRY gene negates the signal to trigger male development. In the situation of XX males, a translocation of the SRY gene onto an X chromosome provides the necessary signal.

The effect of testosterone on male development also results from differential gene expression. Testosterone is not a transcriptional factor but is an activator of another protein, known as a testosterone receptor, which serves as a transcriptional factor. This system functions as a second level trigger for male development. Some individuals have a mutation in the testosterone receptors, which makes them unresponsive to testosterone. Those individuals, including the individual described in the beginning of the chapter, develop as females, even though they have XY chromosomes and have a normal SRY gene. These individuals have a genetic disorder, known as androgen insensitivity syndrome (androgen is the general term for testosterone and similar hormones). The most severe form is known as complete androgen insensitivity syndrome (CAIS). These individuals have XY chromosomes, possess normal female external genitalia, but lack ovaries and uteri.

Amphibian eggs
Amphibians make no investment in parental care. *(GNU Free Documentation License)*

III. What are Females?

In some human societies, females are considered the weaker sex. They are perceived as smaller, weaker, and less aggressive than males. However, there are many examples in the biological world that counter these viewpoints. For example, in nearly all of the predatory bird species, such as eagles, falcons, and hawks, the females are generally larger and more aggressive than males. In many invertebrates, such as the spiders, the females are significantly larger than the males. In some spiders, such as the black widow, the females are as much as ten times larger. Why is there such diversity in female forms among different animal species? How does one define a female? What are the common characteristics shared by females of all animal species?

III.1. Why females?

Femaleness is defined by the production of large gametes that contain the nutrients to sustain the development of the embryo. In all females, including humans and other placental mammals, the egg is much larger than the sperm. It appears inexplicable at first why placental mammals still need large eggs, since the placenta provides all the nutrients for embryonic and fetal development throughout pregnancy. Nevertheless, during the first five days of embryonic development, all the cell divisions are entirely fueled by the nutrients stored in the human egg. This may be a vestige from the times when eggs were released directly into the ocean.

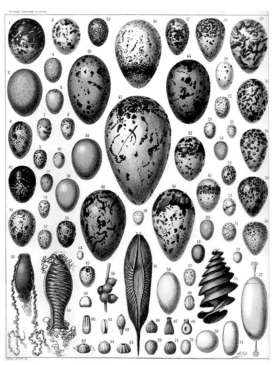

Avian eggs
Maternal investment in creating eggs with protective shells and nutrient supplies. *(Public Domain)*

For many organisms, early embryonic development relies entirely on the nutrients present in the egg. One example is a species of land crab living on Christmas Island. For a few days during certain times each year, the entire population of female land crabs (over several million individuals) marches toward the sea to lay their eggs in the water. Each crab sheds as many as 100,000 eggs, which are swept away by ocean currents. Many predators gather around this time of the year to feast on the eggs. Normally, only a few eggs survive. The surviving eggs rely on the nutrients in the eggs to develop and hatch into larvae.

With luck, the ocean currents sweep them toward the island, and they clamber onto land to perpetuate the species.

Most aquatic animals use this strategy for the development and growth of their young. They produce a large number of eggs at a low cost, with the expectation that only a few will survive. For land animals, it is not feasible to scatter the young throughout a wide area and to let them fend for themselves. Furthermore, an embryo needs an aqueous environment within which to develop. Terrestrial females have developed strategies for developing their embryos within a protective aqueous environment. There are two basic strategies used by terrestrial animal species.

The first strategy is the development of a protective enclosure in the form of an egg that provides not only nutrients but also a shell, which seals in the fluid in order to ensure an aquatic environment. This strategy imposes new demands on the females. To produce an egg, the females must invest a significant portion of their energy intake. The eggs provide all the nutrients during early development and also provide some level of protection. In some cases, the females also incubate the eggs in order to provide an environment of sufficiently high temperature. This temperature is conducive to the growth and the development of the embryos. At the same time, the females guard the eggs against predators. This strategy has been successfully used by birds and some reptiles.

The second strategy is used by marsupial and placental mammals. In this strategy, the females provide continuing support of the young until they reach independence. In humans and in other placental mammals, the young remains connected to the mother through the placenta prior to birth. The placenta provides both nutrients and a constant environment. Since the young are located inside the womb, the mother has greater mobility when looking for food as well when evading predators. However, this second strategy has created even a greater demand on the female. Also, she cannot conceive again until the first pregnancy is terminated. These two different strategies appear very different, but the end result is the same.

For the Christmas Island land crabs, each crab produces as many as several million eggs over her lifetime. These females invest heavily in egg production but minimally in parental care. Consequently, the survival rate is poor, and each female crab might have only three or four offspring that survive. On the other hand, a human female might only give birth to three or four offspring, but if they all survive, the end result is the same as that for the female crab. Therefore, females of different species rely on different strategies to achieve their reproductive goals.

Marsupial strategy

Kangaroos carry their young in a pouch for protection and nourishment. *(GNU Free Documentation License)*

III.2. What makes a female?

The basic biological plan for a female consists of the presence of ovaries for the production of eggs and a ductile system to expel the eggs. For aquatic organisms, the system is very simple. Since fertilization occurs outside the female body, a simple system to discharge the eggs is adequate. In fish, such as salmon, the reproductive process is simple and straightforward. When a female begins to shed her eggs, the males swim around her, pushing each other in anticipation. Immediately after she releases her eggs, the males eject their sperm.

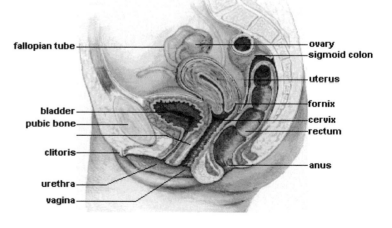

Female anatomy

The female anatomical features are designed for sheltering the developing embryos. *(GNU Free Documentation License)*

The requirements of fertilization for land animals are very different. The sperm must be delivered directly into the female reproductive system. All terrestrial animals have tubular tracts that accommodate the penis during sexual reproduction. In female mammals, this tract is the vagina; in female birds and reptiles, it is the cloaca; in insects and in other invertebrates, it is the oviduct. The human vagina is a highly muscular tissue with secretary glands along its wall to provide lubrication during sexual intercourse. The muscular tissues of the vagina serve to grasp the penis during sexual intercourse to stimulate ejaculation. This ensures that the sperm are delivered into the female genital tract.

Joining the human vagina and the uterus is the cervix, which consists of muscular tissues that normally keep the cervix tightly closed. It opens at the height of sexual intercourse to allow the sperm to pass from the vagina into the uterus. The human uterus is similar to that of other mammals. It is mainly a muscular structure that is capable of expanding to accommodate a developing fetus. The lining of the uterus is known as the endometrium. The endometrium undergoes cyclic changes every month. After fertilization occurs, the blastocyst is implanted in the endometrium. However, during the months when fertilization fails to occur, the endometrium is shed, resulting in menstruation.

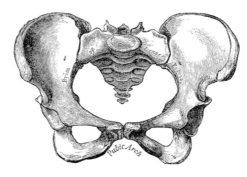

Female pelvis

The large opening is necessary during childbirth. *(Public Domain)*

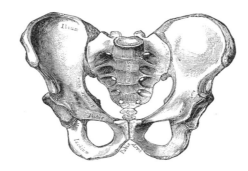

Male pelvis

The smaller opening and thicker bone mass is partially responsible for greater male strength. *(Public Domain)*

Why does menstruation occur? Why does the menstrual cycle occur only in a few primate species? Most other female mammals have estrous cycles in which the endometrium is reabsorbed by the uterus at the end of the cycle. The estrous cycle is regulated by an internal biological clock, and it is only during this cycle that the females become reproductively receptive to the males. The estrous cycle has important biological implications. In many species, the cycles are timed so that the females give birth at a time when food is in abundance and the condition is right for the newborns to grow and develop. The menstrual cycle is a vestige of the estrous cycle, and there are many aspects of the menstrual cycle that remain unclear.

The human menstrual cycle is also regulated by an internal biological clock. The biological clock is located at a region near the center of the brain, known as the pineal gland. The pineal gland also controls the circadian rhythm and the sleep/wake cycle. Many pathological conditions can affect the function of the pineal gland, such as strokes and severe depression. Abuse substances such as alcohol, cocaine, and methamphetamine also disrupt the action of the biological clock, leading to an irregularity of the menstrual cycle.

The uterus is the part of the female reproductive system where the embryo implants and forms a placenta. After fertilization, the zygote (fertilized egg) undergoes a rapid cell division in the next several days. It is moved by the cilia on the surface of the Fallopian tube toward the uterus. Upon contact with the uterine wall, part of the blastocyst forms a placenta, which contains a network of fetal and maternal blood vessels. Nutrients from the mother diffuse from the maternal blood circulation to the fetal circulation. However, the maternal and fetal blood never mixes. Since the fetal tissues contain paternal transplantation antigens, the fetus is equivalent to a transplanted organ. Through mechanisms that remain unknown, the maternal immune system tolerates the fetus.

III.3. How do females develop?

In many ways, the human female reproductive system is more complex than the male reproductive system because of the demands of pregnancy. Furthermore, the menstrual cycle requires several sex hormones to coordinate ovulation, the construction of the uterine wall, and the shedding of the endometrium. It is inconceivable that the same set of genes is responsible for the formation of both the male and female reproductive systems. Through differential gene expression, the same set of cells can become part of either the male or female reproductive systems. The presence of a single gene, the SRY gene, is sufficient to cause the switch between the male and female reproductive systems.

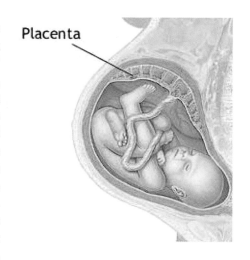

Placenta

The uterus
The uterus is a special organ designed for pregnancy. *(Public Domain)*

The default path of embryonic sexual development is female. If the SRY gene is absent, the primitive gonads develop spontaneously into ovaries. Without the SRY protein, the genes for testes development become silenced, and the genes for ovary development are automatically activated. More importantly, in the absence of the testes, there is no testosterone production. In its absence, the cells that make up the Wolffian ducts gradually die, and this ductile system withers away. There is a second ductile system, known as the Mullerian ducts, which starts to grow and differentiate into the female reproductive system.

From the Mullerian ducts, the female embryo develops the Fallopian tubes, the uterus, and the cervix. The development and differentiation of the Mullerian ducts can only occur in the absence of testosterone. Similarly, in the absence of testosterone, the cloaca develops into the external female genitalia, which includes the vagina, the labia majora, and the glans clitoris. These structures share the same embryonic origin with that of the male reproductive system. In other words, these structures develop from the same group of cells. One notable example is the glans clitoris, which has the same tissue origin as the glans penis in

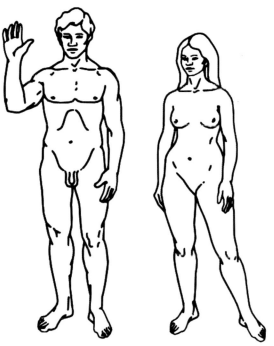

The male and female body plans
Minor genetic disturbances can alter these body plans. *(Public Domain)*

the male. These structures share the same innervations and connections to regions of the brain that stimulates sexual pleasure.

During fetal development of the female reproductive system, disturbances in the sex hormones can lead to developmental abnormalities. One example of this is a disorder known as congenital adrenal hyperplasia. At birth, the external genitalia have characteristics of both males and females, making it difficult for doctors to determine the sex. In actuality, these individuals are females who have ovaries, Fallopian tubes, and uteri. The male appearance of the external genitalia is due to an excessive production of testosterone by the adrenal gland. This genetic disorder results in an excessive production of testosterone during the 2nd trimester of pregnancy. By that time, most of the female reproductive system is formed, but the external genitalia are still under development. The presence of testosterone causes them to take on a partial male structure.

There are other sexual developmental disorders due to genetic mutation. Some of the most common sexual developmental disorders result from sex chromosome nondisjunction, which is the failure of chromosome pairs to properly separate during meiosis. One such disorder is Turner syndrome, which occurs in 1 in every 2,500 female births. The afflicted individuals have only one X chromosome, with a total of 45 chromosomes. These individuals have abnormal female reproductive systems, and they are sterile. They also suffer from other health risks, particularly cardiovascular disorders. The most common form of sex chromosome nondisjunction is Klinefelter syndrome, which occurs in about 1 in 500 live male births. Affected males have an extra X chromosome, making them XXY with 47 chromosomes. The principle effects are small testicles and reduced fertility. The severity of the disorder is greatly varied, and many boys and men with the condition do not exhibit any outward symptoms.

Sexual development is a complex process, and many genes are involved in the process. Therefore, it is not surprising that there is a wide range of "maleness" and "femaleness." Male and female is not a dichotomy; it is a continuum with subtle variations. It is unfortunate that males and females are often considered to be yin and yang or black and white by the general public. Understanding the biological basis of sexual determination is important in understanding and critiquing how society addresses issues regarding sex and gender. There is now biological evidence proving that males and females are equal but different. The same genes are responsible for both sexes; it is only in gene differential expression that the sexes differ. This information should dispel any misconceptions about one sex being superior to the other. It is the specialization of the gametes that have occurred over our evolutionary history of sexual reproduction that has given rise to this cooperative process of creating individual variations.

Chapter 7

Behavior

Why do you behave the way you do?

What makes the peacock flashy?
The peacocks must grow these extravagant tail feathers in order to attract the attention of the female.
However, they also become more vulnerable to predators.   *(Public Domain)*

CHAPTER 7. BEHAVIOR

Do the sexes cooperate or compete with each other? The answer to this question is not straightforward and depends on many factors. For many species, it appears that the sexes compete with each other more than they cooperate. The males of these species spend their time and energy chasing after the females and fighting among themselves over the females. In turn, the females are constantly subjugated by the males and are unable to choose their mating partners. Furthermore, the sex role of the males is limited to merely providing the sperm, leaving the entire nurturing role to the females. In these cases, it appears that the males have the easier role, and the females bear most of the responsibility for sexual reproduction. However, the studies of animal sexual behavior, including human sexual behavior, tell a more complex story.

I. WHY DO MALES COMPETE?

In general, human males are more competitive than females. They are more interested in competitive sports, war games, and fighting. In fact, they are responsible for 98% of all the violent crimes that are committed in modern society. Many observations have suggested that competitiveness in human males is derived from their genes. However, how does the same genetic makeup make a human female peaceful but a human male aggressive?

I.1. *What is the operational sex ratio?*

Operational sex ratio (OSR) is a simple and powerful biological concept that predicts how the sexes will behave. The concept is based on the economic theory of supply and demand. When there is an abundance of goods, the buyers exercise their choice. If the commodities are in short supply, the buyers will compete for the available goods and exercise little or no choice. The operational sex ratio is based on the same economic principle. It is defined as the ratio between sexually-receptive males and sexually- receptive females. If there are more sexually-receptive males than sexually-receptive females, then the mate choice belongs to the females. If, however, there are more sexually-receptive females, then the males do the deciding.

At the level of the gametes, the choice is biased toward the female gametes, because the sperm exist in much larger quantities than the eggs. Therefore, the sperm must compete with each other to fertilize the eggs. The sperm will always mate with the first egg they find and forego any choice. Each male produces a great abundance of sperm, and the majority of them will not fertilize an egg. On the other hand, each female invests heavily in each egg and can only produce a limited number of eggs. Because of this, each female should only choose sperm of the highest quality to ensure the successful development of her eggs into offspring.

In primitive organisms, male competition is restricted at the level of the sperm. For example, corals are sessile and cannot compete with each other. Therefore, the only competition that exists in this species is between their sperm. Sperm are simply released into the water from where the animals are located and are sent towards the nearest eggs. However, when animals become motile, they become an extension for their gametes. In aquatic animals, for example, the males deliver their sperm in the vicinity of the females when they lay their eggs. In many aquatic animals, males constantly compete with each other so that they can have the best position (closest to the eggs) from which to release their sperm. For terrestrial animals, the males compete with each other to gain direct access to the reproductive tracts of the females. In aquatic environments, females choose where they will deposit their eggs, and in doing so, indirectly select the males to fertilize their eggs. In the terrestrial

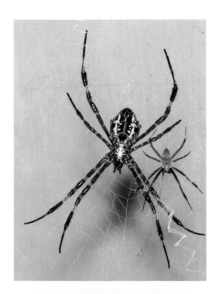

Reverse sexual dimorphism

In this spider species, the male is significantly smaller than the female. *(Public Domain)*

Sexual dimorphism

In most species, the males are generally more ornamented. The female is on the left and the male is on the right. *(Public Domain)*

environments, females exercise an even greater choice by determining who they will mate with.

When the OSR is skewed toward the males, the males need to compete with each other for access to the females. Furthermore, if the male gametes are slow and ineffective when searching for female gametes, then the species becomes extinct. Therefore, male gametes must compete, and only the fastest and most effective male gametes pass on their genes. In other words, the evolution of male gametes is towards greater efficiency and effectiveness. Similarly, the female gametes also evolve; in this case, it is towards greater selectivity in the male gametes.

The improvement in the efficiency and effectiveness of the gametes can also be seen in the behavior of multicellular organisms. Genetic variations in each individual male can cause a slight improvement in their mating strategy. These successful males will leave more offspring, and their genes will pass onto the next generation. Even though the overall change might be small for the first generation, it will eventually result in larger changes with each succeeding generation. In other words, the genes causing the improved mating strategy will be found in more individuals over time.

Male competition
The male fish compete for the best position next to females to release their sperm. *(Public Domain)*

OSR is important in determining how the sexes behave during sexual reproduction. Not only are males more aggressive and competitive during mating, but they also have stronger sex drives than females. Since it is unnecessary for males to invest in nurturing the young, they are always sexually ready. OSR also explains human male sexual behavior and aggression. Men are 1,000 times more likely to view pornography, practice polygamy, commit rape, be pedophiles, and perpetrate violent crimes. In a recent survey of college students that asked how often they thought about sex, 96% of the male students, but only 54% of the female students, think about sex every hour.

I.2. How do males compete?

In the biological world, how males compete is diverse because of the life history of the species and because of environmental factors. Nevertheless, the biological principle is the same: the goal of the males is to fertilize as many eggs as possible. Therefore, each male looks for ways to deliver their sperm to the females. Male competition begins with the sperm, and the sperm in many species have developed sophisticated structures, which gives them an edge when competing with other sperm. This form of sperm competition is common in those species where the female can receive and store sperm from multiple males before using them to fertilize her eggs.

Even though male competition begins with the sperm, this level is not the most important. Male competition occurs mainly at the level of the whole organism. Male competition is divided into five categories: direct physical contest, gaining access, providing resources, offering gifts, and sexual attraction. Each of these strategies is used by different animal species, including humans. The female role in these strategies, however, is not passive. Females observe, judge, and then pick those males who they recognize as "winners." In other words, the females are the ultimate judges in the mating competition.

The most familiar form of male competition is physical contest. Some of the physical contests between the males are spectacular. One such example is the contest between male ibexes, which are mountain goats found in the rugged mountain ranges of East Africa and the Middle East. These males possess huge curved horns that appear out of proportion to their body size. The horns, however, are not used for defense; instead, they are used for battling each other. When a male with large horns fights a male with smaller horns, he often wins and then takes over the harem of females that had belonged to the losing male.

Another species that uses male physical contest is the elephant seal. The males of this species are three times larger than the females and are well-suited to fight physical battles. In the beginning of each mating season, the males fight each other for the best beach territories. They do this before the arrival of the females, who are coming ashore to give birth. The females become sexually receptive immediately after giving birth, and the male who is in control of the territory where they give birth will have first access to them. In this system, the females select the males based on the territories that they hold. The best territories are those that are close to the ocean and that have few rocks. To protect his territory, the male must continually fight off intruding males who were unable to stake out their own territories but who are trying to mate with the females.

Ibex competition

They use huge horns to fight for control over the females. This leads to extreme sexual dimorphism. *(GNU Free Documentation License)*

Elephant seal competition

Because of male competition, the males have become nearly three times as large as the females. *(Public Domain) (GNU Free Documentation License)*

In any mating strategy that involves physical contest between the males, the males are larger than the females. This is known as sex size dimorphism. Among the great apes, which include the orangutans, gorillas, chimpanzees, and humans, the size difference between the males and females can be as large as 50%. In humans, however, the size difference is about 15%. This observation has suggested that human males must have originally used physical contest as a mating strategy, but once the species evolved, competition by physical force was replaced by other forms of competition. This, in turn, has led to a gradual reduction in sex size dimorphism.

In physical contest, the winners of the physical battle generally have mating rights to a large number of females. For example, in elephant seals, a successful beach master assembles a harem of as many as 50 females. Moreover, many males have no mating opportunities during the entire breeding season. In this type of male competition, only the females provide parental care, because the males are focused on fighting with each other. This type of male competition strategy only works when the environment allows for the females to be the sole nurturers of the offspring.

1.3. What are the consequences of male competition?

The strategy of male physical contest has resulted in some bizarre physical characteristics that are only found in males. One such feature is the antlers of the extinct Irish elk, which was one of the largest deer that has ever lived. It is believed to have lived 8,000 years ago and to have roamed across Eurasia, from Ireland to Russia during the last ice age. The Irish elk male stood about seven feet at the shoulders, but it had antlers measuring 12 ft from tip to tip. Why would the males need such large antlers? Researchers have concluded that the antlers were used mainly by the males for display and occasionally battling with each other for mating rights.

Irish Elk
It is an extreme example of sexual dimorphism. *(Public Domain)*

Another example of a male-specific anatomical feature that had evolved for the sole purpose of physical contest is the large canine teeth in male primates. Since most primates are fruit eaters, it is doubtful that these teeth are necessary for eating. Instead, the main purpose of these canine teeth is to fight with other males. Yet another example comes from observing the horns on the extinct triceratops. It is likely that these horns were not used as defensive weapons against predators. They were most likely used in male competition and in dominance displays, much like the antlers and horns of modern reindeer, mountain goats, and rhinoceroes.

These types of bizarre male features are not only limited to mammals and to other large animals. Male insects have also evolved such features. For example, one of the largest species of beetles, known as the rhinoceros beetle, also has horn-like structures that the males use in mating battles. The mating contests of rhinoceros beetles, however, only occur when the contestants are equally matched and both have a chance of winning. In most battles, the outcome is not lethal, as the victors are more interested in driving the loser away than in killing him.

Rhinoceros beetle
The male beetles are equipped with a huge horn-like structure for mate competition. *(Public Domain)*

One puzzling feature of the exaggerated male anatomical characteristics is the observation that many of these features affect the well being of the males. For example, the large size of the male elephant seals reduces their life span, which is 25% shorter than the female elephant seals. Charles Darwin proposed the theory of sexual selection to explain this phenomenon. This theory is based on the observation that the largest males pass their genes onto a greater number of offspring than the smaller males because of their mating success. The resulting male offspring are larger and achieve even more mating success. With every new generation, larger males are created. In other words, the features that provide the greatest mating success will become more and more exaggerated. The theory of sexual selection explains how male or female traits are selected through the mating process.

The sexual selection theory can also be applied to other forms of sexual dimorphism. The exaggerated peacock tail is also an example of sexual selection. In this case, the males who have the most extravagant tail plumage get the most mating opportunities. The genes regulating the tail plumage are then passed onto the males of the future generations. With each subsequent generation, the tails become more extravagant.

Sexual selection also occurs in human society. Traits such as aggression, language, and intelligence are used by human males when competing for mates. Similarly, many female traits, such as breast size, are also subjected to sexual selection, even though the size of a breast has no impact on breastfeeding. Therefore, sexual selection is a powerful mechanism of evolution for changing the physical and behavior traits of a species that are used for mate competition.

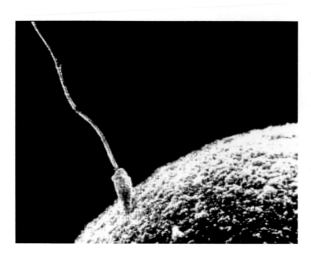

Male function

All males have only one role, which is to deliver sperm to the eggs. *(Public Domain)*

II. How do Females Choose?

Through sexual selection, the traits of a biological species are constantly modified by the mating choices of males and females. Based on the operational sex ratio, male organisms (and their gametes) exist on the supply side of the equation. In contrast, female organisms (and their gametes) are in demand. This situation allows for the females to choose their mating partners. By selecting certain traits over others, the females can affect the genetic makeup of the future generations. If such choice is exercised consistently, the traits of the entire population can change, resulting in the evolution of the species.

II.1. Do females really choose?

Do females really choose? The female egg does not pick a particular sperm to form a zygote. However, some male sperm are more successful than others. In this situation, it appears that the female egg makes a "choice." The basis of this "choice" is genetic variation among the sperm. Of the 300 million sperm that a male produces during sexual intercourse, none are identical. The different genetic combinations make them unique with regards to their genes and to their behavior. One sperm, because of its genetic composition, might be more efficient and effective in reaching and fertilizing the egg. Therefore, the female eggs do not actually choose, but they set the conditions for the sperm to compete in. The first sperm to meet these conditions will win and fertilize the egg.

Another important area where sexual selection, or choice, has been important is gamete recognition. In certain environments, such as aquatic environments, the gametes of many different species exist together. In these situations, it is critical that the gametes of a species recognize each other. Misidentification leads to sterile zygotes and failure in reproduction. Therefore, all species have evolved specific mechanisms to ensure that only the gametes of the same species can form zygotes. These mechanisms include chemical molecules that act as attractants (also known as pheromones) and specific protein receptors on the surface of the gametes to facilitate binding.

These recognition mechanisms are essential for successful sexual reproduction. However, due to genetic variations, alternations of these recognition mechanisms occur. Some of the variations cause defections, some have little or no impact, and some make improvements. The gametes that have become more effective will pass these traits onto their offspring and give them a competitive edge. With time, this trait will spread throughout the population.

At the gamete level, female gametes do not choose male gametes. Some male gametes possess genetic variations that make them more competitive. Furthermore, female gametes must recognize the male gametes of their own species in order to not fuse with male gametes of another species. This principle also applies at the organismal level. For example, two closely-related species might live in overlapping habitats. It is important for the members of each species to tell each other apart to avoid infertile hybridization.

If two species differ from each other only by color spots on the wings of the males (eg, one with red and one with green spots), it is important for these spots to be properly recognized. In other words, these spots serve as mating cues for members of the respective species. Any misidentification results in a failed reproduction. In this case, the genes responsible for the misidentification will not pass on. However, in some cases, slight variations in the color of the wing spots (eg, darker shade of red) can still be recognized by the females. If some females prefer this color over the original one, then it would appear that the females are making a choice.

Mating choice consists of variations in identifying mating partners of the same species. Many different traits can be used for species-specific identification. These traits are morphological, biochemical, and behavioral. They serve to tie all members of the same species together. When these ties are broken, members of the resulting populations cease to reproduce. As a result, new species evolve.

II.2. *What are the consequences of female choice?*

Many argue that human females make conscious choices in selecting mating partners. What is the biological basis of this choice? The answer to this question concerns the biological principle that mating must occur between members of the same species. The following examples of animal mating behavior illustrate the biological basis of female mate choice. The first example concerns the elephant seals. In this species, male contests appear to determine the outcome of mating. However, it is more complex than what it first appears. The females are not simply willing subjugates of dominant males. Even though the females do not choose the males, they choose the beach sites to give birth to their young. If these females produce more young, then the genes encoding for this instinct pass on to their offspring.

Another example concerns a humming bird species. In the beginning of each mating season, the male humming birds fight with each other to establish their territories. The size and the food source of the territories improve in direct proportion to the quality of the males. Once the territory disputes are settled, the males sing to attract the females. The females then choose the territories upon which to build their nest. Up to several females can build their nests in a large territory that has an abundance of flowers. The male guarding this territory then mates with all the females in his territory. Like the elephant seals, the females choose based on resource availabilities rather than directly based on the quality of the male. Those females that have more food availability will produce more young, and the genes from the successful male will be passed on.

Humming bird male competition
They compete for the best territories to attract the females. *(Public Domain)*

In some species, particularly the birds, the species-specific signals have become greatly exaggerated in the male. The most notable example is the peacock and its extraordinary tail plumage. For many years, it was not known why peacocks have such extravagant plumage.

In the wild, it makes the peacocks highly noticeable to their predators and creates difficulties in flying. Do peahens pay attention to the peacock tails? If they do, what do they look for? Researchers discovered that peahens preferentially mate with peacocks that have large eyespots on their plumage display. Individuals with the largest number of eyespots will have the most mating opportunities. Why do the peahens choose to mate with them?

It has been observed that the peahens that mate with peacocks with the greatest number of eyespots are the most fertile. They give birth to more and to healthier offspring. Therefore, somehow the peahens know which peacocks make good mating partners and have the best genes. Do the peahens make conscious choices? It is unlikely. Instead, they have inherited the genes for making this behavioral preference. The mothers of these peahens mated with peacocks having abundant eyespots and passed these genes to their daughters. If these males are more fertile and leave more offspring, then these offspring are likely to have plenty of eyespots. With time, the entire population consists of males that have a lot of eyespots and females that prefer to mate with males having abundant eyespots.

In some species, the males develop unusual behavioral traits that they use to compete with each other. One example of this is a species of birds found in Australia and New Guinea known as bower birds. They live in the tropical rainforests, which are abundant in food and do not have many predators. To attract females, the male bowers build hut-like structures (bowers) using twigs, leaves, and flowers. Each male bird collects different objects to display in his bower based on his own sense of design.

Bower Bird

The males possess skills to build and decorate their bowers to attract the females. *(GNU Free Documentation License)*

During the breeding season, the females tour the bowers. If a bower meets her approval, she mates with the owner of the bower. She then flies away and raises the young on her own. The male birds never see their offspring, but the genes of their bower-building behavior are inherited by their male offspring. What is the basis of female choice in this case? It is most likely that the males who build the best bowers (according to the taste of the female bower birds) are also the most fertile males. Their male offspring are also more fertile and possess the same paternal behavior trait for bower building. This phenomenon is also observed in humans, and the same biological principle can be used to explain why children inherit certain talents from their parents.

II.3. *What are the benefits of female choice?*

Sexual selection is important for shaping the traits of future generations. However, the results of the "choice" are not apparent to the current generation. Animals, including humans, simply like what they see. They cannot predict how these traits will affect the fertility of their future offspring. Nevertheless, these preferences are passed to the future generations. If the preferred traits improve the fertility of the future generations, they will become signals for fertility. These are outward signals that animals look for when choosing their mating partners, and they are known as fertility signals.

The fertile potential of the males is displayed through the use of secondary sex characteristics. Sexual organisms possess two types of sex characteristics, known as the primary and secondary sex characteristics. The primary sex characteristics are those that are directly related to the reproductive system of the sex. For males, they include the testes, the vas deferens, and the secretory glands that are associated with sperm delivery. The primary sex characteristics are formed during embryonic development and are not visible externally. Their development relies heavily on the production of testosterone for a brief period during embryonic development. After this period, the testosterone level decreases and does not rise again until sexual maturity.

The male secondary sex characteristics result from the rise in testosterone during sexual development. This transformation occurs in teenage boys as well as in animals. Testosterone stimulates the development of masculine characteristics, including physical and behavioral traits. This surge of testosterone also stimulates further development of the testes and initiates sperm production. The quantity and quality of the sperm are directly affected by the amount of testosterone produced. In many male animals, all the traits (body size, bird song, antlers, horns, plumage color, and bower building skill) that are related to male competition are directly affected by testosterone. These secondary sex characteristics provide a strong indication of male fertility, and they serve as fertility signals for females.

Sex hormones

Testosterone on the left and estrogen on the right. Notice their nearly identical chemical structure.

Through sexual selection, females have evolved to recognize fertility signals. Therefore, the female mate choice is a behavior that has a genetic base rather than being a conscious choice. Similar fertility signals are also displayed by females, but with the OSR bias toward males, the female fertility signals are less important. However, there are situations where the OSR is balanced between males and females. In these situations, the female fertility signals become equally important.

Another feature that is important for female choice is health. For example, a bright plumage on a male bird is a demonstration of good health. In addition, a big and strong body indicates good nutrition. Only animals in an excellent health status can afford to grow large horns or antlers, and only well-fed birds can devote the energy to build elaborate bowers. These features of good health

Bright plumage of a pheasant

This is an indication of a high testosterone level. *(GNU Free Documentation License)*

appear obvious to humans, because humans use similar criteria when selecting mates. However, this behavior is a complex one and is based on genetics. Only the females who successfully choose their mating partners through these preferences will leave strong and genetically-endowed offspring.

Studies on female mate choice have resulted in a better understanding of the genetic basis of sexual behavior. This has also led to a better understanding of how sexual selection shapes the morphology and behavior of both sexes. Over a long period of time, the species will evolve and have new traits and behaviors. However, the ultimate driving force of these changes is whether the traits that appear in one generation can help the next generation to produce more offspring. Through reproduction and sexual selection, the genes for these traits will either increase or disappear from the population.

III. What are Mating Systems?

In the study of sexual reproduction, researchers have discovered that there are many different types of behavioral interactions between male and female animals. The vast majority of male and female relationships are based on the biological principle of the operational sex ratio. Since males produce an excessive amount of sperm, the primary reproductive goal of the males is to impregnate as many females as possible. However, there are many exceptions to this general rule. For example, in some species, the male pairs with a female for life. Why do these males act against their biological instinct and mate with only one female? This is an interesting and relevant question, because human male mating behavior faces a similar dilemma. The studies of mating behaviors of different animals provide interesting insights into the evolution of different mating systems.

Lion pride

Lion prides are a good example of polygamy, one lion mating with several lionesses. *(Public Domain)*

III.1. What is polygamy?

Polygamy is a mating system where one individual mates with many individuals of the opposite sex concurrently. When one male mates with multiple females, it is known as polygyny. When one female mates with multiple males, it is known as polyandry. Based on the biological principle of the operational sex ratio, the expectation is that all males are biologically driven to mate with multiple females. For example, of the 4,400 mammalian species, over 97% of the species are polygynous. Among invertebrates, nearly 100% of the species are polygynous. However, among the bird species, nearly 94% are monogamous. The human species is also generally monogamous, although there are some exceptions.

Polygyny has resulted in males evolving some remarkable physical and behavioral characteristics. In a polygyny mating system, the mating is often monopolized by a small number of males. For example, less than 10% of the males of the elephant seals mate with all the females during a mating season. In the case of the bower bird, 5% of the males claim paternity of all the offspring. With only a small portion of the males carrying out the mating, their genes are disproportionately passed onto the next generation. Their offspring carry the genes for the traits that will help them to be successful in competing with other males. These male traits will become magnified in each generation. They will become grossly exaggerated, leading to a set of male-specific traits that are very different from the female. Therefore, polygyny is a powerful driving force for sexual dimorphism.

There are variations of polygyny, and males of different species use different strategies to compete with other males. The strategies used by the elephant seals and the ibexes consist of battling with other males to drive them away from the females. These types of strategies lead to males that are stronger and bigger than the females, a form of sexual dimorphism that is based on the evolution of size and of specialized weapons. The peacocks are an example of male polygyny that use flashiness to attract the females. Another form of polygyny is based on providing food gifts to the females.

In some cricket species, the males produce a gelatinous bolus, known as a spermatophore, which contains sperm and proteinaceous materials. The male transfers the spermatophore to the female's ovipore during copulation. The spermatophore remains attached to the female's ovipore. Instead of removing it, the female consumes the spermatophore, a process that allows for maximum sperm transfer. This type of food gift is also known as a nuptial gift. This gift allows the

Food gift

In many cricket species, the males offer the females a nuptial food gift during the mating to prolong the copulation. *(GNU Free Documentation License)*

male to gain mating opportunities, because females shun males who do not offer the spermatophore. The males that produce the largest spermatophore are likely to be most successful in copulating and in transferring the largest number of sperm to the females.

The polygyny mating system has led to the evolution of extraordinary mating behavior. One such mating behavior is known as scramble competition. In central Europe, the males of a butterfly species use an unusual method to compete with each other. These males have evolved the ability to sense the chemical signals of

a female butterfly that is undergoing metamorphosis. The male butterfly stays by the female as she hatches from the chrysalis. As soon as the female emerges, he immediately mates with her even before her wings have expanded. After mating, he deposits a gelatinous plug in the opening of her ovipore. A few hours later, the plug hardens into a sharp spine that prevents any other males from mating with her.

Scamble competition

Males search out the newly hatched females and mate with them before any other males. *(Public Domain)*

The extraordinary variations in the physical and behavioral traits of polygynous males are based on one important biological condition: the males do not make any contribution to parental care. In other words, the females assume the entire responsibility for raising the young. This allows the males to devote all their energy to pursuing the females in the same way as the sperm pursue the eggs. The fierce competition rewards the males that have evolved novel traits that give them a competitive edge. In situations where the successful males get most of the mating opportunities, these traits are more likely to be passed onto the next generation and become exaggerated.

III.2. Why do males choose monogamy?

Based on the biological principle of the operational sex ratio, males are driven to mate with as many females as possible. Among mammals, more than 97% of the species are polygamous. However, in the remaining 3% of the species, males mate with only one female at a time. The duration of the monogamy may be one breeding season, multiple breeding seasons, or an entire lifetime. Humans are among the few of the mammalian species that practice monogamy. Why do males of these species abandon their biological instinct and become monogamous?

Among the primates, there are only a few species that are monogamous. Examining their life histories offers insights into the environmental conditions that have led to the evolution of monogamy. One such example is a species of monkey that lives in the upper canopy of the South American rainforest. The males and females pair for life, because without the help of the males in providing parental care, the species would become extinct. In this species, the males have a strong parenting instinct. They carry their babies everywhere, because the females devote all their energy to breastfeeding the young. If the males abandon their families, the babies would either starve or fall to their deaths, because the females could not do all the work. For the species to exist, the males must contribute to the care of the young.

The development of monogamy is another example of sexual selection. In the case of the rainforest monkey species, the male monkeys that demonstrate behavioral traits for parental care will leave more offspring. The genes for these traits will pass onto their offspring. Females that prefer males with these traits will also pass this behavioral preference to their female offspring. After many generations of selection, a species of monogamous monkeys has evolved. This is a social solution to a biological problem. This example demonstrates that parental behavior can be selected in the same way as bower building behavior.

Wandering albatross

They perform courtship dances for several seasons before forming lifelong pair-bonds. *(Public Domain)*

The wandering albatross is a species that has evolved one of the strongest pair-bonds in animals. These seabirds live solitary lives most of the year. They spend their time searching for food over the open seas. Each year, they gather on remote islands to undertake courtship rituals. The young birds spend several years performing the courtship dance as a group. Eventually, two birds form a pair, and they perform the courtship rituals each year after they return to the island. In the third year, they consummate their union, and the female gives birth to a single chick. It takes an entire year for the chick to mature, and the parents take turns flying to the sea to bring back food to feed the young. They often fly for several hundred miles to find food. Because of the harsh conditions, both parents must cooperate in raising the young. The pair returns year after year to the same island to resume their courtship.

More than 94% of bird species use monogamy because of the need for both mating partners to contribute to parental care. However, there are different types of monogamous relationships. The type of monogamy in which the mating partners have paired for life is known as life-long monogamy. There are also monogamous relationships that last only for the breeding season. In this system, the mating partners

Emperor penguin
They breed under some of the worst climatic conditions. They form seasonal rather than lifelong monogamous relationships. *(GNU Free Documentation License)*

enter into new monogamous relationships during each mating season. This is known as serial monogamy. The third type of monogamy is known as social monogamy, in which the mating partners share the responsibilities in providing parental care for the young, but they continue to mate with other individuals. In monogamous bird species, researchers have discovered that more than 90% practice social monogamy. In addition to mating with their partners, both males and females engage in extra pair copulations.

Humans evolved pair-bonding and became monogamous about 2.5 million years ago. Researchers have suggested that the harsh environment of the savannas required the assistance of the males to care for the young. Also, humans started to give birth to young that were less mature. This occurred because the human skull had enlarged to accommodate a larger brain. A larger brain required a larger skull, and this large skull was more difficult to pass through the human birth canal. The long childhood also posed a greater demand for parental care. For early humans, the survival of the offspring was at stake if the male abandoned the family. The modern social concept of family values has a biological root, and human monogamy is an evolved biological trait.

III.3. How does environment affect sexual behavior?

Male competition, mate choice, and mating systems are the consequences of the interactions between genes and the environment. In the biological world, polygyny is the most common mating system because of the biological roles of the sperm and eggs. Under conditions where it is unnecessary for males to assume parental responsibilities, it is more valuable for the species if the males expend their energy searching for females. The result is males that are aggressive, flashy, and sexually driven. On the other hand, females are quiet and content to stay in one place, so that they can raise their young without being noticed by predators. However, environmental conditions can reverse the role of the males and females in the mating process. The most well-known examples of this are the behaviors of male lions and female jacanas, a bird species that lives on lily pads in crocodile-infested water.

Lions form a pride with one or two male lions living with 8 to 15 lionesses. The male lion mates with all the females in the pride forming a polygyny mating system. The male lion does not hunt, leaving the hunting to the females. Its main role is to protect the pride from marauding male lions that are looking to take over a pride. Such protection is crucial, particularly for the cubs. If the male lion dies or is killed by an invading male lion, the pride is in danger. Immediately after assuming control of the pride, the new male lion commits infanticide by killing every cub in the pride. The females are helpless in preventing the slaughter. The killing might seem cruel, but from the biological standpoint, it has two reasons. First, the male lion does not want to protect cubs that do not carry his genes. Secondly, after the death of the cubs, the females cease to nurse and become receptive to mate with the new male.

With the jacana, the role is reversed, because the female jacana is the leader of the pack of five to six male jacanas. After laying the eggs, the task of incubating the eggs is left to the males. The female jacana is bigger and more aggressive than the male, and she defends the territory against other female jacanas. If the female jacana is killed, another female jacana will invade the territory and assume control over the male jacanas. The first action of the female after taking over the colony is to search for and destroy all the eggs laid by the previous female jacana. She then mates with the males and lays a new batch of eggs for them to incubate. This type of mating system is known as polyandry, where one female mates with multiple males.

Jacana
The female mates with multiple mates in a role reversal mating system known as polyandry.
(GNU Free Documentation License)

This role reversal is driven entirely by environmental conditions. The jacanas live on lily pads in streams or lakes teeming with crocodiles, which prey on their eggs and young. In order to lay more eggs to compensate for the loss, the species has evolved a strategy by having the males incubate the eggs, freeing the females to lay as many eggs as possible. Since the males are preoccupied with egg incubation, they are not available to mate with other females. This shifts the balance of the operational sex ratio to the females; there are more sexually-receptive females than males. Since the females compete with other females for males, they are larger and more aggressive. Therefore, sex roles depend largely on environmental demands.

In human society, the environment also affects human sexual behavior. Even though human male aggression is a biological instinct, the environment has significant influences on male behavior. Like many other behavioral traits, both nurture and nature affect male and female behaviors. An understanding of how both genes and the environment play a role in sexual behavior will aid both personal and societal decisions.

Chapter 8

Union

Why must we procreate?

Is there a battle of the sexes?

Even though males and females of a species must come together to procreate, the males and females want different things. These create conflicts between the sexes that are often difficult to resolve. *(GNU Free Documentation License)*

Dfrnt: Couldn't they find a "different", less offensive way to market cell phone ring tones?

Cesare Paciotti: Another fashion victim--literally, it appears. Designers sure do love to show off their clothes on fallen women.

Sex sells

Advertisements use sex appeal to push their products. They are often offensive to wormen.

(Education Fair Use)

David

This sculpture is often considered to be the perfect male figure. Why is it so appealing? *(GNU Free Documentation License)*

CHAPTER 8. UNION

"Sex sells" is an undeniable fact of modern advertisement, because the desire for sex is an essential ingredient for sexual reproduction. For sexually-reproducing organisms, sexual attraction is necessary for the opposite sexes to recognize each other and to mate. There are many signals given off by both males and females to indicate that they are members of the same species and are ready to mate. For humans, recognizing and giving off these signals are as natural as finding and eating food. If members of the species lack the ability to communicate with these sexual signals, then their genes will not be passed to the next generation because they will not reproduce. By understanding how sexual communication occurs, we can gain a better appreciation of our behavior and how sexual signals shape our society and culture.

I. What is the biological Basis of Beauty?

From the biological standpoint, beauty reflects our instinctive desire. The human desire for beauty has biological roots that are encoded in the genes of the human species. Despite variations in what is considered to be the most beautiful features in a human female, there is a general agreement on beauty across both time and culture. Similarly, most people can agree on the characteristics that make a good looking human male. These observations have suggested that there is a genetic commonality of human desire, and it must have evolved to promote the reproductive success of the species. What is the biological basis of beauty? Do other animals also appreciate beauty? Finally, how does beauty promote reproductive success?

I.1. *What is the biological basis of beauty?*

Is beauty really in the eye of the beholder? Is there a standard of male and female beauty? By casually browsing through *People Magazine* or other similar tabloid publications, one can quickly conclude that there are some common standards of male and female beauty. These standards change slightly from time to time, but the basic characteristics that define these standards transcend time and culture. People around the world share some common perceptions of what beauty is in males and females. Among the different ways to define beauty, the human face has received the most attention. This is not surprising when considering that greater than 80% of human communication is through facial expressions.

The scientific study of facial beauty began in the 19th century by Francis Galton, a first cousin to Charles Darwin. Galton began his research with the hypothesis that it was possible to predict a person's character by studying his or her facial features. He took photographs of many subjects, ranging from criminals to clergymen. He wanted to look for facial features that were unique to "bad" and "good" people in society. He compiled a composite of the faces in the "bad" group and compared them to the composite of the faces in the "good" group. To his surprise, the composites of the "bad" and "good" groups were almost indistinguishable from each other. Furthermore, the composites of both groups were judged by many to be more attractive and beautiful than any of the individuals in the groups.

A similar study was conducted in 1886 using photographic portraits of members of the National Academy of Sciences and the graduating seniors of Smith College.

Hot or Not Composite Images

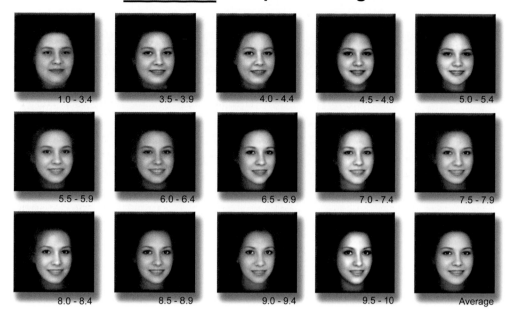

1.0 - 3.4	3.5 - 3.9	4.0 - 4.4	4.5 - 4.9	5.0 - 5.4
5.5 - 5.9	6.0 - 6.4	6.5 - 6.9	7.0 - 7.4	7.5 - 7.9
8.0 - 8.4	8.5 - 8.9	9.0 - 9.4	9.5 - 10	Average

Beauty of averageness
The most beautiful face is the composite (average) face. *(Creative Commons Attribution)*

Galton's observation was confirmed: the average facial features (averageness) of a group of individuals were more attractive and beautiful than the facial features of the individual members of the group. However, no further work on this idea of facial beauty was pursued in the next 100 years. In 1990, when computer-based programs were developed to conduct mathematical analyses of facial features, the concept of averageness was re-examined. In one study, researchers took 192 male and female Caucasian faces and generated a series of composite faces, which were then rated by 300 judges on a 5-point scale. The faces that were judged most attractive had the most average features. In 2005, a similar study was conducted with Miss Universe contestants. A composite of the beauty pageant contestants was created and compared to the composite faces of the general public. Surprisingly, the two composites were nearly identical.

Miss Universe 2005 Composite Images

| Africa - 9 delegates | All - 81 delegates | Europe - 28 delegates |
| Asia - 14 delegates | Finalists - 15 delegates | Americas - 30 delegates |

Miss Universe contestants
Beauty in averageness Is also apparent among the contestants from every corner of the world. *(Creative Commons Attribution)*

Why is averageness the standard of human beauty? There are two reasons from the biological perspective why averageness is preferred. The first reason is related to the individual's genetic status. When researchers studied the various aspects of the most beautiful or "average" face, they discovered that the arrangements of various facial features are the most symmetrical in the "average" face. Furthermore, they also discovered that the relative dimensions of different facial features are in "perfect" proportions. These include the distance between the eyes and the size of the nose relative to the size of the face. All the facial features appeared to be just right. Researchers discovered that this does not occur by accident. During development, the genes that are responsible for developing body symmetry are also responsible for these facial features. Symmetrical facial features are a reflection of genetic quality, not just symmetry of the face but also of other aspects of the individuals. Therefore, good facial symmetry provides an indication of the overall health status of an individual.

The second reason that averageness is preferred is based on the subconscious, individual preferences for traits that are most common in the population. This

Koinophilia

Members of the same species are generally alike in appearance. *(GNU Free Documentation License)*

type of preference is responsible for creating members of a mating population that differ from each other by only minor variations. For example, all squirrels in central Illinois share the same appearance. Similarly, different human populations that were geographically separated in the past share the same physical appearances. Why do individuals within a population take on similar traits as other members of the group?

Recently, researchers have developed a theory, known as koinophilia, to explain this phenomenon. According to this theory, natural selection favors traits that improve reproductive success. These traits are passed on and are spread throughout the population. Individuals who show a preference for these traits are likely to be reproductively more successful because these traits have been tried and tested. Extremes of these traits are avoided because they reduce reproductive success. Therefore, choosing the average traits is the safest and most reliable strategy. If parents prefer these traits, the genes for these preferences are passed onto their offspring. Therefore, beauty has a biological basis and is important in ensuring the reproductive success of the offspring.

I.2. Is beauty an indication of fertility?

What is the origin of male and female physical beauty? The other term for male and female physical beauty is sexiness, and everyone knows that sexiness is directly related to reproduction. Therefore, physical beauty or sexiness is a set of communication signals that are sent to potential mating partners of an individual's fertility. These communication signals are no different from those used by peacocks, hummingbirds, elephant seals, and bower birds. In recent years, through the study of the sexual behavior of other animals, the communication signals used by humans during mating have become understood. It is not surprising that our social and cultural sophistication have hidden the biological significance of these communication signals.

These communication signals are collectively known as fertility signals, because they are used to demonstrate an individual's fertile potential. What is fertile potential? Fertile potential is considered at two levels, the gamete level and the behavioral level. At the gamete level, the fertile potential is simply the production of gametes. For males, fertility is correlated to the production of a large amount of gametes of the highest quality. In females, it is the production of high-quality eggs. However, fertility is also affected at the behavioral level. Can a male compete successfully against other males? Is the female able to nurture the young? These are secondary qualities that are necessary to ensure the success of the offspring. How do animals communicate these fertility signals to their potential partners?

The gamete fertile potential is controlled by sex hormones: testosterone in males and estrogen in females. These two sex hormones are among the most remarkable biological molecules for two reasons. First, they are very simple molecules that are derived from cholesterol but have extremely powerful effects. Second, they are very similar to each other, and both are synthesized in the same biochemical pathway. Furthermore, neither hormone has a direct biological activity. Instead, they both act as transcriptional regulators (triggers for gene expression). They do not directly bind to DNA but bind to specific protein receptors, which then activate appropriate genes. In other words, these sex hormones serve as master switches to turn on other switches.

Testosterone is vital for the embryonic and fetal development of the testes and for other components of the male reproductive system. The testosterone level dramatically drops to an almost undetectable level immediately after birth. Before puberty, the testes remain dormant, and male children show almost no male physical traits. However, at the time of puberty, the testes are stimulated by hormones that are

Fertility signals of the female body

High estrogen and low testosterone levels drive the female body form that human males find attractive. *(Public Domain)*

released from the pituitary gland in the brain. The testes complete their development and start to release a copious amount of testosterone into the blood. Genes in many tissues are activated by testosterone, which then direct the tissue development along the male pathway. These include all the male traits that we commonly recognize. Physical appearance, such as enlarged lower jaws, hair growth, and a deepening voice, result from the effects of testosterone on tissues and organs that are not part of the male reproductive system. These traits that are affected by testosterone are known as secondary sex characteristics.

Similar biological events occur in female sexual development, except that the sex hormone involved is estrogen. Estrogen is important for the development of the female reproductive system during embryonic and fetal development. Like testosterone, its production also stops immediately after birth. When the ovaries start to mature at puberty, they release a large amount of estrogen into the blood. Estrogen acts on similar tissues that testosterone does, but it induces the expression of a different set of genes. The results are features that we associate with female secondary sex characteristics. Some of these traits contribute to successful pregnancies and in caring for the young. However, many of these traits have no direct contribution to the reproductive process.

Some of the secondary sex characteristics contribute to sexual reproduction, but many do not. However, since these traits are directly influenced by the sex hormones, they become indicators of both the level as well as the body's response to the sex hormones. Since sex hormones are important in the development of the reproductive system, the secondary sex characteristics are a visible indication of an individual's fertility. If those individuals who express strong secondary fertility signals mate more often and have more offspring, then their genes will pass onto the future generations. These offspring will then instinctively mate with individuals who also have strong secondary sex characteristics. Therefore, beauty is a secondary sex characteristic that reflects individual fertile potential.

Breasts as a fertility signal
High estrogen levels during puberty enhance breast development. Breasts serve as secondary sex characteristics.
(Public Domain)

I.3. *What is the difference between sex and gender?*

For many years, sex was divided into two separate aspects: the genetic aspect that contributes to the biological properties of the reproductive system and the psychological aspect that contributes to the recognition of one's gender. In the past, psychologists believed that gender was a social construct created only by nurture. Many developmental psychologists had provided evidence that the home environment and society shape gender roles. Any deviations from these gender roles were attributed to the environment rather than to the genetics of sex determination. This view was prominent in addressing the environment rather than genetics as the underlying cause of homosexuality and transsexualism.

One study in 1972 provided the first evidence that gender awareness is genetically based rather than solely environmentally based. This study followed one of twin boys who had sustained a surgical accident during his circumcision, leading to severe damage to his penis. Instead of having him grow up as a male who had a dysfunctional penis, the doctors suggested sex reassignment surgery. With surgery to create female genitalia and with the appropriate hormone therapy, the boy was brought up as a girl, and the parents vowed they would never disclose this fact to the boy. This case was intensely studied, and researchers reported that he grew up as a well-adjusted girl. Based on this evidence, they claimed that gender could be completely molded by environment.

However, as the boy grew older, he felt increasingly uncomfortable as a girl. He preferred boy activities over girl activities and started to experience depression and other psychological problems. By the age of 14, he was finally told that he was a boy and the reason why he was raised a girl. He decided immediately that he wanted to

Homosexuality
This ancient Chinese painting depicts a woman spying on two male lovers. *(Public Domain)*

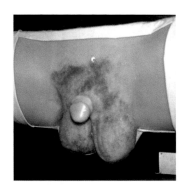

Genetic basis of gender

The Nova program "Sex Unknown" explores the genetic basis of gender. *(Education Fair Use)*

Congenital adrenal hyperplasia

A condition known as intersex leads to ambiguous external genitalia. *(Public Domain)*

live as a boy, because he never felt comfortable as a girl. He continued to have difficultly coping with his past, and he struggled to come to terms with his gender. Unfortunately, he committed suicide as a result of his many psychological difficulties. This case and other similar cases changed the thinking that gender results entirely from the environment and also led to the search for the biological basis of gender.

For many years, it was unclear how the male and female brains differ. The assumption was that the brain and mind were largely shaped by the environment. With improved brain imaging techniques, researchers have discovered that the male and female brains are different in both structure and function. These differences begin very early in life during embryonic and fetal development, when the testosterone and estrogen levels are high. The basic structural differences between the male and female brains are established before birth. These differences account for the male and female differences that can be detected as early as several weeks after birth. By age two, these differences are particularly noticeable in the behavior of children.

The effect of testosterone on fetal development is seen in the genetic disorder congenital adrenal hyperplasia (CAH). In this disorder, the defect results in excessive testosterone production during the second trimester. In addition to masculinizing the genitalia of a female fetus, it also masculinizes the brain. Even after surgery and hormone treatment, these female children often become tomboys. These individuals are also more likely to become involved in lesbian relationships. Research in CAH and sexual development has provided evidence that gender development is strongly genetically based.

Even though researchers have yet to identify the genes, indirect evidence indicates that genes are important in the development of gender identity. One example of this evidence is transsexualism. Individuals who are transsexual find themselves trapped in the body of the opposite sex. Their biological sex does not match their gender, even though many have spent their entire life in the opposite gender role. Many of such individuals do not find satisfaction in life until they undergo sex reassignment surgery in adulthood.

In summary, both the biological basis of sex and the psychological awareness of gender are genetically based. The male and female brains are strongly affected by testosterone and estrogen, leading to differences in both structure and function. Therefore, the human brain also exhibits secondary sex characteristics. Disruption of these secondary sex characteristics can result in the alteration of sexual behavior.

II. WHY IS COURTSHIP NECESSARY?

Courtship (dating) is an intense social activity that humans engage in before choosing their mating partners. During courtship, individuals explore their compatibility and decide whether or not to make a long-term commitment in forming a sexual partnership. Almost all animals carry out some type of courtship. As animals become more complex both in structure and function, so does the complexity of courtship. The courtship in monogamous animals is generally more elaborate than that of polygamous ones. In a monogamous mating system, the males have some influence in selecting their female partner because they also invest heavily in the relationship. In polygamy, courtship is generally defined as the males attracting the females. Courtship is driven by the same strong biological instinct that exists in every aspect of sexual reproduction. An appreciation of the biological basis of courtship will help us to understand our personal life experiences as well as the social aspect of courtship.

II.1. *What is the significance of fertility signals in courtship?*

Love at first sight does not routinely happen in human courtship, but getting noticed by a potential mating partner does. In humans, young males and females are constantly enhancing their fertility signals through clothing, makeup, speech, behavior, and even posture so that they can appear sexy to potential mating partners. This occurs subconsciously without the realization that the intention of such behavior is to attract the attention of potential mating partners. The understanding of human courtship came from studying the courtship behavior of different animals. These examples have demonstrated that the biological basis of courtship is the same for all animals.

In one study, some males of a species of tropical bird were noticed to have a tuff of feather on their foreheads. The females gave particular attention to these males. Researchers assumed that this feather was a fertility signal that was used by females when selecting their male mating partners. The researchers also hypothesized that if they enhanced the appearance of some males by gluing synthetic feathers onto their tuffs, then these males would be more successful in courting the females. The results confirmed their hypothesis; these males were five times more successful than the normal males. Furthermore, if the feather tuffs were cut off of some males, those males received no attention from the females.

Sexual dimorphism

The differences in the male and female duck are indications of courtship signals. *(GNU Free Documentation License)*

In another study, researchers observed the courtship behavior of a spider species and found some interesting results on fertility signals in courtship. In this spider species, the male spiders possess a set of bristles on their front legs. When the male spiders encounter females, they need to send the correct courtship signals. Otherwise, the females take them as prey rather than as potential suitors. To prevent misidentification, the males wave their front legs at the females to show off their bristles. Researchers have discovered that the females are most interested in males who have large bristles. It is these males who cause the females to become sexually receptive. It was also observed in this study that the females would respond to images of the male spiders. When the females were placed in front of a monitor and shown images of male spiders, they responded to the images as if they were real-life male spiders. They also became more excited when shown images of males that had large bristles. More interestingly, the females also responded equally well to stick figures of spiders with bristles.

In human courtship, fertility signals are critical for catching the attention of the opposite sex. Both sexes perform fertility enhancement tactics to make them more noticeable and to stand out from the crowd. The breasts are an important human female fertility signal. Enhancing the female breasts by certain types of clothing or surgical procedures is common in cultures from ancient to modern times. Another important female fertility signal is smooth skin, and human females have used ointments and makeup to enhance the smoothness of their skin. Both of these are important secondary fertility signals because they are directly influenced by estrogen. High estrogen levels during development enhance female breasts and promote smooth skin.

Male fertility signals

Facial features indicate a high testosterone level during puberty. *(Creative Commons Attribution)*

Males use slightly different strategies to attract the attention of the females. Physical fertility signals are important, but females also look for other aspects in choosing males as mating partners. In an interesting study, females were asked to look at set of male faces on the computer. The researchers morphed the face from highly masculine, with a large lower jaw and thick eyebrows, to a more feminine face.

Female fertility signals
They are associated with a high estrogen level during puberty.
(Creative Commons Attribution)

The female subjects were asked to choose one for both a short-term and a long-term relationship. Not surprisingly, most females chose the masculine face for a short-term relationship and the more feminine type for a long-term relationship. They felt that the masculine-type would be "fun" for a short-term relationship, whereas the more feminine-type was better for a long-term relationship, because these males were perceived as being more supportive for raising a family.

Interestingly, when the subjects were tested repeatedly, the researchers discovered that the females often gave different answers. Further analyses demonstrated that the answers were correlated with the stages of their menstrual cycles. They tended to pick the masculine-type when they were ovulating and to pick the more feminine-type when they were not ovulating. These differences suggested that the females were most responsive to strong fertility signals when they were the most sexually receptive. When they were not sexually receptive, they tended to consider other aspects of the partnership.

II.2. Is there a biological basis of love?

What is love? All of us have felt love sometime in our life, but most of us have a difficult time defining the feeling. In the past twenty years, biologists and psychologists have joined forces to study the various aspects of love. The scientific views of love have included various disciplines such as evolutionary psychology, behavioral biology, neuroscience, biochemistry, physiology, and anthropology. Using the most advanced brain imaging technology, scientists have located the brain regions that are involved in the feelings and experiences of love. This knowledge is relevant to everyone because we all experience love at some point in our lives. Having this knowledge enhances our experience and helps us manage the intense emotions that are associated with love.

When people are in love, they do things that they normally would not do. This phenomenon, however, is not unique to humans. Studies on animal behavior have observed animal courtship behaviors that are similar to human behavior. For example, humans are not the only ones who dance when they are in love. A species of water bird that is common in Europe and North America uses courtship behaviors that have great resemblances to human couples when they are in love. Their courtship begins by exchanging gifts between potential mating partners. This is followed by both birds trying to replicate each other's actions. After these early courtship rituals, the pair performs a perfectly synchronized dance by walking on the water surface. Once these steps have been completed, the pair consummates their union. Even though they are paired for life, they never repeat these courtship rituals again.

The pair-bonds between some animals are exceedingly strong. The wandering albatrosses form pair-bonds for their entire life, which can last for over 50 years. Even though they go their separate ways each year to find food in the open ocean, they rejoin the next year at the same place and time. If a mating partner fails to return, the other bird exhibits "sorrow" for the rest of its life, and it will not pair with another bird. This is a type of pair-bonding that humans can recognize. However, other species form pair bonds that last only for the breeding season. It is clear that environmental factors are important in the evolution of pair-bonds.

Dancing in courtship
The partners evaluate each other through coordinated physical activities. It is a courtship behavior common in animal courtships.
(Public Domain)

Pair-bonding is the outcome of love. Love is a strategy that has evolved to ensure that mating partners stay together until their offspring reach adulthood. In the early 1990s, researchers proposed that love could be divided into three discrete stages. The first stage is lust, which is dominated by fertility signals that trigger an intense longing for physical intimacy. In animals, this stage is characterized by uncontrollable behavior, such as showing off or restlessness. The second stage is attraction; this stage focuses on actions, such as giving gifts, doing things for each other, grooming (conversations in humans), and performing synchronized activities (such as dancing).

The third stage is attachment. It is during this stage when a strong bonding between two individuals starts to form.

During the attachment stage, there are three elements of love that are vital for long-term bonding. These elements form the triangular theory of love. According to this theory, all three of the elements must be present before long-term bonding can occur. The first element is intimacy, which encompasses the feelings of closeness, connectedness, and bondedness. The second element is passion, which encompasses the drives that lead to romance, physical attraction, and sexual consummation. The third element is decision/commitment, which encompasses, in the short term, the decision that one loves a partner, and in the long term, the commitment to maintain that love.

Biologists believe that humans are not the only animals capable of loving in a way that encompasses all these elements. All animal species that must maintain a partnership between the males and females to raise their young also possess these elements in their relationships. These animals have evolved the genes to develop these relationships with their mating partners. What exactly these genes do is yet to be resolved. However, recent research has confirmed that love has a biological explanation. Studies of the neurochemistry of the brain during various stages of love have shown that biology can explain many aspects of love.

II.3. *Is love a biological response?*

When people fall in love, there are many physiological changes that occur in the body, ranging from the dramatic to the barely noticeable. Love is an emotional response, and at the height of excitement, the physiological responses of love are indistinguishable from those that occur when a person faces extreme anger and fear. The physiological consequences include pupil dilation, dry mouth, palpitations, sweaty palms, accelerated heart rate, and heavy breathing. These physiological changes are also known as the fight or flight response, because they are the typical reactions that occur when an animal prepares for action. These physiological changes are beyond any conscious control, and they are mediated by part of the nervous system known as the autonomic nervous system.

The autonomic nervous system is divided into two components, which have opposing functions. The sympathetic system is used to initiate the fight or flight response, and the parasympathetic system is used to maintain normalcy. All the emotion and excitement that are associated with the many feelings of love are caused by the release of one of the most well-known hormones, adrenalin, also known as epinephrine. At the height of sexual excitement, the brain sends a signal to the adrenal gland, and adrenalin is released into the blood circulation. Adrenalin binds to adrenalin receptors, which are located on many cells, and induces profound physiological changes. These changes include an increase in cardiac output to provide more oxygen to the brain and muscles and the release of glucose by liver cells. However, adrenalin also inhibits certain functions, such as digestion.

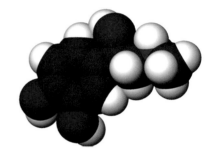

Adrenalin

A simple molecule that produces the physiological reactions of excitement in love.

The feeling of love is a neurological response and is mediated by neurotransmitters (chemical messengers) in the brain. The neurotransmitters that are involved in love include: dopamine, norepinephrine, serotonin, oxytocin, and vasopression. Sex hormones, such as testosterone and estrogen, are also important. Recently, a small protein hormone, nerve growth factor, has also been found to be involved. The neurotransmitters have received a great deal of attention because they are also involved in mediating the addictive effects of abuse substances and certain psychological disorders. These types of interactions further suggest that a close link exists between love and other mental processes, including substance abuse and mental diseases.

Based on the studies of neurotransmitters, love is divided into two separate neurological processes that use two different sets of neurotransmitters. The first neurological process is the sexual attraction phase. In this phase, the neurotransmitters that are involved are dopamine, norepinephrine, and serotonin. Both dopamine and norepinephrine are positive regulators for sexual attraction, whereas serotonin is a negative regulator. Elevated levels of dopamine and norepinephrine in the brain heighten sexual attraction and induce the psychological state of lust. Elevated serotonin levels reduce the obsession with the love interest. Patients who have been treated with antidepressants, such as Prozac and Paxil, have high levels of serotonin. Some of these patients are not particularly interested in falling in love.

The second neurological process is the attachment phase. Two neurotransmitters, oxytocin and vasopressin, are involved in promoting attachment. Both of these neurotransmitters are important in pair-bonding. This observation was discovered by studying the behavior of voles. There are two species of related voles, the prairie vole and the montane vole. These species, however, have different mating behaviors. The prairie voles form life-long pair bonds, whereas the montane voles are polygamous. Researchers recently discovered that the biological basis of these behavior variations was because of differences in the brain in responding to oxytocin and vasopressin. The neurons of the prairie voles were many times more responsive to these two neurotransmitters than were the neurons of the montane voles. Recent studies have also revealed why sexual intercourse promotes attachment between mating partners. After orgasm, the brain releases bursts of oxytocin and vasopressin that reinforce the neuronal connections for attachment.

The role of oxytocin and vasopressin is not restricted to building attachments between mating partners. These hormones are also released during breastfeeding, strengthening the bonds between mothers and infants. Recent studies have also suggested that these hormones are important for building family bonds and are released during times of close physical contact, such as hugging and kissing. Because of their actions, oxytocin and vasopressin are often referred to as the cuddling neurotransmitters and hormones. From these observations and others, it is clear that love has biological and biochemical components that can be traced to physiology and neurobiology. This knowledge does not take away the beauty and mystery of love. Instead, it creates a greater appreciation of the wonder of love.

Vole behavior

The prairie voles are monogamous, whereas the montane voles are polygamous. Their different behaviors have a neurological origin. *(GNU Free Documentation License)*

III. WHY IS SEX FUN?

For humans, sex is a highly pleasurable activity, although the amount of sex that is desired varies among individuals. Furthermore, human males have much higher sex drives in comparison to females. Humans seem to enjoy sex far more than almost all other animal species. Human mating partners engage in sexual activities even when there is no chance for the female to become pregnant. In contrast, other animals engage in sexual activities only during the breeding seasons, which are usually limited to a brief period during the year. During this period, the females advertise their sexual readiness, and once mating has been completed, the females and males do not mate again. However, in humans, the time of ovulation is hidden and is not known to either the female or the male. Therefore, human mating is an ongoing process, and this particular sexual behavior has great evolutionary significance.

III.1. *What is the biological basis of the sex drive?*

All sexually-reproduced biological organisms, including humans, must possess a strong desire to procreate. Without this desire, the survival of the species would be endangered. However, there are wide variations among human individuals regarding their desire to mate with their sexual partners. Individuals who have excessive sex drives can create personal and social problems in a highly complex society. On the other hand, individuals who have little or no desire for sex can also create problems, especially in their relationships with their mating partners. Until recently, sexual desire was considered a psychological issue, with environment playing the key role in shaping individual sex drives. However, recent research has provided evidence that individual sex drives have a biological basis.

In general, humans find great pleasure in sexual activities. However, it was not until the early 1950s that the neurological basis of human sexual pleasure was discovered by researchers at Tulane University. They had implanted electrodes in the brain as a desperate attempt to help patients who had untreatable clinical depression. Using these electrodes, they stimulated different parts of the brain looking for regions of the brain that are responsible for depression. Accidentally, they discovered that the stimulation of some regions of the brain led to the feelings of sexual pleasure. Some patients were delighted to gain control of the switch, and they called it the sexy button. This was the first evidence that sexual pleasure has a neurological basis.

The region of the brain that gives sexual pleasure is known as the nucleus accumbens. It is a small region deep in the center of the brain. It is part of the dopaminergic neural pathway; this pathway is called this because dopamine is the primary neurotransmitter that is involved in the communication of neurons within this region. This discovery was a major breakthrough because it demonstrated that sexual pleasure is not merely psychological and that it can be attributed to a specific part of the brain. The research at the time was controversial, because it overturned the long-held dogma that sexual pleasure can only be explained by psychological theories. These early studies were later confirmed by animal studies, which led to the development of neurological theories to explain how neurotransmitters, such as dopamine and epinephrine, elicit sexual pleasure.

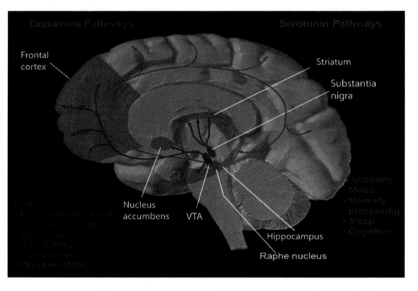

Dopamine pathway
The nucleus accumbens is the pleasure center of the brain. It is part of the dopamine pathway.
(Public Domain)

The understanding of the neurological basis of the sex drive and sexual desire provides a scientific explanation for the variations in sex drives between the sexes and between individuals of the same sex. Recent studies have demonstrated that testosterone is the key molecule in modulating sex drives. Studies with rats have provided evidence that high testosterone levels in the blood of male rats are positively correlated with their libido. It was also observed that the sex drives of female rats can be significantly augmented by administering testosterone. Such correlations have also been found in humans. Males who have high testosterone blood levels are more aggressive and have high sex drives. However, human females produce small amounts of testosterone in their adrenal gland, and their blood testosterone level is less than 1/50 of that of human males.

Genetic differences in testosterone levels are partially responsible for individual sex drive variations in both human males and females. Other genetic factors that can contribute to human sex drive levels include variations of the gene that encodes the testosterone receptor. These variations affect how cells respond to testosterone. Genetic variations can also occur in the production of neurotransmitters, such as dopamine, epinephrine, and serotonin in the brain. These variations can cause a sexual aversion disorder, in which the affected individuals avoid sex. This is the most common sexual disorder, and it affects more women than men.

However, sexual aversion disorder can also be caused by external factors, psychological or physical, that affect testosterone levels or neurotransmitter production in the brain. One of the most common causes of sexual aversion disorder is menopause. Due to the lack of sex hormone production, sex drives decline significantly. In addition, poor nutrition and starvation negatively affect the sex drive, because in these conditions there is a reduction in the dietary components that are required to produce sex hormones. Obesity or being underweight also affects the sex drive. In these conditions, there are often certain metabolic irregularities that can affect the balance of sex hormones. Furthermore, psychological experiences, such as rape and incest, can have a profound impact on neuronal circuits in the brain, which can cause imbalances of neurotransmitters. Psychoactive drugs that affect these neurotransmitters can also lead to a drastic reduction in the sex drive. With this knowledge, the medical community has realized the biological basis of sexual desire and can now teach patients how to maintain a healthy sex life.

III.2. Why do humans enjoy sex?

When researchers studied sexual reproduction among animals, they discovered that sexual reproduction for most animals is a biological necessity rather than a pleasurable activity. Human sexual reproduction is one of few examples in which both males and females enjoy the experience. For most other species, the males are driven by their sex hormones to pursue the females, and the females are generally unwilling participants. Furthermore, sexual activities only take place during a small portion of their annual breeding cycles. During the breeding cycles, sexual activity is a constant battle between the males who are fighting to gain access to the females. In addition, the males battle with the females to transfer as much sperm as possible.

Human sexual activities are enjoyable for both males and females, because both sexes can achieve orgasm. Most studies on animal mating suggest that the females do not receive the same type of "pleasure" as males. For example, in chimpanzees, our closest biological relative, the males usually force the mating on the females, and intercourse lasts less than 15 seconds. The same is true for most other animal species. The purpose of mating for these species is for the males to transfer sperm into the female reproductive tracts. Furthermore, there is a constant battle between the sexes regarding how much sperm is sufficient. Each male wants to transfer more sperm than the other males, whereas the females want to limit the amount of sperm transferred. Therefore, sex for other animals is more of a battle between males and females rather than a pleasurable activity.

This battle between the sexes has led to the evolution of some interesting sexual behavior. In one species of a predatory fly, for example, the males must keep the female in a copulatory position for 30 minutes or longer to transfer as much sperm as possible. In this species, the females copulate with several males and store their sperm in their oviduct. Therefore, each male tries to maximize his sperm transfer to outcompete other males. To keep the females occupied, the males capture prey insects and entice the female to come to feed. While the females are busy feeding, the males take the time to transfer their sperm. When the transfer is complete, the males eject the females and keep his food "gift" to entice another mating partner.

The most extreme example of how males maintain the interest of their mating partners is a phenomenon known as sexual cannibalism. Preying mantis males use this strategy. During the mating ritual, they offer their body parts to the females in order to maintain their interest and willingness to mate. If a male preying mantis is lucky, his loss is limited to a few limbs and some body parts. The males have a remarkable ability to regenerate these parts for the next mating opportunity. In some cases, the females bite off the heads of the males, which brings an abrupt end to their mating opportunities. These mating strategies seem bizarre, but they have evolved to be successful for these groups of organisms.

The most bizarre form of sexual cannibalism is the sexual suicide that is performed by the male red-back spider, a poisonous spider species found in Australia. The red-back females are ferocious predators and are nearly eight times larger than the males.

Sexual cannibalism
Female praying mantis feasting on the male while the male is copulating with her. *(GNU Free Documentation License)*

They are very impatient with the males and are often unwilling to cooperate in the mating process. The red-back males have evolved one of the most unusual mating strategies to deal with the females. When the males approach the females' web, they tap the web to send their mating signals. If the female responds favorably, the male crosses the web and climbs onto the back of the female to mate with her. In the middle of the mating, the male makes a bizarre move; it flips it abdomen directly into the jaws of the female. The female instinctively stabs its fangs into the male and proceeds to feed. While the female feeds, the male continues to transfer his sperm. This strategy allows the male to transfer more sperm. However, more importantly, the male's body contains chemicals which function as anti-aphrodisiacs. These chemicals prevent the female from mating with other males for a period of time.

Female red-back spider
The male red-back spiders commit sexual suicide during mating. *(Public Domain)*

Human sexual activities are very different from those of other animals. For humans, both mating partners take great pleasure in the process. This occurs because there are brain regions that have evolved to reward sexual activities for both males and females. For nearly all other animals that have been studied thus far, the goal of sexual activity is to bring the male and female gametes together. Therefore, the mating only takes place when the eggs of the females are ready for fertilization. It makes evolutionary sense, because it is not energy efficient for males and females to engage in sexual activities when there is no chance for the sperm to fertilize the eggs. For many years, the continuing receptivity of the human female to sexual activities was a biological mystery.

III.3. How did human sexuality evolve?

The special characteristics of human sexuality only became apparent when the sexuality of other animals was studied. It became clear that the differences in sexuality between various species serve important evolutionary purposes. They are adaptations to the particular environments that the species live in. All the variations of sexual behavior serve to perpetuate the species. In some species, their sexual behavior remains constant and unchanging, whereas for other species, their sexual behavior changes rapidly in response to environmental changes. Recently, researchers have discovered how environmental changes have created different sexual behaviors between two nearly identical species.

Humans have two closely related biological cousins, the chimpanzees and the bonobos. Both species are found in the jungles of Africa, but they live apart from each other. The chimpanzees are more common and familiar, and they are slightly larger than the bonobos. Because of their smaller size, the bonobos are also known as pygmy chimpanzees. The chimpanzees live in forests that also have gorillas, which live on the forest floor. The chimpanzees can only forage on the forest floor when the gorillas are not present. In contrast, gorillas are absent in the forests where the bonobos live, and the bonobos spend more time on the forest floor than the chimpanzees to forage. This difference in their respective habitats was vital in the evolution of their sexual behavior.

Common chimpanzee
They have a male dominant society with violent sexual behavior. *(Public Domain)*

The chimpanzee society is highly patriarchal, with one dominant male and several subordinate males who take charge of the group. The males form strong bonds, and they defend their territories against neighboring groups of chimps using violent warfare. Any intruding chimps from neighboring groups are severely beaten or even killed. Females are routinely terrorized by the males and are subjected to forced mating during the height of their reproductive cycle. Chimpanzee sexual activities are short and violent, lasting a mere 10 to 15 seconds. Chimpanzees also have a promiscuous mating system, where females mate with every male in the troop. This mating system evolved to prevent infanticide; males are never certain which infant has been fathered by them. Sexual life in the chimpanzee society is violent and oppressive for the females.

Bonobo

They have a peaceful matriarchal society. Sexual behavior is gentle and tender. *(Public Domain)*

The bonobo society is matriarchal, with the females ruling the group and the males playing a subordinate role. The interactions between bonobos are friendly and gentle, and they use sex as a way to build bonds among both male and female members as well as to diffuse tension. Bonobos regularly engage in sex, both heterosexual and homosexual, even when the females are not reproductively receptive. They find sex fun and completely enjoyable and have found many different ways to engage in sexual activities. Researchers were puzzled by the differences in the sexual activities of these two closely related species.

The answer to why the two related species behave so differently with regards to sex lies in how the species obtain their food. The chimpanzees must feed quickly on the forest floor because of the gorillas. Since the females need to care for their young, they are unable to keep up with the males. Consequently, they feed solitarily, and they are unable to build bonds with other females. The bonobos, however, live in areas without gorillas, allowing them to feed leisurely as a group. In this situation, the females form bonds with each other and have learned to use sexual activities as a way to cement political alliances. This female solidarity allows them to dominate the males, and sex becomes a social activity.

Human sexuality also serves an important social function for creating strong pair-bonds between mating partners. Such pair-bonding is essential if the males are to contribute to raising the young and caring for the females during pregnancy. The hidden ovulation has an important evolutionary purpose; the mating partners will continue to engage in sexual activities not knowing when ovulation will occur. Together with the neurological design for sexual pleasure, human sexual behavior is designed to ensure the development of attachment for life or for the length of time until the offspring become sufficiently independent. This attachment sometimes wears off, leading to what is popularly known as the seven-year itch. In summary, sexual reproduction serves a single objective, which is to bring two sets of genes together. However, the variation by which this is accomplished in the biological world is both extraordinary and intriguing.

Chapter 9

Population

You are one of 6.7 billion people alive.

Why are there so many people?
Hong Kong is a major city with the highest population density in the world. With its crowded city, the Hong Kong population has the lowest fertility rate in the world. (Creative Commons Attribution)

CHAPTER 9. POPULATION

Genghis Khan

People around the world can claim to be his descendents. *(Public Domain)*

A young accountant, who was living in Chicago and working for a cell phone company, wanted to find out his relationship to Genghis Khan, the 13th century founder of the largest contiguous empire in history. He wanted to do this because according to a family legend, his paternal line was of Mongol descent, and he wanted to know whether this legend was true. He was curious about his ancestry and about how he fits into this world. He contacted a biotechnology company through the Internet and had his DNA tested using the recently-developed genealogical DNA analysis techniques. What is your biological ancestry? Where do you come from? How do you fit into the human world or into the biological world? These are fascinating questions, and many are interested in finding the answers. We are curious about our purpose of existence. These questions were once only considered to be the domain of philosophy and religion, but some important insights in this area have recently come from discoveries in biology.

I. HOW DO YOU FIT INTO THE HUMAN WORLD?

Four weeks later, the Chicago accountant checked the company website and found that he was indeed a descendent of Genghis Khan. He had tested positive for a genetic marker on his Y chromosome that had been passed down by Genghis Khan. He also learned that nearly 8% of men living in Asia carry this marker and hence, are related to each other. Around the world, approximately 0.5% of men are descendents of Genghis Khan. The Chicago accountant realized that he was a part of this large family and that he was related to 1 in every 200 people on Earth. Having this knowledge made him feel connected to the past. He also started to consider how he will be connected to the future through his offspring.

Genetic geneology

DNA testing allows individuals to trace their ancestry around the world. *(Education Fair Use)*

I.1. How many people are there in the world?

We are connected to the past through our ancestors, and we are connected to the future through our offspring. This is the biological connectivity that binds all humanity together. It has been estimated that the human species began nearly 250,000 years ago and had evolved from earlier human species. Since then, there has been approximately 12,500 generations (assuming each generation is 20 years) of humans. Recorded history occupies only a small fraction of this. For example, the Great Pyramids of Giza were built less than 150 generations ago, and the independence of the United States occurred only ten generations ago. However, the last ten generations have experienced remarkable changes within the human population. We are now at a crucial point in the biological history of our species.

In the past 200 years, the most remarkable change in the human population is its growth. For over 250,000 years, the human population grew slowly and occasionally suffered from a decline in its population. Genetic studies have provided evidence that the human species nearly became extinct about 100,000 years ago. However, a band of several thousand individuals barely survived in East Africa. As the environment became more favorable, the population maintained a steady but slow growth rate. About 40,000 years ago, humans began to spread from Africa to other parts of the world. Around 10,000 years ago, humans invented agriculture and formed small villages and towns. With a steady supply of food, the human population increased around the world.

By the time of the Roman Empire, the human population had reached 100 million, with China and India being the most populated regions. However, natural disasters, such as droughts and earthquakes, periodically caused a decline in population. Infectious diseases were also devastating and limited population growth. For example, during the 14th century, nearly three quarters of the population in Western Europe was killed by the Black Death (plague). Because of the combination of natural disasters and diseases, the world population maintained a steady state of 500 million people during the Middle Ages. Even though many children were born, many died during infancy and childhood. It was a rarity for families to have all of their children reach adulthood. In some families, more than half of their offspring died because of childhood diseases.

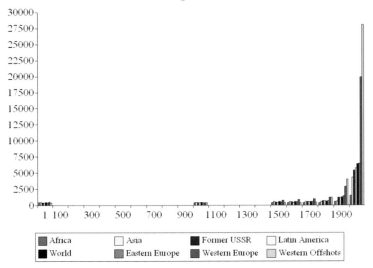

The 18th century was a turning point for human population growth. The Industrial Revolution created the first wave of mechanized farming, increasing the efficiency of crop production. The population around the world increased as food became more available. By the beginning of the 19th century, the world human population reached one billion people. It took 250,000 years for the first humans living in East Africa to leave Africa, to occupy every corner of the world, and to cross this important population milestone.

The human population took less than 125 years to gain its next one billion people. This seemed remarkable, especially when considering that it took nearly 250,000 years to reach the first billion mark. Since then, the human population has gone from two billion people in 1927 to six billion people in 1999. The fastest growth rate of the human population occurred between 1987 and 1999; it was during this time period that the world increased by another billion. The U.S. Census Bureau has set up a web page known as the U.S. and World Population Clocks to track the growth of both the U.S. and the World Population. According to this web page, approximately four babies are born around the world every second, 261 births occur per minute, and 376,000 people are added to the world population each day.

According to the World Population Clock, the world population was 6,670,119,808 as of May 26, 2008. In 2050, the world population will have increased by nearly three billion people and have reached a total of 9.5 billion people. The impact of this population growth on the planet is uncertain, but there have been many predictions. Some predict that this population will exceed Earth's carrying capacity, a term describing the environmental and natural resources that are able to sustain certain populations. Others, however, predict that human ingenuity and technology will adjust to the change. The future is uncertain, and only our knowledge can help us face this major challenge.

Industrial revolution

The growth of gross domestic product was dramatically increased as a result of the Industrial Revolution. (*Creative Commons Attribution*)

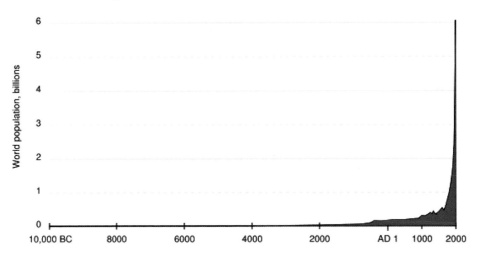

Human population growth

The exponential human population growth occurred after 1800. (*Creative Commons Attribution*)

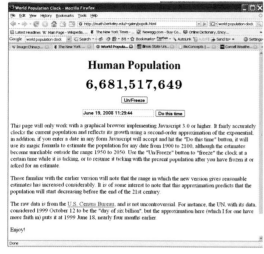

World population web page

The page is constantly updated to show the growth of the world population. *(Education Fair Use)*

I.2. *What is the population around the world?*

Where are all the people living on Earth? How will the human population distribution affect the world 50 or 100 years from now? Will the current distribution pattern of the human population cause political, social, and economic instability in the future? What will the world be like when you turn 60? Will there be mass chaos and suffering or peace and prosperity? These are important questions that require global attention, because human population growth and distribution are more than only regional issues. They affect the entire planet. Since humans are biological organisms, the biological principles that govern population growth and distribution of other living organisms also apply to humans. Studies of these biological principles have provided insights into the understanding of the growth and distribution pattern of the human population, both in the past and into the future.

Studies on the human population distribution pattern of the past have offered an interesting explanation of the current world population distribution. In 1750, the world population was 791 million, with 64% of the world population located in Asia, 21% in Europe, and 13% in Africa. North America, South America, and Australia had less than 3% of the world population. The two most populous nations were China and India. These countries had been prosperous for several thousand years because of advances in agriculture, technology, and medicine. Europe at this time had emerged from the Middle Ages and was just beginning to enter the Industrial Revolution. In addition, the Europeans were just beginning to colonize the Americas. Furthermore, Africa had not experienced the same technological advances that other parts of the world had after the height of the Egyptian civilization.

In 2000, it was observed that the human population distribution had changed only slightly since 1750. Asia remained the most populous continent with 61% of the world population. Africa and Europe had nearly equal populations, each with approximately 12%. North America (U.S. and Canada) had 5% of the world population. Latin America (South America, Mexico, and the Caribbean) had nearly 9% of the world population. Oceania (Australia, New Zealand, and the Pacific Islands) accounted for the remaining 0.5% of the human population. However, the number of people had changed dramatically. In 1750, the Asian population was 500 million, and in 2000, the population had increased over seven times to 3.6 billion people.

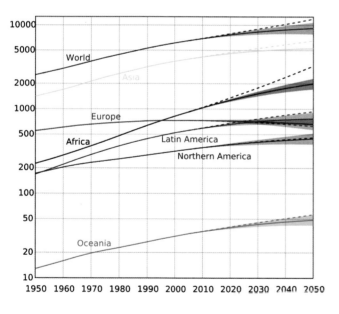

Population change on different continents

The Y axis is millions of people on a logarithmic scale. *(Public Domain)*

By understanding the past population growth patterns, it is possible to project the distribution and growth of future populations. Based on the current population modeling, the world population is projected to increase by 50% from six billion to nine billion people between 2000 and 2050. The biggest population expansion will come from Africa, which is expected to grow from 767 million to 1.8 billion people (an increase of 130%). The Asian population will increase by 45%, from 3.6 billion to 5.2 billion people. The Latin American population will grow by nearly 60%. Northern America, however, will only have a modest 27% increase in its population. Most surprisingly, the European population will decline by 14%, decreasing from 628 million to 517 million people.

What will the world population be in 2150? Will the human population growth continue? The current population model projects that the human population in 2150 will be 9.7 billion people (a modest 9% increase over the population in 2050). Over 100 years (from 2050 to 2151), the greatest population increase will come from Africa, which is expected to have an increase of 24% (from 1.8 billion to 2.3 billion people). The Latin American population will expand by 11%, and the Asian population will grow by a modest 5.3%. North America, however, will grow only by a mere 1.5%. The European population is expected to continue its decline by decreasing another 22%.

The projections of a decreased population growth rate are comforting for the future. The current population growth rate cannot be sustained by the present food production capacity and available natural resources, including energy and water. Human survival could be severely threatened by environmental crises that could be created if the current growth rate continues. It is good news to many that population modeling predicts a dramatic decline in the human growth rate that started its rise over 200 years ago. But, why should it slow down? Why do some populations even experience a decline? Is this trend against the biological principle of reproduction and expansion of the species? In fact, the decline of the human population is completely in agreement with the biological principle of population dynamics.

I.3. How many children do you plan to have?

Recently, an informal survey was conducted among a group of American college students on how many children that they were planning to have. The average was 1.8 children, with male students preferring a lower number than female students. This was a dramatic difference from similar surveys that were conducted as recently as 50 years ago. In these surveys, the average number of desired children was 3.6. In the mid-19th century, the goal of most American families was to have as many children as possible. Women married as early as sixteen years of age and immediately began to have children. Having six or seven children was a necessity because many died in infancy or in early childhood due to childhood diseases. There was hardly any family that did not have some of their children die prematurely. For farming families, children were especially important because they provided help on the farm and at home.

In the U.S. as well as in many developed nations, the child bearing age and the age of first marriage have increased dramatically. In the U.S., the child bearing age has increased from 22 in the early 1950s to 26 in 2000. In some other countries, the change has been even more dramatic. In Japan, young adults have delayed the age of first marriage to 28 for females and 32 for males. Furthermore, these adults have extended the time that they live with their parents. A typical example would be the 29-year-old young news executive in Japan who still lives with her parents. Her parents clean her room, do her laundry, and cook her meals. Since she does not pay rent, she can save her money to pursue hobbies, such as scuba diving and traveling. Her parents enjoy her company, and the arrangement seem to work well for her as well as for many Japanese young adults.

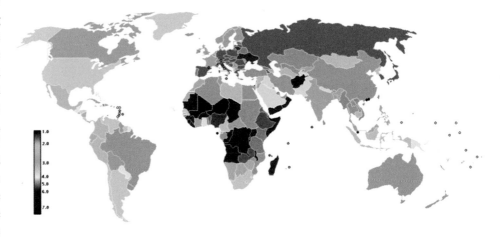

Global fertility rate

Map of fertility rate by countries. The highest fertility rate is in Africa as these nations were the last to make industrial transitions. (*Creative Commons Attribution*)

This growing number of young, unmarried adults creates a potentially serious issue in Japan's population demographics. Japan is a crowded nation with a population of 128 million people. However, the current trend of delaying marriages and having children later has resulted in a rapid drop in Japan's fertility rate. The

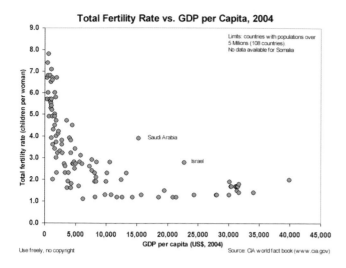

Total Fertility Rate vs. GDP per Capita, 2004

Limits: countries with populations over
5 Millions (108 countries).
No data available for Somalia

Saudi Arabia

Israel

Total fertility rate (children per woman)

GDP per capita (US$, 2004)

Use freely, no copyright

Source: CIA world fact book (www.cia.gov)

Living standard and fertility rate

Countries that are poor have higher fertility rates. (*Creative Commons Attribution*)

fertility rate is defined as the number of a woman's offspring that reach sexual maturity and reproduce. Birthrate is defined as the number of children that a woman gives birth to regardless of whether or not those children reproduce. A fertility rate of two is needed for a woman to replace herself and her mating partner. This is also known as the replacement rate. In 2000, Japan's fertility rate was 1.32. If this fertility rate is maintained, Japan's population will decline by 50% to 64 million people by the end of the 21st century.

A high-ranking Japanese television producer gave birth to her first child when she was 34 years old. She spent most of her life pursuing a career that she enjoyed, and she married another television producer when she was 30 years old. They delayed having their first child so that they could advance their careers. After having her daughter, she went back to work and had work days as long as 12 hours. Her daughter sometimes spent 14 hours at daycare when her mother had to meet production schedules. Because of their work situation, this couple has decided not to have any more children. This case is typical; many families stop at one or two children. In most families, both parents need to work so that the family can maintain a middle class lifestyle. With the increasing cost of raising a successful and educated child, most families cannot afford to have more than one or two children. In fact, in many industrialized nations, women need to work to maintain the family's economic status.

China, however, faces a different situation from that of many countries. China has purposefully decreased their fertility rate through political means. When the Chinese Communist Party took control of China in 1949, the population was about 400 million people. In less than 20 years, the population increased by more than 100% to 850 million. During the late 1950s and early 1960s, China was affected by the worst famine in human history, and nearly 50 million people starved to death. To prevent such a tragedy from happening again, the Chinese Communist government, in the 1970s, established the one child per family policy to curb its population growth. If this policy had not been instituted, the current Chinese population would be 2 billion rather than 1.3 billion.

Interestingly, the fertility rate of a neighboring "country," Hong Kong, is now even lower than that of China. The fertility rate of Hong Kong is 0.9, and it has resulted from personal choice, not governmental policy. Until 1997, Hong Kong had been a British colony for over 100 years. It was considered by many to represent the epitome of capitalism, which was in stark contrast to Communist China. Hong Kong has flourished as a center of international trade and manufacturing since 1949, the same time when China isolated itself from most of the world. In 1997, Hong Kong was repatriated back to China with the condition that it would remain a separate entity from China for the next 50 years. The situation in Hong Kong is similar to that of Japan, and young adults postpone marriages and childbearing for the same reasons. From studying these countries, it appears that career opportunities for women and economic well-being reduce fertility rates. Is this a social consequence? Is there a biological basis for this change?

II. HOW MANY YOUNG SHOULD ONE PRODUCE?

When a couple starts a family, they often decide how many children they are going to have based on different factors. For those living in an industrialized nation, it is understood that the success of the children depends on a good education. If they want to send all their children to college, they often choose to have fewer children. However, if the couple lives in a poor rural area and relies on subsistence farming, they need help to do the farm work. Then, having more children to share the work is an advantage. Therefore, the choice of how many children a couple would like to have depends on the environment that they are in. This choice appears to be socially and financially driven, but it is actually governed by biological principles that apply to all living organisms. There are two important biological theories, known as r-selection and K-selection, that explain human population dynamics.

II.1. What is r-selection?

The highest birthrate in the world today is in the poorest countries that are located in sub-Saharan Africa. When an African youth marries a local girl, who is often only 14 years old, his parents have already decided for them that they need to have at least six children. They hope that most of them are boys, because boys will help with farm work and tend to stay close by their parents for the rest of their lives. The girls leave home after they get married and become the "property" of their husbands' families. Newlywed couples are always poor and have no future educational plans for their children. On occasion, some children can attend a local primary school, but the children often only spend a half day at school. For the remaining part of the day, they help with farm chores. In this situation, the parents cannot invest much in their children. Therefore, they can afford to have as many children as possible.

The reproductive strategy that is used in Africa consists of producing as many young as possible without investing too much in each. Energy is spent to produce the young but not to nurture them. Many biological organisms find that this reproductive strategy works well when environmental conditions are uncertain and opportunities for the young are limited. A good example of how this strategy works is the Christmas Island land crab. The reproductive life history of this species is for each female to produce as many eggs as possible. Because the eggs are deposited into the open ocean, the chance for any egg to survive is slim. Eggs are often swept away from the island and are lost. They are also eaten by predators in the ocean. The chance for the eggs to survive is so poor that in some years, all the eggs are lost. For most years, less than several thousand larvae, out of the billions of eggs that were spawned into the ocean, survive and return to the island.

Some sea turtles also use the strategy of producing many young. Each year for a few nights, 400,000 female turtles come ashore to lay and bury their eggs in the sand. Each female lays as many as 500 eggs in the same vicinity along the same beach. The turtle traffic is so heavy that the females crawl over each other to find an open space. Six weeks later, all the eggs hatch at about the same time, at a rate of 5,000 each hour. Over the next several nights, 40 million eggs hatch, and the beach is filled with baby turtles dashing for the ocean. Predators of all species are waiting to feast on them. Many of the baby turtles are eaten, but many escape. For every ten hatchlings, one escapes into the water, and for every 100 of those entering the ocean, one reaches adulthood. For each breeding, only one in ten females produce a young that reaches adulthood. In this case, the fertility rate is only a small fraction of the birthrate. However, over the lifetime of each female, their fertility rate ranges from five to ten.

Hawaiian green sea turtle
Each female turtle lays as many as 250 eggs during each breeding season, an example of r-selection. (*Creative Commons Attribution*)

This type of reproductive strategy is known as r-selection (or the small egg strategy). In this strategy, the maternal investment in each egg is minimal so that each female can produce as many eggs as possible. The eggs are also small because they contain the least amount of nutrients that are needed to support the embryonic development of the young. For many species, the eggs cannot be made any simpler or smaller and still retain their function. This small egg strategy has both advantages and costs. The most important advantage is that the large number of eggs ensures that some will survive and find favorable environments in which to grow and develop. Another advantage is that the small egg strategy allows for a quick expansion of

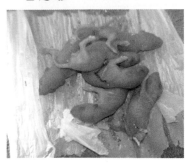

1-day-old baby mice

Some mammals also use the r-selection strategy and have large multiple litters annually. *(GNU Free Documentation License)*

the population during times when suitable growth conditions become unexpectedly available. The reproduction of dandelions represents an example of this small egg strategy. Under good conditions, they can spread and take over rapidly.

The small egg strategy also has its costs. This strategy only works for simple organisms where the young can develop with little nutritional support from the eggs. Furthermore, the young must fend for themselves very early in life, making them susceptible to predators. In addition, this strategy is inefficient because a large proportion of the young die before they even hatch. For simple organisms, however, such as corals, houseflies, herrings, and Christmas Island crabs, this strategy works and is the best one that is available to them.

Complex organisms can also use the small egg strategy. Rabbits and mice have many young, but only a few survive to sexual maturity. They invest minimally in maternal care, and their young are easy prey. Nevertheless, this strategy works for these species because it allows them to rapidly colonize new territories. When the conditions are right, they can take control of an area and rapidly expand their population. Even humans sometimes use this strategy. In those parts of the world where resources are scarce and uncertain, humans tend to produce more offspring to ensure that some survive. In addition, in these situations, there is little investment in parental care.

II.2. What is K-selection?

The low fertility rates of some countries has caused sufficient alarm that governments give out baby bonuses to entice couples to have more children. Singapore was one of the first countries to use this strategy to improve the fertility rate of its population. In the United States, the situation is not as problematic because the fertility rate remains at 1.9. This has resulted mainly because of the high fertility rate of immigrants. The fertility rate of non-immigrants is 1.4, almost as low as Japan. Low fertility rates are also found in the biological world. Some species have very low birthrates and hence, low fertility rates. Why do some species choose this reproductive strategy?

The low birthrate strategy is also known as K-selection or large egg strategy. In this strategy, the females invest heavily in only a few eggs. One of the most striking examples of this strategy is the kiwi, a flightless bird found in New Zealand. The kiwi is about the size of a chicken, weighing around seven pounds. Kiwis lay only one egg during each breeding season.

North Island Brown Kiwi

Females only lay one egg each year, which is an example of K-selection. *(Public Domain)*

The wandering albatross also uses the K-selection strategy. In this species, the overall investment includes not only the maternal investment of producing a large egg, but also significant parental care by both parents. The investment of parental care by the albatross in their young lasts over an entire year. During that time period, the young is cared for by at least one of the parents, while the other parent searches for food. By focusing parental care on only one egg, the survival of the young is almost ensured.

The K-selection strategy also involves keeping the developing young with the mother until they are ready to live independently. The mother both nourishes and protects the young. In marsupial mammals, for example, the young remain safely in a pouch. The joeys (babies) of the kangaroos spend their first nine months in a protective environment next to the mother. When they leave the pouch, it is like a second birth.

In placental mammals, the entire embryonic development and fetal growth occurs in the internal environment (uterus) of the mother. However, different species use varying amounts of maternal investment. Some species use r-selection and have large litters. In these cases the young are born in an immature state. Rabbits, for example, have large litters of immature young. In contrast, other species, such as horses, cattle, and deer, have single births of mature young. In many cases, the newborns can stand at birth and are ready to run within ten minutes.

Primates also have single births, but their newborns require extended maternal care after birth. Some primates do not conceive again until the previous young have developed independence. Others, however, are ready to conceive as soon as the current young have completed nursing. Moreover, each species has its own birthrate. Birthrate is a genetic trait, which is based on the female reproductive cycle, the length of pregnancy, and the need for care of the young. As a species, human females have an average birthrate of seven. Until recently, human females had little control over their birthrates. However, with the development of contraceptives and of other reproductive technology, human females now can have full control of their birthrates.

II.3. How do animals control their birthrates?

For humans, one way to control birthrate is through abortion. Abortion has a long history dating back to antiquity. The earliest description of abortion is from an Egyptian papyrus, which was dated back to 1550 BC. Throughout history, abortion has been subjected to many different opinions, from acceptance to demonization. Regardless of its legality, abortion is practiced nearly everywhere. In 2003, over 42 million abortions were performed worldwide. Since the implementation of its one-child policy in 1979, China has used abortion to control its birthrate. However, the widespread practice of abortion in China has also led to sex-selective abortion. The use of sonograms and amniocentesis has allowed for the prenatal determination of fetal sex. The Chinese traditionally prefer sons, and this has led to the selective abortion of female fetuses. In India, the cultural preference for sons has also led to sex-selective abortions. To counter this, both the Chinese and the Indian governments have enacted laws against sex-selective abortions.

Why do humans choose abortion? What is the biological significance of an individual's decision to terminate a pregnancy? From the biological standpoint, the K-selection strategy provides an explanation for why an individual would want to terminate a pregnancy. In the K-selection strategy, the heavy maternal investment that is required for raising the young makes it essential that a female has the right number of offspring. Humans are constantly searching for the balance between the demands of the offspring and the available resources. If the number of the offspring is greater than what the available resources can support, then there will be insufficient food for all. In this situation, the entire family might perish. If, however, there is excessive food and the number of offspring is low, then parents could miss an opportunity for having more young.

Human K-selection
Human females invest heavily in maternal care. *(GNU Free Documentation License)*

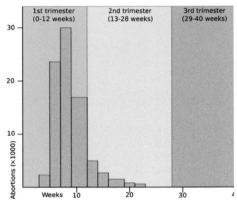

Abortion rate by gestational age
Most abortions occur early during pregnancy to minimize maternal investment. *(Creative Commons Attribution)*

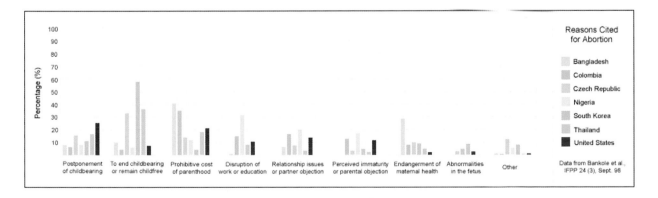

One species of water fowl, the American coot, has developed a strategy to keep the balance between the number of young and the available resources. The females

Why do women choose abortion?
The primary reasons are based on availability of financial and emotional resources. *(GNU Free Documentation License)*

American coot family size control

The parents selectively starve some of the chicks when food resources are limited. (*Creative Commons Attribution*)

Great white pelicans

Pelicans control their brood size by allowing intense sibling competion. With insufficient food sources, the weaker chicks are killed by their siblings. (*Public Domain*)

lay seven to eight eggs each breeding season. After hatching, both the males and females bring food to the chicks, which have voracious appetites. When the chicks get bigger and require more food, the parents might not be able to find enough food to feed all the chicks. In this situation, the parents will preferentially feed only some of the chicks. The others will not receive any food and will be subjected to abuse by having their heads shook by both their parents. These chicks gradually stop begging for food and die. At the end of the season, only three or four chicks survive. Occasionally, when the food is abundant, all the chicks survive. This approach seems cruel, but it allows the parents to maximize their reproductive potential.

Pelicans also have a way of keeping a balance between food availability and maximum reproductive potential. During the breeding season, a female lays three eggs. These eggs, however, are not laid at the same time but are laid a few days apart. They all hatch at about the same time, with the first laid egg being the biggest. Initially, the parents feed all the chicks equally. As the chicks grow, the bigger chicks get more food. They then start to attack the smallest chick and eventually push it out of the nest. The parents never intervene, and they let the fallen chick die. Shortly after, the two remaining chicks start to squabble, and finally, only one chick is left in the nest. Occasionally, more than one chick survives if the fishing is good. In this strategy, the parents use siblicide as a means to remove offspring.

With sex serving both reproductive and social roles, it is important for human females to control their birthrate through means other than abortion. The introduction of the oral contraceptive pill was a milestone in human reproduction. With the pill, couples can choose when to have children and how many children they want. In addition, both males and females can choose to spend more time in individual development through education and career advancement before they have children. By delaying their childbearing, females can spend more time receiving education, improving personal health, and garnering the necessary resources to raise successful children. With reduced infant mortality in the developed nations, maternal investment has shifted from quantity to quality.

For Japan, many European countries, Hong Kong, and the United States, the human reproductive strategy is shifting from r-selection to K-selection. With rising living standards, higher educational levels, and greater opportunities for women, the population has been shifting toward smaller families. This trend can already be observed in Japan, Hong Kong, and in many developed nations around the world. The people of other, less fortunate countries, however, continue to have large numbers of offspring. Therefore, for the prosperity of the human species, governments around the world must break down their national boundaries and promote shared prosperity and economic interchanges. The developed nations must help the economic development of the poor nations. Raising the living standard for every human being on this planet is the only way to control human population growth.

III. WHAT IS THE FUTURE OF THE HUMAN POPULATION?

In a Tao temple in China lives a turtle that is thought to be the oldest living animal in China. There is a legend that says this turtle was once a god and that it was sent to Earth to safeguard the Chinese people. The monks tell the story of how it came to live at the temple in 1855. No one knew exactly how old it was then, but they estimated that it was about five years old. If this is accurate, then it is now over 150 years old. During its lifetime, many dramatic changes have occurred. What changes will you see during your lifetime? What will the world be like 50 years from now, when you are 70 years old? Will you still be working or will you be retired? What will the world population be like? Is there anything you can do now to ensure that your future is good? These are probably not questions that you think about very much, but it is necessary that you realize how important it is for you and society to consider them.

III.1. How long can you expect to live?

Turtles are sacred in many parts of the world because of their longevity. They are the longest living animals, and some species can live up to 150 years. In the biological world, it is genetically determined how long different species live. The turtles are genetically endowed to live longer than any other animal. Most invertebrates, however, live for only one to two years, although some insects can live up to 15. Among mammals, the smaller species, such as mice and rats, do not live more than three years, whereas the larger species, such as elephants and dolphins, can live as long as 70 years. When animals are kept in captivity, they live longer than when they are in the wild. Regardless of how long different animal species live, they all go through the distinct cycles of growth, reproduction, aging, and death. Humans go through the same cycles.

Galapagos giant tortoise
With a life span of 150 years, they are among the oldest living animals. *(GNU Free Documentation License)*

To appreciate changes in the human population, it is important to understand the human life cycle. There are two important biological concepts regarding the human life cycle. The first concept is life span, which is the length of time from birth to death. Life span is a biological property of a species. Each species has evolved to live a certain length of time that is necessary for the individual members to successfully reproduce. However, individuals should die shortly after fulfilling their reproductive role, so that the next generation can take their place. Recent research has shown that aging is the consequence of this evolutionary strategy. It occurs when the internal biological clock triggers a decline in the tissues and organs, making the individuals more susceptible to predators and infectious agents.

The process of this biological decline determines how long the members of the species live beyond their reproductive period. The evolution of life span is based on the biological need of the species to successfully reproduce. Life span also represents the biological adaptation to the environment that a species lives in. One species that demonstrates the significance of life span is a species of cicada. These cicadas reproduce once every 17 years, and they die immediately after they reproduce. As soon as the larvae hatch from the eggs, they bury themselves underground and feed on root saps. They live like this for 17 years, and through unknown communication mechanisms, all larvae emerge at once and molt into adults. As many as ten million adults mate simultaneously, and their vast numbers overwhelm their predators. The life span of this species is important for their life cycle.

17-year cicadas
They spend all their lives as juveniles underground. They only emerge to reproduce as adults for a few days and then die. *(Public Domain)*

In other species, the life span of its individuals is difficult to define. From an evolutionary standpoint, each species has evolved to reproduce. Once the role of reproduction is completed, individual members have completed their task and their existence is no longer important for the success of the species. Physiological systems begin to decline and death eventually occurs. For many species, this decline takes place naturally, and they eventually succumb to predators and infectious agents. For animals living in the wild, most individuals die before they have the opportunity to get old, and only a very few live into old age. Therefore, for most species, it is difficult to determine their life span.

No one knows for certain what the human life span is. The best estimation is based on the oldest person who has ever lived. Currently, the human life span is set at 122 years. This number is based on a French woman who died in 1997 at that age. Human life span is an important biological parameter because it indicates the durability of human organs and tissues. The studies on human life span will also advance the understanding of the genetic mechanisms of aging.

Oldest person who ever lived
Jeanne Calment on her 119th birthday. She died three years later. *(GNU Free Documentation License)*

Another important parameter that is used in determining how long an individual will live is the biological concept of life expectancy. Rather than being genetically determined, life expectancy is almost entirely influenced by the environment. In the U.S., the average life expectancy has undergone a dramatic change in the past 100 years. At the turn of the century, life expectancy in the U.S. was 47 years of age, and in 2008, it is 77 years. This remarkable change of 30 years occurred over only one century. Not surprisingly, life expectancy has changed over the course of human history. During the Stone Age, human life expectancy was estimated to be around 20 years. By the time of the Roman Empire, human life expectancy increased slightly to 25 years of age. Over the Middle Ages, however, human life expectancy remained unchanged. The next increase for life expectancy occurred after the Industrial Revolution. By the early 20th century, life expectancy had reached about 35 years around the world. The current world average is 67 years, with an average life expectancy of 33 years in Swaziland and 81 years in Australia. This change to human life expectancy is the key to understanding the expanding human population growth.

Global life expectancy

Countries that have higher fertility rates also have lower life expectancies. This is an example of r-selection. *(GNU Free Documentation License)*

III.2. What caused the increase in human life expectancy?

Jeanne Calment took up fencing at age 85, and she beat several people who were 20 years younger. At 100, she was still riding a bicycle. She only decided to move into a nursing home shortly before her 110th birthday after a cooking accident caused a fire in her apartment. She was in good health and able to walk without assistance until a fall at the age of 114 years. She was talkative and received frequent visitors until her 122nd birthday. Her health then declined, and she died five months later. You might not live to be 122 years old, but many of you might celebrate your 100th birthday. In Japan, which has the longest average life expectancy in the world, people are not only living longer but are many times healthier than their parents were at the same age.

What caused this remarkable increase in human life expectancy? To fully appreciate this increase, it is important to understand that life expectancy is calculated by averaging the age of death of the entire population. If many people die young, the average life expectancy is low, even if some individuals have long lives. There are several points in the human life cycle, and death occurs disproportionately in each of them. The first point occurs during childbirth. In the past, the mortality of women during delivery has been high, due to difficult labor and infections. Modern obstetric care, sterile techniques, and surgical procedures have eliminated most birth-related mortalities, except in some parts of the world where basic healthcare is still unavailable.

The second point of mortality is childhood infectious diseases, such as smallpox, diphtheria, whooping cough, measles, and polio. At one time, smallpox was a particularly serious and dangerous threat during childhood, killing as many as 15% of children in Europe and Asia. Until the 19th century, less than 50% of children reached adulthood because of these childhood infectious diseases. Today, very few children die from these diseases, because they are protected by immunization at a young age. The discovery of the vaccination against smallpox was one of the most important milestones in human population expansion. With more children living into adulthood, the average life expectancy rose.

The third point of mortality of the human population is the spread of infectious diseases. All through human history, major epidemics, such as the bubonic plague, cholera, and influenza, have devastated the population. It was not until the mid-19th century that the microbial nature of these diseases was understood. Sanitation measures were developed for providing safe water, treating sewage, and preserving food from spoiling. Because of these advances, the occurrence of major epidemics was dramatically reduced. Furthermore, the discovery of antibiotics offered ways to treat infectious diseases, further reducing the impact of epidemics.

With more children entering adulthood and less people dying from infectious diseases, the average life expectancy increased dramatically during the 20th century. The parts of the world that experienced the greatest impact were regions where basic healthcare was not previously available. With more children receiving immunizations, the population around the world grew rapidly during the second half of the 20th century, particularly in the developing countries.

Vaccination in reduction of childhood diseases
Life expectancy increases as more children survive into adulthood. *(Public Domain)*

With the world population increasing by a billion every 13 years during the mid-20th century, the fear of massive famine and starvation in many parts of the world was understandable. One of the greatest successes in modern agriculture occurred: the Green Revolution. By the early 1960s, it appeared that world food production would not meet the needs of the human population expansion. To solve this problem, a group of scientists in the U.S. developed high-yielding varieties of corn, soybeans, wheat, and rice. Together, with the use of pesticides, advanced irrigation practices, and synthetic nitrogen fertilizers, these new high-yielding varieties doubled agricultural output. Through the Green Revolution, the world grain production increased by 250% between 1950 and 1984. This agricultural success has also allowed for the expansion of the human population.

III.3. *What will be your life expectancy?*

In a rural area of Japan, a couple lives on a farm that has been in the family for nearly two hundred years. The land is only suitable for growing a particular type of tea, but it has provided for the family over many generations. However, the couple has been considering selling the land because all their children have left for jobs in the cities. Furthermore, there are hardly any young people left in the small town in which they live. In fact, they are closing down the primary school because the only student in the school will graduate this year.

This type of scenario is happening everywhere in Japan, and the government is deeply concerned. Today, nearly 20% of the Japanese population is "officially" retired, although many of them take part time jobs to supplement their income. By 2050, if the current fertility rate remains unchanged, nearly one quarter of the Japanese population will be over 65 years of age. Furthermore, the fastest growing population segment in Japan is those over 80 years of age. Although many of them are healthier than the 65-year-olds of the previous generation, most of them cannot work. This scenario is concerning because there simply will not be enough people in the work force to support the massive numbers of older people. This is a major demographic transition that was completely unexpected 20 years ago.

The U.S. will face a similar situation when the baby boomer generation enters retirement in the coming decade. Both public and private retirement systems will be pushed to the limit in order to accommodate the largest cohort of retirees in history. Many of the retirees do not have sufficient savings and must continue working to support themselves. The U.S. would be facing the same serious situation as that of Japan if it was not for the continuing influx of immigrants. With their initial high fertility rate, they provide the needed workers to maintain a productive and vibrant economy. In fact, the U.S. is the only developed nation that has not suffered from a population decline. These immigrants are vital in supporting the ever-growing aging population.

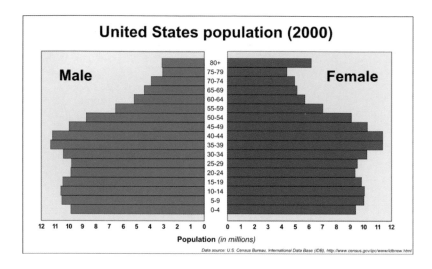

U.S. population pyramid

The population distribution is constantly changing because it is affected by many factors. *(Public Domain)*

In the next several decades, the populations of the developing nations in Africa and Asia will be increasing. Because of their struggling economies, unstable governments, poor healthcare, and inadequate educational systems, these countries have high fertility rates (r-selection strategy). In countries like Kenya, Nigeria, and South Africa, a large number of youth will enter the reproductive age in the next several years. With poor economic development, many young people will not find jobs to support their families. As the populations expand rapidly, there will be an increasing pressure for many people to immigrate to other parts of the world. However, nationalistic sentiments and racism will impede immigration as well as the integration of any immigrants into the mainstream society. This is clearly a serious problem, as tensions between the wealthy and poor nations will lead to political instability and social unrest.

The other significant threat to global stability is the struggle for resources between the developed nations and developing countries such as China and India, which are just beginning to industrialize. These countries want to achieve the same economic success and affluence as the developed nations. However, with their respective populations being many times larger than the developed nations combined, the demands for natural resources will place a heavy burden on the environment. Unless the developed nations can decrease their needs, the situation could destabilize and lead to political and military conflict. The world will be a dangerous place in the coming decades, as governments continue to have a nationalistic outlook rather than a global one.

The time is now to take action in addressing the human population growth from a global perspective. The human population cannot be greater than the carrying capacity of the earth, because overpopulation threatens the survival of the human species. Therefore, we must work toward shared prosperity and environmental sustainability both at the individual level as well as at the societal level. To build a future that we can live out our life expectancy with comfort and fulfillment, it is important that collective action be taken to improve the lives of every member of the human species.

Chapter 10

Development

What is the origin of your intelligence?

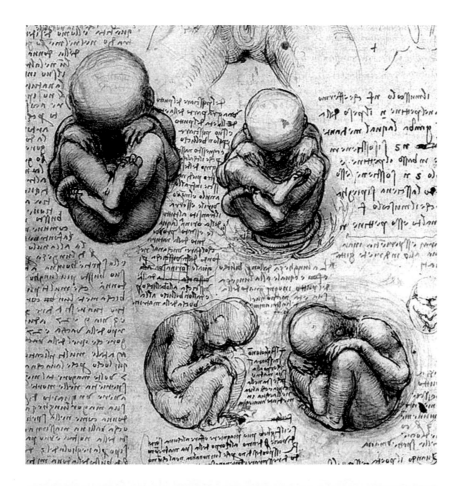

"Views of a Fetus in the Womb" by Leonardo da Vinci, ca. 1510-1512.

To understand the formation of humans prenatal development has been studied throughout history .

(Public Domain)

CHAPTER 10. DEVELOPMENT

All newborns are miracles. They start from a single cell, and in nine months, a human being with several trillion cells emerges from the mother's womb. All the information that is required for this complex biological creation resides in the genes. Somehow, these genes direct the process for creating new cells, which then interact with each other to form tissues, organs, and eventually, the entire individual. It appears that genes are solely responsible for shaping an individual, but that is not the case, particularly when it comes to brain development. The environment plays a subtle but important role in shaping the developing brain, particularly during embryonic and fetal life. Biologists have gradually revealed how this process takes place. It is now understood that early development is important in shaping adult human behavior.

I. HOW DO NEURONS FORM A BRAIN?

It was mid-July, the sun was hot, and the sea was calm. A man and his two children swam leisurely just beyond the beach. The father noticed something unusual drifting near the surface of the water toward one of the children. He called out to warn them, but it was too late. The boy came into contact with the floater, and almost immediately, he screamed in pain. His father swam over and pulled him to safety. He then realized that his son had been stung by a jellyfish. By the time they got ashore, the boy's leg was swollen. The lifeguards brought their first aid kit, which included a bottle of vinegar. Acetic acid, found in vinegar, disables the stingers of the jellyfish, preventing them from releasing neurotoxins into the bloodstream. The boy recovered several days later, but the incident was etched in his memory. What are jellyfish? Do they have brains? It is now known that they do not have brains; instead, they have neurons.

I.1. What is the origin of neurons?

Jellyfish are classified as cnidarians, a group which includes corals, sea anemones, and Portuguese Man O' War. Cnidarians are among the earliest and simplest forms of multicellular organisms. The early forms of cnidarians are also the ancestors of more complex multicellular animals, including humans. In fact, the cnidarians were the first organisms to evolve muscle for movement. One of the cnidarians, the hydra, represents a good example of how muscle movement occurs. Hydras live in freshwater ponds and are predatory animals that capture their prey using stingers located on their muscular tentacles. To coordinate the movement of their tentacles, hydras possess a neural network that controls muscle contraction. Both muscle cells and neurons were first evolved in cnidarians, and their basic structure and function remain essentially the same today.

Hydras belong to a group of cnidarians known as sea anemones, because of their plant-like appearance. They have two sets of muscles that run in horizontal and longitudinal directions. To control their muscles, hydras have a nerve network that spreads throughout their body wall. They also possess light-sensing cells that are connected to the nerve network, which serve to provide information about the external environment. However, hydras do not have brains. Hydras, and other cnidarians, have never evolved to have one. To them, a brain is unnecessary. They have survived every conceivable change on Earth, including earthquakes, volcanic eruptions, continental drifts, and meteorite strikes, without the help of a brain. It is also likely that they will still be around long after humans go into oblivion. Whatever they have, it has been enough for them to flourish for over 550 million years.

Even though the cnidarians appear simple, their nervous systems have many similarities to that of humans. When researchers examined the hydra nerve network,

Moon jelly

It is one of the simplest organisms on Earth, but it has all the components for it to have survived for over 550 million years. *(GNU Free Documentation License)*

Portuguese Man O' War

They possess stinger cells that can deliver a powerful toxin to kill their prey. *(GNU Free Documentation License)*

they discovered that its cells and the cells of the human nervous system are essentially identical. These cells are known as neurons. It has now been established that all neurons are basically the same. The main difference between the nervous systems of simple and complex animals lies in the number of neurons and in the complexity of the connections between the neurons. The cnidarians have the simplest nervous system. Their nervous systems consist of only several hundred neurons that connect with each other to form a circuit, not unlike an electrical circuit.

Using a sensitive apparatus, researchers can visualize electricity flowing across the entire cnidarian nerve circuit. Neurons use electrical currents to communicate with each other, and they also use electrical currents to stimulate muscle contraction. The neurons morphologically resemble an octopus. They have a central body with many tentacle-like extensions. Some of these extensions are a hundred times longer than the cell body. These extensions are known as dendrites and axons, and they serve as communication cables between neurons. The electrical current always starts from the dendrites and travels toward the cell body. From the cell body, the current then travels along the axon. The type of electrical current that flows from one end to the other of a neuron is known as an action potential.

Hydra
One of the simplest animals and an active predator. It has all the basic components of a complex nervous system. (*Creative Commons Attribution*)

An electroencephalogram (EEG) is a device that measures electrical activity or action potential of the human brain. The activity is recorded on paper as peaks and valleys. By comparing the EEG of individuals suffering from neurological disorders with that of a normal individual, diagnoses are made for different types of disorders, such as seizures and strokes. EEG is also used for determining the depth of a coma; this is done to make a clinical prognosis of possible recovery. In many states, EEG is used to determine the presence of brain death.

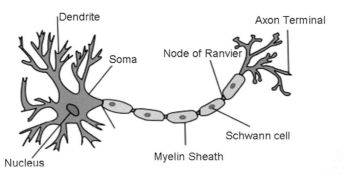

Dendrite · Soma · Node of Ranvier · Axon Terminal · Schwann cell · Myelin Sheath · Nucleus

Structure of neurons
Neurons communicate through the axons and dendrites.
(*Public Domain*)

For cnidarians, the distance for an electrical current to travel is relatively short, generally only a few millimeters. As animals increase in size, the distance for electrical current to travel becomes larger. In the human body, for example, the longest neurons extend from the base of the spine to the big toe. To increase the speed of transmission and to reduce loss of the signal strength, mammalian neurons are insulated like an electrical wire. This insulation is accomplished by sheathing the axons in myelin, a high fat protein. If the myelin sheath is damaged, communication is impaired and neurological symptoms develop. Multiple sclerosis is one condition that results from damaged myelin. In this disease, the immune system attacks and destroys the myelin sheath, resulting in gradual physical and mental disability and eventual death.

Electroencephalogram
It is the measurement of electrical activity produced by the neurons of the brain as recorded from electrodes placed on the scalp.
(*GNU Free Documentation License*)

I.2. How do neurons communicate?

Because of the connections between axons and dendrites, neurons in the simple cnidarians can form a nerve network. Axons of one neuron come into contact with the dendrites of another neuron. To communicate with each other, the neurons use an electrical current. Using this mechanism, electrical signals are communicated throughout the entire nerve network of the cnidarians. The same communication mechanism is also used in the nervous system of complex animals, including humans. However, it was discovered that the axons and dendrites do not actually touch each other. Therefore, how does the electrical current flow across this gap? This was a mystery until an accidental discovery occurred in the early 1950s.

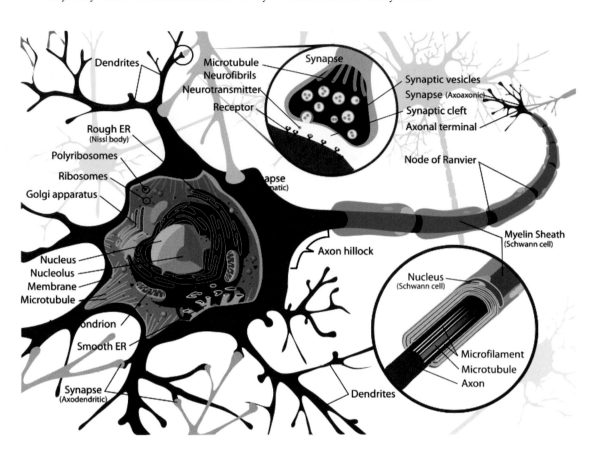

Overview of neurons
Neurons communicate through the formation of synapses between axons and dendrites of different neurons.
(Public Domain)

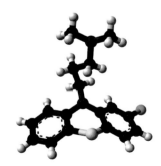

Chlorpromazine
It was the first drug that was effective in treating a mental disorder.

How neurons communicate with each other was answered by the accidental discovery of a drug to treat schizophrenia, which is a serious mental disorder. Schizophrenic patients suffer from hallucinations, delusions, and disorganized speech and thinking. For many years, no treatment was available, and patients remained institutionalized for their entire lives. In the early 1950s, chemists in France synthesized several simple chemical compounds that were useful for treating asthma and other allergic disorders. Researchers tested one of the compounds, known as chlorpromazine, in rats and noted that the compound had a sedative effect on the rats. Based on this observation, chlorpromazine was tested as a possible sedating agent for schizophrenic patients.

In 1951, chlorpromazine was first given to those schizophrenic patients who had the most severe symptoms. The initial results were promising because chlorpromazine had a calming effect on the patients. The researchers attributed this effect to the drug's action in reducing levels of stress hormones. However, after several weeks of treatment, the patients' mental state also changed, showing an improvement in overall behavior. Their episodes of hallucinations and delusions were reduced, and some patients were even completely free of these mental disturbances. Furthermore, the emotional and cognitive behaviors of some patients became normal, allowing them to return to society. The discovery of chlorpromazine is one of the most important breakthroughs in the treatment of mental disorders.

The effectiveness of chlorpromazine, a simple chemical compound, in mitigating a complex behavioral disorder such as schizophrenia was astounding at the time. If simple chemicals could alleviate hallucinations and delusions, then it was concluded that human behavior must have a chemical basis. Instead of relying only on an electrical current to send signals across the neural network, chemicals must also be involved in the communication process. The effectiveness of chlorpromazine in treating schizophrenia began the search for this chemical basis of neural communication. In schizophrenia, these chemical signals must somehow have become unbalanced. Chlorpromazine somehow restores normal chemical communication. This was a great insight at the time, and it began the era of neurochemistry.

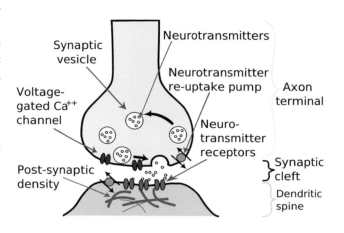

Subsequent research led to the discovery of neurotransmitters. Neurotransmitters are simple chemical compounds that are used by neurons to communicate with each other. They serve as chemical messengers, because neurons do not make physical contact with each other. When an electrical current travels to the end of an axon, it triggers the release of neurotransmitters into the gap between the axon of one neuron and the dendrite of the next neuron. These neurotransmitters diffuse across the gap and bind to specific protein receptors on the surface of the dendrite. This binding then elicits a new electrical current that travels toward the cell body. The space between the two neurons is known as a synapse. The neuron with the axon is known as the pre-synaptic neuron, and the neuron with the dendrite is known as the post-synaptic neuron. Why neurons evolved to communicate chemically rather than by electrical current presented a mystery for neurobiologists.

Structure of a synapse

A synapse is a microscopic gap that is formed between an axon of one neuron and the dendrite of another neuron. *(GNU Free Documentation License)*

Chemical communication between neurons may have evolved to increase the flexibility and the control of signals between the neurons. One advantage of using neurotransmitters is the ability to adjust their amounts in the synapses. Neurons have two methods by which to regulate neurotransmitter levels. In the first method, the neurotransmitters are rapidly removed from the synaptic gap immediately after their release. This is accomplished by transporter molecules present on the surface of the pre-synaptic neurons. These transporters act like vacuum cleaners that suck up the neurotransmitters and store them away for future use. By blocking the transporters, the neurotransmitters will remain elevated in the synapse for a longer time. These chemical blockers are known as specific reuptake inhibitors (SRI). In the second method, degradative enzymes are released by either the pre-synaptic or post-synaptic neurons to destroy the neurotransmitters. Blocking these degradative enzymes also increases the level of the neurotransmitters. Therefore, the presence of specific transporters and of degradative enzymes can precisely control the level of neurotransmitters in the synapse and modulate the electrical signal that is elicited in the post-synaptic neurons.

I.3. How do neurotransmitters function?

From the nerve network of the cnidarians to the complexity of the human brain, neurons form the basis of behavior. Ever since the cnidarians "invented" neurons 550 million years ago, their basic structure and function have remained unchanged. The neurons of humans and cnidarians are so similar that they can be swapped with each other and still function perfectly. The neurotransmitters that are found in humans also have the same effects on the neurons of cnidarians. This observation demonstrates the commonality of life in which a successful biological strategy is passed on from generation to generation and from species to species. This is also one of many pieces of evidence indicating that all life on Earth shares a common ancestor. Humans and jellyfish are distant biological cousins.

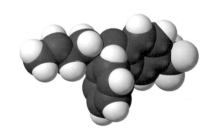

Fluoxetine (Prozac)

Fluoxetine is one of the first chemicals that was discovered to affect the neurochemistry of the synapse.

How neurotransmitters affect human behavior has been an area of intense study for several decades. Surprisingly, some understanding in this area came from a group

Magic mushrooms

Psilocybin mushrooms contain powerful chemical ingredients that affect the communication between neurons. *(GNU Free Documentation License)*

Opium poppy

The milky sap of the poppy pod is the source of opium. *(Public Domain)*

Coca plant

Cocaine is extracted from the leaves and berries of the coca plant. *(Public Domain)*

of mushrooms that have been used for thousands of years in religious rituals. These are the psilocybin mushrooms, also known as magic mushrooms. They were consumed by ancient as well as by modern day shamans to create mystical experiences, such as communicating with dead ancestors. The active substance in these mushrooms is a small chemical compound, known as psilocybin, which is remarkably similar to the neurotransmitter, serotonin. Because of this similarity, psilocybin mimics the action of serotonin in the brain. However, after ingesting the mushroom, the psilocybin concentration reaches a level 100 times over the normal serotonin level. This extreme elevation creates the hallucinogen effects by affecting neural transmission.

There are other plants that produce compounds that have chemical structures similar to animal neurotransmitters and can thus mimic their actions. The opium poppy produces a milky substance in its sap that can be manufactured into opium. Opium is a powerful painkiller and sedative. Throughout history, it has been used recreationally to produce a general sense of well-being, euphoria, and pleasure. At high doses, opium is toxic, leading to respiratory failure, seizures, coma, and death. The active ingredient in opium is morphine, which resembles the natural neurotransmitter endorphin. Morphine binds to the endorphin receptors in the brain and induces the same neurological reactions that endorphin would naturally elicit. Because morphine has the same biological activities as endorphin, it is known as an agonist. Similarly, psilocybin is an agonist of serotonin.

Another plant that produces chemicals that can affect neural function is the coca plant. Cocaine is produced from its leaves. Cocaine can create a sense of euphoria and well-being by affecting the neural transmission in certain regions of the brain. However, cocaine is not an agonist of natural neurotransmitters. Instead, when it enters the synapses, cocaine binds and blocks the normal activity of the transporters that are normally responsible for the reuptake of dopamine, a neurotransmitter. By preventing its reuptake, cocaine elevates the concentration of dopamine in the synapses and alters the neural transmission. Cocaine targets a certain region of the brain that is responsible for pleasure, and the elevation of dopamine in this region is responsible for the pleasurable sensation of cocaine.

The production of substances that resemble neurotransmitters by plants was at first a mystery, because plants do not have neurons and nervous systems. There is no apparent physiological need for the plants to produce these chemicals. Are these evolutionary accidents? Further studies have revealed that plants produce these chemicals as toxins to harm or even kill herbivores. The psilocybin mushrooms produce psilocybin that kills insect browsers. The opium poppies produce morphine to deter animals from eating the seeds before they mature, and the coca plants produce cocaine in their leaves to poison leaf-eating herbivores. These compounds form the chemical arsenals with which plants use to fight against animals by poisoning their nervous systems. Nevertheless, these "accidental" neurotransmitters have been valuable tools for studying the natural neurotransmitters that are found in animal nervous systems. By studying their neurological actions, they have provided researchers with clues that were used to identify natural neurotransmitters, such as endorphin, serotonin, and dopamine.

Neurotransmitters are divided into four groups based on their chemical properties. The first and most common group is the small-molecule neurotransmitters, such as dopamine, serotonin, acetylcholine, glutamic acid, and norepinephrine. The second group is the small proteins known as neuroactive peptides. Some common examples are endorphin, vasopression, and oxytocin. The third group is ions, such as zinc and calcium. The fourth group is gases, such as nitric oxide and carbon monoxide. Together, these neurotransmitters form a complex chemical network that can enhance or suppress the electrical communications between neurons. These interactions allow for precise and subtle adjustments of the electrical activities in the nervous system.

II. How do human brains develop?

The human brain has more than 100 billion neurons. With each neuron making as many as 10,000 synapses with other neurons, the total number of synapses is as high as one quadrillion, a number higher than all the stars in the universe. This complexity gives rise to emotions, intelligence, creativity, altruism, and consciousness. However, the human brain has only two main types of cells: the neurons and the glial cells. The neurons form the wiring of the nervous system, and the glial cells support the neurons by forming the myelin sheaths. From just these two cell types, the human brain is constructed. From the standpoint of cell types, the brain is the simplest organ in the body. Most other organs are formed from far more complex cell types. However, from the standpoint of organization, the human brain is extraordinarily complex. How all the billions of neurons form such complex networks remains one of the greatest mysteries in biology. However, based on recent advances in neuroscience, this mystery is on the verge of being solved.

II.1. How has the human brain evolved?

The human brain came into existence after a long evolutionary history. It is the result of changes and modifications of the simple animal brains that evolved 500 million years ago. Animal brains have become more complex, with human brains being the most complicated. However, animals with brains similar to those first animals still exist, because their simple brains are sufficient for them to survive in their environments. Having a brain that is larger than necessary is inefficient and a waste of energy. Some animals are better off using their energy to produce more offspring. Natural selection favors animals that leave the most offspring and not the "smartest" animals.

Why do humans possess such large brains? The human brain never rests and consumes more energy than any other organ of the human body. It is the only organ that demands a continuous supply of oxygen and glucose from the blood. The neurons die when the blood flow to the brain is stopped for as little as five minutes. With an average weight of less than three pounds, the human brain makes up 2% of the total body weight. However, it consumes approximately 20% of the body's energy output. With this high energy demand, animals cannot afford to have a bigger brain than what they need. In fact, simple animals with small brains are by no means inferior as long as they can survive in their environment.

One group of animals that has a simple brain and has done well is the land flatworms. Despite having very small brains, they have survived for over several hundred million years. The land flatworms measure only several centimeters in length but are fearsome predators of earthworms. Their brains are very primitive and have less than several hundred neurons clustered together to form nerve ganglions. However, there are several important features of this brain that all other animals have inherited and modified. The first feature is the brain location, which is placed in the front of the body. The second feature is the formation of sensory organs, such as a pair of primitive eyes and nose-like chemo receptors, which are located next to the brain. The close proximity of the sensory organs is important because it permits rapid communication with the brain.

The third feature is bilateral symmetry, where the left side of the body is a mirror image of the right. The human body has a body plan consisting of bilateral symmetry. By having paired sensory organs, animals can sense directions of incoming signals. The ancestors of the flatworms had evolved this body plan because of the need for hunting. Because of its effectiveness, this body plan has been passed down to nearly all animals, and it has influenced the structure of their brains. To process incoming sensory signals separately, the primitive brain has been divided into two halves. Sensory information from one side is sent to the opposite side of the brain.

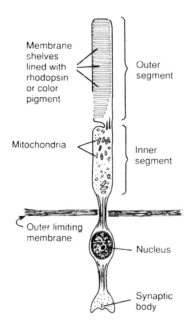

Photoreceptive cells
Functional parts of the rods and cones, cells for monochrome and color detection. *(Public Domain)*

Common buckeye

The exquisite patterns on the wings of this butterfly are one example of bilateral symmetry. *(Public Domain)*

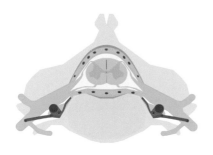

Evolution of the vertebrate

The spinal cord is located in the vertebral column protected by bones. *(GNU Free Documentation License)*

For example, the motor function of the left side of the body is controlled by the right side of the brain, and vice versa. The two halves of the brain are connected by a bundle of nerve fibers that function to facilitate communication. From this legacy, the human brain has derived its two hemispheres.

As animals increased in complexity to adapt to new environments, they evolved more complicated behavior. These animals required a bigger brain to interpret sensory information, to make decisions, and to coordinate behavior. More neurons were added to the primitive brain and more nerve circuits were used to control additional muscles or to receive input from new sensory receptors. As the animals increased in size, the peripheral neurons aggregated into a bundle of nerve tissue in the center of the body to form the spinal cord. The spinal cord gradually became protected by bones (the vertebral column). The fish in the sea were the first animal to evolve this nervous system nearly 400 million years ago. Their brains, however, have remained small, as the demand of their environment needs no more than what they have.

As fish evolved into reptiles and conquered the land, the demands of terrestrial living required a bigger brain for more complex behavior and mental functions. The reptile brain gradually evolved because of the addition of more neurons to the fish brain. This reptilian brain was sufficient for the dinosaurs, which dominated Earth for nearly 150 million years until they disappeared 65 million years ago. To meet the requirements for even more complex behavior, the mammalian brain evolved by adding more neurons to form the cerebral cortex, a new layer of neurons covering the reptilian brain. Therefore, the complexity of the human brain arose over 500 million years ago from the simple brain of the flatworm. Every circuit in the human brain has been tested through evolution, and only those that worked were passed onto the next generation. The human brain and the brains of all other living animals are the masterpieces of nature.

II.2. How does the human embryonic brain form?

From the time of fertilization, a human zygote will divide about 100 times and form several trillion cells by the time the baby is born. After the first few divisions, a zygote forms a group of identical cells, known as totipotent cells. Each of these cells can still develop into a new embryo, as in the case of identical multiple births. After several more cell divisions, however, the cells start to change in relation to each other. Differential gene expression forms the basis of these changes. Furthermore, each new cell division is affected by the previous cell division. As each new cell emerges, a different set of genes is activated to make different proteins, which gives it different properties. The entire process of development appears complex and mysterious, but the differentiation of each cell type is simple.

Each step during the early stages of embryonic development has become precisely choreographed through several hundred million years of evolution. The earliest stages of embryonic development between all animals are essentially the same. The embryos of a fish, frog, chicken, and human have nearly identical appearances, because their developmental pathways are the same. The human zygotes develop into blastocysts that are nearly indistinguishable from that of a snake or a blue whale. Despite the complexity and variations of the human body, the developmental pathways that are etched in our genes are the same. It is minor differences that occur during embryonic development that give rise to our unique structure.

The early stages of human brain development are no different from that of a fish or a frog. The notochord (the embryonic spinal cord) is the first part of the nervous system to form. At this stage, the human embryos share the same morphology as the fish embryos. The next stage of development is the enlargement of the notochord to form the primitive brain. At this point in development, the fish brain stops forming.

The human brain, however, continues to enlarge and reaches a stage that resembles the reptilian brain. If the embryo is from a reptile, then brain development stops at this point. For humans, the brain continues forming and a layer of neurons envelop the reptilian brain to form the cerebral cortex. The cerebral cortex is a unique feature of the mammalian brain.

The mammalian brain is characterized by a layer of neurons that is situated above the reptilian brain and forms the cerebral cortex. The mammalian brain has increased in complexity through the enlargement of this cerebral cortex. Some mammals, such as mice and rabbits, have cerebral cortexes with only one or two layers of neurons. Other mammals, which have complex behavioral traits, have thicker cerebral cortexes consisting of three to five layers of neurons. In other words, brain complexity is increased by the addition of more layers of neurons. Primates have large cerebral cortexes, and their cerebral cortexes are reflective of their intelligence and complex behavior.

The great apes have the largest cerebral cortexes. In these species, the cerebral cortex also takes on a wrinkled appearance. The folding of the cerebral cortex to form the wrinkles serves to increase its surface area. Instead of adding more layers of neurons and increasing the thickness of the cerebral cortex, the brain increases its size by folding into itself. This folding allows for the accommodation of more neurons in the cerebral cortex. The human brain has the largest cerebral cortex, which accounts for nearly 75% of its neurons.

The human brain is modular with each module serving different functions according to its evolutionary ancestry. The part closest to the spinal cord is the brainstem, which controls the most basic physiological processes and has the earliest ancestry. The part above the brainstem is the reptilian brain, which controls aggression and emotion. The part above the reptilian brain is the cerebral cortex, which regulates cognitive functions and other higher mental functions. During embryonic development, each part of the brain develops sequentially with the cerebral cortex formed last.

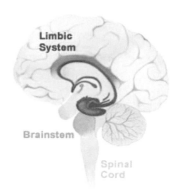

Brainstem and limbic system
They are the two most basic components of the central nervous system, as they are found in primitive vertebrates. *(Public Domain)*

II.3. How does a baby's brain develop?

Human pregnancy is divided into three trimesters of approximately three months each. This division is based on the developmental stages of the embryo and fetus. These divisions are not absolute demarcations, but they serve to provide reference points during pregnancy. The first trimester starts from conception and ends at the 10th week of pregnancy. Embryonic development occurs during this trimester, and the young is referred to as an embryo. From the 11th week onward, the young is known as a fetus. The second trimester begins at the fourth month and ends at the sixth month of pregnancy. The third trimester is the last period of pregnancy and lasts from the sixth month to the ninth month.

All organs, including the brain, undergo their most critical stage of development during the first trimester. The basic pattern of the body is formed by this point, and any mistake that has occurred only becomes magnified during the later stages. Any cell that goes down an incorrect developmental path can cause serious consequences. It has been estimated that nearly 30% of pregnancies end in a spontaneous abortion during the first trimester and that most of these abortions are unknown to the women. Brain development is crucial during these early embryonic stages, and the neurons must make appropriate connections with each other as well as with other tissues and organs.

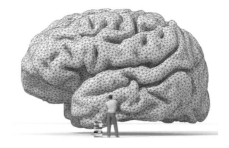

Complexity of the human brain
Image of a human brain generated from MRI data. *(GNU Free Documentation License)*

The development of the nervous system begins with the formation of precursor neurons from pluripotent stem cells as early as the blastula stage (three to four days after fertilization). These precursor neurons migrate to different parts of the embryo to form the notochord, which is the first part of the nervous system to form. From the notochord, the neurons send out axons and dendrites to innervate muscles and other tissues and organs. The neurons also migrate and divide to form the structure of the brain. Studies in rats and in humans have demonstrated that the surrounding tissues produce a matrix of proteins that serve as "highways" for the neurons to migrate on. These molecular highways also contain "road signs" to guide the neurons to precise locations.

The basic architecture of the brain is formed by the end of the first trimester. The developing embryo has a "built-in" checking mechanism to ensure that all neural circuitry is properly formed. If the wiring is wrong, the brain is capable of making some repairs. If the mistake is irreversible, however, the embryo is aborted spontaneously. By the end of the first trimester, the brainstem is developed, and it starts to assume control of many of the physiological processes, including heartbeat, blood glucose level, nutrient absorption, and body temperature. These basic functions are essential for the embryo to enter the next stage of development.

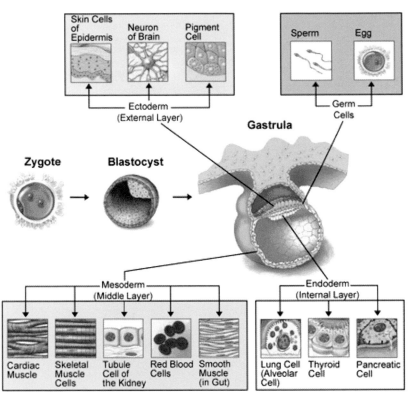

Embryonic development

Embryonic cells differentiate into a variety of cells. *(Public Domain)*

In the second trimester, the embryo is called a fetus. Its brain becomes one of the most prominent features, and it starts to take on a distinctive human shape. By this time, its nervous system is sufficiently developed to direct movement of its limbs. The mother starts to feel the movement of the fetus, a situation often referred to as quickening. The basic structure of the brain is fully formed by the end of the 2nd trimester, with the brainstem being the most developed. During this time period, the cerebral cortex is still growing rapidly with the constant addition of new neurons and the formation of synapses between existing neurons.

During the third trimester, the fetus enters into the growth stage, as the basic structure of the organs and tissues are already in place. This is the time when prematurely born babies have a 90% probability of surviving outside the mother's womb with the support provided by a modern neonatal intensive care unit. Even though most of these babies do well from a physiological standpoint and catch up developmentally with babies born at term, they are more likely to suffer from minor to serious mental disorders later in life. Studies on premature births have revealed that the brain, particularly the cerebral cortex, requires the uterine environment to further its development.

III. WHAT IS BRAIN PLASTICITY?

Premature births have raised some interesting questions regarding the development of the fetal brain. How much growth and development does the fetal brain still need during the third trimester? What is the significance of the uterine environment during these final three months before the infant enters the world? These are important questions, and the answers could determine how mothers should care for themselves during this period. This information is also useful for physicians and other medical personnel of neonatal intensive care units in developing their treatment strategies. Until now, the main focus of the treatment has been to keep the preterm babies alive. However, physicians have become increasingly more aware of the importance of protecting an infant's mental development. This awareness has been derived from studies indicating that both fetal and infant brains are flexible. This flexibility is known as brain plasticity. It has also been shown that during critical periods of development, the environment has a tremendous impact on brain development.

III.1. *What is fetal brain plasticity?*

By the beginning of the third trimester, all the organs and tissues are formed and are working properly. At this point, miscarriages rarely occur, and the chance of survival for the fetus is excellent. The heart is now working on its own to circulate blood throughout the body, the kidneys start to produce urine, and the liver is fully functional. The lungs are also ready for the baby's first breath after birth. The closer the fetuses get to full term (at least 37 weeks) the more likely that they will be born without complications. However, with advances in life-support technology, preterm babies as young as 24 weeks have an excellent chance of survival.

During the past two decades, the rate of preterm births in the United States has risen by nearly 30%. In 2003, more than half a million babies were born prematurely, accounting for approximately 12% (1 in 8) of all births. Prior to the advances in neonatal intensive care, premature births were the leading cause of neonatal deaths and accounted for 25% of those deaths. The ability to save preterm babies has been one of the most important medical advances of the last 30 years. As more preterm babies have entered childhood and early teens, studies have become available on their physical and mental development. Most preterm babies born after 28 weeks of gestation have experienced almost no physical growth delay in comparison to full term babies. However, studies have suggested that there are difficulties with their mental development.

Human infant in incubator
Preterm babies are saved by increasingly more sophisticated medical technologies. *(GNU Free Documentation License)*

Recent studies have reported that as many as 50% of children born prematurely suffer from behavioral and mental difficulties, including delays in motor development, attention deficient hyperactivity disorders, aggressive behaviors, and difficulties in socialization. Children born prematurely are three times more likely than full-term children to experience these difficulties. The long-term effects of being born prematurely are yet to be determined, because the number of preterm babies who have entered adulthood remains too small for conducting full investigations.

Recent studies in animals have suggested that environment is critical for brain development. In one study, newborn rats were taken away from their mothers as soon as they were born and were hand-fed by humans. These rats became aggressive and anti-social in contrast to their litter mates. When their brains were compared to the "normal" rat brains, they showed clear neurological differences. These observations led to the hypothesis that the brains of newborn rats are highly plastic and that environment influences their development. Could this plasticity also apply to the human neonatal brains?

Recent research has revealed that fetal brains are 100 times more active in establishing synapses between neurons than adult brains. These synapses are dynamic because they are constantly forming, breaking, and reforming. Experiences of all forms, such as sound, light, color, touch, smell, and pain, affect this synapse formation. As the brains enter into the third trimester, most of the neurons are permanently located in specific regions of the brain. From these positions, they extend their axons and dendrites, touching each other to form synapses. With nearly 100 billion neurons and with each neuron capable of forming as many as 10,000 synapses, the fetal brain forms several thousand synapses every second. Could the differences between the maternal womb and the stark world of the neonatal intensive care units shape the fetal brains by affecting their synapse formation?

To test the hypothesis that the bright and noisy environment of the neonatal intensive units has negative effects on fetal brain development, researchers created an environment that is more similar to the maternal womb. In this experiment, some premature babies were kept in specially designed facilities that were quiet, dark, warm, and filled with soothing background water sounds. Mothers were encouraged to hold their babies against the warmth of their skin as frequently as possible. The brain development of these babies was then compared with that of term babies using brain imaging techniques. These babies were followed up with behavior tests at various ages. Thus far, the results are promising, indicating that premature babies who were cared for in this type of environment were more comparable to term babies. Large clinical studies on this approach are under progress, and many neonatal intensive care units have considered using this approach for providing care for premature babies. If the preliminary results are confirmed, this could become a new treatment strategy for premature babies.

III.2. How does experience shape brain connections?

There are good neurological reasons for you not to remember your baby years. The infant brain is far from being fully functional. Even after birth, the brain continues to develop. Neurons continue to make new connections with each other. The brain of a newborn baby has twice as many synapses as that of an adult brain. Even though very few new neurons are produced, the existing neurons send out axons and dendrites to build a complex and intricate network. These processes require a great deal of energy. The infant brain uses 60% of the body's energy, whereas the adult brain only uses 20%. This is an indication of the intense activities going on in the infant brain. During the first year, infants need to save all their energy to support their brain development.

One of the best examples to demonstrate the dynamic development of the infant brain is an eye disorder that occurs in some newborn infants. The lenses of the eyes of some babies are opaque, preventing them from seeing. This condition, also known as cataract, also occurs in the elderly as a common result of aging. Before the development of a surgical procedure to remove the defective lens and put in a new synthetic lens, the patients became blind in the eye that was affected by the cataract. This surgical procedure always helps the elderly patients regain their sight but not all infants. If the babies who have cataracts do not have their lenses replaced early in life, they will lose their sight.

To understand why such a difference exists between elderly patients and infants, it is important to first learn about the neurological process of visual perception. The eye is a light-sensing instrument that collects information on light intensity and frequency using light sensitive cells that line the interior of the eye. These light sensitive cells, known as rods and cones, respond to light stimulation by generating an electrical current which then travels to the synapses of the optic nerves. The optic nerves extend from the eye at the front of the head to the visual cortex, which is located in the occipital lobe at the back of the head. The left eye is connected to the right visual cortex and the right to the left visual cortex.

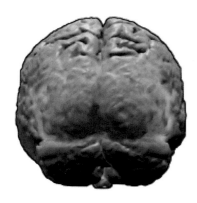

Visual cortex

The red region is the brain area that is most actively involved in visual interpretation. *(GNU Free Documentation License)*

The visual cortex of a newborn is underdeveloped, even though all the neurons are already present. The neurons have yet to be properly connected to each other. When newborns first open their eyes, the image they see is blurred. However, their visual acuity improves rapidly within the first two weeks. The improvement takes place because of reorganization within their visual cortex. Several million new synapses are formed every hour because of visual stimulation. In other words, the more an infant sees, the more developed his or her visual cortex becomes. The visual cortex continues to undergo changes for the entire first year of an infant's life.

When an infant's eye is affected by a cataract, the visual cortex of that eye fails to develop because it receives no visual signal from the defective eye. If corrective surgery is not carried out within six months, the infant will not see with this eye, even if the defective lens is replaced. The neurons in the visual cortex start to die if they do not receive any visual stimulation. This part of the brain will decrease in size in comparison to the visual cortex that is connected to the functional eye. This disorder demonstrates that visual perception occurs at the level of the brain, not at the level of the eye. Without a functioning visual cortex, the eye is of no use. Furthermore, the development of the infant brain relies on the need to use this part of the brain.

A baby girl who had a prenatal cataract had it surgically corrected at four months of age. After surgery, her parents were instructed to put a patch over her normal eye for as much as 90% of her waking hours. Without patching her normal eye, her brain will automatically rely on the normal eye to acquire visual information. Her "corrected" eye will get little use, and the development of the visual cortex for this eye will lag behind. By patching her normal eye, the visual cortex of her "corrected" eye will catch up. For the next five years, her normal eye must be patched to allow the other eye to gain its full function. This example demonstrates that the infant brain is plastic and can remain changeable until late childhood. In an adult, however, the visual cortex is fully developed, allowing the vision to be regained immediately after cataract surgery.

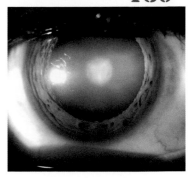

Cataract
The development of the cloudiness of the lens that can gradually lead to blindness. *(GNU Free Documentation License)*

III. *What is fetal alcohol syndrome?*

The plasticity of the brain during fetal development suggests that chemicals in the environment could alter the embryonic and fetal development of the brain. One such chemical is alcohol, which is the most common recreational chemical that has been consumed over the course of human history. Heavy consumption of alcohol during pregnancy has long been prohibited, dating back to biblical, ancient Greek, and ancient Roman times. However, the first medical report on the connection between maternal alcohol use and fetal damage appeared in 1899. This report described a study in which there were higher rates of stillbirths for alcoholic female prisoners than there was for their sober female relatives. Since then, other studies have provided further evidence linking alcohol and fetal development.

A child wearing an eye patch
The good eye is patched to allow the visual cortex of the "corrected" eye to catch up. *(Public Domain)*

During the 1960s, several studies revealed that children born from alcoholic mothers displayed significant developmental abnormalities at birth, including below average birth weight, small head circumference (microcephaly), and cardiovascular abnormalities. Further studies of the brains of these infants revealed malformations in different regions of the brain, particularly in the cerebral cortex. Some of the infants who were born dead had abnormal development of neurons in nearly every region of the brain. Instead of forming neurons five to seven layers deep, these infants had only three to four layers of neurons. Furthermore, these neurons were arranged in a disorganized pattern, suggesting that they were disrupted during their embryonic migration.

Infants from alcoholic mothers also show behavioral disorders, including learning disabilities, impulse control problems, memory problems, attention deficiencies, hyperactivity, and general cognitive deficits. In 1973, all the alcohol-related fetal developmental disorders were named collectively as fetal alcohol syndrome (FAS). The diagnosis of FAS is based on meeting four criteria: 1) growth deficiency, 2) FAS facial features, 3) central nervous system damage, and 4) prenatal alcohol exposure. Using these criteria, the FAS prevalence rate in the United States is estimated to be between 0.2 to 2 cases per 1,000 live births. However, the milder form of FAS, which is only limited to brain development, is the leading known cause of mental retardation in the Western world.

The correlation between alcohol consumption and abnormal fetal brain development is well established, but the biological mechanism that causes this remains unclear. Only 30% of women who are alcoholics give birth to children with FAS. The remaining 70% of pregnant alcoholic women give birth to normal babies. On the other hand, some women, who only drink modestly during their pregnancy, give birth to FAS infants. In some cases, the drinking is limited to a short period, such as the first trimester, when the women are unaware of their pregnancy. With these uncertainties, the U.S. Surgeon General has advised pregnant women to abstain from alcohol to reduce the risk of the syndrome.

The variable effects of alcohol on fetal development suggest that alcohol has different biological effects at different stages of embryonic and fetal development. If alcohol consumption occurs during the first trimester when the embryo is at its early developmental stages, the outcome could be fatal. Even if the embryo survives this early developmental insult, the impact on the baby could be extensive with multiple organs affected. If alcohol consumption occurs during the second or the third trimester, most major organs, such as the heart, liver, and kidney, are already formed and are likely to be only minimally affected. However, brain development is still highly sensitive, because of the continuation in synapse formation.

The mother's physiology and genetics are also important. When alcohol enters the blood stream, the body converts it to other products, which are responsible for the intoxicating effects of alcohol. Whether alcohol or its by-products are able to efficiently cross the placenta barrier and enter the embryonic/fetal circulation depends on the genetic makeup of the mother and the fetus. These genetic differences are most likely the reasons for the variations in whether alcoholic mothers give birth to FAS infants or not. Because of these uncertainties, the U.S. Surgeon General has recommended that women avoid any alcohol use even while planning a pregnancy. This is done to avoid damage that can occur during the earliest stage of embryo development, a time when many women are not aware of their pregnancies. Today, the U.S. Alcoholic Beverage Labeling Act has required that warning labels be placed on all alcoholic beverage containers.

Warning

Education to help women make the right decisions during their pregnancies in terms of alcohol use. *(Public Domain)*

Chapter 11
Language

How do you develop your language?

Are they fighting or playing?
In this encounter, the two dogs are playing. The communication signals including their play faces and tail signals suggest a play fight rather than a serious aggressive episode.
(GNU Free Documentation License)

CHAPTER 11. LANGUAGE

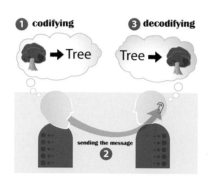

Language is a complex process
It involves coding and decoding information; the sender and receiver must use the same system. *(GNU Free Documentation License)*

Human language is the masterpiece of biological evolution. Even though there are over 6,000 languages in existence today, all languages are the manifestation of a biological trait that is shared by every member of the human species. If there is one trait that links all humans together, it is our ability to learn any language in the world. An infant can learn any language that is spoken in his or her environment. For children, learning their first language is no different from the instinctual act to drink from their mother's breasts. However, learning is one of the most complex mental functions that our brains are designed to perform. These complexities have only recently been unraveled by biologists, psychologists, and linguists. The insights that have been gained have allowed us to understand human intelligence, consciousness, and creativity.

I. WHAT IS LANGUAGE?

Language is exclusively a human mode of communication, even though other animals make use of sophisticated communication systems. However, none of them make use of the properties that linguists use to define language. Over the past several decades, biologists have searched for the existence of animal languages and have trained animals to use human language. Many birds, such as parrots and cockatoos, have been trained to say human words or even short phrases, but they have never mastered the essence of human language. Other great apes, such as chimpanzees, bonobos, gorillas, and orangutans, have been taught to use human sign language, and some have even learned to understand human speech. However, none of them can use human language in its full capacity. Therefore, language is a unique human genetic trait.

I.1. *What is the significance of biological communication?*

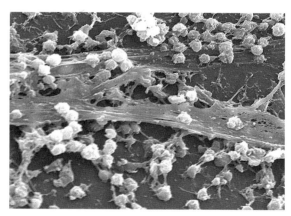

***Staphylococcus aureus* biofilm**

When there are enough bacteria present, they communicate with each other to form cell aggregates known as biofilm. *(Creative Commons Attribution)*

All living organisms communicate with each other, even the simple bacteria. The discovery of communication between members of a simple bacterial species known as *Pseudomonas aeruginosa* has had important medical implications. *Pseudomonas* bacteria are commonly found in hospital environments and exist as free-living organisms. However, under certain conditions, they produce a protein matrix and aggregate together to form colonies known as biofilms. These bacterial aggregations block intravenous lines and other medical equipment, leading to infection and inflammation in patients. The aggregation of the bacteria occurs when there are enough individual bacteria present in the vicinity. They sense each other's presence and send out chemical signals for the aggregation to occur. This mode of bacterial communication is known as quorum sensing, and it has been found in many other bacterial species.

Simple biological organisms communicate mainly through chemical signals. However, complex animals also use chemical communication, and most of these chemical signals are used for mating. For example, male moths have elaborate antennae that are designed to detect scent molecules that are released by females. In some species, the males can detect the scent trails of females that are located several miles away. These chemical molecules that are used for sexual reproduction are known as pheromones. Mammals, both males and females, also use pheromones to attract the opposite sex. Consequently, many mammals have excellent senses of smell that are 100 or even 1,000 times more sensitive than the human sense of smell.

As animals became more complex, behavioral signs evolved to communicate sexual readiness and receptivity between mating partners. Mating partners, such as the albatrosses and grebes, perform elaborate courtship dances. Many male members of the species have evolved elaborate displays to attract female mating partners. The peacocks and the bower birds are examples of these mating communications. Some species, such as frogs, song birds, and whales, have evolved auditory displays in the form of courtship songs to communicate with their partners. The various forms of communication have resulted because of adaptations to different environments. However, they all share the same goal of achieving successful sexual reproduction.

Emperor gum moth
The feathery antennae on the moth is a remarkable device for sensing chemical signals. *(GNU Free Documentation License)*

As animals form larger social groups, communication between members of the group is crucial for cooperation and for resolving conflicts among members. Both males and females develop communication signals that are used for cooperation, competition, and conflict resolution. For mammals, many of these signals involve facial expressions for emotions, such as sadness, happiness, and anger. Humans can recognize these emotions in other animals, such as dogs, because these facial expressions have been conserved through evolution. The reverse is also true, as many dog owners will confirm. As the social groups increase in size, effective communication is vital for the survival of the group in defense, hunting, food gathering, and cohesiveness.

Primates have evolved complex behaviors that are used to build relationships between members of the group. Members form alliances with each other to maintain control of the group, to set up mating priorities of the males, and to provide self-defense against predators and outside groups. All primates, except humans, use grooming as a social means to build friendships and alliances. Some primates, such as the baboons, spend up to 50% of their waking hours grooming each other. Most primates also develop a gesture system, not unlike human sign language, to communicate information. Some mammals, such as the sea mammals (dolphins and whales), communicate with each other by sound.

Japanese macaque monkeys
Social grooming is an important daily activity of primates. *(Public Domain)*

Humans are the only species that communicate with complex vocal sounds or speech. Human speech is unique because it uses abstract symbols to represent real life objects. To a lesser extent, dolphins and the great apes also use abstraction in their communication, but they are limited by the lack of human-like language. With the ability to describe a wide range of objects and events, human speech has become a tool to share information and to build alliances. Instead of grooming, humans have evolved the use of speech to build relationships between group members. About 500,000 years ago, the enlargement of the human brain most likely coincided with the evolution of human language.

I.2. What is the biological basis of human language?

The origin of human language is unclear, and most of the early research had focused on the learned aspect of human language. The accepted theory in the 1950s was that human language was a learned behavior. In other words, the human mind began life as a blank slate and did not have any neuronal circuits for language. Furthermore, this theory suggested that there were no brain regions that had evolved specifically for language. Researchers at the time discounted the idea of a language center in the brain and considered language to be the result of only the environment. Children learned all the rules of grammar and syntax through imitating adults.

Noam Chomsky
He proposed that language is a genetically endowed human intellectual skill. *(Creative Commons Attribution)*

In the 1950s, several linguists, mainly Noam Chomsky, questioned these assumptions. He and others observed that children have a remarkable ability to learn language without much effort. At a young age, children can hear the subtleties of a language that most adults ignore. Children also learn the syntax and grammar of

Infants' language skills

They learn language naturally as part of their development. (*Creative Commons Attribution*)

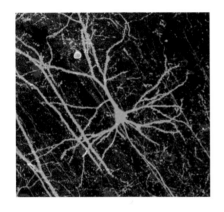

Neuron connections

Infants have ten times more connections than adults. They are gradually pruned by experience. (*Creative Commons Attribution*)

Robert E. Lee

Shortly before he died, he suffered a stroke and lost his ability to speak. (*Public Domain*)

their native languages at an age far below their assumed intellectual capabilities. In addition, they can learn and make use of as many as five new words everyday without any effort. This ability, however, does not exist throughout life. There is a "window" of opportunity in the neuronal development for learning language. This window gradually closes just prior to puberty.

An infant can distinguish between two very similar sounds. For example, a six-month-old-baby can tell apart two nearly identical pronunciations in a foreign language that non-native speakers ignore. In one study, the brain waves of eight-month-old babies were recorded during the playback of two similar pronunciations. Researchers detected a subtle shift in the brain waves during the playback of these pronunciations, indicating that the infants could tell them apart. However, in the same experiment with one-year-old babies, the brain waves were indistinguishable, suggesting that these older babies have lost the ability to separate these two pronunciations. This loss is partly responsible for why we speak with our own accents when we learn a foreign language as an adult. We have lost the ability to hear the subtleties of the foreign language.

These studies demonstrate that during brain development, there exists a set of neurons that are ready to be stimulated and form the synapses appropriate for the particular language that a child is learning at an early age. Once those synapses are formed, the circuits are set for only those sounds that are important for this language. All other language sounds are largely ignored. This strategy has the advantage of increasing the sensitivity to the native language by setting a filter to eliminate those sounds that are irrelevant and potentially distracting. This ability develops early in life and disappears once this critical period has passed.

Another innate ability of the brain in acquiring language is to learn a language's grammar and syntax shortly after the second birthday. Within months, children start to speak in full sentences with appropriate syntax and grammatical construction. They pick up all the grammatical rules of their native language effortlessly. They know what is correct, as native speakers will say: "This sounds right to me." However, for anyone who has attempted to learn a foreign language, mastering the grammatical rules and syntax of a new language is extremely difficult and requires years of intense study. For many non-native speakers, some grammatical rules can never be mastered without conscious effort and continuous vigilance.

In one study, researchers have obtained clear evidence that the brain is genetically endowed for grammar and syntax. In this study, a group of deaf orphans living in Central America were observed. Due to political unrest in their country, this group of deaf children, ranging from 2 to 12 years of age, was placed together in a make-shift camp. Nearly all came from rural areas and had no opportunity to learn sign language. However, they started to communicate with each other, inventing their own system of sign language. When researchers studied their language system, they discovered that the language the orphans had created was as rich and as complete as other established languages. Their language also had a complex system of syntax and grammatical rules. This study offers proof that language is an innate skill of the human brain and that genes have encoded all the basic neural structures for learning and utilizing language.

I.3. What is the neurological basis of language?

During the 19th century, psychiatrists suspected that there is a specific region of the brain that is responsible for speaking and that there is another region responsible for understanding speech. They had observed that some patients had lost the ability to understand speech after they suffered a stroke, but they could still speak. In other patients, the stroke rendered them speechless, but they still could understand other people's speech. During autopsies, they discovered that the patients who could not speak suffered damage in an area of the brain that was different from patients who could speak but could not understand. This type of neurological condition that affects language comprehension and generation is known as aphasia. One of the most famous sufferers is the Confederate General Robert E. Lee. Shortly before he died, Lee suffered a stroke that left him without the ability to speak. He died two weeks later.

A stroke occurs when the blood supply to the brain is impaired. A stroke can affect any part of the brain that has had its blood supply markedly decreased. The brain demands a constant supply of blood to fuel the activities of its neurons. A disruption in the blood flow lasting only a few minutes will lead to irreversible damage or death of the neurons. There are two causes of stroke. The first cause is the blockage of local blood vessels by a blood clot that was released from another part of the circulatory system. The cessation of blood flow quickly leads to the death of neurons, and the extent of damage depends on how much of the area is affected. In some cases, the damage is extensive, leading to paralysis of the entire body. In other cases, the damage affects only a small area and a certain specific function. This type of stroke is known as an ischemic stroke.

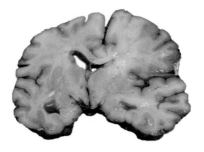

Pathology of stroke
Autopsy of a brain with damage from a stroke. *(GNU Free Documentation License)*

The second cause of stroke is due to the rupture of a blood vessel in the brain. This type of stroke is known as a hemorrhagic stroke. A hemorrhagic stroke can result from a previous brain injury that had weakened a blood vessel wall. This type of stroke can also be caused by microbial infections or a head injury that had resulted from a fall or a sports accident. The risk of a hemorrhagic stroke is nearly the same for all ages, but ischemic strokes affect predominantly the elderly population, particularly those suffering from high blood pressure, atherosclerosis, and diabetes. Strokes usually occur without warning and are often fatal. Strokes are the number three cause of death in the United States, following heart attacks and cancer.

By studying the locations and the effects of strokes, the functions of the different parts of the brain have been determined. The brain is divided into three main parts. The first part is the brainstem, which is joined to the spinal cord. The brainstem is the most primitive part of the brain and controls all the basic physiological functions of the body. A stroke in the brainstem is fatal because it destroys the neurons that control heart rate, digestion, and body temperature. The second part of the brain is the mid-brain, which includes the limbic system and the cerebellum. The limbic system controls emotion and memory. A stroke in this area results in the loss of memory, particularly in the formation of new memory. The cerebellum is vital for controlling body movement, maintaining balance, and learning physical activities. A stroke in this area leads to an inability to walk and to conduct physical activities.

The last part of the brain is the cerebrum or cerebral cortex, which accounts for 75% of the neurons in the brain. The cerebral cortex is responsible for all the cognitive functions, including sight, sound, touch, language, logical thinking, and planning. The cerebral cortex is further divided into four major parts based on the furrows (also known as sulci) on its surface. The back of the cerebrum is known as the occipital lobe. This region is also known as the visual cortex because strokes in this region destroy visual perception. The area in front of the occipital lobe is the parietal lobe. This region has many functions. Strokes in this area affect motor behavior and the perception of motion. The area below the parietal lobe is the temporal lobe. This region also has many functions, including language skills. One part of the temporal lobe is known as the Wernicke's area, named after Carl Wernicke, who discovered in 1874 that a stroke in this area destroys the ability to understand speech. This type of aphasia is known as receptive or Wernicke's aphasia.

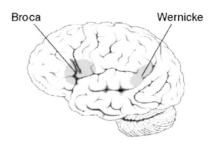

Brain language center
The Wernicke's area is involved in understanding language. *(Public Domain)*

In front of the parietal lobe is the frontal lobe, which is the largest region of the human brain. This region also possesses different functions, including the ability to produce speech. Strokes in the part of the frontal lobe known as Broca's area prevent the patients from generating sentences. They can only produce words or short phrases known as telegraphic speech. This condition is known as expressive or Broca's aphasia. Patients affected by this type of aphasia are generally frustrated because they are usually aware that they cannot speak properly.

II. How do humans acquire language?

The finding of Broca's and Wernicke's areas provided evidence for the existence of language centers in the brain. However, these are not the only areas of the human brain that are involved in producing and comprehending speech. With the development of new imaging technologies, it has become possible to observe neural activities in different regions of the brain when individuals are asked to perform various language tasks. In the past few years, this research has led to an appreciation of the immense complexity in the generation and understanding of human language. These studies also revealed the plasticity of human brains even in adulthood. The brain can be trained to perform new tasks.

II.1. How do humans speak and listen?

Most speakers of a foreign language can seldom master the pronunciations that are unique to that foreign language. They must work repeatedly to acquire this skill. In most cases, the difficulties are impossible to overcome. For example, speakers of the Chinese language Cantonese face great difficulties in pronouncing the "th", "r", and "l" sounds. Similarly, English speakers find it almost impossible to pronounce some of the Cantonese words. However, infants from every part of the world and from every ethnic group can master any language in the world and speak it in a manner that is indistinguishable from the natives. This remarkable skill is due to the ability of the infant brain to adapt and change, whereas the adult brain has lost this flexibility.

Human speech is remarkably complex, and generating human speech requires separate processes. The first process is the ability to generate sound through the human vocal tract, which includes the tongue, lips, teeth, jaws, palate, larynx, and the vocal cords. The various components of the vocal tract work in a coordinated fashion, with each component functioning in synchrony. Through precise neural control of the muscles attached to some of the components, the human vocal tract can produce sounds faster and more accurately than any other animal. With appropriate training, a singer can generate the precise sound frequency to shatter a wine glass. To generate sufficient air with precision, the human larynx has been placed below the esophagus. This arrangement, however, can cause food to accidentally enter the larynx (the wind pipe) and lead to choking. No other animals have this arrangement.

The second process that is needed to generate human speech is speech perception, which is needed to stimulate the development of the neurological pathways in the brain for language development. When sound enters the auditory system of the ears, the electrical signals travel to the brain region known as the primary auditory cortex. This region is located in the temporal lobe between the Wernicke's and Broca's

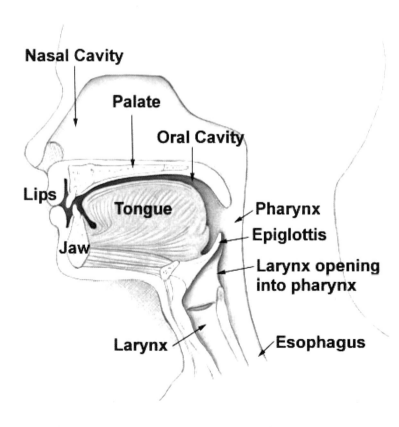

Human vocal tract

Generating human speech is one of the most complicated motor activities that we perform unconsciously. *(Public Domain)*

areas. The primary auditory cortex provides feedback to the two language areas. This feedback is essential for speech development. Individuals who suffer from congenital hearing impairment are unable to develop spoken language, and their overall language development is inhibited.

Language development is affected differently by the varying forms of hearing impairment. There are two main forms of hearing impairment. The first form is known as pre-lingual hearing impairment and is caused by the mutation of genes that are involved in the auditory pathways. The pre-lingual hearing impairment precludes the acquisition of speech and language through the primary auditory cortex. If a child has this type of hearing impairment and if the hearing loss is not quickly detected, then the child will have lasting problems in language acquisition. In this case, the lack of stimulation of the neurons in the language centers can have lasting effects in both language and in cognition, even when the child is taught sign language later. The second form of deafness is post-lingual hearing impairment, which is caused by infectious agents or physical trauma. Since the child has already acquired language prior to the loss of hearing, there is no impact on the child's language development.

During development, the region of the brain near the primary auditory cortex is the center of neural activities. Using EEG and brain scanning techniques, the neurons in this region have been shown to be critical in constructing the neurological pathways that are important for speaking and comprehending spoken language. Since most children learn only one language during their early years, this brain region is dedicated to a single language. However, some children of immigrant families face the task of learning two languages. They will first learn the native language of their parents. Then, they will learn the language of their new homeland usually within one or two years. In some cases, they learn both languages almost simultaneously. Researchers have been interested in determining how the developing brain allocates neural pathways for two languages.

It was discovered that even though the brain can accommodate multiple languages during early development, only one language can occupy the main language center. This is the first language that an infant is exposed to. Using brain scanning techniques, the researchers observed that when the baby was listening and speaking the first language, intense brain activities were focused in this region of the brain. However, when the baby was using a second language, the brain activities occurred in many different parts of the brain. These studies demonstrated that the human brain is designed for one primary language and that other parts of the brain are recruited to learn a second language. This is another example that demonstrates the plasticity of the human brain.

Chinese native speakers
There are more Chinese native speakers than native speakers of any other language in the world. *(Public Domain)*

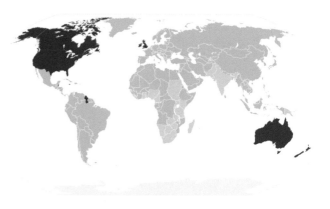

English speakers
There are more people speaking English as a second language than any other language in the world. *(Public Domain)*

II.2. How is language related to consciousness?

From the psychological perspective, language has been linked to consciousness. Through language we can describe our thoughts, sensations, perceptions, moods, emotions, and dreams. Language is a reflection of our physical existence, and language is critical to create an awareness of self. Therefore, an understanding of the integration of language with other neurological functions is essential to the understanding of consciousness. One of the most important questions in psychology and neurobiology is the physical basis of consciousness. Which parts of the brain create self awareness? What is the relationship between self awareness and consciousness? Many researchers believe that understanding the neurological basis of language could provide insights into understanding consciousness.

During the last two decades, researchers have studied patients who suffer from severe epileptic seizures. From these patients, they discovered that language is central to the mental state of consciousness. These patients suffer from the most severe form of epileptic seizures, known as tonic-clonic seizures or grand mal seizures. During a seizure, these patients experience unprovoked electrical activities in many regions of the brain. This massive electrical activity causes neurons to fire randomly, often leading to the loss of consciousness. In addition, their muscles rapidly contract and relax, causing convulsions. The convulsions may range from exaggerated twitches of the arms and legs to violent shaking of the stiffened extremities. A seizure can last from a few seconds to several minutes.

The seizures can occur suddenly without warning. In some individuals, the seizures occur sporadically, whereas in some, the seizures repeatedly occur. In the most severe cases, epileptic patients can experience more than 100 seizures each day. In the past decades, many drugs have been developed to control epileptic seizures, but for some patients, none of the drugs work. In these patients, disconnecting the left and right hemispheres of the cerebral cortex appears to be the only way to stop the seizures. Remarkably, after this procedure, the patients are cured from the seizures and show no significant adverse consequences from the surgery. However, they do exhibit some fascinating abnormalities in their language ability.

To examine the effects of disconnecting the two halves of the brain, these patients were subjected to a split vision test. In this test, they were asked to view words or objects that were flashed on the left and right sides of their visual fields. They were then asked to name or draw the objects that were presented. In one example, a patient was shown a picture of a hammer in his right visual field and a nail in his left visual field. When he was asked what he saw, he replied that he saw a hammer. However, when he was asked to draw the object that he saw, he drew a nail. He had no idea why he drew a nail, because he knew that he only saw a hammer. This study suggests that perception and action are distinct in the conscious mind and that language does not necessarily need to correlate with action.

This discrepancy between perception and action is the result of disconnecting the left and right hemispheres of the brain. The left and right hemispheres of the human brain are linked by a group of nerve fibers known as the corpus callosum, which allows for neural communication between the hemispheres. Disconnecting the corpus callosum cures the severe form of epileptic seizure for reasons yet to be determined. Severing this connection between the two halves of the brain causes them to work independently, and most patients can adjust to it. Their overall perceptions are not affected, except when being tested by the split vision tests.

The split vision test has provided important insights into how the human brain functions. Researchers have learned that the language center is located in the left hemisphere based on how information is perceived by these subjects. When the previously-described patient saw a hammer in his right visual field, the information went to his left hemisphere. The language center processed the information, and he could name the object. However, when he saw a nail in his left visual field, the information went to his right hemisphere. Normally, this information would be passed to the language center in the left hemisphere for speech processing. Since the connection between the two hemispheres had been cut, he could not name what

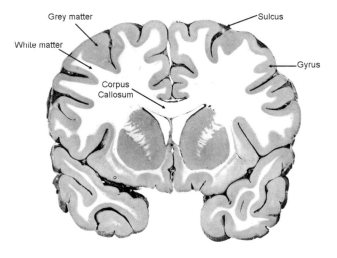

Grey matter

White matter

Sulcus

Gyrus

Corpus Callosum

Corpus callosum

This is a bundle of nerve fibers that link the two hemispheres together. *(Public Domain)*

he saw. However, the information was received in the brain, and he could draw the nail. This is a remarkable demonstration showing that language represents human consciousness. Without language, we lose conscious awareness, even though the brain still processes the information.

II.3. How flexible is the brain in learning language?

The studies on the patients who had severe epilepsy revealed that the two halves of the brain can function independently. Severing the corpus callosum cures their epilepsy but affects the communication between the left and right hemispheres. The disconnection alters the function of the brain, leading neuroscientists to discover that the left and right hemispheres have separate and specialized functions. The left hemisphere is the primary brain area for processing language and speech. For conscious awareness to occur, the information must go through the language center of the left hemisphere. Therefore, it was perceived that language and consciousness cannot exist without the left hemisphere.

In one rare type of epilepsy, the left hemisphere is the source of the electrical storm. This form of epilepsy was devastating for a seven-year-old girl who had been having them since she was four years old. She regularly suffered from tonic-clonic seizures, and some days, she had as many as 100. The impact was so severe on her mental development that she lost the ability to speak. After trying different seizure drugs for four years, her physicians recommended removing most of her left brain. The procedure had proven to be effective in treating this type of seizure, and more than several hundred children in the United States have had this surgery to cure their seizures.

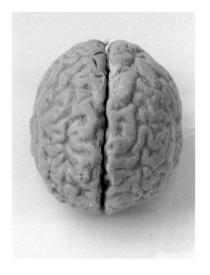

Human brain

Showing the left and right hemispheres separated by a deep grove. *(Public Domain)*

The perception prior to the success of this type of surgery was that for proper cognitive functions to occur, the entire human brain is required. It was believed that removing half of the brain would destroy the nervous system and cause death. However, these types of surgery were considered possible based on some earlier animal studies, in which various portions of the brain had been removed. Depending on the age of the animals and on the areas of the brain, most animals recovered most of their normal functions after significant portions of their brains were excised. One of the most interesting studies was the removal of the occipital lobes from the brains of ferrets.

Ferrets are domesticated mammals that are similar to weasels, and they have been used for neurological studies of visual perception. In one study on the plasticity of the ferret brain, researchers removed the occipital lobes, which are the sites of the visual cortex. The optic nerves were rerouted to the primary auditory cortex in the temporal lobe. The intention of the experiment was to determine whether parts of the primary auditory cortex could be transformed into a visual cortex. Indeed, the regions of the primary auditory cortex that were connected to the optic nerves developed the typical patterns of the visual cortex of the occipital lobe. The ferrets regained some of their sight, but it was not as good as the normal ferrets. Nevertheless, these results suggested that the brain is highly plastic and has the capability of transforming one type of neuron into another.

Ferrets

They are domesticated mammals and have been used to study visual processes. *(Creative Commons Attribution)*

These animal studies suggested that after the removal of the left hemisphere in the epileptic patients, their right brain could take on many functions normally performed by the left brain, including language functions. In one patient who undertook this surgery four years ago to cure his unrelenting epilepsy, researchers undertook a detailed study of his recovery starting immediately after his surgery. He completely lost his speech after the surgery, but he retained his comprehension of spoken language. This observation suggests that both the left and right hemispheres perform a comprehension function, whereas speech is located entirely in the left hemisphere. However, as he recovered, he started to learn and to speak like an infant.

A similar recovery of speech was seen in a seven-year-old girl. Her parents were amazed that she acted as if she was learning how to talk for the first time. She began by making the same range of sounds as an infant and gradually learned new words. In about two years, she started to use full sentences in her speech. When researchers studied her brain with brain scanning techniques, they discovered that some regions of the right hemisphere had taken on the function of the brain language center that is normally located in the left hemisphere. This research provides further evidence that a child's brain is highly plastic and can assume new functions when it becomes necessary. This plasticity, however, gradually decreases with age, making learning a new language as an adult nearly impossible.

III. WHAT ARE LANGUAGE DISORDERS?

Language acquisition is an important developmental milestone of childhood. There are normal variations of the time at which children learn to speak, read, and write. These are interconnected activities and there are wide variations in these abilities among individuals of the general population. Some individuals of normal, or even exceptional intelligence, can have delays in language development. On the other hand, language delay can be a sign of mental retardation. Difficulties in reading are also an indication of a learning disability, but some individuals possess normal intelligence even though they are unable to read. Research in language development has led to effective approaches in treating language disorders. There are also many language disorders in adults due to physical and mental abnormalities. These disorders have provided further insights into the role of language in human consciousness.

III.1. What are the common language disorders?

Language disorders are the most common challenges for children in school. The most common form of childhood language disorders is language delay, in which the underlying knowledge of language is affected. One of the most famous people who suffered from language delay is the physicist Albert Einstein. During his childhood years, his parents thought he was mentally retarded because he had difficulties speaking until he was about five years old. Nevertheless, he proved to be highly gifted, becoming one of the top students in his elementary school. Most cases of language delay, however, affect the intellectual development of the children.

Albert Einstein

He had difficulties speaking until he was five years old. His parents thought he was mentally retarded.
(Public Domain)

There are two types of language delay. The first type is receptive language delay, in which the children have difficulties understanding what is said to them. In this type, their brain circuits for processing incoming speech are not as effective as normal. The second type is expressive language delay, in which the children have difficulties finding the right words or constructing the sentences to communicate what they think, need, and want. Both types of delays can extend into early adulthood or even throughout an entire life. Early recognition of these language delays is important in order to provide training to overcome these difficulties.

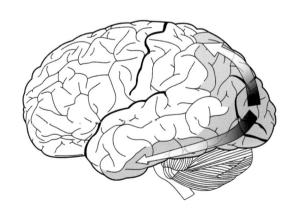

Visual processing

Visual information is first processed in the visual cortex before being transferred to the frontal and temporal lobes. *(GNU Free Documentation License)*

The other common language disorder involves reading, which is a neurologically complex process that involves many parts of the brain. Reading starts with the visual acquisition of written symbols. This information is decoded in the visual cortex before being processed by brain areas in the temporal and frontal lobes. This information is then passed to the language center to generate speech. Next, this speech is conveyed inside the brain to the primary auditory cortex, which decodes its meaning. This complicated neural processing of reading creates an internal voice of what is being read. Using brain scanning techniques, researchers have identified at least 17 areas of the brain that become active during reading.

Individuals have a wide range of reading skills due to genetic variations and individual experiences that shape the neural circuits that are involved in reading. However, reading is one aspect of human language that does not develop naturally. Reading is a learned skill, and a child is taught how to read. To become a good reader, a child must receive reading training that spans their entire childhood. In modern society, reading is the primary source for acquiring information, and difficulties in reading affect intellectual development and social adjustments. Studies have shown that Americans who learn to read by the third grade are less likely to be imprisoned, drop out of school, or take drugs. In fact, literacy rates in the United States are more correlated to monetary earnings than are individual IQ scores.

One of the most common reading disabilities is dyslexia. Children with dyslexia are unable to read even with intense tutoring in reading. Before the 1970s, when the neurological basis of dyslexia was unknown, many children with dyslexia were considered mentally retarded. Children were often held back repeatedly in school due to their inability to read, take tests, and follow written instructions. The recognition that there could be a neurological disorder in these children was made as early as 1896, when a British physician published a description of a "reading-specific" learning disorder. He described a 14-year-old boy who had great difficulties when learning to read but was adept at other activities typical of children his age. In the 1990s, researchers also discovered that dyslexia is a genetic disorder that "runs" in families.

The exact neurological basis of dyslexia remains unknown, but there are several hypotheses based on studies of dyslexic children that used brain scanning techniques.

Complications of reading

Reading is a complex process of information gathering and interpretation, considering how little can be seen during one eye stop. *(Public Domain)*

When a normal child reads, there are many parts of the brain that become active. However, when a dyslexic child tries to read, some areas of the brain remain inactive, suggesting that some information processing pathways in the dyslexic child are suppressed. The pathways that are critical for converting written words into speech in the primary auditory cortex remain either inactive or less active. This suggests that creating the inner speech during reading is a critical part of reading comprehension. With this knowledge, new reading approaches have been used to teach dyslexic children to create the inner speech. The preliminary results are promising, but further research is needed to improve the process.

III.2. What is auditory disturbance?

Dreaming is an important part of human experience, and through language, we can describe our dreams. We cannot be sure whether other animals have dreams, but most pet owners will tell you that their pets behave as if they are dreaming during their sleep. In dreams, we see visual images and hear our own voices and the voices of other people. Every night, we dream, whether we remember the dreams or not. Our brains are fully capable of creating sounds and images from the real life experiences that we store in our memory. Through them, we also create our inner voice that we can listen to as if we were hearing it in the real world. Despite its realism, we know it is not real, just a dream.

John Nash

He is Nobel laureate and suffer of schizophrenia with auditory hallucinations. *(GNU Free Documentation License)*

A Beautiful Mind

This is a book and movie based on the life of John Nash. *(Education Fair Use)*

However, for some people these inner voices can become erratic. Ten years ago, a 35-year-old sailing enthusiast decided to take six months off from his job to pursue a life-long ambition to sail across the Pacific alone. He planned his trip carefully for the two month long journey. Other than equipping his sailing vessel with navigation equipment and an emergency two-way radio, he brought nothing that could produce music or voice. About half way into his journey, he started to repeatedly hear a poem that was recited by an unknown female voice. It was not a poem that he recalled, and at first he enjoyed listening to it. Soon, it became annoying and intrusive, and he could not shut it off. This voice did not go away even after he returned to the United States.

This type of auditory hallucination is common among people who become deaf later in life or in people who have been isolated from the world as part of a religious ritual or in solitary confinement in prison. These individuals are mentally sound and have no other delusional thoughts. They cannot understand the origin of the voice. In some individuals, the auditory hallucination is a song that is repeatedly played. In some cases, the hallucination will stop for a few hours to a few days, only to come back again. When these individuals are examined by brain scanning techniques, researchers discovered that neurons in their primary auditory cortexes are active without external stimuli. Some other parts of the brain are also active. These spontaneous activities appear to be neurons that have become "bored" due to lack of stimulation. In other words, these neurons are creating activities of their own.

Another auditory disturbance that has a more serious impact on individuals is the auditory hallucinations that are associated with schizophrenia. In one typical example, an 18-year-old girl was driving home from work, and she heard two voices in her head, as though she was hearing thoughts in her mind that were not hers. The voices identified themselves as Andrew and Oliver, two angels. Oliver was having a conversation with Andrew and stated that the girl was going to die of a brain hemorrhage in the coming days. She hurried home and was afraid to tell anyone. At first she thought that her imagination had gone wild, and there was nothing to worry about. However, the voices returned repeatedly, and each time they gave her dire predictions of what might happen to her.

When she finally sought psychiatric help she was diagnosed with schizophrenia. She was prescribed an antipsychotic, risperidone, and her hallucinatory voices gradually subsided. However, they were never completely gone, and they reappeared on regular intervals. Despite their presence, she attended college and tried to create a life for herself. She read and learned about her condition, but somehow, when the voices appeared, she could not discount them. She also realized how difficult it is for other people to understand her condition without them having experienced it themselves. Then, she discovered a grassroots organization called Hearing Voices Network that provides support for individuals suffering from auditory hallucinations. She also discovered that there are far more people suffering from it than she had ever imagined.

By developing a better understanding of the neurological basis of language, scientists can understand the cause of auditory hallucinations. Throughout human history, auditory hallucinations have been important in charting the course of societies and cultures around the world. Auditory hallucinations have also been viewed as the work of malignant supernatural forces. With a new understanding of the biological basis of these neurological processes, it has become possible to find treatments for individuals who are tormented by these inner voices.

III.3. *What is aphasia?*

The medical literature is filled with cases of various language disorders. The first recorded case comes from an Egyptian papyrus, which details a speech problem in a person who experienced a traumatic brain injury to the temporal lobe. These types of language disorders are associated with a loss of ability to produce and/or comprehend languages due to a physical injury to brain areas that are specialized in language. These types of disorders are collectively known as aphasia. Aphasia, however, does not result from deficits in sensory, intellect, or psychiatric functioning. It is also not due to muscle weaknesses or to cognitive disorders. Aphasia is usually due to damage to either the Broca's area or to the Wernicke's area within the language center of the brain.

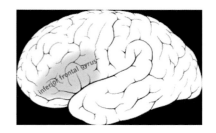

Broca's area
Damage to this area leads to the inability to speak. *(Public Domain)*

One example of aphasia is an opera singer who suffered a stroke at a relatively young age of 42. After her stroke, she was unable to speak spontaneously, and every word that she said required great effort. She was unable to form sentences, and her enunciation was poor. She also had great difficulties pronouncing multi-syllabic words. However, she had no problem comprehending other people's speech. She abandoned her singing career because she felt that she could never sing again. Two years later, when she attended an opera that she once performed as a singer, she unconsciously started to sing the lyrics quietly. She then realized that she could still sing even though she experienced great difficulty when speaking.

This opera singer suffered from Broca's aphasia due to damage to her Broca's area from her stroke. Broca's area governs language production by processing cognitive information coming from other parts of the brain. The neurons in the Broca's area have links to many different parts of the brain. During speech, the neurons in the Broca's area become highly active. Researchers hypothesize that these neurons are responsible for generating grammatical rules and syntax when converting thoughts into speech. The information is then communicated to the motor neurons that control muscles in the vocal tract. However, when a person sings, the neural activities in the Broca's area are minimal. Most of the neural activities for singing are found in the primary auditory cortex. This provides an explanation of why the opera singer could sing but not speak.

In a different type of aphasia, known as Wernicke's aphasia, individuals lose their ability to understand. They find other people's speech unintelligible. In one example, a 35-year-old college professor of ancient Greek history suffered a hemorrhagic stroke in the temporal lobe. Before his stroke, he was articulate and eloquent. After he recovered from his stroke, however, he could not have a simple conversation. Even though his hearing was not affected, he could not understand simple speech. He could still speak fluently and in abundance as he did before the stroke. However, his speech consisted of intelligible words that appeared to be strung together randomly. For example, he would say: "I called my mother on the television and did not understand the door." Similar to Broca's aphasia, individuals with Wernicke's aphasia can still understand and repeat songs.

In most cases, neither the Broca's aphasia nor the Wernicke's aphasia affect the ability to read or write. In the case of the opera singer,

The National Aphasia Association
This national organization provides sufferers and their families a better understanding of these types of language disorders. *(Education Fair Use)*

she wrote a book about her experience with Broca's aphasia. However, in some cases of Broca's or Wernicke's aphasia, the patients lose either the ability to write or to read. The extensiveness of the damage caused by the stroke to these brain regions can range from mild to severe. One example is an individual who developed stuttering after a mild stroke that affected the Broca's area. In this case, the stroke had caused mild damage to the neural circuits, leading to less efficient speech processing. As predicated, stuttering was not a problem when this person sang.

For both Broca's and Wernicke's aphasia, speech therapy can improve the language deficiencies even in older adults. There is evidence from brain scanning techniques that the neurons in the neighboring areas can fill in the space left by the dead neurons. This provides further evidence that the brain remains plastic even in old age. By trying to use the destroyed regions of the brain, the neurons are able to respond to the demands. They expand or even divide to fill in the new niche. Through the study of language and its disorders, neurobiologists have gained a new appreciation of the functions of different regions of the brain in producing language. In addition to many practical applications in treating language disorders, this knowledge has led to a better understanding of human consciousness.

Chapter 12

Addiction

Do you have any addictions?

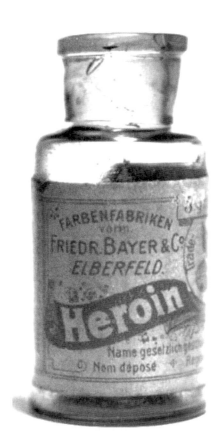

Antique heroin bottle

From 1898 to 1910, the German pharmaceutical company Bayer (also the developer of aspirin) marketed heroin as a non addictive morphine and cough suppressant.

(Public Domain)

CHAPTER 12. ADDICTION

Addiction is a biological issue that has significant personal and social consequences. Addiction occurs when someone relies on a substance for normal function. In addiction, withdrawal symptoms occur when the substance is abruptly removed. Withdrawal exists in many different forms, ranging from mild yearnings to drastic physiological changes. These changes can be so dramatic that they inflict severe physical or psychological damage on the body. A sudden cessation after a long and constant use of many addictive drugs often results in an uncontrollable shaking, known as delirium tremens (DTs). Furthermore, the mortality rate that is associated with some withdrawals is as high as 35%. Because of withdrawal symptoms, many addicts try desperately, but unsuccessfully, to discontinue their drug use. They often fully realize that discontinuing the drug is in their best interest, but they are unable to stop. Why do people become addicted and cannot escape from the addiction despite their best efforts? Is addiction a psychological or a biological problem?

Chocolate

Chocolate creates intense cravings in some individuals, as it produces a sensual pleasure. *(Creative Commons Attribution)*

I. DO YOU HAVE AN ADDICTION?

We have all experienced some form of addiction. In the broadest sense, addiction refers to any physical or psychological dependence. Some people, for example, have a yearning for chocolate, and they continuously look for chocolate to eat. In this case, they have an addiction to chocolate. When people fall in love, they are also briefly addicted to their lovers. Their love interest is constantly on their mind, and they have a deep yearning to be close to the loved one. Most of these addictions are mild or transient, and they can easily be overcome. However, there are other forms of addiction that can create intense psychological dependence. These include gambling, food, sex, pornography, work, exercise, shopping, religion, and e-mailing. Removal of these activities can induce depression and a sense of hopelessness, failure, rejection, and anxiety. However, none of these addictions are as powerful as an addiction to a psychoactive substance. Unbeknownst to most of us, we are addicted to one or more of these psychoactive substances.

I.1. Do you use psychoactive substances daily?

The use of psychoactive substances dates back to prehistoric times. Archeological findings suggest that the earliest use of psychoactive chemicals by humans occurred at least 10,000 years ago. The opium poppy was depicted in prehistoric art as well as in ancient Egyptian murals. Alcohol was also most likely discovered accidentally by early humans eating fermented grapes or berries. Undoubtedly, early humans found enjoyment from the sedative effects of alcohol. Many plant leaves also contain psychoactive substances that were consumed by early humans. However, the link between psychoactive plants and animals is not restricted to humans. Many other animal species have also discovered psychoactive plants and actively seek them. The love that cats have for catnip is a well-known example.

Opium poppy

Poppy crop grown in the Malwa region of India. *(Public Domain)*

Nearly all psychoactive substances are products or chemical derivatives of plants. All are simple chemicals that either act as neurotransmitters or as chemical agents modifying the functions of the neurotransmitters. The existence of these psychoactive chemicals in plants appears contradictory unless an evolutionary perspective is considered. Since most of these chemicals have no direct benefit for the plants, it seems wasteful for the plants to retain the genetic information to produce the chemicals. There are two main hypotheses to explain how these chemicals do, in fact, benefit the plants. The first hypothesis suggests a defensive role for these chemical compounds. Many compounds are toxic at high doses, and animals can become very ill or even die after ingesting these compounds. This negative experience will deter the animals from consuming the plants in the future.

The second hypothesis proposes that frequent visits by animals to the plants somehow assist the propagation of the plants. Through natural selection, many animals have evolved to seek plants that produce psychoactive substances. If these types of relationships have mutual benefits, then the plant's offspring will continue to produce the substances, and the animal's offspring will evolve the necessary behavior to seek these plants. In addition to the production of psychoactive chemicals, some plants produce chemicals that have a medicinal value. These plants have also developed evolutionary relationships with animals. Not surprisingly, humans have benefited from these animal-plant relationships. Some native cultures from the tropical rainforests contain references to animals that had introduced local inhabitants to the use of medicinal plants. When you drink your next cup of coffee, consider the possibility that an animal just might have been responsible for introducing humans to one of their most common habits.

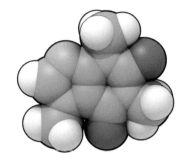

Caffeine
It is a simple chemical compound found in plant leaves and is used as a defensive chemical against herbivores.

Consuming caffeine in tea, coffee, and soda is the most common method of self-administering a psychoactive substance. Caffeine is a simple chemical compound that is produced in varying quantities in over 60 plants in their beans, leaves, and fruits. Caffeine is produced by plants to serve as an insecticide. When insects consume plants that have high levels of caffeine, they become paralyzed and often die. To keep insects from consuming their seedlings, plants produce high levels of caffeine during this early stage of development. Larger or older plants do not need as much caffeine for protection because they often have other means of protection. Coffee beans are high in caffeine because of the plant's need for protection against browsing animals. A high caffeine level is also found in young tea leaves, because they lack any mechanical protection against browsing insects. For this reason, young leaves of many tea plants are the most valued.

At high levels, caffeine is a neurotoxin, and it kills insects by disrupting their neural transmission. The effect of caffeine on insects and on other invertebrates is interestingly demonstrated with spiders. After being given caffeine, the orb-web spiders can longer weave a normal web. Instead, they weave highly irregular webs that are no longer functional. These types of experiments have demonstrated the powerful neurological effects of caffeine. In humans and other mammals, caffeine functions as a central nervous system stimulant and has the effects of temporarily warding off drowsiness and restoring alertness.

Coffee drinking ritual
Men gathered to drink coffee in a Palestine coffee house in 1900.
(Public Domain)

Caffeine is the most commonly consumed psychoactive substance in the world. Over 90% of adults consume caffeine daily in the United States. It is one of a few psychoactive substances that are legal and unregulated. However, caffeine has a profound effect on the central nervous system. Similar to the actions of many psychoactive substances, caffeine quickly induces tolerance and causes withdrawal for many users. Withdrawal symptoms include headaches, irritability, an inability to concentrate, and stomach aches. In addition, consumption of caffeine in excess of 300 mg (about ten cups of coffee) can cause caffeine intoxication, which includes symptoms such as restlessness, rapid heart beat, nervousness, insomnia, irritability, and muscle twitching. In much larger overdoses, mania, depression, disorientation, delusion, hallucination, and death can occur.

I.2. Is tobacco addictive?

Tobacco is the next most commonly consumed psychoactive substance around the world. Tobacco has been growing on both American continents since about 6,000 BC and has been used by native inhabitants since about 3,000 BC. It has a long history of ceremonial and ritualistic use by Native Americans. However, the process that was required to make smoking tobacco had limited its use for many years. It was not until the 19th century when cigarettes became available that tobacco use spread worldwide. Currently, the tobacco industry is among the most profitable business sectors. It produces approximately 5.5 trillion cigarettes globally each year. These cigarettes are used by nearly 1.1 billion people, which is more than one sixth of the world's population.

People smoke tobacco for the same reasons that they consume caffeine. Tobacco is a psychoactive substance that creates desired effects on the central nervous system. Like caffeine, it also results in addiction, tolerance, and withdrawal. However, tobacco has far more serious consequences than caffeine on the health of the user. Tobacco is prepared from dried leaves of tobacco plants, and it contains over 100 ingredients. During cigarette smoking, the burned tobacco creates over 500 different compounds. Smokers inhale these burned residues into their lungs, which, in time, can cause serious damage to lung tissues, resulting in emphysema, pneumonia, and lung cancer. According to the World Health Organization, tobacco smoking is the second leading cause of death worldwide and has been responsible for about 100 million deaths in the 20th century.

Tobacco cultivation

A farmer inspects the readiness of a broad leaf tobacco variety.
(Public Domain)

The active ingredient in tobacco is nicotine, a simple chemical compound that shares some common features with caffeine. Nicotine is present in the nightshade family of plants, which includes tobacco, coca, tomato, potato, eggplant, and green pepper. Nicotine is synthesized in the root of the plants and is accumulated in the leaves. Like caffeine, it functions as a natural insecticide for the plants' chemical defense. It is a potent neurotoxin that causes paralysis and death for many insect herbivores. Nicotine has also been commercially used as an insecticide in the past, and currently, some nicotine derivatives are widely used.

Due to its neurological properties, it is not surprising that nicotine has neurological effects on humans and other mammals. Each cigarette contains approximately 1 mg of nicotine. At this concentration, nicotine acts as a stimulant of the central nervous system. On average, it takes about seven seconds for nicotine to reach the central nervous system upon inhalation because it is rapidly absorbed by the blood and can cross the blood brain barrier. Despite its rapid diffusion, the amount of nicotine that enters the body by inhalation is significantly lower than that caused by chewing tobacco and snuff, which are held between the lips and gum or are taken by inhalation.

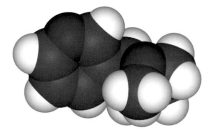

Nicotine

It is the psychoactive ingredient of tobacco leaves and is also used as a plant defensive chemical.

The exact neurological action of nicotine is unclear, but researchers have discovered nicotine receptors on the surface of neurons in the central nervous system as well as on neurons in the adrenal gland. In the central nervous system, the binding of the nicotine receptors leads to an increase in dopamine levels in the brain reward circuit, which is located in the limbic system. In the adrenal gland, nicotine elicits the release of the hormone adrenalin (epinephrine), which then causes the activation of the sympathetic nervous system. This leads to a general sense of alertness due to an increase in heart rate, blood pressure, respiration, and blood glucose level.

The effect of nicotine is subtle in comparison to the effects of many other psychoactive substances. It creates a mild, but clearly perceptible, euphoria due to its impact on dopamine levels. It is also this effect on dopamine that makes it highly addictive. Despite its negative health effects, the number of people in the United States who smoke has remained stable. Currently, 33% of all males and 22% of all females smoke. The American Heart Association, one of the organizations that fight against cigarette smoking, has stated that nicotine addiction has historically been one of the hardest addictions to break. Several recent studies have shown that nicotine is more addictive than cocaine and heroine. This makes quitting smoking extremely difficult.

I.3. Should alcohol be legal?

During an archeological excavation of the Neolithic village of Jiahu in Northern China, an archeologist discovered pottery jars that dated back to over 9,000 years ago. Chemical analyses of the materials that had been absorbed and preserved in the wall of the jar revealed that it once held a fermented beverage of rice, honey, and fruit. This was the first evidence indicating that humans have consumed alcoholic beverages since prehistoric times. This trend has continued into the 21st century despite the many negative effects of alcohol on society. One of the most serious effects of alcohol concerns traffic deaths. In the United States alone, nearly 18,000 people died in 2006 in alcohol-related traffic accidents. This represented 41% of the total traffic deaths in the U.S. Overall, 500,000 people were injured in alcohol-related automobile accidents in the U.S. in 2003. Despite the many negative health and social effects of alcohol, people continue to consume alcoholic beverages.

Alcohol is a psychoactive substance that has a far greater impact on the mental state than does both caffeine and tobacco. Similar to other addictive substances, alcohol induces tolerance, dependence, and withdrawal. The alcohol that is present in alcoholic beverages is ethyl alcohol, or ethanol, which is a fermentation product of yeast. Alcohol has a subtle but long lasting effect on the central nervous system. After consumption, alcohol rapidly crosses the blood brain barrier. Its effects on the neurons of various parts of the brain vary depending on its concentration. At low concentrations, alcohol is a sedative. It stimulates a group of neurons that release the neurotransmitter glutamate. Glutamate causes a sense of relaxation and a reduction in anxiety. This is the pleasurable feeling that most people seek when consuming alcohol.

Similar to many psychoactive drugs, alcohol induces tolerance, and individuals need to consume greater amounts of alcohol to achieve the same feeling. Tolerance to alcohol is caused by physical changes to certain neurons that result in a need for higher concentrations of alcohol to activate these neurons. The result is a gradual increase in alcohol consumption. At higher doses, alcohol also affects the brain region that controls motor functions, resulting in a reduction in reaction time. It also affects neurons in the region of the brain known as the hippocampus, which is involved in the formation of new memories. The blackout phenomenon occurs when an individual fails to remember any events during a drinking episode. At very high doses, alcohol blocks the electrical activities of neurons, leading to convulsions, cardiac failure, and occasionally, death. In addition, repeated episodes of excessive drunkenness kill neurons, leading to permanent brain damage.

The impact of alcohol consumption varies widely among individuals. In general, males are more resistant to the effects of alcohol than females. Consequently, the ability to withstand the effects of alcohol is considered a sign of masculinity. However, this idea has been proven false. Researchers have also discovered that individuals who can tolerate the effects of alcohol are five times more likely to become alcoholics than individuals who cannot. In one study, two college students were asked to consume the same amount of alcohol that they would have drank over the course of the evening. They drank it in ten minutes, and both had the same blood alcohol content. They were also asked how they felt. They gave very different assessments of their mental states. One student complained of a headache, dizziness, and lack of coordination. The other student, however, experienced no effect and felt that he could repeat the drinking exercise a few more times.

The varying effects that alcohol has on different individuals are caused by genetic differences in metabolizing alcohol by an enzyme known as alcohol dehydrogenase. When alcohol enters the body, it is converted by alcohol dehydrogenase to acetaldehyde. The buildup of acetaldehyde in the blood leads to hangover-like symptoms, such as flushing, nausea, and dizziness. Mutations in the alcohol dehydrogenase gene

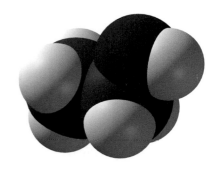

Ethanol

It is one of the simplest forms of alcohol. It is produced by yeast as a metabolic byproduct during fermentation.

Alcoholic beverages
The drinking of alcoholic beverages is often an important part of social events in many societies. *(Public Domain)*

create different versions of this enzyme that has varying efficiencies. Individuals who have a low tolerance for alcohol have an enzyme that is more efficient in converting alcohol to acetaldehyde. Therefore, they cannot drink much before feeling sick. On the other hand, for individuals who have low enzyme activity, the accumulation of acetaldehyde is much lower. Consequently, they can drink more before feeling any effect, often not until a hangover occurs.

Individuals who have a high tolerance to alcohol are far more likely to become alcoholics than those who have a lower tolerance. Furthermore, the trait for high tolerance can pass from one generation to the next in the same way that any other genetic trait can. Some individuals of Asian descent have inherited a mutation of the alcohol dehydrogenase gene that encodes for a highly efficient enzyme. In addition, these individuals also have a mutation in the gene that encodes for a less effective form of another enzyme: the one that converts acetaldehyde to the harmless acetic acid. Therefore, these individuals can accumulate high levels of acetaldehyde. This causes them to suffer from the alcohol flush reaction, leading to severe and immediate hangover symptoms. These individuals are less likely to become alcoholics.

II. WHY ARE THEY ILLEGAL?

In 1972, President Richard Nixon declared the War on Drugs. This was the beginning of a prohibition campaign that was undertaken by the United States government with the assistance of participating countries. It was intended to reduce the illegal drug trade by curbing supply and diminishing demand for psychoactive substances deemed "harmful or undesirable" by the government. The first "War on Drugs" (the Opium Wars) was conducted in China during the 19th century by the Qing government to prevent the British government from importing opium from India (at that time opium was traded in an attempt to restore trade balances with China). Until the Opium Wars in the 1800s, the trade of drugs was similar to that of tobacco and alcohol, and it had full legal status with the governments controlling and regulating the trade. Only after legislation was enacted to prohibit the possession or the sale of psychoactive substances was the illegal drug trade created.

II.1. Why is there a high demand for cocaine?

Cocaine is a powerful and damaging psychoactive substance. It has a strong addictive effect on its users, and a cocaine addict is often compelled to do anything to satisfy the drug habit. This drive to obtain the abuse substance at any cost has created many social problems. This is the basis for making the possession and sale of cocaine illegal. In one example, a cocaine addict described how his entire life was focused on getting high. He would borrow, cheat, and steal to buy cocaine. He described that if several people were doing cocaine together and if one fell down dead, no one would call for help. There would then be more cocaine for the rest. Only recently have researchers uncovered the biological basis for cocaine addiction.

Coca plant
Cocaine is extracted mainly from the coca leaves. *(Public Domain)*

Cocaine is found in the coca leaf (not to be confused with cocoa bean, which is a source for chocolate). It has a similar structure to caffeine, and it is produced as an insecticide by the plant to fight against insect herbivores. The coca plant is indigenous to South America, and for many centuries, the native inhabitants had chewed the coca leaves for vital nutrients as well as for its psychological effects. After the coca leaves were brought to Europe in the 19th century, cocaine was found to be useful as an anesthetic. In addition, it was observed that cocaine also created a euphoric sense of happiness and an increase in energy. As a result, it was marketed as a medicine for treating depression and fatigue. It was also used as a beverage supplement, including being used in Coca Cola, during the early 1900s. However, cocaine was soon found to be addictive and because of this property, it was made illegal in virtually all parts of the world.

Cocaine is a potent central nervous system stimulant. Individuals experience hyperactivity, restlessness, and euphoria with an increase in heart rate and blood pressure. Sexual interest and pleasure are also often magnified. These effects last from 20 minutes to several hours, depending upon the cocaine dose taken and method of administration. For some individuals, the euphoria is sometimes followed by feelings of discomfort and depression. Within a short time after using cocaine, most people experience a craving and want to experience the drug again. With increased cocaine use, many, but not all, individuals feel an insatiable urge to take cocaine. They also lose interest in other pleasurable activities, such as food, friendship, and even sex.

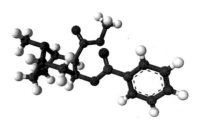

Cocaine

Cocaine is a simple molecule and a powerful central nervous system stimulant.

Research on the neurological effects of cocaine has led to an improved understanding of its addictive properties. Cocaine affects the pleasure center of the brain called the nucleus accumbens. When an individual experiences a pleasurable sensation, the neurons in the nucleus accumbens release dopamine into their synapses. The amount of dopamine in the synapses is controlled by dopamine transporter molecules on the cell membrane of the pre-synaptic neurons. These dopamine transporters bind to the dopamine molecules in the synapse and reabsorb them. This action terminates the pleasurable sensation. This important feedback mechanism controls the intensity and duration of the pleasurable sensation. Daily activities, such as eating, can also induce pleasure through this regulatory mechanism.

Cocaine and dopamine have similar molecular structures. Cocaine, however, is unable to bind to the dopamine receptors on the post-synaptic neurons. Therefore, it cannot directly stimulate neural activities. Instead, cocaine binds to the dopamine transporters and prevents them from binding to dopamine. In effect, it shuts down the dopamine transporters, leading to the accumulation of dopamine in the synapse.

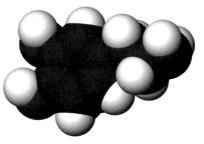

Dopamine

It is one of the key neurotransmitters in the reward pathway.

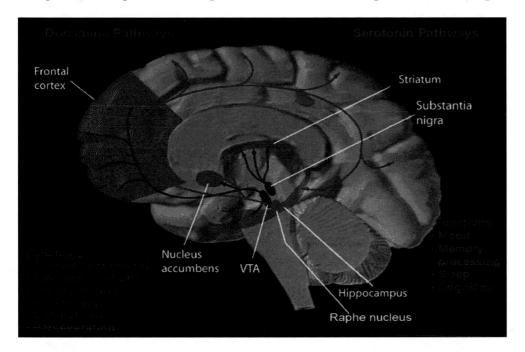

Frontal cortex

Striatum

Substantia nigra

Nucleus accumbens   VTA

Hippocampus

Raphe nucleus

The dopamine pathway

It is the pathway important for reward and pleasure. *(Public Domain)*

The concentration of dopamine during a cocaine high is as much as 30 times higher than the dopamine concentration that occurs during an orgasm. Prolonged exposure of the neurons to high concentrations of dopamine eventually leads to a structural change within the neurons. It is this change that is responsible for the addictive properties of cocaine.

Methamphetamine is another psychoactive substance that has gained popularity around the world in recent years. Methamphetamine was first widely used by German soldiers during World War II to increase their alertness during battles. Methamphetamine, unlike cocaine, is a designer drug, because it is chemically

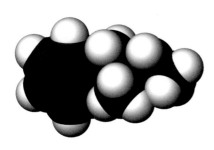

Methamphetamine

It is known as a designer drug because it is synthesized from other over-the-counter drugs. It stimulates dopamine production in the reward pathway.

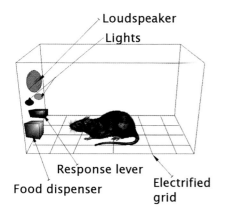

Loudspeaker

Lights

Response lever

Food dispenser

Electrified grid

Skinner box

This is a model system for testing the brain reward system in rats.
(GNU Free Documentation License)

synthesized from other drugs, such as over-the-counter cold medicines. However, it is a stimulant that has similar psychoactive properties to those of cocaine. Methamphetamine also acts by increasing dopamine concentration in the synapses of neurons in the nucleus accumbens. Through a mechanism not yet fully understood, methamphetamine induces the pre-synaptic neurons to produce more dopamine, creating a feeling of euphoria in its users.

II.2. How does cocaine cause addiction?

Addiction to cocaine is more intense and debilitating than is addiction to tobacco and caffeine. It causes greater harm to the well-being of individuals. Addiction to cocaine often results in harmful consequences to an individual's health, mental state, and social life. The addiction is so strong in most individuals that they are unable to stop taking cocaine on their own. Because of the many dangers associated with cocaine, its addiction, along with the addictions of other psychoactive substances, is considered a mental disorder rather than a lifestyle preference.

Recent research in animals has provided evidence that addiction alters the physical properties of the brain. The neurological basis of addiction was first discovered by two neurobiologists, James Old and Peter Miller, at McGill University, Canada. They discovered that the electrical stimulation of the nucleus accumbens in the rat brain produced pleasurable sensations in the rats. In their experiments, they trained rats to deliver electrical stimulation to their brains by pressing a paddle in their cages. The rats enjoyed the effects so much that they would continuously press their paddle and would only stop when exhausted. The researchers then placed two paddles in the cage and separated them by a metal grid. When the researchers turned off one of the paddles, the rats learned to cross the grid to use the other paddle. The rats would run across the grid even when it was electrified and delivered painful shocks to their feet. Interestingly, the rats often refused to brave the shocks to obtain other pleasures, such as food or water. These results suggested that the stimulation of the pleasure center of the brain can have a powerful effect.

When the rats were exposed to cocaine through their drinking water, it was observed that they developed a similar desire for the cocaine that human addicts do. They even fought with each other when there was shortage of cocaine-laced water. They also would run across the electrified metal grid to reach the water bowl containing cocaine. Their cravings and desires for cocaine were as high as those of human addicts. These studies demonstrated that the neurological mechanism for cocaine addiction is the same for humans as it is for other mammals. Just like the rats, human addicts will do everything they can to satisfy their addiction without considering the harmful effects.

The biological basis of addiction results from physical changes in the structures of the neurons. These changes occur over a long period of time, and once the changes have occurred, the neurons cannot easily return to their original structure and configuration. The main change that neurons undergo is at the level of the neurotransmitter receptors on the surface of the post-synaptic neurons. In a normal individual, the number of neurotransmitter receptors on the surface of the post-synaptic neurons is calibrated to the amount of neurotransmitters that are ordinarily released into the synapse. This calibration is critical to ensure that the post-synaptic neurons will not become over or under activated. In addicts, this balance has been altered by a psychoactive substance.

In cocaine addiction, the high level of dopamine in the synapse overwhelms the post-synaptic neurons, causing them to fire continuously and uncontrollably. This over activation of the post-synaptic neurons is responsible for the euphoria and overwhelming feeling of pleasure. When cocaine is repeatedly administered, the post-synaptic neurons undergo changes to control their firing rate. Each neuron reduces the number of dopamine receptors on its surface, so that stimulation is controlled despite the high dopamine concentration in the synapse. This reduction is known as receptor down regulation, and it is the mechanism that causes drug tolerance.

To achieve an adequate feeling of euphoria, addicts must continuously increase the drug's dose. This increase, in turn, results in a further reduction in the number of dopamine receptors. Because of the down regulation of the dopamine receptors, activities that were once enjoyable are no longer pleasurable. In time, cocaine addicts continue to use cocaine at increasingly higher levels just to have enough desire to live. Furthermore, if the cocaine use stops abruptly, addicts will go into withdrawal and have both psychological and physiological symptoms. These symptoms result from the imbalance of neurotransmitters and their receptors in the brain.

Down regulation of receptors

Cocaine causes the down regulation of dopamine receptors on the surface of post-synaptic neurons. *(GNU Free Documentation License)*

II.3. *Why does the brain have a pleasure center?*

The discovery of the nucleus accumbens was important in understanding the biological mechanisms of addiction to psychoactive substances, such as cocaine, methamphetamine, and caffeine. Nearly all addictive psychoactive drugs target this small area of the brain, suggesting that this is the brain region that is responsible for feeling pleasure. Pleasure, however, can also result from other activities, such as eating and sex. Therefore, the nucleus accumbens must also be involved in rewarding behaviors that are vital for the reproduction and survival of organisms. Furthermore, it must have evolved to help organisms fulfill these important biological needs.

Researchers have looked for brain regions in other mammals and in primitive organisms that are similar to the human nucleus accumbens. They discovered that similar brain regions are part of the primitive brains of reptiles and amphibians. Together with the brainstem, they constitute the reptilian brain. In addition to the nucleus accumbens, there are several other components in this region of the brain. They are the amygdala, which is responsible for emotion, and the hippocampus, which is involved in forming memory. The nucleus accumbens, amygdala, hippocampus, and several other components form the limbic system. The limbic system is comprised of a set of neural pathways that are collectively known as the reward pathways. These reward pathways are responsible for ensuring that humans obtain what is required for survival and well being.

Love, friendship, altruism, self-esteem, and spirituality were once considered the domain of philosophy and psychology. One psychological theory, which was proposed by Abraham Maslow, a cognitive psychologist, attempted to explain the various levels of human behavior. In his theory, Maslow proposed that there are five levels of human needs for survival and for leading a successful life. Humans must continue to strive to meet these needs, and the progression from one level to the next can occur only after having satisfied the lower level of needs. The first level is related to biological needs. All living organisms must fulfill certain basic physiological needs, such as oxygen, food, and water, for their survival.

The next level of human needs is the need for safety and security. These needs are reflected by the common human yearning for a predictable, orderly world in which injustice and inconsistency are under control, the familiar is frequent, and the unfamiliar is rare. These needs can appear in different ways, such in the form of job security, financial security, personal health, and well being. After the physiological and safety needs are fulfilled, the third level of human needs that must be met are social needs. Since humans are highly social, these needs are important for group cohesion and harmony. Another important part of the social needs is the need for sexual and emotional relationships.

The fourth level of human needs is the esteem needs. These include the needs to be respected, to have self-esteem, to have self-respect, and to respect others. Humans have emotional drives that allow them to strive for recognition, to have a sense of contributing something important, to feel accepted, and to feel valued. Imbalance at this level leads to low self-esteem. The last level of the human needs is the growth needs, also known as self-actualization needs. This is the need for intellectual development that occurs because of curiosity, exploration, and self-realization. The growth needs can only be adequately pursued after the other four lower levels of needs have been met. These sets of needs are known collectively as Maslow's hierarchy of human needs.

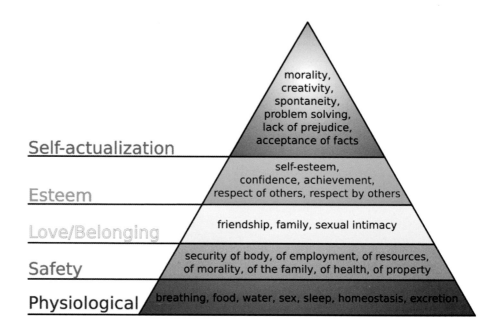

The hierarchy of human needs

Diagram of Maslow's hierarchy of human needs, represented as a pyramid with more primitive needs at the bottom. *(GNU Free Documentation License)*

Why would humans pursue these needs? What motivates them to pursue these needs? Is there a biological basis for humans to seek fulfillment of these needs? From studying the effects of abuse substances, researchers have realized that the reward pathways of the limbic system form the biological basis in motivating human behaviors. Also, it has been determined that human behaviors are genetically encoded and that these behaviors are rewarded within the reward pathways in the same way that cocaine "rewards" an addict.

III. WHAT ARE OTHER HUMAN ADDICTIONS?

Based on the biological studies of psychoactive drugs and on the psychological studies of human needs, researchers have concluded that human behavior has a biological base. Understanding the biological mechanisms of human behavior can provide valuable insights into the nature of human emotions that are important in love, friendship, anger, and jealousy. This type of understanding is also important for understanding the evolution of love, courtship, and pair-bonding. In the past ten years, great progress has been made in unraveling the neurological process of love, attachment, and pair bonding. This understanding can help individuals to better manage their emotional lives and to gain a better appreciation of their intimate relationships.

III.1. Is love an addiction?

Can love become addictive and obsessive? The answer is clearly yes, and the consequences of obsessive love can be dangerous and tragic. John Hinckley shot the President of United States, Ronald Reagan, in an assassination attempt because he wanted to catch the attention of actress Jodie Foster. He wanted to use this action to have her fall in love with him. As seen in the news, obsessive love is often the cause of stalking, rape, suicide, and murder. The victims are often the targets of an obsession. Why does love go wrong and become obsessive? What are the conditions that cause love obsession?

From the neurological standpoint, love has many similarities to addiction to psychoactive substances. There are three phases of love: the lust phase, the attraction phase, and the attachment phase. The lust phase is the first phase of love. In this phase, the physical attachment is strongest because of stimulation by the fertility signals. The excitement of the lust phase is enhanced by the production of norepinephrine in the brain and by epinephrine in the adrenal gland. During sexual intimacy that includes kissing, touching, embracing, and talk-teasing, neurons in the nucleus accumbens are stimulated to produce dopamine. Through dopamine and through several other neurotransmitters, the reward pathways are stimulated to seek repetition of these behaviors. During the lust phase, a high level of dopamine is produced and a euphoric experience is generated that is similar to the effect produced by cocaine.

Sexual orgasm produces the highest level of dopamine in the nucleus accumbens. This level then affects the other regions of the limbic system. One of the structures of the limbic system is the hypothalamus, which is triggered to produce the peptide hormones, oxytocin and vasopression. The targets of these hormones are thought to be located somewhere in the reward pathways within the limbic system. The exact function of these hormones is unknown, but they have been shown to be important in forming strong pair-bonds.

Love obsession most likely results because of strong neurological connections between the nucleus accumbens and the amygdala. All animals that form monogamous pair-bonds possess these neurological pathways. Because of the neural connection, they develop an obsessive love relationship with their partners. When their love is not returned, they become aggressive and act violently. One interesting example of this pair-bonding is the relationship that occurred between a woman and her pet macaw. Macaws are New World parrots that are found in Mexico, Central America, and South America. They are monogamous and pair for life. They are fiercely devoted to each other and are very possessive of their partners.

When a macaw is raised as a pet, they treat their primary caretaker as their mating partner. In one case, a male macaw, which had bonded with the lady of the house, got into a nightly tussle with her husband when he tried to kiss her goodnight. This example demonstrates that love, as well as attachment, is a biological process and is not restricted to humans.

As monogamous organisms, humans have evolved powerful neurological mechanisms to reward behaviors that are conducive for pair-bonding. The reward pathways of the limbic system contain all the necessary neurological components to reinforce this behavior. However, psychoactive substances, such as cocaine, can hijack these pathways and cause addictive behavior that, in many ways, is not that different from the neurochemistry of love.

III.2. *What are psychological addictions?*

Our behavioral inclinations to love and to be loved are genetic traits that have evolved to ensure the survival of our species. These behavior traits are critical for sexual reproduction and for the care of the young. Nevertheless, individual variations also create a wide range of sexual behaviors. Some individuals are hyposexual, showing little interest in sex, whereas some individuals are hypersexual. Many of these individuals suffer from abnormal behaviors that are driven by neurological

Assassination attempt of Reagan

Chaos outside the Washington Hilton Hotel after the assassination attempt of President Reagan by John Hinckley. *(Public Domain)*

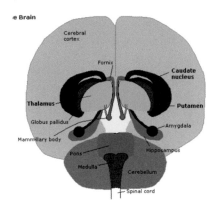

The amygdala

The human brain as viewed from the underside, with the front of the brain at the top. Amygdalae are shown in dark red. *(GNU Free Documentation License)*

Macaw

They form life-long pair-bonds. *(Public Domain)*

processes. Only in recent years has the neurological basis of these various sexual behaviors become understood.

One example of these behavior variations is a condition known as sexual addiction, in which the affected individuals feel such an overwhelming need for sex that this drive interferes with their jobs and relationships. They pursue their addiction in the same way that a cocaine addict does. No matter how hard they try, they fail repeatedly at attempts to reduce or control their sexual activities or desires. Their major symptoms are nearly identical to those of a cocaine addict and include compulsiveness, obsession, and continuation to take any risk for satisfaction despite the consequences.

The neurological basis of sexual addiction was determined by examining the hormonal profiles and the neurotransmitter production in animals and humans who had symptoms of sexual addiction. They all showed a higher level of blood testosterone (testosterone is the hormone that is primarily responsible for sex drive). Furthermore, they showed a higher than normal level of dopamine during sexual activity in their nucleus accumbens. These individuals also had a low number of dopamine receptors on the surface of their post-synaptic neurons. Because of these abnormalities, these individuals had a continuing demand for sexual activity. The lives of these individuals are as miserable as those of the cocaine addicts. Instead of seeking cocaine, they are constantly seeking sex.

Sexual addiction can be caused by many different factors, including genetic factors, developmental impairments, psychological factors, and physical trauma. One interesting case of sexual addiction that demonstrates the neurological basis of this disorder is a woman who developed symptoms of sexual addiction after suffering a head injury from an automobile accident. Understanding the neurological basis of sexual addiction has important social implications. This knowledge could result in better treatment of sex offenders, such as pedophiles and serial rapists. This understanding can also help individuals who have a sex addiction to better understand their psychological conditions.

Sex addiction is also an example of a psychological addiction, which is a dependency of the mind that if prevented, can lead to withdrawal symptoms, such as craving, irritability, insomnia, and depression. One of the most common forms of psychological addiction is work addiction or workaholism. Individuals who have a work addiction do not enjoy their work but feel compelled to work. Workaholism in Japan is considered a serious social problem, leading to family difficulties, poor health, depression, and other mental problems. In severe cases of work addiction, some individuals simply work themselves to death.

Many other normal behaviors can become addictive if they become uncontrollable, such as gambling, Internet addictions, computer addictions, pornography addictions, reading, eating, shopping, self-harm, vandalism, and shoplifting. The causes of psychological addictions are many, but their neurological mechanisms are most likely similar and are linked to the reward pathways in the limbic system. They also share many features with psychoactive substance abuse. In both cases, there is an imbalance of neurotransmitters, which results in an inappropriate stimulation of the nucleus accumbens and in other parts of the reward pathways.

III.3. Are there proper uses of psychoactive substances?

Love and many other psychological addictions demonstrate that all behavioral traits exist in a broad range, and sometimes, defining normalcy is subjective and depends on the situation. However, when the behavior becomes compulsive and harmful to the individual, the criteria for addiction becomes applicable. When love for an individual reaches a point of excessive jealousy, rage, violence, and abuse, the line of normal behavior has been crossed. Similarly, the use of psychoactive

Ancient sex addiction
Pornographic image shown on an ancient oil lamp. *(Public Domain)*

substances also exists in a broad range, from harmless to detrimental. It is important to understand the various aspects of the use of psychoactive substances.

One example of the broad range of effects is the use of alcohol. When considering the negative effects of alcoholism, the legality of alcohol can be questioned. However, moderate and controlled use of alcohol is not harmful and could even be beneficial. For example, medical research has shown that drinking one glass of red wine each day protects against heart disease and Alzheimer's disease. Therefore, alcohol consumption is not illegal, because responsible use of alcohol is not only pleasurable but also has health benefits.

The effects of alcohol and many other psychoactive drugs span the spectrum of beneficial to harmful. At one end of this spectrum is the beneficial use of psychoactive substances. Coffee and tea are useful to increase alertness and to promote work efficiency. In addition, many psychoactive substances are valuable medicines when used at appropriate doses. For example, morphine, cocaine, and cannabis have been used to relieve pain. Benzodiazepines and other related sedatives have been very effective in relieving psychological tension and in promoting sleep. In fact, many psychoactive drugs have been used for beneficial purposes.

The next level is the recreational but nonproblematic use of psychoactive substances. Social drinking and the use of alcohol for relaxation fall into this category, and so does the controlled use of cigarettes. The occasional use of cannabis and hallucinogens is also appropriate for this spectrum of use. This level of use has negligible health or social effects. The next level of use creates negative consequences, including problems with personal health, financial well-being, emotional stability, social relationships, work, and other social situations. For example, driving inebriated, spousal abuse, and missing work are some examples of behavior in this category. The most serious level is chronic dependence, when the usage of the psychoactive substance becomes habitual and compulsive, leading to a complete disruption of personal life and to serious health damage.

The number of psychoactive substances that are available through both legal and illegal means has increased dramatically over the past 100 years. Many prescription drugs have found illegal outlets for recreational use. Your understanding of the

Spectrum of Psychoactive Substance Use

Casual/Non-problematic Use

- recreational, casual or other use that has negligible health or social effects

Chronic Dependence

- Use that has become habitual and compulsive despite negative health and social effects

Beneficial Use

- use that has positive health, spiritual or social impact:
- e.g. medical pharmaceuticals; coffee/tea to increase alertness; moderate consumption of red wine; sacramental use of ayahuasca or peyote

Problematic Use

- use that begins to have negative consequences for individual, friends/family, or society
- e.g. impaired driving; binge consumption; harmful routes of administration

A public health approach
From drug controls in Canada.
(Public Domain)

addictive properties of these substances is important for you to make appropriate decisions if you come into contact with them either through leisure or medical situations.

Several years ago, a medical journal, *The Lancet,* compiled data on dependence and on the physical harm of common psychoactive substances. The data from 20 psychoactive substances were analyzed and plotted on a graph that was designed to show the relationships between addictiveness and physical damage to the users. As expected, heroin topped the list in both addictiveness and in physical harm. Cocaine was second, followed by methamphetamine, barbiturates, and street methadone. Tobacco was shown to be almost as addictive as cocaine but with less physical harm. Similarly, alcohol is less addictive than tobacco but causes more physical harm.

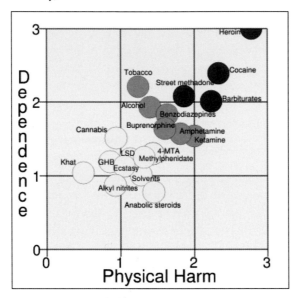

Dependence versus physical harm

Comparison of the perceived harm of various psychoactive drugs.
(GNU Free Documentation License)

The understanding of addiction to psychoactive substances provides an important window into the neurochemistry of our mind. As researchers gain a greater appreciation of the integration of the different parts of the human brain, some of the deepest mysteries of human behaviors, such as morality, altruism, and spirituality, will be understood.

Chapter 13

Disorders

How normal are you?

Kurt Cobain with Nirvana, 1992

Kurt Cobain suffered from bipolar affective disorder. In 1994, he was found dead in his home with a self-inflicted shotgun wound to the head. (*Creative Commons Attribution, R.B. Page*)

CHAPTER 13. DISORDERS

Maslow's hierarchy of human needs provides justifications for why humans need to have desires to survive. Only through these desires will individuals seek fulfillment of the physiological and emotional requirements for survival. The ultimate goal of all living organisms is to reproduce. Meeting the human physiological, safety, social, esteem, and cognitive needs are essential before an individual can find a mate, reproduce, and successfully raise offspring. However, the desire for these human needs varies widely in individuals because of genetic variations and differing environments.

Love is an example of how desires can vary. Love is a critical social need for reproduction and for raising offspring. However, love can become obsessive and out of control. Through the studies of psychoactive substances, researchers have gained an understanding of the neurological process by which the brain directs human behavior in meeting human needs. This understanding is also important to the understanding of behavioral disorders.

I. WHY DO WE HAVE EMOTION?

Everyday when we go through life, we take a roller coaster ride of emotional feelings. We are so accustomed to them that we do not notice them most of the time. However, occasionally these emotional feelings overwhelm us, making us either grateful that we are alive or wondering what the purpose of life is. These emotional feelings are vital for our survival and help us make choices in our lives. Without these emotions, life would be uncertain and aimless. Recent research in animals has discovered that human emotions have a deep evolutionary root. Even simple organisms, such as snakes, also have emotional responses, and their neurological basis of emotion is identical to that of humans. Of course, their emotional responses are more basic, but they are as important for their survival as human emotion is for us. What is the biological significance of emotion?

I.1. *What is the biological significance of emotion?*

Emotion has deep evolutionary roots, and recent research has demonstrated the existence of human-like emotion in many animals. At the biological level, one of the most important functions of emotion is to enhance an organism's ability to encode its experiences into long-term memory. Emotion also heightens an organism's attention and focus so that it can evaluate the importance of situations that provoke past memory. Emotion also allows an organism to make decisions when developing the best strategies for survival and reproduction. In other words, emotion strongly affects both memory and future behavior. A positive emotion creates pleasure and causes the animals to repeat their experience. A negative experience, however, creates anxiety and fear which cause the animals to avoid such an experience in the future.

One method by which to study emotion in humans is to examine those individuals who have lost the ability to use emotion. In a rare example, a 35-year-old man suffered a stroke in his limbic system that affected his emotion. After he recovered, he lost nearly all emotional feeling. He showed no fear, empathy, or pleasure in his daily life. Before he had the stroke, he was a loving husband and father. He enjoyed watching movies and playing sports with his children. Each year, he took a great deal of time to plan their family vacation, and he always looked forward to it with great anticipation. After the stroke, however, he has no desire for nearly anything, including the activities that he once enjoyed. He could no longer work, because his ability to make decisions was also lost. He spent his entire day sitting at home. To his wife, he became an entirely different person after the stroke.

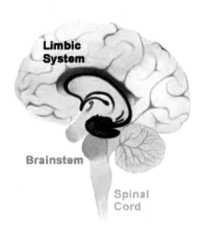

Limbic system

It is the region of the brain that plays a central role in human emotion. *(Public Domain)*

Capgras delusion is another example that demonstrates the importance of emotion in our daily lives. A man was involved in an automobile accident and suffered severe head trauma. He was in a coma for several weeks, and fortunately, he made a nearly full recovery. The head injury affected the movement of one of his arms, but otherwise he was fully functional, with one exception. He complained to friends that his parents were not his real parents but were imposters. He could not explain why he felt that way. He admitted that they looked exactly how he remembered his parents looked. However, he did not feel any emotional feelings toward them when he saw them. Therefore, he felt that they must not be his real parents because he could not feel love and closeness toward them.

Fear of snakes
The human fear of snakes is the result of activation of the limbic system. (*Creative Commons Attribution*)

Both of these examples demonstrate the importance of emotion in our lives. Without emotion, individuals would not have the motivation or desire to pursue the necessities of life. Emotion is also the driving force for humans to meet the different levels as described in Maslow's hierarchy of human needs. To navigate the paths to reach these needs, humans, as well as other animals, must possess the neurological and physiological mechanisms that allow them to respond to environmental cues. Emotion is the neurological mechanism by which animals respond to these environmental cues. Through emotional responses, animals can make appropriate choices.

An emotion is defined as a neurological and physiological state that reflects a wide variety of feelings regarding mental conditions and behaviors. Emotion is also a prime determinant of the sense of individual well-being. It is highly subjective, but it plays a central role in human activities. The classical approaches to the study of emotion are mainly sociological, philosophical, and psychological. Emotional feelings are also explored in literature, art, and music. Until recently, emotion was considered beyond the realm of scientific investigations, but advances in biology over the past several decades have provided many insights into the different forms of emotion and has revealed that there is a common physiological and neurological basis to all forms of emotional feelings.

Throughout history, there have been many theories on how to classify emotion. According to most researchers, there are six basic emotions. They are anger, disgust, fear, happiness, sadness, and surprise. These basic emotions can be combined into more complex emotions, such as satisfaction, frustration, anxiety, excitement, embarrassment, guilt, relief, sadness, depression, shame, and jealousy. Primitive animals, such as reptiles, have only basic emotions, such as fear, anger, and surprise. In mammals, these emotions are well developed, and social species, such as dogs and primates, have complex emotions that are similar to humans. The great apes have nearly all the emotions that are found in humans. Based on these observations, it has been concluded that all human emotions must have a biological basis.

I.2. What is the physiological basis of emotion?

When a person experiences an emotion, their body undergoes typical physiological reactions, such as sweaty palms, pupil dilation, dry mouth, palpitations, accelerated heart rate, and heavy breathing. These changes also occur without any conscious control. The classical example of the effects of emotion at the physiological level is the well-known fight or flight response. This behavioral response is common to nearly all animals. This physiological response has a deep evolutionary root because it is important to the survival of the organisms. Consequently, the biological mechanism of this response is nearly identical in all animals.

A lion in the hunt
Its fight or flight response is activated as it pursues its prey. (*Creative Commons Attribution*)

The fight or flight response is an exaggerated physiological response that prepares an animal to undertake extreme physical activities to either fight or flee. Interestingly, all the extreme physiological changes of the body are triggered by a single hormone, known as adrenalin or epinephrine, which is produced by the adrenal gland. This hormone has profound effects on almost every cell in the body. The effects of adrenalin result because of the presence of adrenalin receptors on cell surfaces. Even though the receptors are the same for all cells, the binding of these receptors with the adrenalin molecules can lead to different biological effects in the cells, which causes them to carry out different actions.

From the biological standpoint, the fight or flight response is a physiological disturbance of normal body functions in preparation to confront a dangerous or life-threatening situation. The fight or flight response is the body's preparedness to devote all its resources to handle an emergency situation. The entire response is reflexive because there is simply not enough time. To understand the working of the fight or flight response, it is important to know that the functions of the human body are under both conscious and unconscious controls. The conscious control is subjected to our thought processes in the cerebral cortex, whereas the unconscious control occurs through the brainstem and the limbic system.

The brainstem manages all the basic physiological processes such as heart rate,

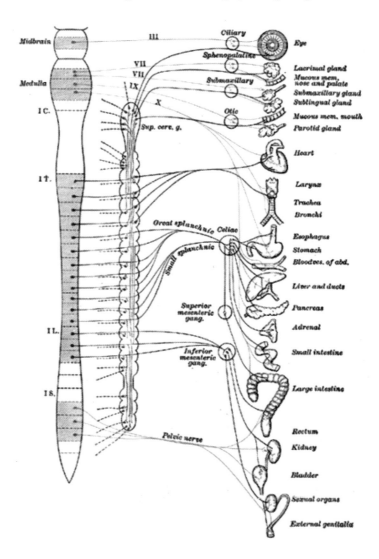

The autonomic nervous system

The brain system controls the basic physiology of the body, including the fight or flight response.

Blue = parasympathetic

Red - sympathetic

(Public Domain)

respiration, blood glucose level, and body temperature. The brainstem uses two peripheral nervous systems, collectively known as the autonomic nervous system. The first system is the parasympathetic nervous system, which functions to maintain a steady state condition known as homeostasis. This condition is optimal for digestion, nutrient absorption, cell growth, and development. The second system is the sympathetic nervous system, which is responsible for directing the tissues and organs to undergo rapid physiological changes in preparation for maximum physical actions. The brainstem maintains the balance between these two opposing nervous systems.

In the fight or flight response, the central nervous system senses a dangerous situation and triggers the brainstem, which then sends a signal to the adrenal gland for the production of adrenalin. Adrenalin travels through the blood to every part of the body, shuts down the parasympathetic nervous system, and activates the sympathetic nervous system. All normal body functions, such as digestion, kidney function, and sexual desire, are shut down. Other activities, such as heart rate, breathing, and blood glucose level are increased. These changes are necessary to increase blood flow so that the maximum amount of oxygen and glucose is delivered to the muscles for the preparation of physical activity.

The fight or flight response is observed in all vertebrates and in many invertebrates. It is the ultimate physiological response that prepares animals for dangerous and life-threatening situations. In simple animals, the fight or flight response serves the basic demands for survival. However, in animals that have complex behaviors, the fight or flight response is modified for managing complex emotions. Nevertheless, the physiological process of these emotions is still the same.

I.3. What is the neurological basis of emotion?

The neurological basis of emotion has become better understood from studies of stroke patients and with brain scanning techniques. Animal studies have also indicated the brain regions that are most involved in the generation of emotion. In one study with rats, researchers discovered that destruction of neurons in a small area of the brain, known as the amygdala, completely eliminated their fear of people. They also found a genetic mutation that caused an inhibition in the development of the amygdala, which then resulted in a modified fear response. These results suggested that there is a region in the brain that is critical for the emotion of fear.

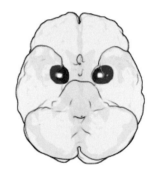

Amygdala
Despite its small size, the amygdala is one of the central controls of neural activities in the brain. *(Public Domain)*

Similar to the nucleus accumbens, the amygdala is located in the limbic system, which is part of the reptilian brain. It has a long evolutionary history because it is prominently present in the brains of all reptiles. Using brain scanning techniques, researchers have demonstrated that neural activities in the amydgala of a snake are increased when it is startled. In one study using human brain scanning, the neural activities of the amygdala were measured after showing subjects a set of photographs of pleasant and smiling faces. The researchers then inserted a face that had an angry and threatening expression. The neural activity within the test subject's amygdala increased immediately, providing strong evidence that the amygdala is the brain region that is used for reacting to fear and other emotional responses.

In the earlier example of the man who was deprived of emotion after his stroke, researchers discovered that the part of his brain that was the most severely affected was the amygdala. With injury to this part of the brain, he lost the ability to experience fear and all other emotions. This example indicates that in the human brain, the amygdala is responsible for the entire range of human emotion. The amygdala is also involved in the Capgras delusion. In these individuals, the neural pathways between the amygdala and the temporal lobe are affected. Normally, visual information is decoded for recognition in the frontal lobe and in the temporal lobe. This information is then sent to the amygdala for assessing its emotional value. The amygdala then reports back to the temporal lobe regarding whether this information has emotional significance or not. In the case of Capgras delusion, the communication between the amygdala and the temporal lobe is disrupted. Without the emotional value, loved ones seem like strangers and are therefore considered to be impostors.

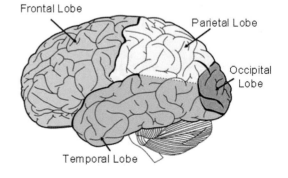

Cerebral cortex
Basic subdivision of the cerebral cortex. *(Public Domain)*

The neural communications between the amygdala and other parts of the brain are also critical for memory formation. There are, however, different types of memory; one type is episodic or emotional memory. We have all experienced the acquisition of episodic memory because these memories are associated with emotional situations, both negative and positive. For example, your high school graduation was an emotional experience, and the details of that occasion are etched in your memory. For many, a traffic accident is another example of episodic memory. Episodic memory is also related to major events in the news. For example, the 9/11 terrorist attack on the World Trade Center Towers will remain forever in your memory. You will never forget your own personal events of that day.

Emotional memory
9/11 terrorist attack. *(Public Domain)*

From studies in humans and in animals, researchers have discovered that emotion and memory are strongly tied to each other. In the brain, the hippocampus is the region that is responsible for memory formation. The hippocampus and the amygdala are parts of the limbic system and are linked together by extensive neural pathways. They are also found in primitive vertebrates, including reptiles, which suggests that they are important for the survival of reptiles as well. The linkage between emotion and memory is vital for animals to pursue activities that are rewarding and to avoid activities that are detrimental. By attaching emotional values to these activities, they can act with purpose and decisiveness.

Emotions have a powerful impact on the memory and on the behavior of humans and other animals. Under normal circumstances, emotions are short-lived. Emotions are mainly elicited during events that are either dangerous or pleasurable. Once the stimuli are removed, the brainstem curtails the physiological impact of the emotion by restoring the normal balance between the parasympathetic and sympathetic nervous systems.

In some situations, however, emotion and its physiological responses persist. In one study of baboons that live on the African savanna, researchers demonstrated that the persistence of emotional response is harmful. Baboons are social animals that have a hierarchy of male dominance. Males establish their rank through both physical violence and psychological intimidation. In this situation, the low-ranking males are under constant psychological stress, which affects both their emotional and psychological health. Their physical health is also compromised because of elevated levels of adrenalin in their bodies. From this type of research, the connection between psychological stress and physiological well-being has been established.

Male olive baboon
Baboons live in a social group and they suffer similar stress disorders as humans.

II. WHAT ARE THE CAUSES OF MENTAL DISORDERS?

What are mental disorders? How do people develop them, and how can they be treated? Are some individuals more susceptible to mental disorders than others? What is the role of emotion in mental disorders? The search for the answers to these questions is ongoing and will most likely continue for several more decades. The descriptions of mental disorders date back to the ancient Greeks, and terms such as melancholy, hysteria, and phobia have origins that are traceable to ancient Greece and Rome. Over the centuries, mentally ill patients have faced severe discrimination and stigmatization. Until the advent of modern psychiatry and psychology, explanations for mental disorders were based on religious beliefs and demonic possession. In Nazi Germany, mental patients were deemed "life unworthy of life," and over 100,000 mental patients were exterminated.

II.1. *What are the different types of mental disorders?*

Nearly all mental disorders are classified as a form of an emotional disorder. The main symptoms are often inappropriate expressions of emotion under normal social contexts. The Muslim doctors in the 9th century were the first to recognize that mental disorders have a biological basis rather than a purely "spiritual" basis. These Muslim doctors were the first to advocate humane treatment of the mentally ill. Still, society at the time failed to accommodate those suffering from severe mental conditions such as psychosis. In the 12th century, the earliest mental institutions were established in Europe. However, most mental patients were chained to their beds, and many were treated worse than livestock.

Modern psychiatry

Philippe Pinel in the 1800s proposed humane treatment of mental patients. *(Public Domain)*

Modern psychiatry began in the early 1800s, when Philippe Pinel in Europe and Dorothea Dix in the United States championed the rights of the mentally ill and created mental asylums. During the late 1800s and early 1900s, Sigmund Freud proposed some of the early theories to explain the etiology of mental illnesses, and Alois Alzheimer discovered the first biological evidence of a mental disorder. However, other than institutionalization, no treatments existed for patients with mental disorders.

In the early 1950s, the discovery of antipsychotic drugs changed the treatment of mental disorders. Chlorpromazine was accidentally discovered as a treatment for schizophrenia, which was previously untreatable by any other means. It was a remarkable discovery, because schizophrenia is one of the most serious mental disorders. Since then, many psychoactive substances have been discovered that can treat a wide range of mental disorders. The neurological mechanisms by which these psychiatric drugs work are similar to the mechanisms that are used by the recreational psychoactive substances. In both cases, the effects of the substances result from an ability to interfere with the activities of neurotransmitters in the synapses.

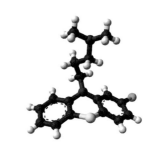

Chlorpromazine

It is the first chemical that was discovered for the treatment of mental disorders.

Another advance in the understanding and treatment of mental disorders was the classification of different mental disorders. This knowledge has led to a better understanding of the different mental disorders and to the development of more specific treatments. At the beginning of the 20th century, there were only a few recognized types of mental disorders. In the early 1950s, the American Psychiatric Association classified mental disorders and published the Diagnostic and Statistical Manual of Mental Disorders (DSM). This publication has become the diagnostic standard that is used by psychiatrists and clinical psychologists. It has influenced the perceptions and treatment of mental disorders in the U.S.

In the first edition of the DSM, there were 192 disorders listed along with descriptions of their clinical symptoms. In the 4th edition (2000), also known as the DSM-IV, the list of disorders was expanded to 374. In addition, the disorders have been divided into five domains or axes. Axis I includes clinical disorders, which are all the mental disorders except personality disorders and mental retardation. Axis II comprises personality disorders and mental retardation. Axis III are mental disorders that are connected to general medical conditions, such as trauma, stroke, or infectious diseases. Axis IV includes psychosocial and environmental problems, such as post-traumatic stress disorder (PTSD). The reason for the increase in the number of mental disorders between the DSM-I and the DSM-IV remains unknown.

DIAGNOSTIC AND STATISTICAL MANUAL OF MENTAL DISORDERS

FOURTH EDITION

TEXT REVISION

DSM-IV-TR™

AMERICAN PSYCHIATRIC ASSOCIATION

DSM-IV

It contains a list of 374 mental disorders with their clinical descriptions. *(Public Domain)*

Discoverer of Tourette's syndrome

A developmental disorder that is common among children. *(Public Domain)*

Typical behavior of autism

An autistic child stacks cans. *(GNU Free Documentation License)*

Typical behavior of autism

An autistic child lines up his toys. *(GNU Free Documentation License)*

The classification of disorders in the DSM-IV was also important because for the first time, developmental time frames were considered. Many groups of mental disorders are usually diagnosed before the patients reach adulthood. For example, Tay-Sachs disease and fetal alcohol syndrome are first diagnosed in infancy. Autism, mental retardation, and attention deficient hyperactivity disorder (ADHD) are diagnosed in early childhood. Bipolar affective disorders, Tourette's syndrome, and obsessive compulsive disorders are diagnosed in early adolescence, and schizophrenia is most often diagnosed in late adolescence. Other groups of mental disorders, however, such as depression and Alzheimer's disease, are often diagnosed in early or late adulthood.

II.2. *What are the causes of mental disorders?*

Many mental disorders have a genetic origin. The most unambiguous example is Tay-Sachs disease. This disease occurs because of a mutation in the gene that encodes for an enzyme that is required in fatty acid metabolism. Tay-Sachs disease is characterized by a gradual loss of both cognitive and motor functions. The child's brain gradually deteriorates, and death often occurs before the fifth birthday. Another example is Down syndrome (trisomy 21); children who have an extra chromosome suffer from mental retardation due to improper brain development. There are many other mental disorders that are caused by mutations in certain genes that lead to developmental problems of the brain. In these cases, there are clear biological mechanisms that are responsible for the mental disorders. In other mental disorders, however, the biological processes that are causing the diseases are unclear.

Autism is a brain development disorder that affects the ability of children to establish emotional and social relationships. Children develop autism by age two and have characteristic behaviors, such as continuously repeating certain tasks, lack of flexibility, and an inability to establish social relationships with parents and siblings. There exists a wide range of symptoms in autistic children, from totally nonfunctional to those who are nearly normal. The mild form of autism is known as Asperger syndrome. Some children who have autism also have special mental capabilities, such as the ability to rapidly perform mental calculations. The movie *Rain Man* portrayed an autistic adult who had such a skill, but he was unable to live an independent life. Other individuals possess talents in painting, music, and exceptional memory. These individuals are known as autistic savants.

Thus far, there is no biochemical or genetic test for diagnosing autism. The brains of autistic children appear normal when visualized with brain scanning techniques. However, behavioral testing has established that multiple regions of the brain are affected in autism. These regions include the brainstem, amygdala, hippocampus, cerebellum, corpus callosum, basal ganglia, and cerebral cortex. All these regions appear to be involved in forming the clinical symptoms of autism. Currently, there is neither a cure nor treatment for autism, although many approaches have been attempted.

During the past ten years, it has been claimed that vaccinations are responsible for the development of autism. One such claim was based on the presence of mercury in vaccinations. Prior to 1999, many vaccines contained the mercury-containing thiomersal, which was used as a preservative. Thiomersal had been used as a vaccine preservative since the 1930s and had never been shown to have any side effects. However, in the 1990s, some parents claimed that the development of autism in their children occurred shortly after receiving vaccinations. Many studies were conducted to examine the causal relationship between thiomersal and autism as well as other brain development disorders. To date, no definitive link has been found. However, as a precautionary measure, the Center for Disease Control and the American Academy of Pediatrics requested vaccine makers to remove thiomersal from vaccines, and presently, all vaccines used in the U.S. and in Europe are free of thiomersal.

Over the years, there has been an intense search for the treatment and cure for autism. In the 1980s, a new method, known as facilitated communication, was described. In this method, facilitators hold the hands of children and help them tap on a keyboard. Using this method, formerly non-communicative autistic children started to "speak" through typing on this keyboard. They could converse with their families, teachers, and other students. Some even started to write poetry and study subjects such as calculus. The success of facilitated communication was astounding, and many facilitators were trained.

However, questions regarding facilitated communication were soon raised. Through her facilitators, one autistic child claimed that she had been sexually abused by her parents and grandparents, an accusation that led to a criminal prosecution. The judge who was assigned to the case requested verification of the effectiveness of facilitated communication. An investigation soon discovered that the facilitators were unconsciously tapping out words that they thought the autistic children would say rather than letting these children tap out their own words. In one experiment, the autistic children were shown objects in the absence of their facilitators. When the children were subsequently asked to name these objects with the aid of their facilitators, they got the answer wrong every time. They only gave correct answers if their facilitators also saw the objects. If the scientific method had been used to thoroughly test facilitated communication and to ensure its reliability, the truth would have been quickly known, and the hopes of many parents of autistic children would not have been falsely raised.

II.3. Could microorganisms be responsible for mental disorders?

Schizophrenia is a mental disorder that primarily affects cognitive functions and leads to emotional and behavioral problems. The clinical symptoms include auditory hallucinations, delusions, disorganized speech and thinking, and paranoia. The disorder generally develops during late adolescence to early young adulthood. It is estimated that approximately 0.5% of the population is affected. Diagnosis relies entirely on clinical symptoms because no laboratory test for schizophrenia currently exists. The cause of schizophrenia remains unclear, and thus far, no genes for schizophrenia have been identified.

Brain imaging
Schizophrenic patients show abnormal neural activities in the red regions of the brain. *(Public Domain)*

In 2006, researchers at Columbia University published findings suggesting that as many as 20% of the schizophrenia cases can be traced to prenatal infections. These and other researchers have discovered that a high correlation exists between schizophrenic patients and their mothers who contracted influenza during the early stages of their pregnancies. The risk of children developing schizophrenia was seven times higher if their mothers had influenza during the first trimester of pregnancy. This is a period when the embryo undergoes critical development of the brain, spinal cord, and the peripheral nervous system. Any disturbance during this time can have long-term consequences.

How the influenza virus causes damage to the fetal brain remains unclear. Unlike alcohol, the influenza virus cannot cross the placental barrier, and therefore, it is unlikely that the fetus becomes infected by the flu virus. Instead, evidence suggests that the mother's immune system is involved. When a mother is infected by the influenza virus, her immune system produces protein molecules, known as cytokines, which are powerful immunological mediators that can induce inflammation and other tissue reactions. Many cytokines also possess neurological activities and can interact with the central nervous system. It is not understood how these cytokines affect brain development, but it is possible that they could induce subtle changes in the fetal brain resulting in inappropriate development during adolescence.

Another common mental disorder is the anxiety disorder known as obsessive-compulsive disorder (OCD). Individuals with OCD have recurrent and persistent thoughts, impulses, or images (obsessions) that are intrusive and inappropriate. These are not simply excessive worries about real-life problems. Even though individuals with OCD recognize their obsessions as products of their own minds and are not based in reality, they cannot ignore or suppress them. Consequently, they perform repetitive and ritualistic acts to neutralize the anxiety that is produced by the obsession. OCD varies in severity and in some cases, keeping a job and maintaining social relationships becomes impossible.

Most cases of OCD develop over a period of several months or even years, but recent research discovered that in some children, the development of OCD is abrupt, with a seemingly "overnight" onset of symptoms. In this form of OCD, the affected children were previously infected by the common bacteria, *Streptococcus pyogenes,* which normally causes strep throat and scarlet fever. How does the bacterial infection cause OCD? Streptococcal infection does not ordinarily involve the central nervous system. However, streptococcal infections can stimulate an autoimmune response against the body's own tissue cells. This autoimmune response occurs because of a similarity between the streptococcal proteins and the body's own proteins. This autoimmune response has been shown to cause kidney damage, leading to kidney failure in severe cases.

There is now evidence suggesting that the autoimmune response that is caused by the streptococcal bacteria also attacks neurons in the brain and causes OCD. This form of OCD was named PANDAS, an abbreviation for Pediatric Autoimmune Neuropsychiatric Disorders Associated with Streptococcal infections. This theory was initially criticized because it went against the conventional view that mental disorders take months or years to develop. It was difficult for most psychiatrists and psychologists to accept that a complex mental disorder such as OCD could develop in only two weeks. Recent research has provided even further evidence for the bacterial origin of this mental disorder. These studies have provided further support of the biological basis of the human mind. The understanding of PANDAS will lead to new approaches in the treatment and prevention of this and other mental disorders.

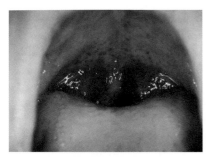

Strep throat
The redness is caused by the inflammation that results from the bacterial infection. *(Public Domain)*

Scarlet fever
This child shows the typical rash on the cheeks. *(Creative Commons Attribution)*

III. Is depression a mental disorder?

Depression is an emotion that we all occasionally experience. Depression, which is the opposite of happiness, is important to us because it provides a type of reality check. Everyone gets depressed occasionally, but there are great differences in the intensity and duration of depression. For most, depression is short, and it provides individuals with the opportunity to examine their situation and to choose the next course of action. Furthermore, if certain environmental stimuli continually induce depression in an individual, it is likely that the individual will learn to avoid those stimuli. From this standpoint, depression has an evolutionary significance for survival. However, prolonged depression at a high intensity creates both psychological and physiological stress that can become pathological. This type of depression is known as clinical depression.

III.1. *What is clinical depression?*

In our everyday lives, we experience fluctuations in our emotions, ranging from moments of happiness to sadness. These minor mood variations are finely tuned and we achieve a level of stability that allows us to pursue our ultimate goals, which are to grow and reproduce. Occasionally, an individual experiences a heightened level of happiness or sadness due to some special event, such as a birthday party or the termination of a romantic relationship. These heightened emotional experiences are generally of longer duration but are still transient, and normalcy is gradually restored over time. Each episode of these emotional experiences adds to the richness of our lives and creates new neural synapses in our brains.

In some cases, the intensity of the emotional experience creates long-lasting changes in the neuronal junctions that take days or even months to return to normal. This situation is similar to that induced by repeated use of cocaine (cocaine causes changes in the dopamine receptors in the post-synaptic neurons). In depression, however, the changes result from high exposure to certain hormones. Recent studies have shown that in addition to the production of adrenalin, another hormone, cortisol, is also produced during the fight or flight response. The effect of cortisol is not as immediate as that of adrenalin on the sympathetic nervous system. Cortisol, however, has a much greater effect on the neurons in the brain. While the biological action of adrenalin is quickly diminished, the effects of cortisol linger on because it modifies the neural synapses, either increasing or decreasing their sensitivity to future stimulation.

Adrenalin and cortisol are referred to as stress hormones, and the levels of their production have profound consequences in the development of clinical depression. During clinical depression, an individual's normal routines are disrupted, affecting work, school life, family relationships, and social interactions. The length of depression can last from several weeks to several months. Normally-pleasurable activities are no longer gratifying, and even the purpose of life is in doubt. Not everyone is susceptible to clinical depression, and there is a wide range of individual variations. However, nearly one third of the U.S. population has experienced clinical depression, with women outnumbering men two to one. One reason that women are more prone to clinical depression is childbirth.

Cortisol
It is a steroidal hormone produced by the adrenal gland.

It has long been known that women suffer from a period of depression, known as baby blues, shortly after giving birth. The severity of the depression ranges from mild to clinical depression. The symptoms include tearfulness, irritability, inability to concentrate, headaches, sleeplessness, and a sense of isolation. As many as 80% of new mothers experience the baby blues. During this period of depression, instead of having positive emotions, new mothers often harbor negative emotions toward their infants. These negative emotions are strongest when the new mother is not getting adequate support from her partner or from her extended family. The depression is shortest, however, when the new mother receives large amounts of emotional and physical support in caring for the baby.

As many as 25% of new mothers experience the most severe form of baby blues, postpartum depression, which is a condition resembling clinical depression. On June 20, 2001, Andrea Yates made headline news worldwide because of her postpartum depression. She methodically drowned all five of her children, including her six-month-old infant. Her postpartum depression had led to a psychotic delusion, which instructed her to kill all her children to save them from eternal damnation. Her initial conviction of first degree murder and life in prison was overturned based on evidence of her mental disorder. The jury found her not guilty based on reason of insanity.

Postpartum depression is detrimental for both the mother and the infant. The affected woman feels a sense of profound sadness, hopelessness, low self-esteem, guilt, social inadequacy, and an inability to care for her newborn. Strong emotional and physical support of the new mother is vital for treating postpartum depression. The prevalence of postpartum depression is the highest among low-income, unmarried women, who receive the least social and financial support. Even though each woman is different in her susceptibility to develop postpartum depression, all women are vulnerable in developing depression after their babies are born. From an evolutionary standpoint, baby blues and postpartum depression result from a need of a new mother to assess the resources that are available to her in raising her young.

Depending on the assessment, she then decides to react either positively or negatively towards her infant.

III.2. Why does clinical depression exist?

There are two different types of clinical depression, sporadic and familial. The familial form is an autosomal dominant trait that involves multiple genes. Less than 10% of clinical depression is the familial form. The remaining 90% are the sporadic form. Most episodes of sporadic clinical depression are linked to significant life events, such as the loss of a spouse or a serious illness. Recovery from sporadic clinical depression is generally complete and without any long-lasting effects. In contrast, familial clinical depression occurs with no clear etiology and erupts without warning. For some individuals with familial clinical depression, their entire lives are centered on the depression.

Cockatoos

With the lack of social interaction, cockatoos can suffer from clinical depression. *(Public Domain)*

Clinical depression has been observed in many animals from dogs to baboons. For example, cockatoos are highly social animals that form life-long pair bonds with their mating partners. Many cockatoos suffer human-like clinical depression in captivity as pets because there are no other cockatoos to provide them with company. They become restless and many pluck feathers from their wings and body. On the African savanna, low-ranking male baboons also exhibit symptoms of clinical depression when they are constantly harassed by high-ranking males with physical violence and intimidation. They appear sad, and their health is severely affected by living in a socially stressful environment.

The high prevalence of clinical depression in humans as well as in other animals suggests that there must be some evolutionary significance of clinical depression. One theory, known as the psychic pain theory, suggests that clinical depression allows an individual to withdraw from a damaging situation when the cost for continuing in that situation is devastating or deadly to its well-being. Postpartum depression could also be viewed as a strategy for the mother to withdraw, abandon, or even commit filicide if there are insufficient resources available to raise the infant. Instead of risking her life, it is better for her to abandon the baby and try again when there are sufficient resources.

Another theory, known as the rank theory, suggests that among social animals that have a dominance hierarchy, clinical depression is a means by which to avoid a lengthy fight for dominance and hence, promotes the survival of the social group. Another theory proposes that clinical depression is a way for members of a social group to call for help in the case of illness, hunger, or starvation. From this perspective, postpartum depression could represent the mother's call for help when she cannot find sufficient support and resources to raise her newborn.

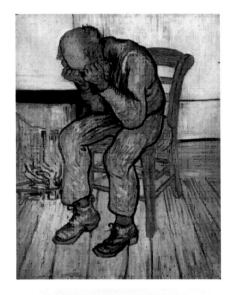

Clinical depression

A painting by Vincent van Gogh, who suffered from bipolar disorder. He committed suicide. *(Public Domain)*

A variation of clinical depression is a mental disorder known as bipolar disorder (or bipolar affective mood disorder). Bipolar disorder has two phases, a depression phase and a manic phase. The depression phase is similar to clinical depression. The manic phase is characterized by an elevated, expansive, and irritable mood. The patients appear to have boundless energy, need less sleep, behave aggressively, and aim for impossible goals. Many also experience higher sex drives, and greater tendencies to use alcohol, cocaine, and other psychoactive substances. For talented individuals, these could be creative and productive periods in their lives. However, when the manic phase passes, they plunge into the dark phase of depression. The emotional roller coaster ride takes a heavy toll, and sufferers of bipolar disorder often take their lives during the depression phase.

There are many examples of talented individuals who have suffered from tormenting mental disorders that have led to tragic ends, such as Kurt Cobain of the alternative rock band Nirvana, who committed suicide at the prime of his musical career. Other names include Ernest Hemingway and Vincent van Gogh, who also terminated their lives despite their literary and artistic talents. With a better understanding of the link between mental disorders and creativity, researchers have suspected that many of the following intellectuals and creative individuals had suffered from bipolar disorder. The list includes Winston Churchill, Charles Dickens, Ralph Waldo Emerson, Scott Fitzgerald, William Faulkner, Jimi Hendrix, John Keats, Marilyn Monroe, Napoleon, Florence Nightingale, Isaac Newton, Robert Louis Stevenson, Mark Twain, Virginia Woolf, and Tennessee Williams.

III.3. Can mental disorders be treated?

The discovery of chlorpromazine to treat schizophrenia ushered in the era of psychopharmacology. Treatments for mental disorders made the transition in the 1960s from the psychoanalytic model to the pharmacological model. However, it was later discovered that both psychotherapy and psychiatric drugs change brain chemistry and that they work synergistically. The greatest success in treating a whole range of mental disorders occurs when psychiatric drugs are supplemented by psychotherapy and counseling. These combinations have proven effective for most mental disorders.

Since the discovery of chlorpromazine, pharmaceutical companies have invested heavily in the research and development of psychiatric drugs. Since most patients need to take these drugs for the rest of their lives, psychiatric medications represent one of the most profitable sectors of the pharmaceutical industry. Most of the psychiatric drugs were discovered accidentally by screening large numbers of synthetic chemicals. However, they all share structural similarities with natural neurotransmitters. They either act as agonists, which enhance the action of a neurotransmitter, or as antagonists, which block the actions of neurotransmitters. Nearly all are synthetic compounds, with only a few being derived from natural sources.

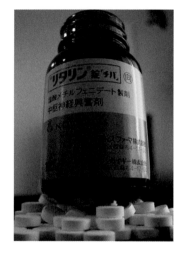

Ritalin in a Japanese bottle

It is a stimulant that is used for the treatment of ADHD. *(Public Domain)*

All the psychiatric drugs can be classified into five basic categories. The first category is known as antipsychotics, and they are useful in treating schizophrenia and other serious mental disorders. The second group is antidepressants, which includes a large group of drugs for treating clinical depression, anxiety disorders, and eating disorders. The third category of drugs is known as mood stabilizers, and they are useful in treating bipolar disorder. The fourth group includes stimulants; Ritalin is one of the most well-known members of this group. They have been shown to be effective in treating attention deficit hyperactivity disorder. The last category is minor tranquilizers (also known as anxiolytics and hypnotics), which have been effective in reducing anxiety and in overcoming insomnia.

The most well-known group of psychiatric drug is the SSRI; they are anti-depressants and include Prozac, Zoloft, and Paxil. SSRI stands for serotonin specific reuptake inhibitor, and their mechanism of action is binding to the transporter that is responsible for removing the neurotransmitter serotonin from the synapses. By blocking the action of the transporter, the SSRI elevates the serotonin level in the synapses. Today, SSRIs are some of the most effective psychiatric drugs for treating clinical depression and anxiety disorders. In addition to their clinical effectiveness, SSRIs have also shed light on the role of serotonin in the regulation of emotion. Interestingly, SSRIs have also been used by veterinarians to treat animals. In one example, a cockatoo was being treated with Prozac for its anxiety disorder, which led it to constantly pluck feathers from its body. The effectiveness of SSRIs on other species provides further evidence of the common evolutionary root of the brain and of the nervous system in all vertebrates.

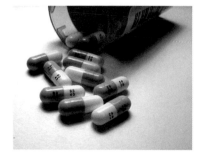

SSRIs

They are effective in treating clinical depression. (*Creative Commons Attribution*)

Bipolar disorder is one of the most difficult mental disorders to treat. Patients often plunge from the manic phase into deep depression without any warning. It is during this transition that the patients are the most vulnerable, when the symptoms of mania and clinical depression occur simultaneously. In this mixed state, the patients often develop a sense of worthlessness, because they realize the futility of the goals that they set for themselves during the manic phase. Deep disappointment leads to a sense of despair and self-loathing. The patients are most vulnerable to suicide at this juncture of the disorder.

Unfortunately, the neurological basis of bipolar disorder remains unclear, and many of the available psychiatric drugs are ineffective in overcoming the depression phase. Incredibly, one effective treatment is known as electroconvulsive therapy. In this therapy, an electrical current is passed through a patient's brain to induce a seizure. This treatment brings the patients out of their depression, but it is not a cure. The disorder usually returns several weeks or months later. This demonstrates the complexity of the brain and the physical basis of our normal as well as our abnormal thought processes. With this knowledge, researchers continue to work toward a better understanding of our mental health and our mental disorders.

Chapter 14

Memory

Why do you forget?

Former United States President Ronald Reagan

In 1994, he informed the country of his diagnosis of Alzheimer's disease in a handwritten letter. *(Public Domain)*

Chapter 14. Memory

Memory is an integral part of our mental process, and we rely on our memory to carry out the simplest and most basic aspects of our daily activities. Without memory, we could not function. Those afflicted with Alzheimer's disease, for example, gradually lose their memory over several years and become unable to care for themselves. The devastating effects of this disease reminds us of the importance of memory and the dependence of the mind on memory. Memory also has an important role in helping animals adapt to new environments. Animals continuously learn from their experiences and store what is learned in their memories. In time, those memories are retrieved and applied to new situations. Without memory, the survival of even the simplest animals would be impossible. In recent years, scientists have discovered the neurological basis of memory and have used this information to treat and prevent memory disorders. This knowledge has been valuable for improving both the efficiency and effectiveness of human memory.

I. Why do we forget?

Our lives depend on our ability to remember. This ranges from where we put our keys to how to find our way in a city. Without memory, our lives would be completely nonfunctional. Yet we take our memory for granted, and only when our memory fails us do we recognize its importance. One young man found himself in such a situation because he had suffered a hemorrhagic stroke during his first year of law school. He recovered from his stroke with no physical impairment, but he lost his ability to form new memories. He still retained memories that he had before the stroke, but he could not remember anything new. For example, he could not remember what he had for dinner or any other activity from the previous day. He still remembered how to take the train to visit his parents, but he could not remember why he was at the train station when he arrived there. Even though his intellectual ability remained much the same, he could no longer pursue a law career. Such loss of memory is unusual, but it provides insights into how memory functions in our brain.

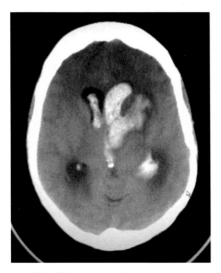

Hemorrhagic stroke

An intracerebral hemorrhagic stroke as revealed by brain imaging. *(Public Domain)*

I.1. What is memory and forgetting?

What is memory? We generally do not pay attention to our ability to remember, until we find ourselves desperately trying to recall a phone number that we have not used for a while or to cram for an examination that is only minutes away. However, once we take a deeper look at memory, we find many interesting questions. Research on the neurological basis of memory has revealed some fascinating aspects of how a collection of neurons in our brain provides us with the ability to remember everything from the trivial to the profound. We now know that memory comes in different forms, and we rely on all of them to conduct our daily lives.

Have you ever wondered why you cannot remember your babyhood? Why do some memories last for a long time, even for a lifetime? Once you learn to swim or to ride a bike, you never forget. Why do some memories, on the other hand, seem to disappear immediately after use? Do you notice that when you look up a phone number to make a call, you forget the number almost immediately after you dial it? For those of you who might have had a drink too many at a party, did you experience a blackout? You woke up and could hardly recall what had happened that night. What happened to those memories?

The study of memory has been an important endeavor of cognitive psychology. Over the past one hundred years, many psychiatrists, most notably Sigmund Freud, have studied various aspects of memory and its role in mental disorders. One of the most interesting findings that resulted from this early research was that memories exist both in our conscious and unconscious minds. The existence of unconscious memories has been shown to have a profound impact on our behavior and mental states. In fact, it is these unconscious memories that are often the source of mental disorders.

Memory has been studied from many different aspects because of advances in genetics, biochemistry, and cell biology. It has established, for example, that memory formation has a genetic basis that is involved in brain development and in the formation of various developmental disorders, including mental retardation and autism. In addition, new approaches using brain imaging techniques, such MRI and PET scan, have allowed researchers to determine which parts of the brain are involved in memory formation. Another aspect of memory formation that has been established is that the physical basis of memory involves neurons and neurotransmitters.

Memory is vital for the storing, retaining, and retrieving of information. Throughout evolution, as living organisms increased in complexity, memory also became more sophisticated. To fully understand memory and its complexities, researchers have classified memory into three properties. The first property is the duration of memory, which is divided into short-term and long-term memory. The second property of memory is its information content, which is divided into physical memory and symbolic/abstract memory. The physical type of memory, also known as procedural memory, involves bodily movements, such as swimming. The symbolic/abstract type of memory is represented by the use of language. The last property of memory is its temporal (time) direction. Memories involve the past and what needs to be done in the future.

We are familiar with all these types of memory because without them we could not carry out our daily routines, reflect on the past, or make plans for the future. However, we also often forget, and one of the most interesting and challenging aspects in the study of memory is the biological mechanisms of forgetting. The most interesting findings in this area come from individuals who have experienced a complete memory loss due to physical trauma or disease of the brain. These individuals have amnesia, a condition which occurs when a significant portion of memory is destroyed.

Sigmund Freud

He was among the first to study various aspects of memory in mental disorders. *(Public Domain)*

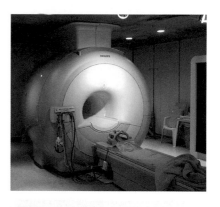

MRI

Magnetic resonance imaging for studying brain activities. *(GNU Free Documentation License)*

I.2. *What is amnesia?*

Amnesia is a common theme in fiction because it seems so improbable that a person could suffer a complete loss of memory. How can memory seemingly disappear without a trace? One such incident of amnesia occurred when a man was involved in a traffic accident. After recovering from his head injury, he could not recall driving his motorcycle prior to his crash. Also, he could not recall the hospital room where he had conversations with his parents in the two days following his accident.

The motorcyclist suffered from two different types of amnesia: retrograde and anterograde. Retrograde amnesia is the inability to recall past events, beyond ordinary forgetfulness. Anterograde amnesia, however, is the inability to convert short-term or immediate memory into long-term memory. The motorcyclist suffered from retrograde amnesia because he could not remember driving his motorcycle. He also suffered from anterograde amnesia because he could not remember talking to his parents shortly after regaining consciousness. By studying these two types of amnesia, researchers have discovered that different regions of the brain are involved in the formation of long-term and short-term memory.

In addition to retrograde and anterograde, amnesia has also been divided into other types. The above story is an example of traumatic amnesia, which generally results from head injuries. Most traumatic amnesias are transient, but some can be permanent. These amnesias can consist of the anterograde, retrograde, or mixed type. The seriousness of the traumatic injuries often determines the severity and duration of the amnesia. Someone who has mild trauma may remember events but forget the details, such as the faces of the people involved in the accident. Also, accident victims often have strong memories of some aspect of the accident, such as the color of the car involved, but fail to recall other details.

Another type of amnesia is dissociative amnesia. This amnesia does not result from neurological damage to the brain but results from psychological causes. One of the most common examples of dissociative amnesia is childhood amnesia (also known as infantile amnesia). This amnesia results from the inability to remember events from childhood. However, there are genetic variations in regard to this amnesia. On rare occasions, an individual has retained vivid memories of his or her infancy. Another well-known example of dissociative amnesia is memory repression. In this type of amnesia, a person is unable to recall information about past stressful or traumatic events, even though the memory has been unconsciously stored. These individuals frequently retain the capacity to partially or completely recover the memory.

The third type of amnesia is associated with chemical disturbances within the brain. Psychoactive substances can cause amnesia by affecting the chemical balance in the brain. Chemicals such as cocaine, heroine, and alcohol can alter neurotransmitter levels in the synapse and lead to amnesia. The most common form of chemically-induced amnesia is alcohol intoxication. When an individual drinks a large amount of alcohol in a short period, the alcohol rapidly infiltrates the brain tissue and blocks neural transmission in regions of the brain that are responsible for converting short-term memory into long-term memory. In a condition known as blackout, an intoxicated individual remains conscious but is unable to convert his or her short-term memory into long-term memory. Consequently, he or she cannot recall what happened the previous evening. This is also an example of anterograde amnesia.

I.3. *What is the neurological basis of amnesia?*

During the past decades, researchers have studied patients with amnesia to identify the brain regions that are responsible for memory. One example of anterograde amnesia that has provided great insights into the neurological basis of memory formation is a man who lost his ability to form memory after contracting a viral infection. He was a very skillful musician and composer before he came down with viral encephalitis. In viral encephalitis, the virus passes through the blood brain barrier and infects the neurons. His symptoms began as a cold and a stiff neck. Shortly after, his symptoms quickly worsened, and he lost consciousness. He remained in a coma for about a week.

After he regained consciousness and recovered from the illness, he was noted to have both retrograde and anterograde amnesia. All his past memory had been lost, and he also had lost the ability to form new long-term memory. In addition, he could only retain information for a few minutes. For example, he would greet his wife during her visit as if he was meeting her for the first time after a long absence, even though he might have just spoken to her. Other than his memory, he had no other physical or mental problems.

Memento

In this movie, the main character suffered from anterograde amnesia. *(Education Fair Use)*

Blackout

Binge drinking can lead to blackouts, a form of temporary anterograde amnesia. *(Public Domain)*

Hippocampus

It is a brain region that assumes a seahorse shape and is responsible for forming new memory. *(Public Domain)*

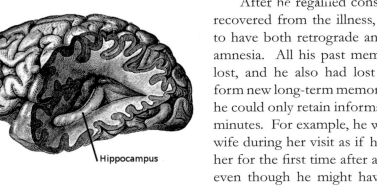

Hippocampus

However, his musical career was over, and he could not live independently. Sadly, he was aware of his condition and was frustrated by his loss of memory.

Brain scan imaging demonstrated that two areas of his brain had been destroyed by the viral infection. The first area of damage was in the frontal lobe, the part of the brain that is normally responsible for processing complex information. This damage was most likely responsible for the loss of his long-term memory. The second area of damage was a small brain region that is located deep inside the forebrain known as the hippocampus, which is part of the limbic system. Its name is derived from the Greek word seahorse for its curved shape. Humans and other animals have two hippocampi, one on each side of the brain. The hippocampus is located near the amygdala, which is the center for emotion. The amydgala is also important in memory formation, particularly in forming the memory that occurs under highly emotional conditions. The third component of the limbic system that is involved in the formation of long-term memory is the mammillary body.

From studying amnesia patients, long-term memory formation has been shown to depend on synaptic formations between neurons. In other words, changes in neuronal synapses are responsible for memory formation. Disruptions of these connections by trauma, psychological stress, or neurological disease affect the formation of long-term memory. Biological memory shares many similarities to computer memory because it results from connections in the neural circuits. Each neural circuit represents the outcome of memory formation. Although the detailed mechanism is unclear, the hippocampus is important for moving short-term information into long-term storage.

In memory formation, two types of neuronal changes can occur: how neurons conduct signals and how neurons can establish new synaptic connections with other neurons. Researchers have demonstrated that both processes occur in long-term memory formation. In the first process, the neurons become sensitized during memory formation to become more responsive to similar signals in the future. This is a process known as long-term potentiation. In the second process, synapses are formed between new neurons, creating a new circuit. The neural circuits of the

Clive Wearing

The musician who lost his memory from a viral infection that destroyed his hippocampus and other parts of his brain. *(Education Fair Use)*

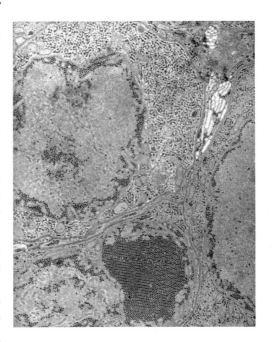

St. Louis encephalitis

The viruses are shown in a mosquito salivary gland. The viruses are transmitted to humans through the bite of a Culex mosquito. *(Public Domain)*

brain are constantly rearranging because of our experiences and are forming new memories to replace old ones.

II. HOW DO WE REMEMBER?

The studies of amnesia patients have resulted in an understanding of the neurological basis of memory. With new brain scanning techniques, researchers can explore the different regions of the brain that are affected. By correlating the neurological damage with the psychological changes, researchers have established how different regions of the brain are involved in certain types of memory. In the case of the musician, the viral infection destroyed the parts of his brain that are important to both short-term and long-term memory. However, certain aspects of his memory remained intact. He still retained the skills to play piano, sight read, and direct his formal chorus group. On one occasion when he was visiting his chorus group, he emphatically stated that he did not know how to play the piano. However, as soon as he sat down at the piano, he started to play and direct the chorus group. Why was his memory for playing the piano undiminished in comparison to his other forms of memory?

II.1. What are different kinds of memory?

The case of the musician suggests that there are two kinds of memory. The first kind of memory involves the ability to recall past events, names, faces, and other factual information. The musician lost this type of information because the region of his brain that controlled this type of memory, mainly the hippocampus, had been destroyed by the viral infection. The second kind of memory, which involved his ability to play the piano, sight read music, and direct a choral group, remained intact. Because this kind of memory was unaffected, it suggested that a different region of the brain was responsible for these activities and that this region was not damaged by the encephalitis.

The type of memory that is characterized by conscious storage and recall of information is called declarative or explicit memory. One form of declarative memory is semantic memory. Our educational system, which is based on attending lectures and studying textbooks, is one example of the use of semantic memory. Semantic memory is formed through the symbolic use of words and symbols. It is not, however, the memory that is formed after experiencing an actual event. Some semantic memory consists of factual information, such as phone numbers, addresses, and birthdays. Other forms of semantic memory are based on concepts and generalizations. Semantic memory is easy to lose, but practice through repetition can reinforce the memory. Regularly used information can be retained in semantic memory for life.

Santiago Ramón y Cajal

He was the first to propose that memories might be stored in the connections between neurons. *(Public Domain)*

Semantic memory

A form of declarative memory that requires studying and practice as in the case of studying for an examination. *(Creative Commons Attribution)*

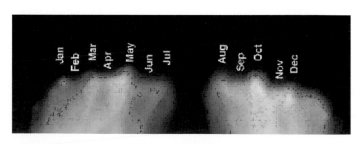

Physical mnemonics

Knuckle mnemonic to remember the length of each month.

Semantic memory can be improved by using mnemonic techniques, such as first letter mnemonics, physical mnemonics, and musical mnemonics. Another more advanced memory-improving method includes the journey method. In this method, a familiar journey, such as a trip to the grocery store, is created, and each item that is to be remembered is placed in a particular location along the journey. With training, some individuals have acquired prodigious semantic memory. For example, Akira Haraguchi of Japan recited pi's first 100,000 decimal places from memory in 16 hours. The 2004 World Memory Champion, Ben Pridmore, memorized the order of cards in a randomly shuffled 52-card deck in 31 seconds.

The hippocampus is the primary site for the formation of semantic memory, and individuals who suffer damage to their hippocampus experience difficulties when forming semantic memory. Other regions of the brain, such as the frontal and temporal lobes, are also involved in the formation of semantic memory. Semantic memory reaches peak efficiency during our early 20s, and a decline in forming semantic memory occurs after the mid-30s. However, brain "exercises" such as memory games can prevent the decline of semantic memory in old age.

Another type of memory is known as procedural or implicit memory. In contrast to declarative memory, the storing and recalling of procedural memory is beyond conscious awareness. Procedural memory is related to motor learning, such as riding a bicycle and playing the piano. It requires much practice to master these skills, and it cannot be easily verbalized. Most procedural memory reflects a simple stimulus-response pairing, making it the most primitive form of memory. It is also the memory that is found in all animals. Procedural memory is long lasting, and once an individual has mastered certain skills that are stored as procedural memory, they are never lost.

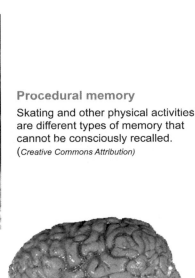

Akira Haraguchi of Japan
He recited pi's first 100,000 decimal places from memory in 16 hours. (*Creative Commons Attribution*)

Procedural memory is stored in the cerebellum, which is located next to the brainstem, below the occipital lobe. Cerebellum means "little brain" in Greek, because of its physical resemblance to the cerebral cortex. Despite its size (10% of total brain volume), the cerebellum contains 50% of the neurons in the brain. In the example of the musician, his cerebellum was unaffected by the viral infection, leaving many of his musical skills intact.

Procedural memory
Skating and other physical activities are different types of memory that cannot be consciously recalled. (*Creative Commons Attribution*)

II.2. What does emotion have to do with memory?

In addition to semantic memory, there is another kind of declarative memory, known as episodic memory, which can be consciously recalled. Episodic memory is frequently associated with special events in a person's life, such as the first day of school, a 21st birthday party, or a wedding. A person often remembers many details in association with such particular events. Some of the details might be insignificant and unimportant, but the person can remember them well. These details could be the song being played on the radio or the fragrance of a perfume. These types of details are generally not remembered in less significant events. Episodic memory often lasts a lifetime, and a single exposure is sufficient for forever linking together the events, times, places, and other conceptual-based knowledge.

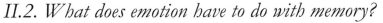

Cerebellum
The little brain, which is the purple region, is located beneath the cerebrum. (*Public Domain*)

Flashbulb memory

Many people remembered trivial details in association with the Challenger space shuttle explosion. *(Public Domain)*

Episodic memory can be further divided into two types. The first type is known as autobiographical memory, and it is the memory that is formed after an individual experiences certain life events. These events include birthdays, baptisms, graduations, weddings, childbirths, job promotions, and professional advancements. Autobiographical memory can be changed over time due to memory distortion. The second type of episodic memory is flashbulb memory. This memory is formed after an intense major event. All personal details are captured together in the memory with the major event. For example, most people can answer questions such as "Where were you on 9/11?" and "When did you learn that Princess Diana had died?"

Episodic memory also relies on the function of the hippocampus. The hippocampus is important in filtering and consolidating the information before transferring it for long-term storage in the cerebral cortex. The neurological mechanism for the strength of episodic memory remains unclear. However, some neuroscientists suggest that the amygdala of the limbic system is involved in the formation of episodic memory because of its role as the emotional center of the brain. The interactions between the hippocampus and the amygdala increase the strength of the neurological signals that are communicated to the temporal and frontal lobes in the formation of episodic memory. Brain scan imaging of the prefrontal cortex also demonstrates an increase in electrical activities during formation of episodic memory, suggesting its involvement. Many mammals, including chimpanzees and dogs, also form episodic memory. Furthermore, a recent study revealed that humming birds also develop episodic memory, suggesting that episodic memory has a long evolutionary history.

Posttraumatic stress disorder

This photo from World War I shows a wounded soldier in the lower left having a dazed "thousand yard stare." This is also known as shell shock. *(Public Domain)*

An anxiety disorder that is related to episodic memory is posttraumatic stress disorder (PTSD). This disorder occurs when the intensity of an experience negatively affects an individual's psychology. PTSD was first recognized during the First World War, when soldiers failed to cope with the psychological stress of the battlefield. It was also known as shell shock or traumatic war neurosis. PTSD is also caused by serious accidents, medical complications, serious illnesses, sexual assaults, witnessing physical violence, warfare, or life-threatening natural disasters. In one case, a man was badly hurt in a traffic accident and was trapped in the car for an hour before he was rescued. For nearly a year, he had recurring recollections of this distressing event.

PTSD is caused by a hyperactive amygdala, which together with the hippocampus, continues to reinforce the episodic memory of the event. The event repeatedly plays out in the mind, and the memory is further strengthened with each repeating episode of recollection. PTSD is an unfortunate anxiety disorder, but it provides an excellent demonstration of the power of emotion in memory formation.

II.3. Why does emotion affect memory?

One important question in the study of memory is the biological basis of episodic memory. Why is episodic memory more vivid and longer lasting than semantic memory? Over the past decades, cognitive psychologists have conducted research in this area and have provided some important insights. One theory suggests that memory formation is associated with the elicitation of emotional responses. Storytelling is an effective teaching tool, because compelling stories elicit emotional responses. The details of the story are more likely to be retained if the story has a high emotional value and elicits strong episodic memory.

The formation of episodic memory is associated with the release of stress hormones. When an animal faces a stressful (both positive and negative) situation, its body releases stress hormones, such as adrenalin and cortisol. The amount of these hormones in the blood circulation prepares the animals for action, depending on the level of arousal. In a highly excited or stressful situation, a large amount of these hormones is circulated in the blood. These hormones enter the brain and increase the strength of synapses leading to longer-lasting memories. Therefore, emotion and memory formation are highly correlated.

Emotional arousal is important for memory formation, because emotion leads to the selectivity of attention. Physiological changes in the body create a condition known as attention narrowing, which causes the individual to decrease their focus on the range of cues from the stimulus. Instead of focusing attention on peripheral details, the attention is concentrated on the arousing details of the stimulus. The consequence is selective encoding of the arousing details into memory at the expense of encoding the peripheral details into memory.

Weapon focus
A Browning pistol. The presence of a weapon has been shown to diminish the accuracy of eyewitness testimony. *(Public Domain)*

One of the interesting phenomena in support of this theory is known as the weapon focus. When a person faces an attacker, it is far more likely that the stronger memory is of the weapon, whether it is a knife or a gun. The memory of the attacker's clothing or vehicle is likely to be the weakest. The weapon poses the greatest threat and generates the maximum emotional arousal for the longest period. Impact of emotional arousal on memory formation can be both real and imaginary, as in the case of emotional arousal that occurs from reading and movies. Many teachers intuitively understand this association and use emotional arousal in teaching. A better understanding of this process can lead to the development of more effective teaching techniques.

Why is emotional arousal so effective in the formation of long-term memory? Episodic memory is likely to be the most primitive form of memory in the animal kingdom, because it is important for survival. During the early development of an animal, trial and error is the process by which it learns about its environment. Through this process, the animal develops a behavioral pattern that its survival depends on. When it enters into dangerous situations, the release of stress hormones creates physiological responses that become encoded into memory. This creates the classical fight or flight instinct. This type of memory is intense, because the animal must remember to avoid similar situations by recalling all the relevant cues in vivid detail. Therefore, it is not surprising that emotion and memory are strongly linked, and the intensity of the episodic memory is directly tied to the intensity of the event. An understanding of this relationship between emotion and memory provides an explanation and possibly treatment for individuals suffering from PTSD.

III. DOES MEMORY HAVE A PHYSICAL BASIS?

From studying patients who have had a stroke or who have had other types of brain damage, researchers have located the regions of the brain that are responsible for different forms of memory. Unlike many other mental functions, human memory functions are built from different neurological components. These components work under a "command center" that integrate their functions. It has been observed that the separate brain regions for memory work independently as well as in concert. Furthermore, these various brain regions have a long evolutionary history, as their human neural counterparts have been found in many other animals, from chimpanzees to birds. Some of these animals have extraordinary memory skills that are beyond most human memory capacities. The physical basis of memory was further demonstrated from studies on Alzheimer's disease. In this disease, the loss of memory is directly associated with structural damage to the brain. As researchers gain a better understanding of the neurological processes of memory, finding cures and preventions for many neurological diseases will become possible.

III.1. What is the physical structure of memory?

From studies of patients who have experienced memory loss resulting from physical damage to their brains, the existence of a neurological base of memory is unequivocal. Structural damage to the neurons in the hippocampus leads to disruption of memory functions as seen in both anterograde and retrograde amnesia. From these observations another question arises: Is it possible to detect physical changes in the brain as the result of memory formation? Current brain imaging techniques lack the sensitivity to distinguish minor changes at the level of individual neurons. However, a recent study of spatial memory of London taxi drivers has provided evidence that the structure of the human brain can be changed because of increased memory demands.

London taxi drivers
Their hippocampi were shown to be enlarged to accommodate their demand for spatial memory. (*Public Domain*)

Spatial memory is the type of memory that encodes information from one's environment based on spatial orientation. All animals use spatial memory to find food, shelter, and escape predators. Laboratory rats use their spatial memory in a maze to find food. Humans use spatial memory to navigate around large cities. Not surprisingly, individual variations exist among humans in their capacity for spatial memory. There are also gender differences in how humans store and use spatial memory.

One of the most extraordinary cases of spatial memory comes from the legendary London taxi drivers. Before the age of GPS, they had to commit to memory thousands of streets, landmarks, and locations. For over 150 years, a candidate had to pass a grueling exam, which the Londoners call "The Knowledge," and it took most people as long as two years to master. Researchers at the University of London used the taxi drivers as way to study the structure of the brain in people who must assimilate a large amount of information in a very short time. They discovered that from the time the drivers started their study of the "The Knowledge" their hippocampi started to enlarge. This result provided evidence that the hippocampus is involved in the encoding of spatial memory. The drivers who had been on the job longest had hippocampi that showed the greatest increase in size.

However, the most extraordinary spatial memory is not found in humans. Researchers have found two animal species that possess the ability to encode up to

Clark's nutcracker
It can remember the locations of 33,000 seeds that it buries during the gathering season. (*Creative Commons Attribution*)

50,000 physical locations into their spatial memory. These species are the Clark's nutcracker and grey squirrel; both are scatter hoarders. The Clark's nutcrackers feed on pine seeds in western North America. As winter approaches, they bury five to ten seeds per cache in shallow pits. Over an area of 12 square miles, each bird buries up to 33,000 seeds in over five thousand locations. Their long-term spatial memory is remarkable because they can recover nearly all their caches as long as six months later in areas covered with as much as three feet of snow.

Another example of extraordinary spatial memory is the grey squirrels, which are native to the eastern and midwestern parts of the United States. They hoard food in small caches in up to 10 thousand locations for later recovery. They possess remarkable spatial memory in accurately pinpointing the location of their caches many months later. Both of these species have been shown to possess large hippocampi. These studies and the taxi driver research have provided a clear indication that our spatial memory has a direct correlation to the physical structure of our brain.

III.2. What is Alzheimer's disease?

The study of Alzheimer's disease provided the first example that linked our mind to our brain. In this discase, the destruction of the neurons in the brain leads to the destruction of the mind, starting first with memory and then gradually progressing toward consciousness. It was first discovered by the German psychiatrist Alois Alzheimer in 1906 after he tended to a 51-year-old woman for five years in the Frankfurt Asylum. She was admitted to the hospital when she was in the early dementia phase. She then gradually transited into the advanced dementia phase, and subsequently died. Her most distinctive clinical symptoms were her gradual and progressive loss of memory. Alzheimer suspected that there could be a physical cause for her condition because her brain had shrunk significantly by the time of her death.

Alois Alzheimer
The German psychiatrist who first discovered Alzheimer's disease.
(GNU Free Documentation License)

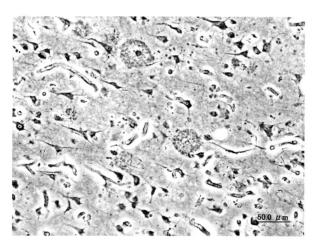

He performed pathological studies of the patient's brain tissue by observing the neural pathology under the microscope. He was surprised to find that a dramatic reduction in the number of neurons had occurred. He also observed that the space between the neurons had become filled by a chalk-like substance, which he called amyloid plaques. Furthermore, he discovered that inside the neurons, the cytoplasm was filled with tangled fiber-like materials known as neurofibrillary tangles. He concluded in his 1906 publication that the neurological symptoms of the disease were caused by a pathological damage of the brain tissue. The scientific community of the time reacted with incredibility, because the general assumption among psychiatrists was that all mental illnesses were psychologically based rather than physically based. Alzheimer's discovery led to a complete revision of the psychiatric dogma of the time.

Amyloid plaques
Histologoical images of amyloid plaques in the cerebral cortex of a patient with Alzheimer's disease.
(Public Domain)

Alzheimer's disease is a gradual destruction of memory, and it is one of the most significant medical problems of the elderly. Currently, there are 24 million people around the world who suffer from Alzheimer's disease, and at present, there is no cure for this debilitating disease. The duration of this disease is between 5 and 20 years, and the financial and social costs of caring for these patients are higher than most age-related diseases. Currently, it is estimated that the annual average cost per Alzheimer's patient is as high as $77,500.

Alzheimer's disease is divided into four clinical phases: predementia, early dementia, moderate dementia, and advanced. The predementia phase can last up to eight years, but generally, it lasts two to three years. During this phase, the patients experience short-term memory loss, which leads to problems in acquiring new information. Of the different memory types, the semantic memory is most affected. In addition, the patients have minor impairments in communication, making them appear apathetic and lacking enthusiasm. The transition to early dementia is gradual and is often unnoticeable, with learning and memory impairment becoming increasingly more severe. The patient starts to have difficulties in word fluency because their vocabulary begins to shrink. They search for the words for familiar objects, and they hesitate when speaking and writing. Procedural memory is also affected because their motor coordination starts to decline. Because of this decline, they often are clumsy. This phase usually lasts for approximately one to two years.

In the moderate dementia phase, language difficulties become clearly noticeable, and the patients have an increase in their loss of reading and writing skills. The most distinct symptom of this phase is a condition known as paraphasia. Paraphasias are characterized by the inability to find the right words, the placing of the words in the wrong order in sentences, and inappropriate sentence construction. The patients are generally unaware of their deficit, and they become frustrated with their difficulties and their inability to communicate. They show irritability with emotional outbursts, aggression, and occasionally, physical violence. In some cases, the patients can no longer recognize their family members. They also sometimes have delusional symptoms, such as believing that people are conspiring against them.

Portion of Reagan's letter

In this letter, Reagan informed the nation of his diagnosis of Alzheimer's disease. *(Public Domain)*

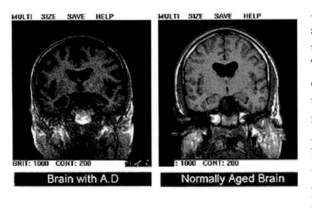

MRI Images

Image of a normal aged brain (on the right) and an Alzheimer's patient's brain (on the left). In the Alzheimer's brain, atrophy is clearly visible. *(Public Domain)*

In the advanced phase of Alzheimer's disease, language ability completely deteriorates, and the patients are incommunicable. They exhibit extreme apathy and exhaustion. They lose the ability to coordinate their muscles and can no longer walk and feed themselves. At this stage, they become bedridden. Further impairment of their motor coordination leads to physiological problems, including cardiac difficulties and respiratory failure. Most die from infections of the respiratory tract, such as pneumonia. The average course of the disease is seven years, with approximately 3% living for more than 15 years.

III.3. How is memory destroyed?

One hundred years later, Alzheimer's assessment of the disease that bears his name has been proven correct. The progression of Alzheimer's disease provides evidence of the link between brain structure and the function of memory. The disease results from both the gradual accumulation of amyloid plaques between the neurons and the development of neurofibrillary tangles inside the neurons. The amyloid plaques destroy the neurons because they are extracellular proteins that affect the ability of the neurons to absorb nutrients from the environment. In addition, the amyloid plaques gradually enlarge as the disease progresses.

The neurofibrillary tangles are fiber-like structures that accumulate inside the neurons. Their origin is unclear, but it appears that environmental factors are responsible for inducing the neurons to produce them. The neurofibrillary tangles block electrical signals in the neurons, which leads to the regression of the synapses between neurons. Both the amyloid plaques and the neurofibrillary tangles form gradually and progressively over a long period of time. They can be found in the brains of most elderly patients long before the expression of clinical symptoms of Alzheimer's disease. This phenomenon provides an explanation of why the occurrence of the disease is less than 5% for the 65-year-old age group but increases to nearly 50% for the 85-year-old age group.

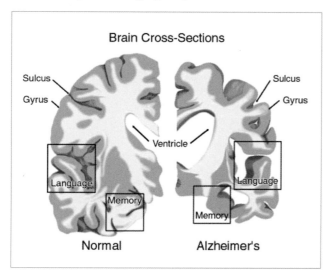

Atrophy of the brain of Alzheimer's patients

Destruction of neurons in brain regions that are vital for memory and langauge are responsible for the decline in speech and cognitive functions. *(Public Domain)*

The deterioration of neurons and synapses due to the accumulation of the amyloid plaques and the neurofibrillary tangles first begins in the hippocampus, which explains the inability to form short-term memory during the predementia phase. The next part of the brain that is affected is the temporal lobe, which leads to a further decline in forming long-term memory. The neurological damage then spreads to the parietal lobe, which contains the motor cortex that is critical for controlling many of the voluntary motor functions. The destruction of the neurons in this area accounts for the loss in motor coordination. As the disease spreads to the frontal lobe, confusion and delusional thinking occur, leading to the advanced state of dementia.

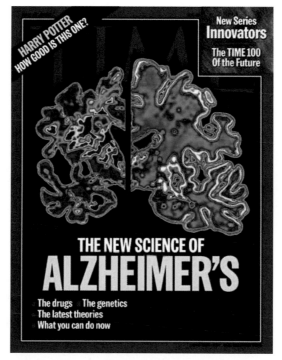

Advances in Alzheimer's research

It is an important disorder with broad social implications. *(Education Fair Use)*

The cause of Alzheimer's disease remains unclear. However, studies on the onset of Alzheimer's disease have provided important insights into its possible causes. There are two forms of Alzheimer's disease based on their times of onset. The first form of Alzheimer's disease is early onset, and it has a pattern of familial inheritance. The early onset Alzheimer's disease accounts for only 5% of the total cases. The symptoms of the disease appear as early as 35 years of age, and the duration of the disease can be as long as 20 years. The inheritance pattern of the disease is largely autosomal dominant, and several genes are involved in the development of the disease. A mutation in one of the genes is responsible for the formation of the amlyoid plaque. A mutation in another gene causes the development of the neurofibrillary tangles.

The other form of Alzheimer's disease is the late onset or the sporadic form. The sporadic form shows no pattern of familial inheritance, but is linked to certain genes. It has been estimated that over 40 genes are possibly involved. However, environmental factors are also important in the formation of the disease. The sporadic form is late onset, starting at 65 of years of age, and is characterized by a dramatic increase in incidence every five years. Of the population over age 85, the rate of the disease is from 35% to 50%. If a cure for Alzheimer's disease is not found in the next two decades, the social and economic impact will be immense as the baby boomer generation enters this demographic group. From the biological standpoint, Alzheimer's disease provides the most convincing argument for the existence of a physical basis of human memory.

Chapter 15

Consciousness

What is reality?

Jacob's dream of a ladder of angels
Why is our consciousness altered in our sleep?
(Public Domain)

CHAPTER 15. CONSCIOUSNESS

Northern sea lion
Pup with adult male and female taking a nap. *(GNU Free Documentation License)*

Defining consciousness has posed a challenge for philosophers and religious thinkers for millenniums. This has resulted because there are various degrees of consciousness, ranging from complete awareness to semiconsciousness. In the past several decades, the study of consciousness has been approached by different scientific disciplines, including biology, psychology, neuroscience, and cognitive science. However, studies on consciousness remain difficult to conduct because defining consciousness is difficult. For most situations, a general definition of consciousness, which has two components, can be used. The first component concerns subjectivity, which is a property of perception from a subject's point of view that is expressed in behavior and/or language. The second component is self-awareness or self-consciousness. However, consciousness must also be closely tied to reality, because the survival of a biological organism relies on its ability to accurately access its environment and behave accordingly. Human consciousness has long been considered a concept that cannot be studied and understood, but recent research has started to unravel some of its mysteries.

I. WHAT IS SLEEP?

I.1. Is sleep an altered state of consciousness?

What is going on when we sleep? Why do we spend as much as one third of our lives sleeping? What happens to our conscious mind during sleep? Sleep occurs in all organisms because it is a necessary survival activity. Even simple animals, such as reptiles, amphibians, fish, and insects, require sleep to function normally. It appears that sleep is important for replenishing and restoring bodily functions. In humans, sleep deprivation leads to physical and mental exhaustion that cannot be replaced by any other means other than sleep. Inadequate sleep has a severe impact on mental functions, leading to psychological and emotional distress. However, the brain does not rest completely during sleep, and during some parts of sleep, the brain is as active as it is during full wakefulness. Because of these properties, studies on sleep abnormalities have led to an understanding of our conscious mind.

Flamingo
They sleep in an upright posture and with at least one cerebral hemisphere awake. Only one half of their brain goes to sleep. *(Creative Commons Attribution)*

One sleep disorder is a strange condition called narcolepsy. Narcolepsy occurs when an individual has excessive daytime sleepiness, even after adequate night time sleep. Narcolepsy varies in severity from mild to severe. In the severe form, a person can nod off in the middle of a sentence. In some rare instances, a narcoleptic person can fall asleep after being provoked by psychological stress. One individual, who suffered from narcolepsy, was a student. Even though he was a very good student and enjoyed learning, he had difficulties staying awake during class ever since high school. During almost every lecture, he would fall asleep as soon as the professor started to talk. His sleepiness continued even after he increased his sleeping at night. Finally, he sought medical help and was diagnosed with narcolepsy. What causes the brain to take such sudden action?

Another type of sleep disorder is REM behavior disorder (RBD), also known as parasomnias. This is a class of sleep disorder that is characterized by individuals who become physically active during their sleep. In fact, some episodes of parasomnia are so strange and bizarre that they provide excellent plots for novels and movies. In some cases, RBD leads to a tragic outcome. In one example, a man attempted to strangle his wife in his sleep. In one of his RBD episodes, the man recalled that in his dream, he was struggling with a deer whose neck he was trying to snap. When he awoke, his hands were on his wife's head and chin. Fortunately, she was able to wake him up and stop him from hurting her any further.

Another equally bizarre episode of RBD involved a woman who had just became a grandmother. She went to stay with her daughter's family two months after the baby was born. One night, her daughter heard the baby crying and discovered that her mother was putting her finger into the mouth of the baby and then holding the baby in such as way that she appeared to be doing mouth-to-mouth resuscitation. Her daughter was horrified and snatched the baby from her mother's arms. Her mother was actually acting out her dream. In her dream, she was trying to save the baby because she saw that the baby had stopped breathing.

RBD demonstrates that the conscious state of waking and the unconscious state of sleep is separated by only a small margin. This fine separation is further illustrated in a case where a middle-aged woman was recently divorced and living alone. She discovered that she had been unknowingly eating in her sleep. She would get up from her bed, walk to the kitchen, open the cupboard or refrigerator, and eat. One morning, she discovered that she had opened a can of mushroom soup and had picked out all the mushrooms. Approximately 75% of the time, she had no awareness of eating during the night. However, about 25% of the time, she remembered dreaming about eating. Interestingly, her nocturnal snacking only stopped after she started taking medication for her depression.

From studying sleep disorders, researchers have discovered that our consciousness and unconsciousness are closely linked. Most of the time, our conscious mind informs and directs our behavior to help us deal with environmental stimuli. However, when we go to sleep, our unconscious mind takes over and plays out dramas that are beyond our conscious awareness. This drama may be important for the health of the mind and the function of the brain. Understanding the abnormal behavior that occurs during sleep has helped to reveal the mysteries of the unconscious mind.

A child asleep
Children need a greater amount of sleep per day than adults to develop and function properly. Newborn babies need up to 18 hours a day. *(GNU Free Documentation License)*

I.2. How do we know when to go to sleep?

One of the first questions that sleep researchers asked concerned the timing of sleeping and wakefulness. Do we get our cue of when to sleep based on the day-night cycle of the earth? Or, do we have an internal clock inside our body? In the 1960s, researchers discovered that when rats were kept in constant light or dark environments, they slept and woke as if they were exposed to a regular day-night cycle. These results suggested that the rats possessed an internal biological clock that regulated their sleep pattern and other physiological activities. Do humans also have an internal biological clock? With the advent of air travel in the 1960s, a person could travel to a place that was the reverse of his or her day-night cycle. The occurrences of jetlag suggested that human sleep and physiology are also governed by an internal biological clock.

To find evidence of a human biological clock, researchers secluded volunteers in a constant light environment. This was done to keep the test subjects from receiving any cues about the time of day. Some volunteers were placed in this solitary confinement condition for as long as two months. They were free to read, write, play games, eat, and sleep whenever they wanted. In the beginning, their daily routine was disrupted. Within a week, however, they had established a schedule for their daily activities, including sleeping and waking. This 24-hour schedule is known as the circadian rhythm. This rhythm is roughly a 24-hour cycle that affects every aspect of the body, not just sleeping and waking. Further studies have shown that this mechanism for biological time keeping (biological clock) is found in all living organisms, including plants, fungi, animals, and bacteria.

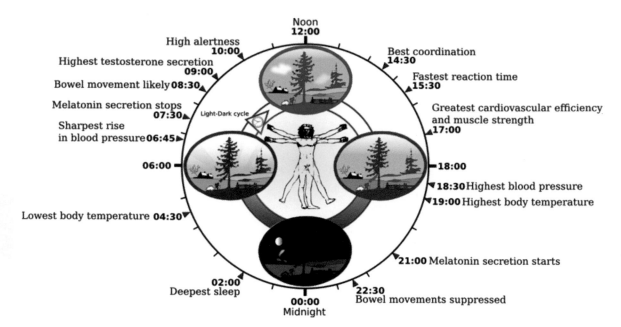

Biological clock

Overview of the human circadian biological clock with some physiological parameters. *(GNU Free Documentation License)*

Pituitary and Pineal Glands

Pineal gland

The pineal gland is located near the pituitary gland. Both are important in the control of the circadian rhythm. *(Public Domain)*

From studying human sleep patterns, researchers have discovered that a small region of the human brain, the pineal gland, is responsible for maintaining the circadian rhythm. Inside the neurons of the pineal gland, a set of biochemical reactions occur spontaneously (similar to the working of a clock) to mark the passage of time. The pineal gland also directs other parts of the brain to release neurotransmitters and hormones to regulate the physiological functions of the body. One hormone that is important to the circadian rhythm is a simple compound known as melatonin. The exact role of this hormone remains unclear, but it is thought to control the sleep-wake cycle.

The human biological clock is not static and unchangeable. Each day, this clock undergoes fine adjustments and is correlated to the amount of daylight that is perceived from external cues. In situations, such as traveling, when an individual's schedule has markedly changed, this adjustment can take as long as one week to become fully adjusted. This is the biological cause of jetlag. There are several ways to treat jetlag by adjusting the biological clock. One way is to be exposed to light at certain wavelengths (resembling natural sunlight) according to the time zone of the destination for several days before the trip. Another way is to take melatonin to reset the biological clock. Nevertheless, the biological clock will gradually and automatically reset on its own if given enough time.

The cycle of sleeping and waking is controlled by many factors. Levels of neurotransmitters, for example, follow a distinct pattern and are partially responsible for the cycle. However, the most important control of the sleep-wake cycle is the hormones that affect the physiological functions of the body. These are the fight or flight hormones, which include adrenalin and cortisol. When a person is ready to sleep, the levels of both adrenalin and cortisol decline to the lowest levels of the day. If these levels remain high, the person is too excited or agitated to fall sleep. Consumption of caffeine increases the level of norepinephrine, which is the counterpart of adrenalin in the brain, and keeps a person awake. During the different stages of life, the circadian rhythm of these hormone levels varies. Most teenagers have levels of adrenalin and cortisol that remain high late into the night, causing them to stay up late and wake up later.

When a person falls asleep, profound changes occur both in the brain and throughout the entire body. Research on the biological mechanisms of sleep has revealed fascinating aspects of the purpose, significance, and benefits of sleep.

This understanding has not only resulted in treatments for sleep disorders but has provided important insights into the biological basis of consciousness. Currently, it is understood that consciousness is based entirely on the biochemistry and genetics of the brain. Also, consciousness is not separate from other aspects of our mental functioning.

I.3. What goes on during sleep?

Narcolepsy provides an interesting insight on what happens during sleep. It is well-known that when we fall asleep, our bodies become limp, and we are unable to move. Why does this happen? Researchers have discovered that in the region of the brain between the frontal lobe and the parietal lobe, there is a strip of neurons known as the motor cortex. All of our voluntary muscle functions are controlled by the motor cortex. Using brain scan techniques, it was discovered that when a person experiences narcolepsy, all activity in the motor cortex abruptly stops. As a result, the person loses all motor control, becomes limp, and possibly falls off his or her chair.

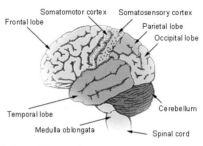

Lobes of the cerebrum

Somatomotor cortex

Region of the brain that controls voluntary muscle movement. It is inactive during REM sleep. (Public Domain)

During normal sleep, the brain gradually changes the neural communications between various parts of the brain. As a person falls asleep, the motor cortex goes into "hibernation." In parasomnias, for reasons yet to be fully understood, the motor cortex remains active, giving the person the ability to move about and to act out whatever is going on in the subconscious. From studying parasomnias, researchers realized that the brain is not at rest during sleep and that sleepers are not usually aware of what is going on. In other words, the brain activities take place unconsciously rather than consciously. These unconscious brain activities occur each night, and when we remember them, we refer to them as dreams.

We do not dream during our entire sleep, and we alternate between the dream and the non-dream state. Researchers have discovered that the electrical activities during the dream state are as active as they are during full wakefulness. This stage of sleep is also known as REM (rapid eye movement) sleep. During this sleep state, the eyes of the sleepers are rapidly moving behind their closed eyelids, as if they were watching a private movie. During REM sleep, the sleepers lie completely motionless, because the motor cortex is "off line," with very little electrical activity. In parasomnias, however, the motor cortex remains active, which allows the sleepers to act out events in their REM sleep.

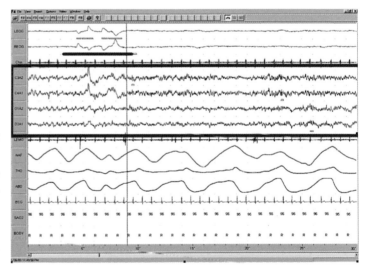

REM Sleep

EEG is highlighted by the red box. Eye movements are highlighted by the red line. (Public Domain)

REM sleep must serve an important biological function, because all mammals and birds have REM sleep. The prevalence of REM sleep in complex animals suggests that it must play an important evolutionary role in the survival of the organism. There are a number of hypotheses on the function of REM sleep. According to one theory, REM sleep is important to consolidate declarative memory. Studies have shown that college students who get adequate sleep before their tests perform consistently better than students who stay up late to study. Another theory proposes that during REM sleep, individuals work out the conflicts that they have by accessing and freely associating memories that are stored in the unconscious mind. This theory explains why some dreams are strange and have sequences that are out of place.

During each night, REM sleep alternates with non-REM sleep. Generally, each period of REM sleep lasts from 30 to 45 minutes, and the non-REM sleep lasts 45 to 90 minutes. Electrical activities in the brain during non-REM sleep are minimal. Interestingly, the tossing and turning that occurs during sleep happens during non-

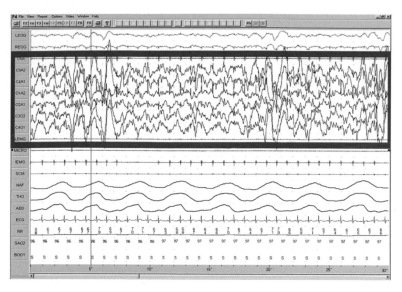

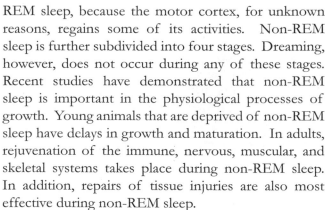

REM sleep, because the motor cortex, for unknown reasons, regains some of its activities. Non-REM sleep is further subdivided into four stages. Dreaming, however, does not occur during any of these stages. Recent studies have demonstrated that non-REM sleep is important in the physiological processes of growth. Young animals that are deprived of non-REM sleep have delays in growth and maturation. In adults, rejuvenation of the immune, nervous, muscular, and skeletal systems takes place during non-REM sleep. In addition, repairs of tissue injuries are also most effective during non-REM sleep.

The results from sleep research indicate that sleep is vital for the physical and mental health of animals. It provides opportunities for young animals to grow and develop, which is why human infants spend up to 80% of their time sleeping. It also helps animals to fight infectious agents. This is why a sick person spends most of the day in bed. The study of the neurological and psychological basis of sleep has also revealed the importance of sleep to mental health. Inappropriate sleep patterns, lack of sleep, and drug-induced sleep disturbances can result in depression and other mental disorders.

Non-REM sleep

This phase of non-REM sleep is known as stage 4, which is the deepest form of sleep. Animals need this sleep to survive. *(Public Domain)*

II. WHAT IS CONSCIOUSNESS?

II.1. What is conscious awareness?

How do we become aware of a chair or a person in the room? Why do we sometimes fail to see something that we are looking for even if it is sitting right in front of us? How do we become consciously aware of something? One way in which researchers have studied awareness is to observe patients who have received surgery to disconnect their left and right hemispheres. This surgery is sometimes performed as a treatment for severe seizures. These individuals can demonstrate the existence of unconscious awareness by a simple experiment. In this experiment, an item is presented in the left visual field of an individual. As a result of the surgery, the individual cannot state what the item is, but they can successfully draw it. This example demonstrates that we are not aware of the many events that are occurring in our unconscious mind.

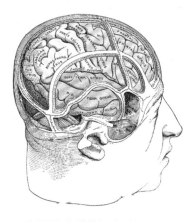

Another condition that has allowed researchers to demonstrate how our mind works is visual neglect. In this condition, an individual's brain does not recognize information that is presented to particular parts of the visual field. One woman, who suffered a minor stroke to her parietal lobe, was noted to have visual neglect. Even though she had recovered from her stroke without any noticeable mental or physical effects, she found that she could no longer draw a complete picture. When her grandchildren asked her to draw a house, for example, she only drew half of the house. In addition, when asked during her psychological testing to copy a star, she drew only half of the star. She was completely unaware of this deficiency until it was pointed out to her. Furthermore, when asked to draw a star from memory, she also only drew half of the star. From studies of patients who have visual neglect, researchers have discovered that the deficiency is not in the patients' visual system (the eyes and the visual cortex). Instead, their problem is located in the parietal lobe, the brain area that is responsible for processing spatial information.

Visual neglect

The parietal lobe (shown in yellow) is the site for processing spatial information. A stroke in this region can cause visual neglect. *(Public Domain)*

Our conscious awareness is a complicated neural process. In other words, we "see" with more than just our eyes. We see with our brain; our eyes are only instruments that collect external light signals in the form of intensity and color (wavelength). In an unusual condition known as blindsight, researchers have discovered that our vision is far more complicated than was previously known. Blindsight occurs when a person can sense something moving but is unable to describe anything else about the object. One individual, who has blindsight, lost his vision because of a severe head injury he received as a child. The physical trauma destroyed the optic nerve of one of his eyes. Even though his eye did not sustain any damage, he could not see with that eye because it was no longer connected to his visual cortex. Interestingly, however, he could sense motion in the visual field of his "blind" eye. This motion was especially noticeable to him when the movement of the object was abrupt. From studying individuals who have blindsight, researchers have discovered that in addition to the visual cortex, the eye uses another neural pathway to process vision. This pathway goes to the limbic system and then travels to the cerebral cortex for conscious awareness.

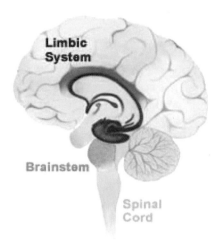

Why do we have a visual pathway that travels through the limbic system? Do other organisms use a similar pathway? Studies have revealed that this pathway is the primary visual pathway that is used by reptiles and amphibians. Detecting motion is vital for these organisms to catch prey, such as flying insects. Blindsight results because of the retention of this visual pathway in our "reptilian brain." This pathway allows for an individual to sense motion, even though there is no conscious awareness of the nature of the object. For conscious awareness of an object to occur, it must be processed in the cerebral cortex.

Reptilian brain
The limbic system is present in reptiles and other lower vertebrates. It is responsible for blindsight. *(Public Domain)*

Even though we are not aware of the information that is processed by the primitive visual pathway, it is vital to us when we simultaneously carry out multiple tasks. Because of this pathway we can, for example, drive and talk at the same time. In this situation, if a truck gets dangerously close we can notice it and make immediate adjustments. Our blindsight is subconsciously keeping track of details, and it only alarms us when absolutely necessary. Another area in which the importance of blindsight is demonstrated is in athletics. Some baseball hitters can "feel" the ball coming without actually seeing it, and some quarterbacks can "sense" the linebacker coming even though they are focused on throwing the ball to the wide receivers. Excellent basketball players, such as Michael Jordon, probably possess exceptional blindsight.

II.2. *Why do we see and feel things that are not there?*

Both visual neglect and blindsight demonstrate that our consciousness is only part of our awareness. We have both conscious and unconscious awareness. It is our brain that determines what we do or do not see at the conscious level. How the brain plays such a role is illustrated in a strange condition known as phantom limb pain. One man who experienced phantom limb pain was seriously injured in an automobile accident, and his arm required amputation because of severe damage. After the surgery, he woke up and felt a terrible pain in his missing arm. He could not understand why he could still feel his arm, even though it was no longer there. At times, the pain that was associated with his missing arm was severe, and he sometimes felt that his hand was caught in an unnatural position. He would try to move his hand, but then he would realize that he no longer had a hand to move. More interestingly, every time he shaved the left side of his face, he felt as if something was touching his missing hand. Some individuals who have phantom limb pain suffer from severe, chronic pain and discomfort in their missing limbs. Furthermore, phantom limbs are not the only body parts to elicit this condition. There are phantom eye (removal of an eye), phantom breast (after mastectomy), and even phantom tooth pain (after the extraction of a tooth). How can we still feel a part of the body that is no longer there?

Blindsight in sports
Good hitters can sense the incoming pitch with instinctual accuracy that is beyond conscious awareness. *(GNU Free Documentation License)*

Sensory cortex

This region of the brain, located near the frontal lobe, maps all the sensory points on our body. However, certain regions of the body receive greater sensory information than others. Our lip and tongue are highly sensitive for this reason. *(Public Domain)*

Phantom limb pain results because of the neurological function of the sense of touch. In the brain, there is a strip of neurons, known as the sensory cortex, in the cerebral cortex that is located next to the motor cortex. The sensory input of the entire body is mapped onto this sensory cortex. For example, sensations, such as pain, heat, and softness, for an arm are felt because of the stimulation of particular neurons in the sensory cortex. When that arm is amputated, however, the sensory neurons for that arm remain. Somehow, these neurons can generate their own signal and create the sensation of pain, even though there are no more signals coming from that arm. Interestingly, researchers have discovered that these signals can be controlled by fooling the brain to think that the hand is still there. Using an apparatus known as the mirror box, the amputee places his or her normal hand in the

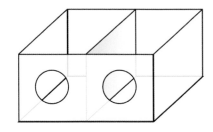

The mirror box

A patient inserts their hand into one hole, and their "phantom" into the other. When viewed from an angle, the brain is tricked into seeing two hands. *(Public Domain)*

box. Using the mirror image, the amputee can "exercise" the missing hand to relieve the pain.

Understanding the structure of the sensory cortex has also provided an explanation of why touching the face of an amputee can also give a sensory stimulation of the missing hand. In the sensory cortex, the sensory neurons for the hand are located next to the sensory neurons for the cheek. After the arm is amputated, the sensory neurons no longer receive any stimulation, and they start to form connections with the sensory neurons for the cheek. This results in these sensory neurons being responsive to facial stimulation. Consequently, an amputee feels the stimulation of the hand in situations, such as shaving, when the face is touched.

In addition to physical changes, mental changes can also induce false sensory perceptions. The Japanese pilgrims are an example of how physical and psychological stress can affect conscious awareness. During late fall of each year, Japanese pilgrims travel to a sacred mountain site to meditate and to gain spiritual renewal. They spend nearly one week with hardly any food in a remote area. Each night, they try to stay awake as long as they can. With near-freezing nighttime temperatures and little food to eat, the pilgrims become exhausted. It is at this point that they experience altered consciousness. Some pilgrims have out-of-body experiences, such as seeing their bodies from above. Some feel that their arms have become detached from their bodies, and some have visions of their loved ones who have died many years ago. Some are even transported to places that they have never been before. These psychological experiences closely resemble hallucinations, altered states of consciousness not unlike the state of dreaming. What is the neurological basis of hallucinations?

II.3. What causes an altered state of consciousness?

The first account that hallucinations have a biochemical base was a report that was written by a Victorian naturalist who collected mushrooms for scientific study and for culinary pleasure. He reported that on one occasion he prepared some mushrooms for his family at breakfast. After breakfast, the entire family, including the four-year-old daughter, experienced hallucinations. They reported seeing bright colors, various geometric shapes, and flashing lights. Some thought the experience was pleasant, whereas others were frightened by the effects. He concluded that the mushrooms they ate were responsible for their hallucinations. It was more than 200 years before the neurological basis of their hallucinations was understood.

Hallucination is defined as perceptions in the absence of stimuli. People who experience hallucinations recognize that their experiences are not real. Most people who experience hallucinations experience them during the time just before falling asleep or waking. They are known as hypnagogic and hypnopompic hallucinations, respectively. However, hallucinations are often induced by psychoactive substances, such as magic mushrooms and LSD. Magic mushrooms have been used by priests and shamans for thousands of years. Magic mushrooms were also used in many ancient cultures, including ancient Egypt, ancient Greek, Maya, Inca, and Aztec. They were mainly used by shamans during religious rituals as a means to contact the dead and the gods. They were intended to induce spirituality, and were consequently, given the name entheogens. The use of entheogens was prohibited by Judaism, Christianity, and Islam. They were considered to be the tools of the devil, and users were persecuted as witches.

Magic mushroom
A species of psilocybin mushroom.
(Public Domain)

Magic mushrooms are also known as psilocybin mushrooms, and their active ingredient is a chemical compound known as psilocin. Psilocin has a chemical structure that is nearly identical to the neurotransmitter serotonin. Because of this similarity, psilocin serves as a serotonin agonist, a substance that can function in the place of serotonin. In other words, psilocin affects the same brain areas that use serotonin. Serotonin has many different neurological activities depending on the region of the brain. Serotonin activities in the frontal lobe and in the temporal lobe, for example, are involved in depression.

Psilocin
Active ingredient of magic mushrooms.

Serotonin
A neurotransmitter with similar structure as psilocin.

Serotonin is also used in the region of the brain known as the thalamus. The function of serotonin in the thalamus is to regulate sensory input. The thalamus is located in the junction between the limbic system and the cerebral cortex. Because of this location, the thalamus has neural circuits that connect it to nearly every part of the cerebral cortex. The thalamus serves primarily as a filter of incoming sensory information. To prevent the overstimulation of the cerebral cortex, it only allows vital information to pass through. Serotonin is the neurotransmitter that regulates these neural pathways. When there is too much serotonin,

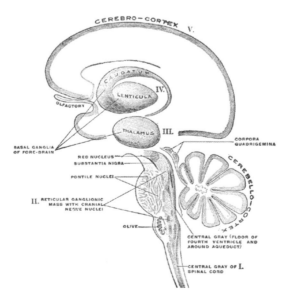

The thalamus
The brain region that filters incoming sensory information. *(Public Domain)*

the pathways that are controlled by the thalamus become activated, and the cerebral cortex becomes overstimulated. When psilocin enters into the brain, it targets the thalamus for reasons yet to be fully understood. The psilocin then opens up the serotonin neural circuit of the thalamus leading to overstimulation of the cerebral cortex and to hallucinations.

When the Japanese pilgrims were studied after their hallucinating experiences, researchers discovered that their self-imposed sensory and physical deprivation resulted in high levels of serotonin in their brains. This result suggested that the pathways used for psilocin-induced hallucinations and for behavioral-induced hallucinations are the same. Both involve the neurological circuits between the thalamus and the cerebral cortex. These results have provided a biological base of the neurological processes that are involved in spiritual experiences. This knowledge is vital for developing a modern view of religion and religious experiences.

In 1938, a semi-synthetic entheogen was synthesized from ergot, a grain fungus that grows on cereal crops, such as rye. The chemical was LSD (lysergic acid diethylamide), and it launched the era of psychedelic drugs. LSD is structurally similar to serotonin and psilocin. It is also a serotonin agonist and acts on the neural circuits in the thalamus. It causes a similar hallucinogenic effect as that caused by the magic mushrooms, providing further evidence of the role of serotonin in regulating the activities of the thalamus. In addition to LSD, there is another family of psychedelic drugs that has been discovered. They are collectively referred to as phenethylamines, and the most prominent example is MDMA, commonly known as Ecstasy. Instead of acting as an agonist, these compounds stimulate the release of serotonin. Marijuana also induces mild hallucinations, but it does so through a serotonin-independent pathway.

III. WHAT IS UNCONSCIOUSNESS?

III.1. *What is a coma?*

In a serious traffic accident, a woman was ejected from her car and sustained a severe head injury. After the EMTs stabilized her condition at the scene, she was lifted by helicopter to an emergency trauma center. When she arrived at the hospital, her condition was dire. She was judged to be in a deep coma because her eyes were not open, she made no sound, and she was completely motionless. There was nothing the doctors could do for her, except to cut a hole in her skull to remove a blood clot that had formed in her brain. For six weeks she remained in a coma, even though her basic physiological functions remained intact.

Head-on collision

The most frequent cause of severe head injuries that lead to comas.
(*GNU Free Documentation License*)

Deceleration injury

Deceleration exerts powerful rotational forces in the brain, causing the brain to ricochet inside the skull.
(*Creative Commons Attribution*)

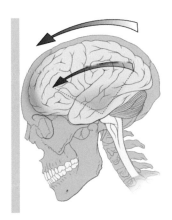

Coma is defined as the death of neurons in the brain to the extent that consciousness is destroyed. There are many different causes of comas, but the outcome is generally the same. The most frequent cause of comas is automobile accidents. Without wearing a seatbelt, a coma can be caused in accidents at speeds as slow as 30 mph. When a moving vehicle comes to a sudden halt, the momentum causes the brain to be shaken violently in the skull, ricocheting back and forth. In this situation, the neurons in the brain are twisted and stretched, resulting in the breakage of axons, dendrites, and synapses. This breakage causes the release of a vast amount of neurotransmitters, which results in inflammation and swelling in the brain.

Since the brain is located in the confined space of the skull, the swelling brain exerts pressure on the blood vessels and cuts off it own blood supply. Without oxygen and glucose from the blood, the neurons start to die. As the blood supply is cut off, the cerebral cortex is the first to die, leading to the loss of cognitive, motor, and sensory functions. The amount of brain tissue death is directly correlated to the length of oxygen deprivation. Unfortunately, after a traumatic injury, very little can be done to decrease tissue swelling.

After spending six weeks in the coma unit, the woman, who was involved in the traffic accident, started to stir. Her family was overjoyed, because the chance for regaining consciousness dramatically reduces with each passing week. Generally, the chance for a patient to awaken from a coma after six weeks is less than 15%. After three weeks, she returned home to recuperate, and it took her another eight weeks to regain most of her motor and cognitive functions. However, the residual effects of her brain damage will stay with her for the rest of her life. In recent years, the incidence of comas that are caused by traffic accidents has been dramatically reduced because of mandatory seat belt laws. In addition, newer safety features in cars have provided better protection for both drivers and passengers.

Comas can be induced by any cause that deprives the brain of oxygen. Drowning, suffocation, strokes, drugs, heart disease, ion imbalances, head injuries, and gunshot wounds are all causes of comas. One of the most remarkable cases of comas was demonstrated by a police officer who was shot in the head and subsequently went into a deep coma. The only part of his brain that remained alive was his brainstem, which was important to coordinate his basic physiological functions, such as breathing, cardiac function, kidney function, and temperature regulation. For seven and a half years, he was in the deepest state of a coma, a condition known as a persistent vegetative state. The prognosis of recovery for individuals in this state is very poor. Also, most coma patients who have been in a coma for more than five years have a negligible chance of recovery. Remarkably, one day he emerged from his coma and started to talk. He recognized his wife and old friends. His emergence from his coma made world news, as this seemed to be medically impossible. However, for unknown reasons, he fell silent again, slipped back into a coma, and died a year later. His case made medical history and reflects the complexity of how the brain functions and repairs itself.

Terri Schiavo
Before her 1990 respiratory and cardiac arrest. *(Education Fair Use)*

III.2. Can consciousness be regained?

Comas are one of the most difficult medical situations for family members and society. It is difficult for individuals and society to decide when the life of a coma patient should be terminated. Currently, there are over 300,000 coma patients in the United States, and nearly 90% of them will never emerge from their comatose conditions. Determining when the lives of coma patients should be terminated has posed both legal and ethical challenges for families, medical personnel, politicians, and ethicists. In 2005, Terri Schiavo, a coma patient, attracted worldwide attention. Her case demonstrated the difficulties of the issues regarding coma patients.

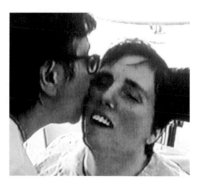

Persistent vegetative state
Terri Schiavo with her mother in hospice. *(Education Fair Use)*

In 1990, Terri Schiavo collapsed in her home from a respiratory and cardiac arrest. Her arrest had resulted from an electrolyte imbalance that had been caused by her self-directed weight loss attempt. She lapsed into a coma as a result of extensive

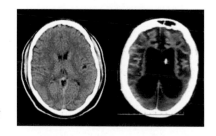

CT scan of Schiavo's brain
The left is a normal brain. The right is Schiavo's brain in 2002, showing loss of brain tissue. The black area is filled with fluid. *(Education Fair Use)*

brain damage. She was later diagnosed to be in a persistent vegetative state (PVS). In a coma, the patient's eyes are closed, and they have no discernable muscle movement. In a PVS, the patient has progressed to a state of wakefulness, and their eyes have opened. However, there is no sign that they have conscious awareness. Using brain imaging techniques, it has been observed that the cerebral cortex of most patients in a PVS has been mostly destroyed. Patients in a PVS can progress into another state, known as a minimally conscious state (MCS). In a MCS, some parts of the brain remain active.

Based on a CT scan and other medical evidence, it was estimated that 50% of Schiavo's brain had been destroyed. In 1998, Terri Schiavo's physicians deemed that her chances for recovering from her PVS were non-existent. Her husband, as her legal guardian, petitioned the court to terminate her life by removing her feeding tube. Terri Schiavo's parents, however, argued against the medical opinions of her physicians and insisted that she was in a MCS rather than in a PVS. Because of this opinion, they felt that her chance for recovery was greater than expected. This began a seven year legal battle that received worldwide attention. Eventually, the Florida Supreme Court granted her husband permission to remove her feeding tube. However, the U.S. Congress went into an emergency session attempting to block the decision to remove her feeding tube. Schiavo's husband finally won the legal battle, and her feeding tube was removed on March 18, 2005. She died 13 days later.

Among the several hundred thousands of patients in a MCS in the United States, there are only a few confirmed cases of patients emerging from this condition. The most well-known case is Terry Willis. After being seriously injured in an automobile accident in 1984, he first entered into a coma but later progressed to a MCS. After 19 years, in June 2003, Willis regained consciousness and started to speak with his family members and friends. Over a three day "awakening period," he regained the ability to move and have full awareness. Remarkably, he still recalled events that had occurred before his accident. He remembered his 19th birthday, for example, and thought that Ronald Reagan was still president. The recovery of Willis suggested to researchers that there must be a brain region that serves as the command center of the brain. When this region is destroyed, all other brain regions cannot function cooperatively.

Another intriguing and rare coma-like condition is known as the locked-in syndrome. With this syndrome, an individual has normal cognitive functioning but appears to be in a PVS. After a severe head injury, a man was in a coma for several weeks, and then he progressed to what was thought to be a PVS. His eyes were open, but he could not move any part of his body. Using a routine brain scan, it was surprisingly discovered that his brain activities were nearly normal. Through further testing, it was also discovered that his cognitive function was intact. The cause for his inability to communicate was due to damage to a critical region in the brainstem that is used for communicating with the cerebral cortex. The destruction of this brainstem region resulted in a complete paralysis of all voluntary muscles, preventing him from making any communicative gestures. The patient was awake and aware but could not move, talk, or communicate in any way. The discovery of the locked-in syndrome has allowed for the identification and the appropriate treatment of this type of patient.

Comas and coma-like conditions have provided us with an understanding of consciousness. From studying coma patients, it has become clear that the brainstem is the part of the brain that maintains all the complex physiological functions of the brain. Conscious awareness, however, depends on the integrity of the cerebral cortex. It is the complex interactions between the brainstem and all other brain parts that allow a human to function normally. Nevertheless, despite its complexity, it has been well-established that the human nervous system consists of nothing more than a neural circuit. By understanding and decoding this circuit, it has become

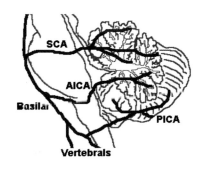

Locked-in syndrome

The neural connections between the brainstem and the cerebellum are destroyed, leading to the elimination of all motor functions.
(Public Domain)

possible to manipulate human consciousness for the benefit of the individuals. The development of anesthesia is an example of manipulating human consciousness.

III.3. How does anesthesia work?

During the American Civil War, soldiers who were infected with gangrene in their legs had two options: to die or to have their legs amputated. The soldiers were given several shots of whiskey and a bullet to bite. Then, the surgeons used their surgical saws to amputate the leg. The soldier was held down by assistants, and the entire operation took less than a minute. A bullet was put between the teeth to prevent the patient from biting his tongue. "Bite the bullet" became a common phrase to describe the need to make a difficult decision. There were other equally horrific surgical procedures, such as giving birth to a child by cesarean section or pulling a tooth out, that were performed without the benefit of anesthetics.

None of the remarkable surgical procedures of modern medicine would have been possible without anesthesia. The pain that is associated with most surgeries is too much to bear. Throughout history, many substances were tried to see if they could induce unconsciousness. Unfortunately, most of these chemicals often killed the patients. It was not until the mid 1800s that effective anesthetics were discovered. The first chemical that was discovered to be an effective anesthetic was ether, a simple chemical compound. In 1846, William Morton, a dentist, performed the first public demonstration using ether on a patient to remove a tumor from his neck. The impact was immediate, and almost overnight surgery was changed from "butchering" to highly sophisticated procedures.

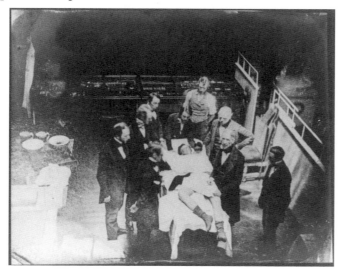

First use of anesthetics
Anesthesia was introduced in 1846. *(Public Domain)*

Ether was the first anesthetic used to render a patient completely unconscious. This type of anesthesia is known as general anesthesia. The patients were given a controlled dose of ether to achieve a certain level of unconsciousness. At the correct dose, ether will affect the cerebral cortex but not the brainstem. If the dose becomes too high, the brainstem shuts down, and the patients die from respiratory failure. In modern times, ether has been replaced by other anesthetics because it is flammable. Furthermore, in modern general anesthesia, a ventilator takes over the breathing for the patients.

Since the development of ether, many other chemicals were discovered or synthesized to serve as anesthetics. New procedures were also developed to block regional pain without rendering the patients unconscious. Spinal anesthesia, also known as a spinal block, is carried out by injecting a small volume of anesthetic directly into the spinal cord, so that the neuronal activities are blocked. The other type of regional anesthesia, known as epidural anesthesia, is less specific but easier

Morphine

Morphine is the active ingredient of opium. Heroin is a chemically modified form of morphine but is nearly twice as potent. Both are highly addictive.

to administer. In this case, a large amount of anesthetic is injected around the spinal cord. Both procedures are commonly used during childbirth to reduce the pain of labor.

Another aspect of pain management is analgesia. Anesthesia differs from analgesia in that anesthesia blocks all sensations, not only pain. Many drugs have been used as analgesics, ranging from aspirin to morphine. Some analgesics act indirectly on the peripheral and central nervous systems, whereas some act directly. Analgesics are the most widely used drugs around the world, and they are important in modern medicine. However, some analgesics are highly addictive, such as the opioids (also known as narcotics). Therefore, their use must be properly controlled and under professional guidance.

In summary, our nervous system is a circuit that contains several hundred billion neurons. It is a communication network that is used for sending and receiving information. We have discussed many components of this extraordinary, complicated network and how this knowledge is vital for us to have. Our understanding has greatly increased our ability to manage this network using psychoactive drugs. Some of these drugs have remarkable effects and have enormous benefits in treating mental disorders and in managing pain. However, many of these drugs are addictive and detrimental to an individual if their usages and applications are not properly controlled. We need to appreciate this knowledge and the benefit of its application.

Morphine advertisement

During the early 1900s, morphine was considered to be non-addictive and was easily available.
(Public Domain)

Chapter 16
Intelligence

What is the origin of your intelligence?

Emperor Tamarin
A social primate, allegedly named for its resemblance to the German emperor Wilhelm II.
(GNU Free Documentation License)

CHAPTER 16. INTELLIGENCE

I. WHY ARE THERE MULTICELLULAR ORGANISMS?

I.1. Why are cells the basic units of life?

Our body is made up of about 100 trillion cells. Our brain has approximately 100 billion neurons. In our circulatory system, we have over 300 billion red blood cells. Even though we may think of ourselves as individual organisms, our bodies are actually communities of many semi-independent cells that can survive on their own. Our skin cells, for example, can be cultured in the laboratory for years after our death. Blood transfusions work because our blood cells can live and function normally in another body. In some manner, our cells can be independent of us. They have no allegiance.

Our bodies also host other cells. Foreign cells, such as bacteria, are present in numbers up to 10 times the amount of our own cells. These cells, however, are generally 50 times smaller. They live on the periphery of our bodies and subsist on any extra nutrients that our bodies might have discarded. They are scavengers and thrive on the waste that our bodies produce. Most of these cells are bacteria, and they colonize our skin, intestines, oral cavity, nasal passageways, and any exposed surface areas of our bodies. They invade our bodies immediately after we have left the protective environment of the womb. Furthermore, our bodies are powerless to eliminate them. We tolerate these bacteria, and our relationship with them lasts our entire lifetime.

Several years ago, it was discovered that despite their simplicity, bacteria can communicate with each other after they colonize our bodies. One species of bacteria that colonizes our teeth aggregates together to produce a special layer of proteins, known as a biofilm. The bacteria use this biofilm for attaching to the surface of the teeth. However, a critical number of bacteria must be present before an effective biofilm can be produced. If an inadequate number of bacteria are present, then the saliva washes them away before they can attach to the teeth. Surprisingly, it was discovered that the individual bacteria of this species can sense each other's presence. When the critical number of bacteria is reached, these bacteria simultaneously begin

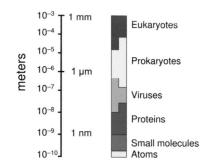

Relative dimensions

The range of sizes of prokaryotes (bacteria) relative to those of other organisms and biomolecules. *(Public Domain)*

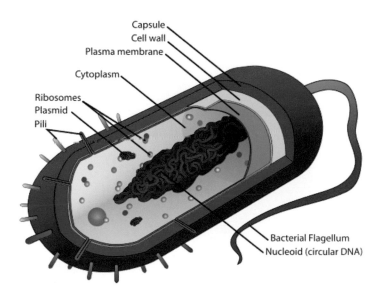

Prokaryote

They lack organelles and have no internal divisions. *(Public Domain)*

to produce the necessary proteins for creating the biofilm. This process is called quorum sensing, and it is considered to be a form of bacterial intelligence.

Bacteria are too small for us to see, but they are everywhere. We rarely consider bacteria and only worry about them after they cause an infection, such as a skin infection, strep throat, pneumonia, or diarrhea. Bacteria belong to the group of organisms known as the prokaryotes. Prokaryotic organisms are unicellular (consisting of only one cell). They are very simple and have no internal divisions within their

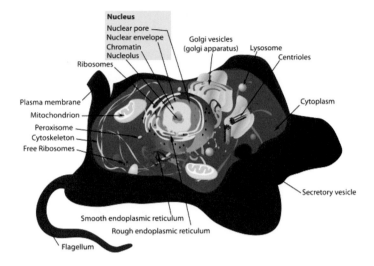

Eukaryotic cell

This is the structure of an average eukaryotic cell with the basic organelles. *(Public Domain)*

cells. In other words, all their components are in one "bag." Despite their simplicity, prokaryotic organisms are the most abundant organisms on Earth.

The other major group of organisms is the eukaryotes. Humans are eukaryotic organisms, as well as all animals, plants, and fungi. Eukaryotic organisms are larger than the prokaryotic organisms, are often formed from many cell types (multicellular), and possess internal structures such as nuclei, mitochondria, and chloroplasts. These structures are known as organelles, because they resemble little organisms. Mitochondria, for example, are organelles that have become specialized to produce energy for the eukaryotic cells. They are similar to bacteria, and they even have their own DNA. Based on this observation and on other evidence, the theory of endosymbiosis was proposed to explain the evolution of eukaryotic cells. According to this theory, some early bacteria incorporated other smaller bacteria into their cells and developed a partnership. This partnership then allowed for these large and complex cells (the eukaryotes) to become more capable of exploring new environments.

Cells are the most basic form of life on Earth. In fact, researchers believe that any life form that might exist on other planets is also based on cells. In 1996, NASA scientists announced that a meteorite from Mars contained evidence of life. Under the electron microscope, they found structures that resembled prokaryotic organisms. This finding was not particularly surprising because on Earth, prokaryotic organisms have been found in the most inhospitable environments, such as the volcanic vents under the ocean. Therefore, many scientists have expected that life beyond Earth would appear like the prokaryotic organisms.

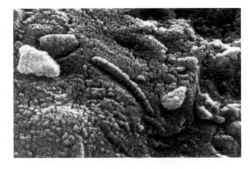

Signs of life on Mars

The electron microscope revealed prokaryote-like fossils on a meteorite from Mars. *(Public Domain)*

I.2. What is the advantage of being multicellular?

The human body is a conglomerate of 200 different types of cells, each with their specialized structure and function. These cells work together in perfect synchrony to maintain the overall function of the body. We often take this cooperation between cells for granted and forget that each cell is an independent entity. However, these cells occasionally "rebel" and strike out on their own. The result is cancer, which is defined as cells that grow and divide out of control. Cancer often results in the destruction of the organism, because a complex multicellular organism relies on the cooperation of every cell in the body.

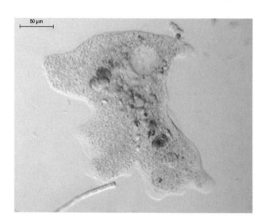

Multicellular organisms have a clear advantage over unicellular organisms. This advantage is demonstrated by those species of unicellular organisms that can, under certain conditions, function as a multicellular organism. One example of this is a species of amoeba-like organisms known as slime mold. Amoebae are unicellular organisms that capture their prey by engulfing them. The members of these species live as unicellular organisms until their normal food source becomes depleted. At that time, some individuals release chemical signals that attract other individuals to aggregate and form multicellular slug-like creatures. This aggregate migrates together and becomes a formidable hunter of prey that is normally too large for the individuals to capture. Furthermore, when the environmental conditions improve, the individuals disperse from the aggregate and return to their solitary existence.

Amoeba

A typical unicellular organism. In the slime mold, individuals can come together to form a multicellular organism. *(GNU Free Documentation License)*

From studying the slime mold and other similar species, it has been suggested that multicellular organisms evolved from the aggregations of unicellular organisms. It was most likely through the use of chemical signals that individual cells aggregated and took the first steps in the evolution of multicellular organisms. In the human body, similar chemical signals can be found and are used by cells to form tissues and organs. In addition, the failure of cells to respond to chemical signals is observed in conditions such as malignant cancers. In these conditions, cancer cells detach from their original tissues and spread to different parts of the body.

Multicellular organisms are also more effective in protecting themselves against adverse environmental conditions as well as against predators. Many unicellular organisms take advantage of this property and aggregate to form spores when their environments become inhospitable. These spores protect the aggregates of individuals by forming a thick outer wall. This wall provides a defense that is better than each individual could make on its own. Many unicellular organisms alternate between their unicellular and multicellular forms according to environmental conditions. Based on these observations and others, it has been concluded that "permanent" multicellular organisms did not evolve suddenly. Instead, multiple intermediate stages occurred before the evolution of true multicellular organisms.

Slime mold

The individual slime mold amoebae come together to form the multicellular aggregates. *(GNU Free Documentation License)*

True multicellular organisms permanently retain their multicellularity and consist of cells that have specialized structures and functions. Sponges are the most primitive multicellular animals. They function with only a few different cell types. One cell type is responsible for producing a protective outer layer, a second cell type is responsible for creating a current of water that flows through the body of the sponge, and a third cell type is responsible for capturing small prey that passes through an inner chamber (resembling a primitive digestive tract). The cells work together and share the nutrients that they obtain. This collaboration allows for multicellular organisms to explore new environments, a characteristic that is not possible for unicellular organisms.

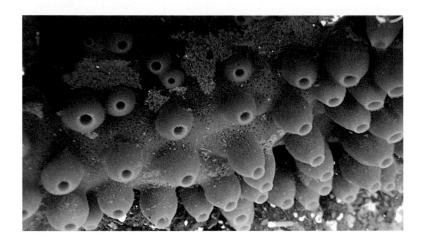

Tide pool sponges
They are the simplest multicellular animals. Their cells are specialized for conducting different functions. *(GNU Free Documentation License)*

The different cell types of the sponge are genetically identical to each other. Their differences in structure and function result from differential gene expression. However, the mere existence of different cell types does not necessarily allow for the existence of a multicellular organism. The cells need to bind to each other. This binding was the next step in the evolution of multicellular organisms. To form a true multicellular organism, there are chemical signals that allow for the different cell types to bind to each other in specific ways. This property can also be observed in the sponges. Because of their simplicity, sponge cells can be physically separated, and the individual cells can be isolated by passing them through a sieve. When the cells are mixed back together, they assemble back into a sponge because of the chemical signals that they produce. From this study and others, it was concluded that multicellularity is based on differential gene expression, which creates different cell types, and on the presence of chemical signals that direct the interactions of these cells.

I.3. Why did multicellular organisms become more complex?

The human body seems incredibly complex with 100 trillion cells and with 200 different cells types. However, the basic biological mechanisms (differential gene expression and chemical signaling) that are responsible for creating multicellular organisms is the same for humans as it is for sponges. In contrast to sponges, the human body requires complex cells, tissues, and organs because humans live in a terrestrial environment. This environment undergoes constant changes in temperature, humidity, and moisture. The body must constantly adjust to these changes and maintain a constant internal environment (also known as homeostasis) for the cells. The sponges live in a more stable environment, so their simple design and structure is sufficient for them to grow and reproduce. Therefore, the complexity of a living organism results from its environmental demand and not from its level of sophistication.

Humans exhibit a behavioral response to light because of visual perception. Nearly all other animals respond to light in a similar manner. Furthermore, many simple animals also use light. In their case, light guides them to their food. One of the simplest light-sensing organisms is the moon jelly (a primitive jellyfish), which feeds on photosynthetic microorganisms. Every morning, thousands of these jellyfish swim toward the surface of the water to harvest their food, and at night, they swim back down to depths of the water. They return to the surface the next day just like commuting city workers. They can do this because they have light-sensing cells in their gelatinous body that detects light intensity. For the moon jellies, seeing an image is unnecessary. They are only as complex as they need to be.

Mediterranean jellyfish
They respond to light and are highly sensitive to touch. *(GNU Free Documentation License)*

The jellyfish, however, also possess some highly complex and sophisticated cell structures. Anyone who has been stung by a jellyfish will testify to the painful effect of their stingers. These stingers (also known as nematocysts) are fired from specialized cells. This firing takes less than a microsecond, making it one of the fastest processes in biology. These stingers are one of the most remarkable weapons that are used by biological organisms. The jellyfish use their stingers to hunt prey, and they are reflexively fired when triggered by touch. One person, who was swimming alone in Australia, was stung by a type of jellyfish, known as the sea wasp, which is one of the most venomous marine animals known. He suffered excruciating pain and was rushed to the nearest hospital. He was lucky to survive, because the chance for survival after being stung by a sea wasp is virtually zero according to the Australian Institute of Marine Science. Despite its simplicity, jellyfish can severely injure or kill a person. As demonstrated by the jellyfish, multicellular organisms can be very simple in some aspects but complicated in others depending on their needs for survival.

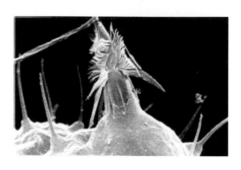

Nematocysts

Highly complex and powerful weapons; the tips of the stingers are coated with toxins. *(Public Domain)*

Some simple multicellular organisms have sophisticated sensory mechanisms that they use to search for prey. Even though a species of flatworm, the Australian flatworm, is less than 4 cm long, it hunts earthworms. It has a small brain that contains only several hundred neurons, but it has an exceptional chemical sensory mechanism. It can detect and track the scent of an earthworm over a vast distance. In other words, this simple organism has a part of its body that is highly complex. Several of these flatworms were accidentally introduced into Great Britain. The result was devastating for a small farming community that was invaded by the flatworms. The fields were waterlogged because all the earthworms were killed by the flatworms. Without earthworms, the soil was not turned and water accumulated. The excess water prevented farmers from planting their crops.

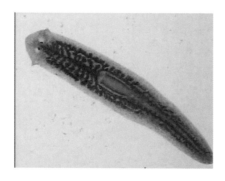

Flatworm

The first primitive animal to have a brain to coordinate its movements. *(Public Domain)*

The Australian flatworms have no teeth or jaws, and their mouths are located in their mid-sections rather than on their heads. When a flatworm catches an earthworm, it quickly secretes a layer of slime to trap the earthworm. It then extends a primitive organ, the pharynx, which injects digestive enzymes into the earthworm's body. When the enzymes digest the earthworm (as food is digested in the human stomach), the flatworm uses the pharynx to suck up the contents of the earthworm. As long as there are earthworms to hunt, this system works well for the flatworms.

If an environment changes, animals can become either more or less complex to adjust to the new demands. Some of the flatworm species, for example, have adapted to a parasitic life inside the intestines of other animals, including humans. Tapeworms belong to a group of parasitic flatworms known as cestodes. These animals have lost both their intestines and their sensory organs. Instead, they have a modified head, the scolex, which has a row of sucking grooves. These grooves function like suction cups to attach the worms to the intestinal wall of their host. Some cestodes even have rows of hooks on their scolex. These organisms have evolved to get their nutrients directly from the intestines of their host. Therefore, they no longer have the need to move and find food. Because of this, they have also completely lost their ability to move. From observing the flatworms and other species, it has been concluded that the complexity of multicellular organisms is nothing more than a reflection of the environment.

z

Tapeworm
The tapeworms have evolved to live in the guts of humans and other animals. They have a modified head known as the scolex with hooks to attach to the host's intestinal wall. *(Public Domain)*

II. WHAT IS SOCIALITY IN SIMPLE ORGANISMS?

II.1. How does complex behavior evolve?

Some human behaviors, such as riding a bicycle, reading a book, or playing a piano, are extremely complex. How do we master these behaviors? Do we start out as a "blank page" or do we develop our behavior based on some innate instincts? We can recognize some innate instincts in newborns. Pediatricians test a baby's instinctive sucking reaction by placing a finger into his or her mouth. Babies will also grasp any extended fingers with their fingers and toes as if they were trying to hang onto tree limbs. Another fascinating response that is only found in babies six to eight months of age is their diving response. When young babies are placed into a pool of water, they instinctively close their airway and start to swim. Many of these instincts are lost as babies become older.

Instinctive behaviors are found in many animals, and some of these behaviors are highly complex. One such complex behavior is demonstrated by the Australian mudwasp. Mudwasps are voracious predators, and they build underground nests for their young. After paralyzing a caterpillar, the female mudwasp places it in the nest and lays several eggs into the caterpillar. When the eggs hatch, the larvae feed on the caterpillar until it dies. To prevent others, namely the parasitic cuckoo wasp, from entering the nest to lay its eggs, the female mudwasp builds a perfectly shaped bell that functions as an entrance. The outside of the bell is rough, but the inside is polished to prevent the cuckoo wasp from entering. The female mudwasp instinctively builds this bell entrance. This complex behavior is encoded in the genes of the mudwasps and has evolved from trial and error over many generations.

Mudwasp
They are capable of building highly complex dwellings and nests. *(Public Domain)(Public Domain)*

Many complex behaviors are instinctive and have a genetic base. Another interesting example involves the female Canadian goose. The female incubates her eggs by sitting on a shallow nest that she builds on the ground. Occasionally, an egg rolls out of the nest, and she diligently rolls it back into the nest. If a frosted light-bulb, however, is placed by the nest, she gets up and rolls it into her nest as if it were her egg. She does the same for a billiard ball or even a red wooden block. Female geese are not too discriminatory and will roll anything that is of the approximate size and shape of their eggs into their nests. How this behavior evolved is not clear, but it probably evolved as a safety mechanism for the young. The geese just play it safe and roll all similar objects into their nests.

Some instinctive behaviors can be acquired unconsciously in childhood. This type of instinctive behavior is known as imprinting. Male goldeneye ducks, for example, are imprinted as ducklings as to what their mating partners should look and behave like. If a male goldeneye duckling is raised by a female mallard, he is imprinted to recognize mallard females, and not goldeneye females, as his mating partners. In the following mating season, the foster male goldeneye ignores the goldeneye females and chases after the female mallards. The female mallards, however, have learned only to recognize the mating behaviors of mallard males.

Goldeneye male
The males are imprinted as ducklings in regards to choosing their mates.
(Public Domain)

Instinctive behavior is often triggered by sign stimuli. One of the most important sign stimuli is fertility signals, which are important for eliciting sexual behavior. However, other sign stimuli are important for eliciting behaviors such as maternal, nest building, and aggressive behaviors. Sign stimuli are often an approximation of the real thing. For example, many objects that resemble an egg can cause a female goose to stimulate her egg-gathering behavior. In human society, advertising has taken full advantage of the biological mechanism of sign stimuli to elicit our behavioral instincts.

An instinctive behavior that results after an encounter with a sign stimulus is known as a fixed-action pattern behavior. Its name is derived from the observation that animals respond the same way each time they encounter a particular sign stimulus. The fixed-action pattern is an important device that allows for biological organisms to respond to their environment when the environment is relatively unchanged. Fixed-action patterns have two advantages over other behaviors. The first advantage is that no time is wasted considering what appropriate behavior should be used, especially when there is only one response for a given stimulus. The second advantage is that it conserves neurological circuits in the brain. Many human behaviors, such as the fight or flight response, are fixed-action patterns. One disadvantage of the fixed-action pattern behaviors is that they cannot be modified easily, because they are encoded in the genes.

II.2. What is eusociality?

When living organisms evolved from unicellular to multicellular organisms, the possibilities for adaptation to different environments were greatly increased. Life began to spread from the ocean to land and eventually conquered nearly every environment on Earth. In multicellular organisms, cells can develop specialized structures and take on different functions. Some cells form protective layers on the surface of the organisms, some transport oxygen, some become gametes, and some form the nervous system. This type of cell specialization allows for a multicellular organism to become more adaptive to its environment. This change is also known as the socialization of unicellular organisms.

If socialization is successful for unicellular organisms, then can it also be successful for multicellular organisms? Socialization has been a successful strategy for multicellular organisms, and humans are an excellent example of the power of socialization. Socialization has also led to some insect species dominating their environments. Insects use a form of socialization known as eusociality, which is different from the socialization used by humans. Eusociality is characterized by the presence of several components including the cooperative care of the young, a reproductive division of labor, and an overlapping of the generations. Eusociality is commonly found in a group of insects known as eusocial insects, which include ants, termites, and bees. Due to their eusocial structure, these insects have become some of the most dominant biological organisms on Earth.

The army ants are a group of ant species that demonstrate the power of eusocial organisms. They are found primarily in central and east Africa. They form large colonies of as many as 50 million individuals. They are formidable predators particularly when they are relocating their colonies due to food shortage. They leave their ant hills and form marching columns of up to 50 million ants. When they pass through an area, they kill every living organism that is in their way, including invertebrates, reptiles, birds, and mammals. With their large numbers, they can overwhelm organisms that are several hundred times bigger than they are. With their scissor-like mouth parts, they dismember their victims with extraordinary efficiency.

Army ants

When they are working together, the army ants can bring down prey many times their size. *(GNU Free Documentation License)*

The termites are another successful eusocial insect that dominate their environment. Termites are found in nearly every part of the world. They feed on dead plant materials, such as dead trees, leaf litters, soil, and animal dung. Termites are a vital part of the ecosystem, because they are recyclers. Some termite species live close to human habitation and cause considerable damage to buildings and crops. Termites live in colonies of up to five million. The largest termite colonies are found in Africa and Australia. They build large termite mounds, known as cathedral mounds, which reach nearly 25 ft tall.

Another familiar eusocial insect are bees. The honey bee species is one of the most eusocial bee species. Honey bees are important to agricultural production because of their role in pollinating many important agricultural plants. A honey bee colony can have as many as 40,000 individuals. There are about 20,000 bee species that have been identified, and they vary in their degree of eusociality. Some species, like the honey bees, are highly eusocial, some are semi-euosocial, and some live solitary lives. By comparing the behavior patterns of these species, researchers have studied the evolution of eusociality. However, the eusocial bee species are by far the most successful species in terms of their numbers and distribution.

The evolution of eusociality

Eusociality evolves in a step-by-step process. This wasp can be considered as semi-social. *(GNU Free Documentation License)*

The eusocial insects are the most dominant animals on Earth. The colonies of eusocial organisms are considered to be superorganisms, because each colony behaves like an individual organism. Moreover, each member of the colony behaves like a specialized cell of a multicellular organism. In a multicellular organism, only certain cells are responsible for reproduction, whereas other cells carry out physiological, defensive, and communication functions. In the colonies of eusocial organisms, such division of labor also exists. The ability of these insects to act as a single organism has given them enormous power. They are the superorganisms of the biological world.

II.3. What is a superorganism?

Humans are highly social organisms, but humans are not eusocial. Imagine what it would be like if we lived in a eusocial society. We would live in a colony of several million people. The head of the colony would be the queen, and she would be the mother of everyone in the colony. We would all be her daughters, and none of us could have children. Some of us would take care of the queen, who would be giving birth to new babies at a rate of one every other minute. Some of us would take care of the newborns, and some would do housework. Most of us would be workers, except the few who would be soldiers. Their responsibility would be to defend the colony. As we became older, we would forage for food and bring it back to the colony. If we were attacked by predators, we would give our lives to defend the colony. Our work would be hard, and our lives would be short, but we would never complain. We would just work until we died.

In reality, human society is very different from that of eusocial insects. The social structure of human society also has a division of labor, but each individual works first and foremost for his or her personal interest and for reproductive success. Socialization is a difficult feat for a living organism to achieve, because sexual reproduction is designed to generate individual variations. With the operational sex ratio bias toward the males (more sexually-receptive males than females), the males must compete. In a eusocial society, there is no competition, because only the queen in the colony can reproduce.

Honey bee eusociality

The workers perform different tasks with perfect integration. *(GNU Free Documentation License)*

Studies on honey bee colonies have offered some interesting insights into eusociality. Eusocial insects have no sex chromosomes. Their sex is determined by their ploidy (the number of chromosome sets that they have), a sex determination system known as haplodiploidy. Females are diploid (2n or 2 sets of chromosomes), and all males are haploid (n or 1 set of chromosomes). The males, also known as drones, contribute only to reproduction. All other members of the colony are female, but only one female, the queen, assumes the reproductive role. She mates only once in her life. This mating occurs during her maiden flight, and she mates with multiple drones. She stores the sperm in her reproductive tract for the rest of her life. Before she lays an egg, she can choose to either fertilize it with the sperm to produce a female or leave it unfertilized to produce a male. In most colonies, the males number less than 1%.

Honey bee eggs and larvae

By feeding the larvae with different nutrients, the workers determine the type of young that will be raised. *(GNU Free Documentation License)*

When a female larva hatches, she has the potential to become either a queen or a sterile non-reproductive worker based on how she is cared for. All larvae are initially fed with a secretion, known as royal jelly, from glands which are located in the heads of the young workers. If the hive needs a new queen, this larva remains on the royal jelly diet and will develop into a fertile adult female. Those who are destined to become sterile workers have their diets switched to honey and pollen. It is not known how the workers know when there is a need for a new queen. It is known, however, that chemical signals in the form of pheromones are responsible for determining what diet is given to the larvae. In addition, the food that is given to the larvae contains chemical signals that induce differential gene expression during larval development.

This gene expression then determines whether the larva becomes a worker or a queen.

How did such a reproductive system evolve? Why does it seem to violate the theory of natural selection? To answer these questions, an evolution theory, known as kin selection, was developed. This theory suggests that some organisms contribute to raising their siblings rather than raising their own offspring. This occurs in eusocial insects. In the haplodiploidy sex-determination system, the reason for this strategy becomes clear when considering genetic inheritance. Even though workers do not reproduce, they are passing on more of their genes (75%) by caring for their sisters than they would by having their own offspring (each would have only 50% of their genes). This occurs because in the haplodiploidy sex-determination system, the workers are more similar to their sisters than they would be to their offspring. This observation has suggested that differences in sex-determination systems can alter reproductive strategies and lead to the evolution of eusociality.

III. What is sociality in complex organisms?

III.1. How did true social organisms evolve?

Human sociality and eusociality have four important differences. The first difference is the requirement of intelligence. Human sociality requires an awareness of a situation, whereas eusociality requires no such understanding by the members of the colony. The second difference is that human sociality is a conscious decision on how to behave. Eusociality is based on the fixed-action pattern of stimulus and response. The third difference is that human sociality is tenuous and can break down anytime, whereas eusociality is governed by pheromones that exert rigid control over the members of the colony. Fourth, human sociality is a transient cooperation, whereas eusociality is a genetically encoded rigid interaction.

There are many levels of sociality among animal species. Instead of promoting the survival of the colony, as in eusociality, the goal of most sociality is to promote individual reproductive success. Since every member of a social group reproduces on his or her own, social behavior will only be inherited if the individuals who participated in the social behavior are able to reproduce successfully. In some animals, forming a group of individuals is sufficient for promoting reproductive success. However, individuals in the group do not interact with each other. In other groups, social interactions among members of the group are necessary to promote individual reproductive success. In humans, an elaborate social structure has been created that resembles the eusocial society of ants, termites, and bees.

The simplest form of sociality occurs when animals form a crowd, such as schools of fish, flocks of birds, and herds of reindeer. The animals come together for various reasons, from mating to escaping predators. The largest gathering of animals for the purpose of mating is the Pacific herring, which can form a group as large as several million individuals. Some unknown signals trigger all the females to spawn in synchrony, releasing as many as 20,000 eggs per female in one spawn. There is such an abundance of eggs that entire coastlines turn milky white. These fish communicate with each other instinctively while swimming

Red-billed Queleas
These birds form enormous flocks containing thousands of members. (*Creative Commons Attribution*)

in large groups. This is probably the first step in developing more interactive social groups.

Emperor penguins

They form large breeding colonies in remote regions during Antarctic winters. *(Public Domain)*

Another type of social grouping is the formation of breeding colonies. Many birds migrate thousand of miles to remote islands to raise their young. Most of these breeding locations are beyond the reach of predators and can provide safety for the young. Thousands of emperor penguins, for example, trek up to 75 miles over ice to their breeding colony during Antarctic winters. Other similar breeding colonies have been found in many sea mammals, such as sea lions and elephant seals. Many insect species, such as crickets, cicadas, and mayflies, also reproduce in large groups.

Other animals aggregate in large numbers during migration to evade predators. Instead of traveling individually or in small herds, animals travel in large groups for protection. Since there are more animals looking out for predators, it is more difficult for predators to sneak up on them. Furthermore, when a large number of animals are in motion, the predators often become confused and unsure of which animals they should bring down. Another advantage of a large group is that the weak and old are the first to be taken by predators, allowing the strong animals to escape.

The aggregation of animals has a survival advantage for individuals. Despite some losses, the overall benefit to the individuals is great. However, this type of social grouping is based entirely on sign stimuli and on fixed-action patterns that are genetically encoded. There are negligible social interactions between members of the group. Furthermore, the level of intelligence that is required for this type of social grouping is minimal.

III.2. How did animal cooperation evolve?

True social cooperation in the animal world is rare. Division of labor in a stable fashion as that seen in eusociality is only found in a few species. However, those species that do use division of labor in their social structure become masters of their environments in the same way as the social insects. Nevertheless, social cooperation is a rarity in the biological world despite its many advantages. This has occurred because social cooperation requires traits that subvert the biological instinct for an individual to reproduce. In males, the instinct for reproduction can cause intense competition that can easily result in the disbandment of a social group. Social groups of any species can only be maintained if the reproductive instincts of the subordinate members are repressed.

Other than the eusocial insects, the naked mole rat is the only other known species that consists of a reproductive queen and a group of female workers. They are found in East Africa, and they live in a harsh underground environment. Social

Naked mole rat

Their social structure is similar to the eusocial insects. *(GNU Free Documentation License)*

cooperation is the only way they can survive. As in eusocial insects, the queen is the only reproductive member of the colony, but unlike eusocial insects, the worker females are not sterile. Instead, they are prevented from sexual development by a pheromone that is produced by the queen. If the queen dies, the worker females compete to become the next queen by undergoing rapid sexual development. A fierce struggle takes place as the workers fight to assume the reproductive role.

Florida scrub jay
They live in a family group.
(Public Domain)

Another species that exhibits high levels of social cooperation is the Florida scrub jay. These birds usually form small family groups of eight members that include the parents and their offspring. The young usually stay with their parents for two to three years to assist in rearing their siblings. They watch for predators and defend the family territory against neighboring family groups. Even though the young reach sexual maturity in the second season, they do not reproduce until they are ready to leave the family group. This type of social cooperation is an example of temporary eusociality. In the harsh environmental conditions that the birds live in, the parents would be unable to successfully raise the young without the help of their older offspring.

Meerkat is also a species that practices social cooperation in raising their young. Meerkats are small mammals that live in the Kalahari Desert of South Africa. They are highly intelligent animals as portrayed by the character Timon in the movie, *The Lion King*. They live in colonies with up to 30 members. The colony is a large family that has one breeding pair, known as the alpha pair. Similar to the Florida scrub jay, the offspring do not breed but stay in the colony to help rear the young and watch for predators. Any member who comes to sexual maturity is ejected from the colony, and any young that are born to members other than the alpha pair are immediately killed. This is the only social system that allows the meerkats to survive in a desert terrain where food and water are scarce.

Meerkat
They also practice social cooperation in raising their young.
(Creative Commons Attribution)

Social cooperation reaches a high level of success in the wolves and in other related species. Wolves are one of the most successful predators due to their cooperative hunting behavior. Their cooperation is due to the social structure that binds the group together. The wolves exist in a family unit that is similar to Florida scrub jays and meerkats. They live in a family-based social group with up to 15 members. The group is led by two breeding individuals, the alpha pair. In the wolf family, there exists a strict hierarchical structure of the ranking members. This structure is maintained by ritual fighting between the group members. The subordinate members do not normally reproduce. If the alpha male or female dies, the next highest ranking member takes over the role and forms a new alpha pair. With this social structure, wolves can hunt down large prey.

Most social animals have a strict social hierarchy that controls the reproductive process. This strategy is similar to that used by the eusocial insects. All members of the group are genetically related, and all belong to the same family. Other than the alpha breeding pair, individual members of the group are prohibited from reproducing through hormonal control, intimidation, or both. Any offending member is ejected from the group or killed. This type of social cooperation has allowed many species to survive in harsh and inhospitable environments. However, this type of social cooperation does not work well when food is plenty, because the urge of the individuals to reproduce on their own is much stronger. One exception to this system is the primates. They have developed a social system through intelligence.

III.3. How do animals cooperate through intelligence?

The eusociality of the social insects is a genetically imposed social system. The individual members of the social group have no control of their destinies. Their development into a queen, a worker, or a soldier is predetermined by how they are raised. The social structure in higher animals, such as the naked mole rats, Florida

Vampire bat
They practice reciprocity in sharing their blood meals.
(GNU Free Documentation License)

scrub jays, meerkats, and wolves, is under strong biological control through hormonal and behavioral manipulations. Most of these social behaviors are instinctive in nature, with sign stimuli and genetically based fixed-action patterns as the major driving forces. However, there is a more sophisticated kind of social cooperation that arose because of an increased level of intelligence.

This type of social cooperation is more subtle and involves reciprocity between the members. Reciprocity is absent in eusociality and in the lower forms of social cooperation. The vampire bats offer an intriguing example of this type of higher level of social cooperation. Each night, vampire bats leave their communal roosting places to feed on animal blood. The bats do not cooperate in raising their young or in hunting for prey. Instead, they practice a special type of cooperation that is more sophisticated and advanced than the social cooperation of other animals. This type of cooperation requires the use of intelligence.

Vampire bats must drink blood every night to survive due to their high metabolism and energy requirements for flight. It they fail to drink blood for more than two days, they will not survive. These bats perform an interesting social behavior that is rarely found in other animals. The bats who did not eat beg their roost mates to regurgitate part of their blood meal from the evening. Researchers discovered that this social cooperation establishes a system of reciprocity. The bats remember who owes them and who has done them a favor.

This type of sociality demands conscious awareness rather than sign stimuli and fixed-action pattern behaviors. For this social system to work, the vampire bats must have the memory to recall all the bats in the roost and the intelligence to determine who they should seek for help and who they should cooperate with. Individuals who are unable to make these distinctions would be at a great disadvantage. Most animals do not have this awareness for sharing their resources. In addition, under most circumstances, this type of social cooperation is unnecessary. Primates, however, are a major group of animals that has developed this type of social cooperation.

Japanese macaques
They bathe together in a hot spring. *(GNU Free Documentation License)*

This type of social cooperation is intelligence based, because members of the social group make conscious decisions whether or not they choose to cooperate. The individual must evaluate the situation and determine the cost or benefit of their participation. The outcome is to promote individual reproductive success. The primates use this type of strategy in their social cooperation, and the sophistication of the cooperation depends entirely on their intelligence. The human species has reached the pinnacle of this intelligence-based collaborative strategy. However, other great apes also have this skill. Intelligence and the enlarged human brain are the cause and effect of the demands of this form of social cooperation.

The remarkable success of the human species in the past 10,000 years is the direct consequence of social cooperation. The sophistication of the social cooperation in modern society rivals that of the eusocial insects. It is only in recent years that researchers from many disciplines have worked together to understand the dynamics of human society from the biological perspective. It is remarkable how far biological organisms have evolved, from unicellular to multicellular organisms billions of years ago. Then, about 200 million years ago, individual organisms formed social cooperations through genetics and programmed behavior. The emergence of intelligence-based social cooperation has brought a new direction in the ability of living organisms to adapt to new environments.

Chapter 17

Great Apes

Are we related to the great apes?

Why is there so much controversy?
Since the 19th century, fossil and genetic evidence have provided unequivocal evidence that humans are great apes.
(Public Domain)

CHAPTER 17. GREAT APES

I. WHAT ARE THE GREAT APES?

I.1. How do humans fit into the biological world?

Plato and Aristotle

Aristotle (on the right) and Plato (on the left) discussed their beliefs about types of knowledge. *(Public Domain)*

Carl Linnaeus

Swedish botanist and zoologist who proposed a classification system for living organisms. *(Public Domain)*

How do humans fit into the biological world? The ancient Greek philosophers were among the first to think about where humans belonged in relation to other biological organisms. The Greek philosopher Aristotle concluded that humans were at the pinnacle of the biological world and that all other living organisms were arranged on a *scala naturae* or "ladder of life." He and other philosophers concluded that all living organisms came into being exactly in the way they are today. Aristotle's idea of the biological world had a powerful influence on philosophical and religious thoughts for the next 2,000 years. His idea of the special creation of living organisms has been the central tenet in Judeo-Christian religious dogma.

Until the 1750s, little effort had been made to classify biological organisms. Carl Linnaeus, a Swedish botanist, zoologist, and physician, was the first to develop a classification system for biological organisms. His system is still used today. Linnaeus diligently compared living organisms to determine their similarities and differences. He discovered that many organisms are similar to each other and could therefore be grouped together. Linnaeus discovered that all biological organisms can be grouped based on their structure and behavior into a hierarchical structure that resembles a tree, with small branches feeding into larger branches.

Linnaeus' system begins with species as its base. He concluded that all members of a species are similar enough to each other to interbreed. The next grouping is genus, which includes different species that have similar biological properties. However, members from the same genus but different species cannot interbreed. He then grouped similar genera into families, similar families into orders, similar orders into classes, similar classes into phyla, and similar phyla into kingdoms. Linnaeus' classification system was a major milestone in biology, because for the first time, a system was established to classify and understand the extraordinary diversity of biological organisms. For this contribution, Linnaeus is considered to be one of the greatest biologists in history.

When Linnaeus came to the classification of humans, he experienced considerable difficulties. First, he observed that humans from various parts of the world have significantly different morphological features. However, he decided that despite these differences, humans belong to a single species. Second, he was surprised and dismayed to discover that humans and the great apes, particularly the chimpanzees, are very similar. He wrote: "It is not pleasing to me that I must place humans among the primates…..I desperately seek from you and from the whole world a general difference between men and simians from the principles of Natural History. I certainly know of none. If only someone might tell me one! If I called man a simian or vice versa I would bring together all the theologians against me." Despite his initial hesitation, Linnaeus chose to put humans with the great apes because of his scientific observations.

Linnaeus' classification of humans with the great apes was largely ignored. During the 18th century, humans were considered to be a special creation. Even though humans share many features with the great apes, it was inconceivable at the time to consider that humans and the great apes could be related. People of the time believed that the similarities between humans and the great apes were created by design for reasons that humans did not understand. Furthermore, during most of the 19th century, biologists perceived that all living species were created with their distinctive features already intact. Therefore, the possibility that humans and the great apes could have evolved from a common ancestor was considered ludicrous.

The view of special creation was shattered when Charles Darwin proposed his theory of natural selection to explain the formation of all the species in the biological world. Based on this theory, all life forms on Earth have evolved from a common ancestor over billions of years. His theory suggested that all species on Earth are related. These relationships could also be depicted as a "tree of life" with different species forming the branches. The human species forms one of these branches, and the great apes form the branches that are adjacent to the human branch. Because of the close resemblance between chimpanzees and humans, Darwin predicted that humans most likely originated from the same place where the chimpanzees live today. He also predicted that fossils of human ancestors would be found in Africa. His prediction has been proven correct by paleontologists.

Systema Naturae

Title page of the 1760 edition of Linnaeus' work on the classification of biological organisms. *(Public Domain)*

I.2. Are humans great apes?

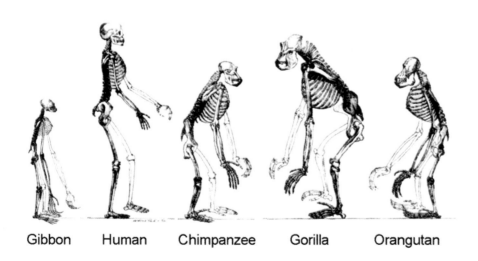

Gibbon   Human   Chimpanzee   Gorilla   Orangutan

The hominoids

A comparison of the skeletons of humans to other apes as depicted in Thomas Huxley's book published in 1863. *(Public Domain)*

The similarities between the great apes and humans have been recognized since antiquity. Even though there are significant differences in morphology between humans and the great apes, there are many anatomical, physiological, and reproductive similarities. For example, all great apes have the same dental formula: 16 adult teeth in the upper and lower jaws. The size of the teeth, however, varies among the great apes. In addition, all the great apes normally give birth to a single infant after a gestation of eight to nine months. Furthermore, all infants of the great apes are helpless, depending on their mothers' care for several years. Also, sexual maturity for the great apes is not reached until 8 to 13 years of age. Additional characteristics shared by humans and the great apes are that no distinct breeding season occurs and that females give birth once every few years.

The relationship between humans and the great apes was unequivocally confirmed by DNA evidence. The chimpanzee genome was completed in 2005 and was subsequently compared to the human genome. It was observed that the DNA sequences between humans and chimpanzees differed by only 1.5%. In addition, the gorilla genome was sequenced and compared to the human genome. The DNA sequences between humans and gorillas were observed to differ by 3%, making gorillas the next closest relatives to humans. During the last several decades, extensive direct and indirect evidence has established that humans are great apes and that humans share a common ancestor with other great apes.

There are only five great ape species, including humans, in the world today. There are two subspecies of orangutans living in Southeast Asia. Two subspecies of gorillas and two species of chimpanzees live in Africa. There is, howver, only one species of humans. Researchers have discovered that many great ape species existed in the past, including many different species of humans. Most of these species, however, have become extinct. All the great apes, excluding humans, are presently endangered, because their forest habitats are threatened due to human development and population growth. It is vital for us to preserve them in their natural habitats, because we have a great deal to learn from them. Many of the insights regarding human nature have come from studying the great apes.

Orangutan
A two-week-old baby orangutan. *(GNU Free Documentation License)*

The orangutans are the largest tree-dwelling animals in the world. They spend almost their entire lives in the trees, moving from one tree to the next. The males can weigh up to 260 lbs, but the females are 50% smaller. The orangutans exhibit the greatest sexual size dimorphism among the great apes. They are native to Indonesia and Malaysia, but currently, they are only found in Borneo and Sumatra. Some researchers consider the orangutans to be the most intelligent organisms next to humans. They build sleeping nests high up in the trees and cover them with leak-proof roofs. They can make various tools, including using leaves to make rain hats. Even though they are social creatures, most adults live solitary lives. They come together only for mating and for the females to care for their young.

Gorilla
A Western Lowland gorilla. *(GNU Free Documentation License)*

In contrast to the orangutans, the gorillas are ground dwellers. There are two species of gorillas living in Africa. One species is known as the mountain gorillas, because they live in the mountainous cloud forests in East Africa at altitudes as high as 14,000 ft. The other species is known as the lowland gorillas. They live in dense forests, lowland swamps, and marshes along the coastal regions of West Africa. The gorillas form small family groups with up to five members. The dominant male, the silverback, mates with all the females in the group. A large sexual size dimorphism exists, with the males weighing up to 500 lbs and the females being half the size of the males. They mainly eat fruits and other vegetation, but they occasionally eat termites and other small animals.

Chimpanzees are the smallest of the great apes, with males weighing up to 150 lb and females weighing up to 110 lb. There are two species of chimpanzees, the common chimpanzee and the bonobo. Both species live primarily in West and Central Africa, with their habitats separated by the Congo River. They are the most social of the great apes, next to humans. Their social units are small family groups of up to eight individuals with an alpha male, beta males, females, and their young. Periodically, these small family units coalesce to form larger bands that can

Chimpanzee
A young, common chimpanzee.
(GNU Free Documentation License)

have as many as 100 members. These large chimpanzee groups have many features that were also found in human primitive cultures. Chimpanzees and humans also share another behavior trait as they both wage war against their neighboring groups due to territorial disputes.

I.3. *How did the great apes evolve?*

The evolution of the great apes has received great interest in recent years because of the discovery that the human immunodeficiency virus (HIV) might have originated from primates. There are two forms of HIV: HIV-1 and HIV-2. Both viruses originated in Africa during the mid-20th century. Both viruses are similar to viruses known as Simian Immunodeficiency viruses (SIV), which are found in primates. Researchers have found evidence that HIV-1 originated in southern Cameroon after it had evolved from SIV. When local inhabitants came into contact with wild chimpanzees, the virus jumped to humans. HIV-2, however, may have originated from the sooty mangabey, a monkey also native to Cameroon. The transmission of these viruses from primates to humans has suggested that a close evolutionary relationship exists. In addition, studies of the relationship between humans and primates can help to prevent the transmission of similar diseases in the future.

The evolutionary relationship between humans and primates was first proposed by Charles Darwin in his book, *The Origin of Species.* Darwin, however, was not the only one to propose the theory of natural selection. Another biologist/naturalist Alfred Russell Wallace independently arrived at the same theory. In the first announcement of this theory to the scientific community, the papers of Darwin and Wallace were read jointly at a professional meeting. However, the reaction to this new theory was unremarkable. By the mid-19th century, different theories had already been proposed for the evolution of life. In *The Origin of Species,* Darwin briefly mentioned that humans are close cousins to the chimpanzees and that both are descendents of a common ancestor. Darwin published another book 12 years later entitled *Descent of Man,* in which he provided a more detailed discussion of the origin of the human species. Darwin received criticisms from many scientists, including some of his close colleagues. They denounced his view that humans and the great apes are related.

The great apes are one branch of the order primates, which also include lemurs and monkeys. The great apes are the most sophisticated and evolved form of primates. Together with the lesser apes (such as gibbons), the great apes are members of the ape family. The great apes and the lesser apes split from each other about 18 million years ago. About 14 million years ago, the ancestor of the orangutans split off from the main branch. Then, about seven million years ago, the gorilla branch split off from the common ancestor of chimpanzees and humans. About six million

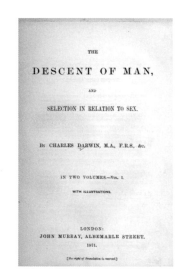

Descent of Man
Title page of Darwin's most controversial book. *(Public Domain)*

years ago, this common ancestor spilt off to form the early chimpanzees and the early humans.

There are several pieces of evidence that demonstrate the kinship between chimpanzees and humans. Fossil records of skulls and bones have indicated that about five to eight million years ago, the common ancestor of chimpanzees and humans formed two groups that lived in different environments. The approximate time when this happened was determined using DNA sequence analyses. Researchers have discovered that human and chimpanzee DNA are 98.5% identical. The differences in the sequences have resulted from mutations. In addition, it has been observed that the rate of mutation, over long periods of time, is relatively constant. Consequently, mutation rates can be used as a clock for determining the time that has elapsed after the splitting of the two species from their common ancestor. Using this approach, researchers have calculated that the human and the chimpanzee species were formed approximately six million years ago.

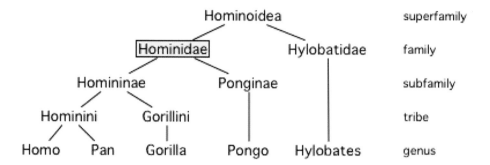

Hominoid family tree

Humans (Homo) and chimpanzees (Pan) are the closest relatives. Pongo is orangutan. *(Public Domain)*

The chimpanzee and human species were formed because of an environmental change. During this period, there was a dramatic climatic change that converted some of the forest into a dry savanna, similar to the Serengeti in today's Africa. Some of the ancestral population was caught in this transition, and they evolved into the ancestors of the human species in order to adapt to this new environment. The ancestors of the modern day chimp, however, remained in the forest. The different environments led to the evolution of different adaptive features, which eventually resulted in two different species.

The six million years that separates humans and chimpanzees is a difficult concept to understand. It may seem like an eternity to us, but from a geological standpoint, it is a very short time. Most of us, however, can relate to generations, because we have had contact with different generations. If a human generation spans 20 years, then there have been 100 generations between the time of Christ and the present. Using this formula, six million years represents 300,000 generations.

II. WHY ARE GREAT APES INTELLIGENT?

II.1. *Can great apes learn?*

Human intelligence is exemplified by our ability to learn, to acquire information, and to perform complicated tasks. How intelligent are the great apes? Do they have human-like intelligence, the ability to use tools, insightful thinking, abstract thoughts, and simple arithmetic skills? If great apes can demonstrate human-like intelligence, then the argument for their close relatedness to humans is even stronger. Indeed, researchers have discovered that great ape intelligence and human intelligence are uncannily similar. They are as curious as humans and show the same desire to learn.

All great apes show intense curiosity toward human activities and even replicate them. One example of great ape intelligence came from studying a group of orangutans that took refuge in a nature preserve area known as Camp Leakey in Borneo. During the past several decades, many of the forests in Borneo have been cleared by loggers. Because orangutans live their entire lives in the trees, this deforestation has displaced them from their natural habitat. Camp Leakey was set aside as a natural reserve for these orangutans. Shortly after the orangutans came into contact with humans at the camp, they started to imitate human behavior. One orangutan had even learned to untie a boat from the dock and paddle it around the lake using his long arms as oars. He has spent hours on the lake and has enjoyed boating as a human would.

Orangutan at Camp Leakey
Boating behavior. *(Education Fair Use)*

Another orangutan at the camp has learned to use tools. After watching carpenters at work, she became interested in performing her own brand of carpentry. She and her daughter have learned how to use hammers to pound nails and hand saws to saw wood. With their skillful hands and excellent coordination, they have learned how to saw a piece of wood in half and to drive nails into wood. Their ability to use tools suggests that they share many human behavioral traits. However, one question remains: Can the orangutans use tools in the wild or does tool using result only after human contact?

Orangutan at Camp Leakey
Using a hand saw. *(Education Fair Use)*

For many years, humans were thought to be the only species in the biological world that could use tools. This assumption was overturned when a 26-year-old British primatologist, Jane Goodall, began her research at the Gombe Stream National Park in Tanzania to study chimpanzee behavior. Prior to this time, most of the studies of chimpanzee behavior were conducted in zoos or in laboratory settings. Goodall spent hours observing the chimpanzees in the wild. Her first discovery of chimp tool use occurred when she observed a group of chimpanzees stripping a twig free of leaves and snapping it into a particular length. The chimpanzees then inserted the twigs into termite holes to pull out the termites and eat them.

Cracking nuts
Chimpanzees can use tools to crack nuts. *(Education Fair Use)*

Her discovery was the first evidence that humans are not the only tool makers or tool users. Chimpanzees also use tools to accomplish their goals and objectives. Further studies of this behavior demonstrated that chimps are not born with this skill; they must be taught by their mothers or their siblings. Some chimps learn quickly and become efficient with using tools. Other chimps, however, have great difficulties in learning the tasks. Interestingly, with regards to learning tool use there are differences between the sexes. Young female chimps generally master the skills almost an entire year ahead of the male chimps. Also, the female chimps are more patient than the male chimps.

Another interesting observation of animal learning and intelligence is the different approaches to a particular task that is used by different groups of chimps. One group of chimpanzees have mastered cracking nuts by placing them in the depression of a fallen tree. They then smash it with a piece of heavy wood. Everyone in this group uses this method. However, another group of chimps all use rocks to smash the nuts. These differences are analogous to human cultural differences in various parts of the world.

II.2. Can great apes solve problems?

One of the greatest achievements of human intelligence is the ability to visualize solving a complicated problem using multiple steps. This type of problem solving requires insight that is used to consider different steps of the problem. One of the ways to accomplish this is to rehearse each step of a multi-step process and to anticipate what might happen. This type of problem solving often involves independently testing each step before putting all the steps together. Practicing before playing a game of tennis is an example of rehearsing the parts, such as the serve and the backhand. Humans are very good at practicing the parts of a complicated task. Can other great apes accomplish this challenging feat?

In Germany, a group of researchers designed an experiment to test the problem solving ability of a group of chimpanzees. They hung a banana on a high wire with a string. The chimpanzees were eager to get the banana, which is their favorite food. However, the banana was out of their reach. The researchers wanted to test whether the chimpanzees could put familiar objects together in novel ways to solve the "banana problem." In the chimpanzee's enclosure, they had placed two wooden boxes, which the chimpanzees had played with before. They frequently jumped on top of them, but had never stacked them. The researchers also left a stick in the enclosure. This was also a familiar object because the chimpanzees had used it before to strike things.

To reach the banana, the chimpanzees needed to stack the two wooden boxes together, stand on the boxes while holding the stick, and jump while swinging the stick at the same time. After many chimps tried unsuccessfully to get the banana, a female chimp began to gather all the pieces together. At first she tried to stand on one box and then two boxes. After failing several times to jump from the boxes, an insight came to her. She picked up the stick, climbed onto the stacked boxes, jumped, and swung the stick as she jumped. The banana was hers. This experiment demonstrated that chimpanzees can solve a complicated problem by using insightful thinking.

Another important human trait for solving complex problems is to conceptually model the problem. An example of conceptual modeling is architectural modeling, in which a small scale model is built to represent the real building. Researchers can use a psychological test to determine the ability of children to think conceptually. In this test, a model of a room is built that matches every aspect of a real room, such as furniture, house plants, and appliances. The test subjects are then shown an object and are allowed to watch where that object is hid in the model room. Next, the test subject is led to the real room and is asked to retrieve the object. Adults can easily perform this task, but children under the age of four cannot. On average, a child gains the ability to conceptually model at about four years of age.

In one study, a female chimpanzee was given the model test. She was shown a can of soda that was hid inside a cabinet of the model room. She was then led into the real room to find the real can of soda. Without any hesitation, she walked to the cabinet, opened it, and retrieved the can. This study has provided evidence that chimpanzees

Chimp problem solving
Using available tools to reach a banana. *(Education Fair Use)*

understand conceptual modeling better than a four-year-old human child. Also, it has been observed that chimpanzees develop the model concept at about the same age as a human child, suggesting that there are similarities in mental development between humans and chimpanzees. However, not all chimpanzees have the ability to understand the model concept.

From these and many other studies, researchers have observed that chimpanzees can solve many different and complicated problems.

Chimp can understand models

Chimps have the ability to use abstract thinking.
(Education Fair Use)

They possess the skills that are needed for solving conceptual and abstract problems. These types of studies have provided clear evidence that chimpanzees are highly intelligent.

II.3. Do great apes have language?

One of the most distinctive biological traits that separate humans from all other animals is human speech. Human speech became possible when the larynx and tongue developed and formed the vocal tract. Because of these anatomical adaptations, humans are one of the few animals that are capable of generating an extraordinary range of sounds in pitch, tone, speed, and intensity. However, the vocal tract alone is insufficient for producing human speech. Other animals, such as the lyre birds, can generate an even more impressive array of sounds than humans, but they do not have speech.

Humans are the only animals that have the ability to convert sound into speech for complex communication. Human speech is part of a sophisticated communication system that consists of more than just the production of sound. It is a language system that uses grammatical rules to manipulate arbitrary symbols. Even though other animals also use sophisticated communication systems, only humans make use of all the linguistic properties. For example, animal communication lacks the capacity to join words together to form sentences. Furthermore, the ability to communicate past and future events does not exist in animal communication.

If the modern great apes are close relatives of humans, then shouldn't they also have the capability for language? During the past several decades, researchers have investigated the language ability of the great apes in various ways. It has been observed that even though the great apes are incapable of speech, they can be taught other forms of communication, such as sign language, using physical objects, and written symbols. Researchers have discovered that all the great apes (chimpanzees, gorillas, and orangutans) have an inborn capacity for learning language.

The ability of the great apes to understand human language was most impressively demonstrated by Kanzi, a male bonobo. Kanzi was trained to communicate using a specialized computer keyboard at a young age. His ability to understand human language was remarkable. When he was eight years old, Kanzi was tested with 416 complex questions, and he answered them correctly over 75% of the time. One day, the researcher asked Kanzi a question: "Can you make the dog bite the snake?" This was a sentence that Kanzi had never heard before. Kanzi searched among the objects present and picked up a toy dog and a toy snake. He put the snake in the mouth of the dog and used his thumb and finger to close the dog's mouth over the snake. Kanzi's ability to understand human language suggests that neural circuits for language are also present in the great apes.

Another well-known study on the ability of the great apes to use and understand human language is Project Koko. Koko is a female lowland gorilla that was raised from an infant by researchers at Stanford University. Koko made international news when she was shown fluently communicating with the researchers using American Sign Language. Koko can use over 1,000 words in sign language and form simple sentences for making requests or expressing her feelings. Furthermore, Koko understands approximately 2,000 words of spoken English. Koko is also the first nonhuman animal to keep pets.

Gorilla language

Gorillas can lean to use human sign language. *(Education Fair Use)*

Later in this research project, the researchers taught another gorilla, named Michael, American Sign Language. Michael was rescued as an infant from poachers who had shot his mother in the jungle. Michael remembered the killing of his mother and surprisingly, described the incident through the use of sign language. These studies further support the hypothesis that the neurological regions for language are present in all the great apes, and it is only in humans that this capacity is fully developed. The behavioral similarities between humans and the other great apes are undeniable. Together with the evidence in genetics, physiology, morphology, and reproduction, the evolutionary connection between humans and the great apes is difficult to ignore.

III. WHY ARE GREAT APES SOCIABLE?

III.1. *What is the great apes' social structure?*

Modern human society is organized and complex, but this was not the case through most of human history. Prehistoric human society was most likely similar to today's chimpanzee society in that it was based on small family units. A typical chimpanzee community has approximately 20 to 100 members, depending on resource availabilities. The larger communities are made up of small family groups, which often split and reform as resources fluctuate. In the common chimpanzee society, an adult male leads the group, supported by a group of beta males. The alpha male can only stay in power if he receives support from the other males. Similar to human political systems, forming alliances is critical for maintaining power.

Chimp community

A group of orphaned chimps rescued from poachers in the bushmeat trade. *(Creative Commons Attribution)*

Common chimpanzees have a patriarchal society in which the males dominate the females. The members practice promiscuous mating, where females mate with nearly all the males. The males provide no parental care and occasionally commit infanticide. The promiscuous mating reduces infanticide, because the males are not sure which infants they have fathered. The male chimpanzees often intimidate the females with the threat of violence and abusive behavior. The male chimpanzees are nearly 50% larger than the females, giving them a physical advantage over the females. The common chimpanzees practice a patrilocal strategy, in which the male offspring stay with the family social group, and the females are sent away to join neighboring groups.

The common chimpanzees are highly territorial. They protect their territories against intrusion by other groups of chimpanzees. The male chimpanzees routinely form patrol parties to secure their territory. If they encounter strange males in their territory, they chase them away. If the stranger fails to rapidly retreat and gets caught, the patrol parties beat the intruder to death. The human species will also routinely kill other members of the same species to protect their territories. The chimpanzees also use tree branches and rocks as weapons during their attack. Because of this violent tendency, chimpanzees in captivity are often highly aggressive toward humans.

When two neighboring groups of chimpanzees have territorial disputes, war often breaks out. Occasionally, one group of chimpanzees assembles a raiding party and invades the neighboring group in a surprise attack. They chase away or kill the males and take the females hostage. They also kill the infants, because their biological instinct is not to raise the young of other male chimpanzees. These aspects of chimpanzee group violence show uncanny similarities to warfare between different human populations. Through the studies on the inter-community violence in chimpanzees, researchers have developed a better understanding of the evolutionary origin of human group violence. This knowledge could be useful in understanding and preventing human warfare.

Another chimpanzee social behavior that greatly resembles a human social behavior is the formation of hunting parties. Chimpanzees hunt monkeys, such as the colobus monkeys. Chimpanzees form organized hunting parties using cooperative hunting strategies with each member playing a different role. When the colobus monkeys see the chimpanzees coming, they move to the forest canopy, where they are safe. Because the chimpanzees are big and heavy, the weaker branches on the top cannot support them. However, the chimpanzees post themselves in strategic positions to cut off the escape route of the monkeys. They then start to scream and scare the monkeys. Some of them try to flee and fall into the traps set up by the chimpanzees. With a success rate of over 50%, the chimpanzees are more efficient hunters than lions.

Colobus monkey
They are frequently hunted by the chimpanzees. *(GNU Free Documentation License)*

After the kill, the high-ranking chimpanzees always feed first, but they do not always eat what they take. Instead, they share their meat with females or low-ranking males to trade for future favors. Researchers have observed that chimpanzees often use their skills of manipulation to create and cultivate long-term relationships. This type of behavior is also common in humans, and the intricate structure of human society is dependent on the ability of individuals to use these skills. Without these long-term relationships, chimpanzee and human societies could not have been maintained. The study of chimpanzee social behavior has helped researchers to gain

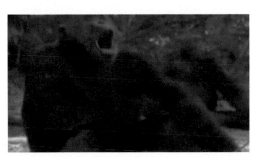

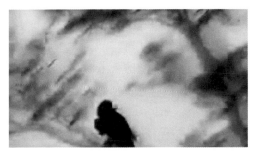

Chimps hunting colobus monkeys
They first scream to scare the monkeys, causing confusion, and then block off their exits. *(Education Fair Use)*

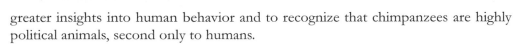

greater insights into human behavior and to recognize that chimpanzees are highly political animals, second only to humans.

III.2. Do great apes have morality?

In human society, some behaviors, such as honesty, sharing, altruism, and empathy are considered to be good behaviors, because they promote harmony within the group. In contrast, behaviors such as cheating, selfishness, and incest are considered bad behaviors due to their negative impact on the survival of the group. Behaviors are sanctioned by the group as either good or bad by using a code of ethics. Chimpanzee society also has a code of ethics that is similar to that of human society, and from these examples, researchers have begun to understand the evolution of human morality.

One example of the application of human morality to chimpanzee society is reciprocity. Chimpanzees will perform tasks for others, but will also expect a favor in return. For example, chimpanzees spend as much as 40% of their waking hours grooming each other. This activity is pleasurable and is important for maintaining their cleanliness. However, if a chimpanzee asks to be groomed, it must return the favor by grooming its partner. The amount of time that they groom each other must also be roughly equivalent in order for the relationship to be maintained. This example demonstrates that the chimpanzees have a moral code of reciprocity. This moral code of reciprocity also applies to food sharing, providing protection for each other, and establishing political alliances.

In one study, the feeding behaviors of a group of chimpanzees in captivity were studied. Every morning, the chimpanzees were given their favorite food in an amount that was enough for everyone. In this group of chimpanzees, the adults always allowed the juveniles to feed first. They were then followed by the high-ranking chimpanzees. The low-ranking chimpanzees, usually the adolescents, were the last ones to feed. It appeared that the chimpanzees knew how much to take and to leave enough for everyone else. Occasionally, some young chimpanzees took more than they should and were "punished" by the older and high-ranking chimpanzees. Researchers have recognized this behavior as an example of establishing a moral code that is actively taught and implemented.

In another study, the social interactions of a group of wild chimpanzees in their natural habitat were studied. Researchers discovered that chimpanzees use punishment to control the behavior of their members. In one case, they observed that one chimpanzee was beaten to death by a group of chimpanzees because of its anti-social behavior, such as stealing food from other chimpanzees and snatching baby chimpanzees. After several months, the group was no longer willing to tolerate the behavior and "sentenced" this offending chimpanzee to death.

Chimpanzees also display altruistic behavior by helping the sick or injured members of the group. In one study of a group of wild chimpanzees, researchers observed that some younger chimpanzees will offer help to sick chimpanzees by bringing them food or by helping them to walk. Occasionally, a female chimpanzee will help to care for the young of another chimpanzee. Even though the display of altruism in chimpanzees is not as extensive as it is in human society, this behavior demonstrates the close relationship between humans and chimpanzees.

Gorilla female with young
Socialization is an important part in raising their young.

Through the study of chimpanzee morality, researchers have discovered the evolutionary significance of human morality. To live in a group, individuals must abide by the rules of the group so that trust is established among the members. These rules also help the group members to know how to behave and are taught to the young at an early age as a moral code. Human society requires this moral code for it to function, and this moral code is also important for the chimpanzee society to function. Therefore, the study of chimpanzee morality has provided an understanding of human morality.

III.3. Do great apes have consciousness?

One of the most distinctive human traits is the conscious awareness of self. Humans have a concept of self, with an understanding that they are individuals separate from other people. This self-awareness leads to the development of empathy, which is the ability to project one's feelings onto another person. With empathy, humans can read the motives, intentions, and emotions of other individuals. From self-awareness, humans become conscious of their actions and develop the ability to understand consequences. This capacity of self-awareness and consciousness is critical for successfully navigating complex social situations.

For many years, biologists considered self-awareness and consciousness unique mental traits of the human species. These traits were thought to separate humans from all other animals in the biological world. However, recent research has revealed that the great apes might also possess self-awareness and consciousness. These findings have led to revisions of the notions of what makes humans distinctive from the great apes and other living organisms. Furthermore, this research demonstrates that humans are members of the great apes and that the biological and behavioral differences between humans and the other great apes are continuums rather than discrete steps.

Several tests have been used to find out whether the great apes possess consciousness. One such test is the mirror test. All humans can recognize themselves in a mirror. However, this is a trait that human babies are not born with but develop as they get older. In this test, a red dot is placed on the forehead of the test subject. If the subject recognizes his or her self-image in the mirror, an attempt will be made to remove the red dot. Using the mirror test, researchers have discovered that a human child develops this self-awareness at about 18 months of age. This experiment demonstrates that self-awareness is a step in human mental development.

Most species, such as the baboons, fail to recognize the animal in the mirror as themselves. Instead, they will relentlessly look for the animal behind the mirror. Many animals have been subjected to the mirror test, and it has been successfully accomplished by only six species: human, chimpanzee, gorilla, orangutan, dolphin, and elephant. The chimpanzees have also been observed to use mirrors in the same manner as humans. They look at their teeth in the mirror, and they even hold the mirror in certain ways to examine parts of the body that they normally cannot see. Koko, the gorilla, uses the mirror to adjust her sunglasses each time when she puts them on. The ability of the great apes to pass the mirror test suggests that they are

Chimp and dolphin with mirrors

Both chimps and dolphins recognize themselves in the mirror and use the mirror like humans. *(Education Fair Use)*

self-aware and are conscious that they are distinct individuals.

Another important human trait that represents consciousness is the ability to recall long-term emotional memory. The understanding that one event is distinct from other events is a hallmark for conscious awareness. Some chimpanzees have demonstrated this ability. In one example, some chimpanzees expressed joy upon seeing a caretaker that they had not seen for many years. During the development of the hepatitis vaccine in the 1970s, a group of chimpanzees were used for experimentation. After the vaccine development was completed, a study was conducted to rehabilitate

Baboon and a mirror

Baboons fail to recognize themselves in the mirror. *(Education Fair Use)*

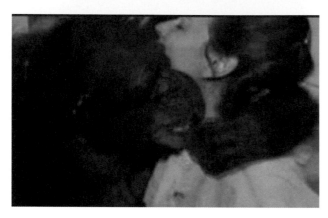

Chimp has emotional memories

A joyful reunion after 18 years of separation. *(Education Fair Use)*

these "laboratory" chimpanzees. A young graduate student cared for the chimpanzees for three years in a reserve and was successful in helping them readjust to a normal life after the harsh experimental treatments. These chimps were allowed to live in a more natural environment for the remainder of their lives. Eighteen years later, the graduate student returned to the reserve for a visit. The chimps recognized her instantly and exhibited joy at the reunion. They behaved as humans would when reunited with old friends after being apart for many years.

Many studies have demonstrated that humans share many behavioral traits with the great apes. We might have evolved to achieve great intellectual heights, but we are still great apes. Research in the areas of genetics, physiology, and behavior has established our unequivocal link to the other great apes. It is vital for us to protect them in their environments, because they can provide us with an understanding of our biology, genetics, and behavior that would not be possible in any other way.

Chapter 18

Human Evolution

Who were our ancestors?

Reconstruction of a Neanderthal hunter
Are they our ancestors?
(GNU Free Documentation License)

CHAPTER 18. HUMAN EVOLUTION

I. EARLY HUMANS

I.1. What have we learned from human fossils?

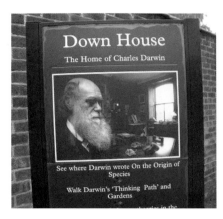

Down House, England

Charles Darwin spent most of his life working and writing about evolution. *(Public Domain)*

After Charles Darwin published his book *The Origin of Species,* the scientific community gradually accepted that humans and chimpanzees are closely related and that the two species must share a common ancestor. Based on Darwin's theory of natural selection, modern humans must have evolved over a long period of time and through different intermediate forms. Such intermediate forms have been found in other species, providing evidence that species evolve because of adaptations to environmental changes. However, where can we find these intermediate forms if they are extinct? The fossil record has provided an answer to this question. By studying fossils, researchers have constructed a family tree of the evolution of modern humans.

During the past 100 years, the evidence for human evolution has come from studying fossil records. The interpretation of some of these fossils, however, has been highly controversial. Researchers have not always agreed on exactly how humans have evolved during the past six million years. In addition, interpretation of human fossils is difficult because many of the fossils are fragmented. Only parts of a fossilized skull, for example, are generally found. Also, understanding fossils requires great skill and expertise. However, some researchers have become extremely skilled at identifying and understanding fossilized remains. During the 19th century, a French paleontologist (a scientist who studies fossils) developed the skills to deduce from a single fossilized bone the morphology, behavior, and diet of an extinct animal.

Sometimes, however, even the experts are fooled, especially if someone intentionally perpetuates a fraud. The most famous hoax in modern science involved a human fossil. In the early 20th century, scientists around the world were searching for human fossils to construct the evolutionary history of humans. By this time, human-like fossils had been discovered in Europe, Africa, and Asia. Also, most scientists had already agreed that humans had evolved from chimpanzee-like ancestors. However, there was no definitive proof because no transitional form (a fossil that has features of both humans and chimps or other great apes) had been found.

Piltdown man

This portrait was painted in 1915 to depict the principals who were involved in the discovery of this fraudulent skull. *(Public Domain)*

In the 1920s, an amateur paleontologist living in Piltdown, England reported the discovery of a human-like, fossilized specimen that appeared to have the lower jawbone of an orangutan and a skull of a modern human. This discovery was considered important because it represented the transitional form that paleontologists had been searching for. This fossilized skull suggested that early humans had a fully developed brain that was similar to modern humans but had the jaw of a great ape. The fossil came to be known as the Piltdown Man and was kept in the British Museum of Natural History. It also brought great pride to England, because England was now considered the site where the evolution of modern man had occurred. Many theories of human evolution that were created during the first half of the 20th century were based on the Piltdown Man. Any fossil that failed to fit into these theories was either ignored or discounted.

Some researchers, however, became increasingly skeptical about the Piltdown Man. With the invention of more sophisticated techniques, the Piltdown Man was finally exposed in 1953 to be a forgery. The lower jaw had been taken from a modern orangutan and colored to give it an ancient appearance. The Piltdown Man was the most famous hoax in the history of modern archeology for two reasons. First, it had misled the research in human evolution for many years. Second, it took over 40 years before it was exposed as a forgery.

The study of human evolution has made great strides since the exposure of the Piltdown Man hoax. Many important fossils have been discovered during the past five decades. These fossils have allowed researchers to construct a clear picture of human evolution starting from the time when humans and chimpanzees split from their common ancestor. The understanding of human evolution has direct and immediate significance at both the personal and societal levels. It helps us to understand our diets, need for physical activity, behaviors, and emotions. It also helps us to understand the relationship between populations in different parts of the world. Because of this understanding, we can also appreciate the impact that technology has had on us, a species that had evolved for living in a very different environment.

Excavating site of Piltdown Man

Someone had planted the fraudulent fossil remains at the site. *(Public Domain)*

I.2. Why are humans bipedal?

After the exposure of the Piltdown Man hoax, the search for human fossils resumed and was focused on Africa. As Darwin and many other scientists predicted, Africa has the richest and oldest source of human fossils. The region that has the greatest wealth of fossil deposits is the Rift Valley, which is located in the eastern region of Africa. This valley had been created by the continuous movement of Earth's crust over time. This movement gradually resulted in the exposure of sand and rock that had been buried for millions of years. Many fossils were also exposed, making the region an excellent place to search for them. Most of the fossils were from animals that had lived in the region millions of years ago. Occasionally, however, fossils from early humans were found. One of the most important human fossils, nicknamed Lucy, was found in this region.

The discovery of Lucy made headline news around the world. It was considered

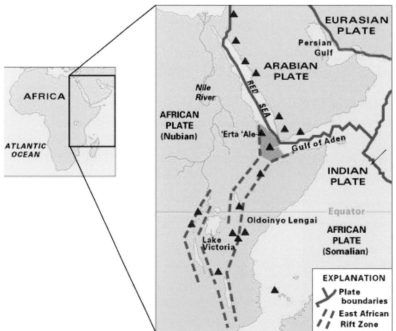

The Great Rift Valley

Map of East Africa showing some of the historically active volcanoes (red triangles). The dark orange area is the triple junction, where three tectonic plates pull away from one another. *(Public Domain)*

one of the most important fossil discoveries in the history of paleoanthropology. Lucy was important for three reasons. First, it is a fossil from one of the earliest human species. Second, it is one of the most complete human fossilized skeletons (40% of the fossilized skeleton) that has ever been found. Finally, it was the first fossil to provide clues as to why and when humans started to walk upright.

We are so accustomed to our upright posture that we rarely think of how unusual it is to be bipedal. Most other organisms get around on four or more legs. Birds are bipedal but only because their upper limbs have evolved into wings for flying. Bipedalism has many disadvantages, such as falling over because of tripping and slipping. However, because of a keen sense of balance, humans can perform remarkable physical maneuverings on only two feet. The greatest advantage of bipedalism is the presence of free hands that can be used to perform other tasks, such as using tools and carrying things. Watching a kung fu master yield a sword provides a quick confirmation that free hands promoted the survival of the early hunter-gatherers. However, both bipedalism and the ability of the hands to perform complex activities are unique to the human species. Even though the other members of the great apes have hands that are similar to humans and can partially walk upright, humans are the only species of the great apes to develop full bipedalism. Until the discovery of Lucy, the reason this had occurred in evolution was a mystery.

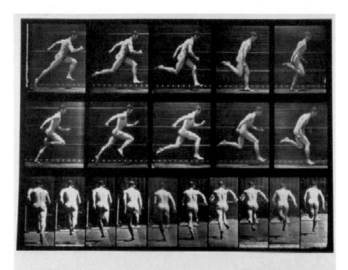

A man running

Bipedalism is highly efficient even though it is not as fast or as stable as quadrupedal locomotion. *(Public Domain)*

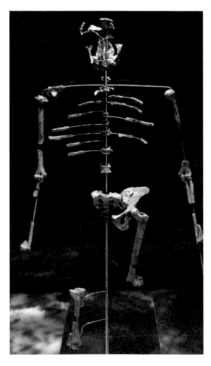

Lucy

She was an early human species known as *Australopithecus afarensis*. She was discovered in the Awash Valley of Ethiopia's Afar Depression. *(Public Domain)*

In 1974, an American paleoanthropologist, Donald Johanson, and his team made one of the most remarkable human fossil discoveries. They discovered a nearly 40% complete skeleton of a human-like female. She was 3 ft 8 in tall and weighed about 65 lb. Her skull resembled that of a modern chimpanzee and had a cranial capacity of 400 cc. Her pelvis and leg bones, however, were almost identical to those of modern humans, a clear indication that she had been fully bipedal. The skeleton was determined to be about 3.2 million years old through radiometric dating, a modern procedure that can provide a highly accurate determination of fossil age. She was nicknamed Lucy, because at the time of her discovery, some members of the team had been repeatedly playing the Beatles song *Lucy in the Sky with Diamonds* on a tape recorder.

The evidence that Lucy walked upright on two legs is demonstrated in how her thigh bones are joined to the pelvis. In other great apes, the pelvic girdle has a configuration that joins the thigh bones in such a way that bipedal movement is inefficient. Even though this configuration allows the great apes to walk upright, they cannot sustain the bipedal posture for any distance. Instead, they prefer a way of locomotion known as knuckle walking. Among the great apes, the chimps, our closest relatives, are the most adept in walking upright. However, their legs were not designed to support their body weight. When the chimps wade in shallow marshes, they walk in a posture that is similar to humans, because the buoyancy of the water provides support for their body. From these observations, it was concluded that the ability to walk upright did not appear suddenly in humans. The species already possessed the genetic tendencies for bipedalism.

Four years after the discovery of Lucy, another group of paleoanthropologists discovered a set of fossilized footprints in Laetoli, Tanzania, East Africa. These footprints had been made in volcanic ash that had been formed over 3.7 million years ago. Three individuals, a male, a female, and a child, had walked across powdery volcanic ash before it was covered again by another shower of volcanic ash deposits. These footprints were indistinguishable from those of modern humans, which suggested that the three individuals had habitually walked upright.

I.3. What caused the early humans to walk upright?

The discovery of Lucy and the Laetoli footprints resolved a long-standing debate. For many years, it was not certain which characteristic had evolved first, a large brain or bipedalism. Lucy had a brain capacity of 400 cc, which is similar to that of modern chimpanzees. However, she and her kind had evolved the necessary anatomy to walk upright. From this observation, it was concluded that the evolution of early humans began with bipedalism and that the evolution of a bigger brain came much later. Researchers have placed Lucy in a group of primitive humans that has a different genus from that of modern humans. Lucy's genus name is *Australopithecus,* and her species name is *afarensis.* Because of her chimp-like brain size, researchers have suggested that her behavior was similar to the chimpanzees. But, why did her species evolve bipedalism?

Laetoli footprints

A set of fossilized footprints in Laetoli, Tanzania, East Africa. These footprints were dated to be 3.7 million years old. *(Public Domain)*

About six million years ago (300,000 generations) Lucy's ancestors were displaced from the tropical rainforest where they lived. Prior to that period, the current Sahara desert was covered with thick vegetation that extended from the lowlands of West Africa to the mountains of East Africa. The ancestors of the modern great apes had adapted to living in this jungle environment and were well-sustained by the abundance of fruits and vegetation. Their anatomy had been adapted for climbing trees and for navigating the tangles of vegetation that were growing on the forest floor.

The climate began to change about eight million years ago because of changes in the earth's geology. The forest in North Africa started to disappear, and the Sahara desert started to form. These changes occurred slowly and are still occurring today, as the Sahara desert continues to expand. At the edge of the desert, rainforests are replaced by savanna, which is a grassland ecosystem. This rich ecosystem consists of scattered trees that are small and widely spaced. In a savanna, sunlight easily reaches the ground and supports a large growth of grass. The largest savanna is the Serengeti, which stretches for 18,600 miles from northwestern Tanzania to south western Kenya.

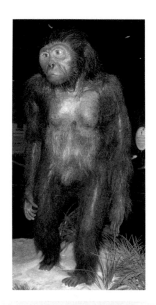

Lucy reconstruction

On display at the Museum of Man, San Diego, California. *(Public Domain)*

Many of the great apes that were living in these areas disappeared when the forest retreated, but some gradually adapted to the new environment over several hundred generations. Those great apes that had evolved (through genetic variations) bipedalism survived better. They were more agile in evading predators and in chasing down small prey. Both of these characteristics were important for survival on the open savannas. Another factor that contributed to bipedalism was the freeing of the hands to carry the young over long distances. With each generation, the anatomical features of these early humans were selected to become more efficient for walking and running.

The African savanna is a rich ecosystem, and it has the largest collection of large mammals in the world. Each year, nearly two million herbivores migrate from the northern hills toward the southern plains and back in search for rich grasslands. This is known as the circular migration, and its exact route depends on the annual rainfall. This migration route, however, is full of danger. Over 250,000 wildebeests perish each year because of exhaustion and predation by the big cats and other carnivores. It is likely that these migrating animals provided food for the early humans.

Circular migration
Occurs annually in search for rain and pastures. (*Creative Commons Attribution*)

A. afarensis
This reconstructed skull shows a cranial capacity similar to chimpanzees. (*GNU Free Documentation License*)

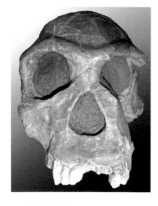

Homo habilis
They were the first human species to make sophisticated stone tools. They are also known as the handyman. (*GNU Free Documentation License*)

The modern-day gorillas and chimpanzees are omnivores. The meat source for chimpanzees consists of small monkeys that they actively hunt. Protein has always been a small, but significant, part of their diets. The early humans most likely expanded their protein intake by eating more meat. However, they were yet to become good hunters to kill large animals, such as zebras and wildebeests. They were most likely scavengers and ate the leftovers from the kills of the big cats. The early humans also were likely intense competitors with the hyenas for the unfinished herbivore carcasses. Researchers have suspected that the meat and fat-rich diets that were consumed by the early humans have led to the meat cravings that are experienced by modern humans.

II. MIDDLE HUMANS

II.1. How did tool use increase brain size?

According to the fossil records, *Australopithecus afarensis* persisted for nearly two million years. They were very successful as small-brained bipedal great apes. Like the modern chimpanzees, they made simple sticks to fish for termites in termite mounds. They also used stones to crack nuts, and they used large tree branches to beat back predators or to battle against each other. Their tool making skills were primitive, but they were well adapted to the environment that they lived in. For nearly 100,000 generations, this early human species thrived on the African savanna. *A. afarensis* was a great success story of the early human species.

About two million years ago, a new human species appeared on the east African plain. This new species had a brain that was nearly 50% larger than that of *A. afarensis*. Its brain capacity was 610 cc, whereas Lucy's was about 400 cc. Based on the fossil records, this new species was bigger and taller than *A. afarensis*. However, the most interesting discovery of this new species was the tools that they used. Whenever fossil remains of this species were found, there were stone tools found nearby, suggesting that they were the makers of these stone tools. These tools are not the same primitive tools that were found with *A. afarensis*. In fact, these tools are so sophisticated that most modern humans would have difficulties making them without first receiving some training.

The tools made by the early humans were made from flint, which is a form of quartz mineral. Flints are widely distributed, but they are often concentrated in certain areas. When a piece of flint is struck by another hard object, small pieces are flaked off. When performed by a skillful toolmaker, a sharp edge is created by repeatedly striking off small flakes of the flint. This was a tremendous innovation in tool making because, for the first time, a specialized tool had been created by biological organisms. This tool is known as a hand axe and it has two cutting edges. It can be held in one hand to use for cutting, slashing, digging, and smashing. The early human species that made this hand axe were the first species to be included in the genus *Homo*. They came to be known as *Homo habilis* or the handyman.

The hand axe was the first human-made tool. None of the other great apes have ever made objects having this level of sophistication. The makers of the hand axe must have possessed a higher cognitive ability to make this tool for several reasons. First, they must have identified the right type of materials. Even though flints are abundant, they can only be found in specific locations. Researchers have discovered evidence that some early humans might have traveled as far as 100 miles to locations where they mined the flints. Secondly, the flint makers must have possessed excellent hand-eye coordination that they used to strike the flint at an exact angle and in a precise location. The process of making a hand axe required a new set of mental skills and physical abilities that none of the modern-day great apes possess.

For over one million years, the hand axes were made in exactly the same manner. This period is known as the Paleolithic Stone Age and lasted from about one million to two million years ago. Researchers have also found the hand axe in great numbers all over Africa, suggesting that this implement was very useful to the Paleolithic humans. This hand axe is often referred to by paleoanthropologists as the Stone Age Swiss Army knife, because the Paleolithic people used the axe for many different purposes in their daily lives. The hand axe was also important because it was the first piece of human technology that transformed the evolution of humans. Because of the hand axe, humans started to evolve in ways that were unimaginable before.

It is believed that the perfection of the Paleolithic hand axe occurred over many generations. During this period, the human brain increased in size, because of the higher physical and cognitive skills that were required for fashioning these tools. In other words, the need for creating a better hand tool led to the evolution of a bigger brain and greater cognitive skills. These changes, in addition to bipedalism, began the formation of the modern human.

Hand axes

These are variations of hand axes made by *Homo habilis*.
(Public Domain)

II.2. How did stone tools change human behavior?

The Paleolithic hand axe was the main stone tool that was used for over one million years. In modern terminology, this is analogous to using the same computer software for 50,000 generations. The impact of the Paleolithic hand axe on the lifestyle and behavior of the early humans was revolutionary. Even certain modern human behaviors including mating, social interactions, hunting, and diet, directly resulted because of the use of the hand axe. This seemingly simple tool made crucial contributions to human evolution. As the tool making process become more sophisticated, the level of human intelligence also increased.

One of the most important contributions of the hand axe was to enrich the human diet with fat and protein from a source that was previously inaccessible. On the African savanna, the carcasses of large mammals were stripped of meat first by the big cats and then by scavengers, such as hyenas and early humans. The bones that were left behind contained a nutritious marrow that was rich in fat and proteins. This marrow, however, was unavailable to carnivores and scavengers because these animals did not have teeth or jaws strong enough to crack open the bones. This changed dramatically after *H. habilis* invented the hand axe and then used it to crack open the bones to consume the marrow. Consequently, they developed a craving for a high fat and protein diet, which continues to be a dietary preference for modern humans. Furthermore, this new food source allowed *H. habilis* to become bigger and stronger than *A. afarensis*.

Researchers have also found evidence that *H. habilis* used the hand axes as digging tools. They also used it to build primitive dwellings by piling soil and rocks for defense against predators. This led to the formation of semi-permanent accommodations (known as home-bases), where the hunters and gatherers could return every night. In addition, women and children could be kept safe in this protective dwelling. Evidence has been found indicating that such home-bases were first constructed about 1.5 million years ago. The home-base was advantageous for both social cooperation and for protection of the young. In turn, the increase in social cooperation led to a further increase in brain size because of the need for greater cognitive skills.

Anthropological evidence has suggested that early *H. habilis* were primarily scavengers, using their hand axes to extract bone marrow from carcasses. They also supplemented their diets with fruit and vegetation. However, as the social groups became larger, they started to develop a hunting lifestyle, with the males forming hunting parties, not unlike the chimpanzees. They began to modify the stone axes into spears for stabbing large animals. With their intelligence and cooperation, these early humans became successful as large-game hunters. Because of the improved diet, several new human species that were bigger and stronger evolved from *H. habilis*.

Another important characteristic that was developed during the period of human evolution was pair-bonding. Pair-bonding was important because it eliminated male competition. Instead of competing for females, the early human males formed pair-bonds with females and developed a monogamous mating system. Because of this mating system, males could form strong friendship bonds with each other rather than competing with each other for females. The bonding that occurred between the males was important for forming the necessary relationships that were used during cooperative hunting. Even today, males still find this type of bonding deeply satisfying, and it can be found in many areas, such as team sports or on battlefields. The social structure that resulted from pair-bonding led to a greater cooperation between group members. Furthermore, this social structure allowed the males to dominate and assume the main responsibilities of defending the social group. In addition, this social structure also led to the evolution of altruistic behavior, where some members sacrifice themselves to protect the group.

The use of flints by early humans also led to the control of fire. Flints were important because they were used to start fires. Fire was important in the evolution of early humans because it provided protection against predators at night and allowed the early humans to live deep in caves. Also, the use of fire resulted in early humans cooking food that was otherwise indigestible. This greatly enhanced the nutritional value of meat and vegetation that was in their diet. Because of this increased nutrition, prehistoric humans grew to the same height and weight of modern humans by about 1.5 million years ago.

II.3. *What was the first human migration?*

From fossil records, researchers have discovered that there were other human species that co-existed with *H. habilis*. These species, however, occupied different habitats. By about 1.2 million years ago, *H. habilis* had been replaced by other species. One species that has repeatedly appeared in the fossil records had a larger brain capacity. It had a brain size of 900 cc, 30% larger than the earlier *H. habilis*. This new species was also taller, more robust, and was named *H. erectus*. *H. erectus* has a special place in the history of human evolution, because it was the first human species to venture out of Africa and to spread to other parts of the world, including the Middle East, East Asia, and Southeast Asia.

The discovery of *H. erectus* was first made on the island of Java in Indonesia by a Dutch anatomist in the 1890s. Similar fossils were discovered at a location near Beijing, China in the 1920s. These fossils caused a great sensation at the time, because their skull structure was clearly different from modern humans, even though other parts of their anatomy were essentially the same as modern humans. Therefore, researchers concluded that these fossils were from a species other than *H. sapiens* (modern humans).

H. erectus left Africa and migrated to the Middle East and Asia about 1.5 million years ago. Some evidence indicates that *H. erectus* were the descendents of *H. habilis*. However, other evidence indicates that they were evolutionary cousins of *H. habilis* and that they and *H. habilis* shared *A. afarensis* as their common ancestor. Nevertheless, *H. erectus* shared many characteristics, such as tool use and social behavior, with *H. habilis*. They also formed typical hunter-gatherer societies and had a monogamous mating system. However, their tools were more sophisticated than the tools made by the earlier *H. habilis*.

After the initial discoveries of *H. erectus* fossils, more fossil remains of this human species were discovered in different parts of Africa. Studies of their skull structure indicated that they possessed human-like anatomy but lacked the

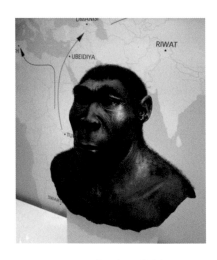

Homo erectus

This was the first human species to migrate from Africa to other parts of the world. *(GNU Free Documentation License)*

anatomical characteristics that are used to produce the complex sounds of modern speech. However, it is likely that they communicated in ways that are similar to the chimpanzees. *H. erectus* was also thought to be the first human species to hunt on a large scale and to establish small scale societies that are similar to modern human societies. There is even evidence that *H. erectus* cared for the sick and the old.

Some members of *H. erectus* left their habitat in Africa because of cyclical climatic changes in northern and central Africa. These cyclic climatic changes were due to many physical factors, including the rotation of the earth, plate tectonic movements, and global weather patterns. The climatic changes resulted in droughts that lasted for thousands of years. These severe droughts affected many regions of Africa resulting in a wide scale devastation of plants and animals. To survive, some members of *H. erectus* migrated from Africa to other parts of the world. In fact, they were the first human species to construct water crafts that were used to cross narrow ocean straits.

Fossil records have suggested that *H. erectus* lived in many parts of the world as recent as 15,000 years ago. It is possible that they co-existed with modern humans (*H. sapiens*) in different parts of the world. In 2003, researchers from Australia and Indonesia discovered a species of humans that was diminutive in size. The full grown adults of this species were less than 4 ft tall. The fossils were discovered on the Indonesian island, Flores, and hence, the species was named *H. floresiensis*. Researchers have suggested that this species had descended from *H. erectus* and that their small size was due to a phenomenon known as island dwarfism. Island dwarfism occurs when large animals become smaller because of a lack of food and the presence of predators when living on remote islands.

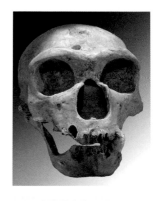

H. floresiensis
They are likely to be descendents of *H. erectus*. *(Public Domain)*

III. Modern humans

III.1. What was the second human migration?

The evolution of modern humans, *Homo sapiens*, is now well-known and can be told as a complete story. Human evolution started about six million years ago, when climate changes in Africa forced the earliest human species to adapt to life on the savanna. This led to the evolution of the bipedal *Australopithecus afarensis* (Lucy). About two million years ago, the first *Homo* species, *H. habilis*, evolved a larger brain and the ability to make and use primitive stone tools. Human behaviors and social structures were dramatically altered because of this technological advancement. About 1.5 million years ago, *H. erectus* (a descendent or cousin of *H. habilis*) became the first human species to leave Africa and to populate other parts of the world.

As climatic conditions improved in Africa, plants and animals, including the early humans, rebounded in their numbers. Even though many members of *H. erectus* had migrated out of Africa, some of them had remained. This remaining human population gradually evolved into a new species known as *H. heidelbergensis* about 750,000 years ago. There is strong evidence that this species is the common ancestor for the last two human species, *H. sapiens* and *H. neanderthalensis*. About 400,000 years ago, Africa endured another climatic disaster with drought threatening many regions of the continent. Researchers believe that a second human migration occurred at this time. Most of the population of *H. heidelbergensis* migrated north into Europe. At that time, Europe was in an ice age, and the new migrants quickly adapted to the colder climate. In time, they evolved into a new human species, *H. neanderthalensis*.

The first fossil remains of *H. neanderthalensis* were discovered in a limestone quarry at the Neander Valley, Germany, in 1856. The workers realized that the skeletons were very old and sent them to the local museum for identification. After careful studies, researchers recognized that this set of skeletons had belonged to a different, previously unrecognized human species. The skeletons were classified

H. neanderthalensis
Their skulls are more robust and have a greater cranial capacity.
(GNU Free Documentation License)

as a new species and became known as the Neanderthals. Compared to modern humans, they were similar in height but had more robust bodies. Furthermore, their skulls were considerably different from human skulls. They had a low, flat, elongated skull; a projecting mid-face, and a prominent browridge. Interestingly, their cranial capacity was 10% larger than modern humans (1,500 cc versus 1,350 cc in humans). However, based on their skull structure, the Neanderthals did not have the anatomical characteristics that are required for complex speech.

Since the initial discovery of the Neanderthal fossils in the Neander Valley, other

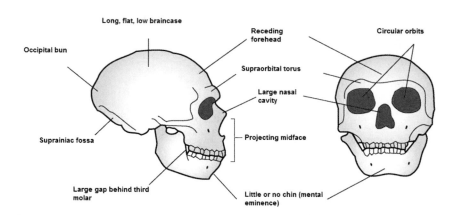

Neanderthal child

Reconstruction based on fossil evidence. *(Public Domain)*

similar discoveries have been made all over Europe and in some parts of the Middle East. None have been discovered in Africa, however, suggesting that the Neanderthals never migrated back to Africa. Therefore, the Neanderthals represented the second human migration from Africa after the exodus of *H. erectus* nearly 500,000 years ago. The evolution of many Neanderthal features resulted from their adaptation to the ice age climate that was present in Europe. Despite the harsh environment, the Neanderthals flourished for over 300,000 years. Their abrupt disappearance occurred about 30,000 years ago, a time that corresponds to when modern humans left Africa and entered Europe.

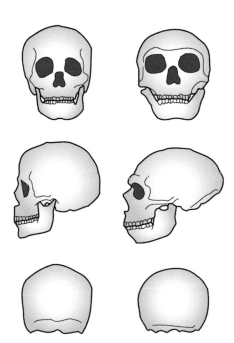

Comparison between modern humans and Neanderthals

Modern human skulls (on the left) and Neanderthal skulls (on the right). *(Public Domain)*

Based on the artifacts that were found with their fossil remains, the Neanderthals had sophisticated behavior and social structures. In one site in the Middle East, an elaborate burial site was uncovered. Several interesting discoveries from this burial site have provided important insights into the Neanderthal culture. The first intriguing find was that the burial site contained many different types of pollen, which were later identified to be from flowering plants of the region. This observation suggests that Neanderthals were buried with flowers, probably in a type of burial ceremony. The other interesting discovery was that the Neanderthal fossil was from an individual who had signs of severe arthritis, suggesting that the Neanderthals cared for their sick. Both of these characteristics indicate that the Neanderthals had sophisticated cultures and social structures that are similar to modern humans.

The extinction of the Neanderthals remains a mystery. The evidence indicates that they disappeared about 10,000 years ago after modern humans entered Europe from Africa. There are several possible causes for their sudden extinction. The first cause could be the invasion of other humans into their habitat. Since both species shared the same biological niche, it is possible that the environmental resources could only support one species. Therefore, it is possible that the Neanderthals were out-competed by the human species and were eventually displaced. The second cause is interbreeding with members of the modern humans. The two species were likely to have easily interbred because of their genetic similarities. Currently, DNA samples have been recovered from several Neanderthal fossils and efforts are underway to sequence the entire Neanderthal genome. This research will help us understand our evolutionary path and will determine how we are related to the Neanderthals.

III.2. What was the third human migration?

After the *H. heidelbergensis* population in Africa split off, the remaining African population was under severe drought conditions for a long period of time. This human population, along with many other animals and plants, were at the verge of extinction. About 250,000 years ago, fossil records suggest that a new human species evolved in Africa from *H. heidelbergensis*. This species shared nearly all the characteristics of modern humans, and they became the earliest form of *Homo sapiens*. Even though they probably did not possess the exact same behavioral and social characteristics of modern humans, their anatomical features are indistinguishable from modern humans. Therefore, this species is frequently referred to as anatomically-modern humans.

The relentless drought conditions in Africa nearly pushed *Homo sapiens* into extinction. Based on genetic evidence, the entire population of *Homo sapiens* dwindled to less than 1,000 people about 140,000 years ago. This small population was located in a certain part of East Africa. From the standpoint of population genetics, this situation is known as a population bottleneck. Because of the small size of the population, there was an increase in inbreeding, which led to a reduction in genetic diversity. In genetic studies of modern human populations around the world, it has been discovered that every single human alive can be traced back to this population.

Genetic studies have also resulted in discovering a phenomenon known as Mitochondrial Eve. This name has been given to the woman who is supposedly the mother of the most common recent ancestor of all living humans. Mitochondria are cell organelles that are responsible for energy metabolism in the cells. Mitochondria have their own DNA, which have been useful in tracking maternal lineages. During fertilization, sperm do not contribute their mitochondria to the zygote. In other words, all humans receive their mitochondria from their mothers. Therefore, by tracking the spontaneous mutations in the mitochondria, it is possible to trace maternal lineages. Using

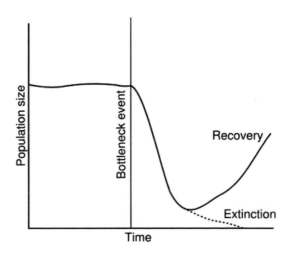

Population bottleneck
Genetic evidence suggests that the modern human population was near extinction about 140,000 years ago. *(Public Domain)*

this method, the Mitochondrial Eve is believed to have lived about 140,000 years ago in what is now Ethiopia, Kenya, or Tanzania.

H. sapiens was the only human species to survive the severe drought in Africa; all other human species became extinct. As the climatic condition in Africa improved, the *Homo sapien* population expanded. About 40,000 years ago, a population of *Homo sapiens* left Africa to populate the rest of the world. This was the third human migration from Africa. This theory of the spread of *Homo sapiens* to populate the rest of the world is known as the out-of-Africa theory. This theory replaced another theory, known as the multi-regional theory. In the multi-regional theory, it was suggested that the current world population had evolved from local populations that had remained from the first and second waves of human migration. However, recent research has provided unequivocal evidence that the out-of-Africa theory is correct.

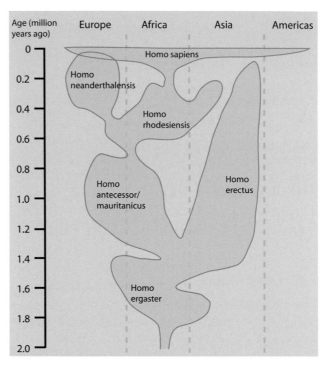

Proposed evolution of human species

When all other human species went into extinction, *Homo sapiens* was the only human species that survived. *(Public Domain)*

The out-of-Africa theory also provides an explanation for the genetic similarities that exist among different populations around the world. The human population is among the most homogeneous of the great apes. In fact, two native inhabitants from different parts of the world have greater genetic similarities than two chimpanzees living in different parts of the same forest. Despite our morphological variations, our genomes are nearly identical. The population bottleneck that was caused by the near extinction of the human species 140,000 years ago created a genetically similar population. This is another reason that race is not scientifically sustainable.

When humans migrated from Africa to Europe and Asia 40,000 years ago, they already had advanced cultures and societies. Human language was fully developed, and speech had become an important form of social interactions. In addition, the *Homo sapiens* had more sophisticated tools for hunting and warfare than the Neanderthals. Even though the Neanderthals were physically stronger than the *Homo sapiens*, they were not as flexible and creative. Consequently, the Neanderthals were replaced by modern humans.

III.3. *Will humans continue to evolve?*

As soon as the human genome was completed, researchers immediately began work on the chimpanzee genome. They wanted to know how humans and chimps had evolved from their common ancestor. The results from the genomic comparison were clear. Humans and chimpanzees are indeed genetic siblings that share the same parentage. However, chimps and humans evolved into two different species during the past six million years because both needed to respond to environmental changes. Through the process of natural selection, individuals who had traits that promoted survival passed their genes to the next generation. Because of this constant change, two new species gradually came into existence.

Over the last six million years, over 20 human species evolved to live on the African savanna, but only *H. sapiens* has escaped biological extinction thus far. However, many traits that are found in *H. sapiens* are the legacies from the species that had failed to survive. Evolution is a continuing process that is driven by mutation and environmental changes. In other words, human evolution is still ongoing. However, humans are currently facing a different challenge: cultural and technological evolution.

Cultural evolution began 10,000 years ago, when humans formed the first agricultural community. With language as the foundation, human society developed rituals, philosophy, religion, science, astronomy, art, music, and literature. These cultural aspects then formed the traditions that affect how people live, how they select mates, and how they interact with each other. Cultural evolution exerts a powerful force on biological evolution because of sexual selection, mating behaviors, and koinophilia (beauty that is associated with averageness).

The invention of the Paleolithic hand axe was a major technological advance in the history of human evolution. It had a profound impact on human evolution that led to dramatic behavioral and genetic changes. The development of agriculture was the next major technological advancement, because it resulted in vast social changes and the expansion of the human population. The technological changes that have occurred since the Industrial Revolution represent another major change in human evolution. Through technology, humans have developed tools that have allowed them to master the environment. The impact on human evolution has yet to be determined. Nevertheless, its effect is inevitable.

For individuals who live in an industrialized society, life has become sedentary. In other words, many of us spend long hours working in an office and have little to no exercise. From studies on human evolution, it is quite clear that humans did not evolve to lead sedentary lives. In addition, the modern diet of processed food is different from the diet that humans have evolved to consume. Many of the foods that we crave are not good for our health. These foods were craved by those living in a hunter-gatherer world because they were in short supply. Now that we can have these foods all the time, they are destroying our health. Therefore, understanding human evolution is vital for us to adapt to our new technologically-driven environment.

Humans are continuously evolving in response to environmental changes, whether those changes are natural or man-made. Because of our population of 6.8 billion, the possibilities for various genetic combinations are limitless. Until recently, human evolution occurred only through random mutation and natural selection. With technology, *H. sapiens* is at the brink of directing its own evolution through genetic testing, gene therapy, and reproductive technology. Will the evolution that is directed by human technology make the human species unfit for the natural world? This is an important question for society to ask before it is determined how these technologies should be used.

In summary, humans do not hold a special place in the natural world, because humans evolved from the common ancestor of the modern great apes. Through the past 6.5 million years, environmental changes had shaped the behavior of early humans from bipedalism to a monogamous mating system. Many species of early humans had thrived and then went into extinction, as natural selection favors those species that possess traits to adapt to changing environments. The evolution of

Homo sapiens was a long process, and many other species had contributed to our biological being. These species were past members of the human family tree, and modern humans are part of this heritage. Having this knowledge is vital for a better appreciation of human's place in the biological world.

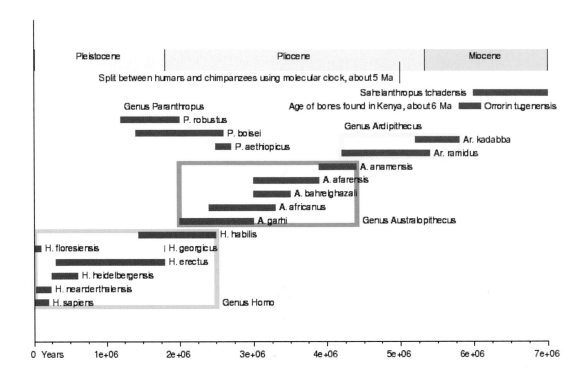

Evolution of humans

There are many human species that have evolved in the past seven million years. *Homo sapiens* is the only species that has not gone extinct. *(GNU Free Documentation License)*

Chapter 19

Diversity

Why are we different from each other?

Why are bulldogs in crisis?

The jaw and the shoulder of the bulldog have become too wide for the pups to pass through the birth canal. Many require Caesarean section to deliver.

(GNU Free Documentation License)

CHAPTER 19. DIVERSITY

What is the significance of biological diversity? This is one of the most important questions in biology. This question also has individual significance and social relevance. At the individual level, we often ask why we are the way we are, and we often see others who were less fortunate in the genetic lottery. Why does such variation exist? What is the biological significance of genetic diversity? It is important to understand the origin of genetic diversity and the range of genetic diversity that exists in a species. This diversity exists in every animal species, from dogs to humans. It is also important to understand that this genetic diversity is vital for the survival of all biological species, including humans. Because of our individual uniqueness, we are the agents of survival for our species.

I. WHY ARE DOGS MAN'S BEST FRIEND?

I.1. How did dogs become domesticated?

If humans are considered the most successful mammalian species of the 21st century, then dogs must be given second place. Today, there are 400 million dogs in the world, far exceeding the population of any other mammalian species, except humans. Interestingly, the ascendance of the dog as a species occurred less than 13,000 years ago, which is only a split second in evolutionary time. It has long been suggested that dogs and wolves share a common ancestor. Modern genetic studies have provided unequivocal proof of the dog's relationship to wolves. In fact, dogs and wolves are so closely related that they are considered the same species, *Canis lupus familiaris*. Dogs and wolves do not breed naturally due to their behavioral differences, but they can be artificially crossed to produce fully fertile offspring.

Fossil evidence has suggested that dogs and humans began to associate with each other when humans started living in small settlements about 13,000 years ago. Since then, dogs have become the most widely kept working and companion animals in human history. For generations, humans have revered and loved their dogs. In many cases, the dogs have been treated as partners rather than as inferior organisms. The partnership of dogs and humans is based on their remarkable ability to communicate with each other. They rely on each other when they hunt, and they comfort each other next to the camp fire. It is amazing how two entirely different species have created such an inseparable partnership. How did this happen? What were the biological processes that allowed the wolf ancestors to adapt to human existence?

Scientists have long tried to determine how early humans domesticated wolves. Wolves are highly intelligent, fierce, and powerful pack hunters. They are at the top of the food chain and are one of the most effective predators in the history of mammals. Why would they abandon their close knit kinship and join humans for co-existence?

Wolves as pack hunters
A pack of wolves surround a bison and look for ways to attack. (*Creative Commons Attribution*)

One of the early theories on wolf domestication has suggested that humans found orphaned wolf cubs and raised them as pets. During the 1970s, researchers attempted to raise wolf cubs, and they found that even after extensive human contact through feeding and handling, the orphaned wolf cubs remained highly dangerous because of their high intelligence, powerful physique, and strong predatory instincts. These studies were conducted in large isolation units that had gates and chain link fences, video monitoring, and 24-hour care by professional staff. The failure of these researchers to tame the wolf cubs indicates that early humans were probably not responsible for the taming of the wolves.

In the 1990s, another theory, known as the self-domestication theory, was suggested to explain how wolves became domesticated. This theory suggests that as human settlements grew in size, the wolves began to congregate near early communal dumps to scavenge food remains and waste. After a short time, some wolves started to follow humans on their hunts. Gradually, the early hunters allowed the wolves to participate in the hunts as well as in sharing the prey. With the strong social instincts that are present in both species, an interspecies alliance was established. Both species became more successful as a result of this alliance. In other words, the domestication of wolves was mutual rather than one-sided.

The self-domestication theory was supported when it was discovered that large municipal garbage dumps in many cities attract feral dogs that scavenge food remains and waste. Hundreds of feral dogs, for example, were observed scavenging for food in municipal garbage dumps on the outskirts of Manila in the Philippines. Early wolves probably did the same. Furthermore, those wolves that were not afraid of humans would have received more food and produced more offspring. These behavior traits would have passed onto the future generations; therefore, within 10 to 20 generations, tame wolves had evolved.

I.2. Why do people like dogs?

Where did the dog evolve from the wolf? Did it occur in only one place or did dogs evolve separately in different places? Recent research using mitochondrial DNA samples from dogs around the world has provided strong evidence that all dogs originated from a single source, some place in East Asia. Skeletal remains of early dogs have suggested that the transformation from wolf to dog might have taken as little as several hundred years, much shorter than was expected for the evolution of a sub-species. In other words, the evolution of dogs from wolves was natural selection in fast forward.

Ancient Roman mosaic

Showing a large dog with a collar hunting a lion. *(GNU Free Documentation License)*

Even though it has yet to be determined how dogs affected human evolution, the evidence of human impact on dog evolution is abundant. The early dog's body plan had evolved from a predator into a scavenger that had smaller teeth and body size that was about half the size of a wolf. The early dogs barked, wagged their tails, had floppy ears, and black and white coats, all of which are traits that are similar to many of the modern dogs. For many years, it was thought that the early dogs appeared the way they did because early humans had bred the dogs to select for these traits. This idea, however, was proved incorrect. The evidence for this came from a pivotal experiment that was performed on a Siberian fox farm.

Dmitry Belyaev, a Russian biologist, was working on a fox farm that produced pelts for coats and hats. The foxes were wild silver foxes that were kept in captivity. They were raucous, aggressive, and poorly bred. Belyaev began a simple experiment by breeding together only foxes that would not attack his gloved hand when it was extended into their cages. In less than 14 generations over a 20-year period, the experiment produced domesticated foxes that were tame and sought human attention. However, the most surprising aspect of this experiment was that these domesticated foxes also exhibited new physical traits, including spotted or black and white coats, floppy ears, tails that curled over their backs, and foreshortened faces and muzzles.

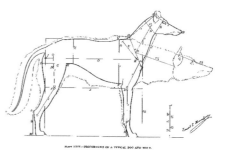

Comparison between dog and wolf anatomy

The dog is smaller, including the head. *(Public Domain)*

Dmitri Belyaev

Breeding tame silver foxes in less than 14 generations. *(Public Domain)*

Russian tame silver fox

They were bred for their tameness. *(Education Fail Use)*

They also displayed puppy-like behavior, such as whimpering and tail wagging, even in adulthood.

Since none of the observed traits were selected for, the researchers found it puzzling as to why the traits appeared. The answer became clear when they examined the fight or flight hormones, adrenalin and cortisol, in the foxes' blood. These hormone levels were significantly lower in the domesticated foxes than in the wild foxes. Since adrenalin and dopamine are closely related and are metabolized through similar biochemical pathways, it was possible that the reduction in adrenalin levels also affected the dopamine levels. In turn, the change in dopamine levels could have influenced the foxes' behavior patterns. Cortisol also shares biochemical pathways with other hormones. In this case, the hormones affect melanocyte (cells that produce color pigments) development. Lower cortisol levels could have a significant effect on other physical characteristics. From these observations and others, it was concluded that the domestication of dogs probably brought forth physiological and morphological changes that were unrelated to their socialization with humans.

Early humans took their dogs with them to hunt in the tropical rainforests, savannas, deserts, and mountains. The dogs that did well in these environments were valued and received better care by the humans. After living in these environments for 15 generations or less, many of these dogs acquired new physical and behavioral traits. In time, these dogs formed specialized breeds. Today, there are seven basic dog breeds: livestock guarding dogs, gun dogs, scent hounds, sight hounds, mastiff-types, bulldog-types, and terriers. Each dog breed has become specialized in certain aspects of their natural instincts as predators. It is through isolating these instincts that breeds of dogs that have specialized skills were developed. The selective process, however, was unintentional. Humans unknowingly selected the instincts for specialization.

Two interesting examples of dog breeds are the salukis and the Alaskan sled dogs. Both epitomize the extraordinary adaptability of the dog species. The salukis became one of the fastest land animals on Earth because of their unique physical and physiological adaptations. They were used in ancient Egypt as hunting dogs for small rodents in the desert. The Alaskan sled dogs rightfully claim to have the greatest physical endurance, because they have the capability of running a distance of five marathons everyday in some of the coldest weather on Earth. They can survive temperatures of -60°F with wind chills down to 100° below zero without the need for shelter. They were used by the Inuit to travel across the coldest regions of the world. Without these dogs, it would not have been possible for humans to survive in such hostile environments. These dogs were valued for their resourcefulness, loyalty, and intelligence.

Salukis and Alaskan sled dogs

They are both bred for playing highly specialized roles in their partnership with humans. *(GNU Free Documentation License)*

I.3. Why do dogs work for people?

When dogs first accompanied hunters in search for food, they most likely ate the prey immediately upon capturing it. This trait is easily observed in some modern dogs. Untrained dogs are sometimes difficult to play catch with because they often run away with an item after fetching it. However, hunting dogs do not eat their prey because otherwise they would have no value to their human owners. The reason that dogs are remarkable as hunting companions is their ability to refrain from their basic predatory instincts.

Wolves are predators and are equipped with strong instincts to hunt in a pack. Their hunting instinct is divided into four separate stages: searching, stalking, chasing, and kill bite. The search step includes scenting and sighting. Wolves possess a sense of smell that is 1,000 times more powerful than human smell. Wolves can pick up and follow a scent trail that is more than two weeks old. Once a wolf locates its prey by sight, it will enter into a high level of alert and will maintain an intense focus on the prey. The next stage is stalking, which is characterized by a low head and crouching posture that indicates a readiness for striking. After a wolf reaches a striking distance, it will begin the chase. The chase is followed by a kill bite, which occurs once the prey is captured.

Dogs have retained their predatory instinct, but they stop at certain steps of this predatory sequence. One of the most intelligent dogs is the border collie, which is often used for sheep herding. The border collies perform every step of the predatory sequence except for the last step. They will search, stalk, and chase the sheep, but they refrain from the kill bite. Why do they stop and not complete the sequence? This question is answered by the theory of pedomorphism (also known as neoteny). Pedomorphism results when the adults of a species maintain a juvenile appearance and/or behavior. In other words, the border collie adults act like juvenile wolves in some aspects of their behavior. Wolves display different predatory behaviors according to their developmental stages. Their cooperative hunting behavior mandates that junior members of the wolf pack must obey the signals given by the leader of the pack during the hunt. A junior member, for example, may sight prey but will not give chase until the leader of the pack gives the signal for the chase to begin. Otherwise, the prey may be alerted before the pack is ready to mount an attack. Similarly, when the prey is brought down, the junior member must defer to the senior and more experienced members of the pack to inflict the kill bite.

Predatory instincts

A border collie utilizes only part of its predatory instincts in herding the sheep. *(GNU Free Documentation License)*

The working dog breeds have retained different juvenile predatory behaviors through deliberate or inadvertent breeding. The gun dogs or the pointers, for example, will locate prey but will refrain from the chase. The sight hound, however, will proceed with the chase but will refrain from the kill bite. The hunting instincts of all dog breeds have been selected to retain some aspects of pedomorphism. This has allowed the dogs to be highly adaptive to various situations. The terriers, for example, have a ferocious and fearless reputation because they were bred to kill vermin (rats and weasels). For this purpose, they were selected to have short legs, which allow them to enter into burrows. Also, they were selected to complete the entire predatory sequence so that they would readily kill any vermin they caught. Another example of the adaptability of dogs is the guard dogs. The social intelligence of wolves, which is necessary for pack living, allowed for their transition into human hunting companions. Their loyalty to the pack and their strong territorial instincts also makes them the perfect guardians of human property.

Pedomorphism

Toy dogs often display an extreme level of pedomorphism, resembling not just infant, but fetal wolves. *(GNU Free Documentation License)*

II. ARE WE DESTROYING OUR DOGS?

II.1. What is wrong with dog standards?

Until about 150 years ago, dogs were mainly working companions for humans. They were bred to do certain jobs, and they were valuable to their human owners. This changed with the development of the modern dog breeds. In many modern dog breeds, appearance, not performance, is the essence of the breed. The history of modern non-working dog breeds dates back to China nearly 2,000 years ago. When Buddhism was adopted by the Chinese during the Han Dynasty, the believers needed a symbol for the mythical lions that were described in the scripture. Since there is no lion-like animal in China, early Buddhist monks started to breed dogs, known as Fu Lion or Foo Dog, which looked like lions. The result was the first non-working dog breed (the Pekingese or the Foo Dog) that was bred specifically for its appearance. The Pekingese were considered sacred for two thousand years and were only found in the Royal Palace and Buddhist monasteries. If any of these dogs were found in civilian possession, the owners were punished by death.

Fu Lion or Foo Dog

The Chinese lions are actually a dog breed (Pekingese) that was selected by early Buddhist monks to take on an appearance of mythical lions. *(GNU Free Documentation License)*

At the close of the 19th century, two empresses from two different cultures played a role in creating a modern dog breed. The Qin Dynasty Empress, Dowager Cixi, loved her Foo Dogs, and she provided her breeders with a precise description of their appearance and temperament. This became the Foo Dog standard, and the breeders had to strive to achieve the standard. When the British ransacked the Empress Dowager Cixi's palace in the 19th century, the Foo Dog keepers killed most of the dogs to prevent them from falling into foreign hands. However, the British soldiers found five Foo Dogs and the written Foo Dog standard. Both were brought to London and presented to Queen Victoria, who was delighted with them. Foo Dogs became a sensation in Great Britain. Other non-working dog breeds were developed, and owning a non-working lap dog became a status symbol for the upper-class British society.

Dowager Cixi and Queen Victoria

Two empresses on opposite sides of the the world were responsible for the introduction of modern dog standards. *(Public Domain)*

Over the next 100 years, over 400 dog breeds were developed by intentionally breeding for the appearance of the dogs. By the beginning of the 1920s, dog shows became a popular way for owners to show off their dogs. In order for dogs of the same breed to compete based solely on appearance, an arbitrary standard was developed for each breed in the same manner of Empress Dowager Cixi's Foo Dog standard. The judges award the winners based solely on whether the appearance of the dog contestants meet the ascribed standards.

Uno, a male beagle, made international news when he won the Best in Show at the Westminister Kennel Club Show on February 12, 2008. When he was brought to the floor to receive his trophy, the entire arena erupted in cheers as if he was a human celebrity. The Westminister Kennel Club Show, which was started in 1887, is one of the longest continuously running "sport" events in the United States. However, for many canine researchers and dog lovers, the dog breeding of the modern society has destroyed man's most faithful animal companions. The negative consequences of this breeding have only recently been felt by both the dogs and the dog owners.

Westminster Kennel Club Show

The 2007 Best of Breed, Komondor, in the show ring. *(GNU Free Documentation License)*

Modern dog breeds represent the worst form of eugenics and have resulted in devastating biological outcomes for both dogs and their owners. Today, over 4.7 million people are bitten by dogs annually in the United States. In addition, many dog owners are unable to cope with their dog's behavior. Out of the 65 million dogs in the United States, one in five, a total of 12 million dogs, will be put to sleep, as either abandoned dogs or by the request of their owners. How did this happen? How did the mutual relationship between humans and dogs become lost?

II.2. *What are the consequences of dog breeding?*

The relationships between dogs and humans for nearly 10,000 years consisted of working relationships. Early on, humans and dogs were hunting partners and later, dogs took on other roles, such as herders, guard dogs, and watch dogs. During the last two to three thousand years, humans brought their dogs with them as their societies grew and their habitat extended to every corner of the globe. When humans met challenges in their newly-settled environments, the dogs were with them and helped them to adapt. Together, the dogs and the humans settled new biological niches.

Bulldog

The bull dog is prone to health issues. They have breathing difficulties due to their short muzzle. *(GNU Free Documentation License)*

Throughout history, humans have selected their dogs through breeding, in the same manner as they have manipulated their crops and livestock. The breeding generally lacked any systematic approach, and the outcome was often uncertain. However, dogs were highly malleable and developed the traits that were desirable to humans. The bulldogs, for example, were bred to have a large head and muscular chest so that they could herd difficult and aggressive bulls. Doberman pinchers were bred as guard and attack dogs. The appearance of these dogs was of secondary consideration, because the emphasis had been placed on their temperament and on their instinctive predatory skills for a specific task.

Before the Victorian craze of the dog fanciers, the appearance of the dogs was not important to dog breeders. Their goals were to develop a dog breed to accomplish a specific task. However, in the modern era, dogs no longer work for their human owners. As a consequence, their appearance and body structure has become subjected to the whims of the dog breed standards. The standard for the head and shoulders of the bulldog, for example, has continued to increase in size. Today, many bulldogs can only give birth through Caesarean section, because their birth canals can no longer accommodate the natural birthing process.

An additional problem that has occurred between human and dogs is that dog owners often fail to understand the breed history of the dog they have in their home. As a result, there is often a serious mismatch between the dogs and the home environment of their owners. Having a border collie in an apartment with small children is an example of this mismatch. Border collies have been bred to herd sheep and to run up and down mountains all day long. Because of their extreme energy and herding instincts, an apartment is not an appropriate place for this active animal. It is not surprising that whenever there is a chance, the border collies try to herd small children into a corner of a room. Owning an Alaskan husky while living in a suburban home is also a bad idea, considering that this dog can run five marathons in a single day while pulling a sled over ice at -40°F. Both dogs and humans are frustrated by these mismatches. These problems have arisen because the dogs have been taken from their original role as human work partners and have been put into a new role as sedentary companions. Many of the breeds have yet to adapt because they are still genetically hardwired to chase, hunt, protect, and kill for their human masters.

Dog breeders have become aware of the damage that has been done to their dogs through breeding. Most recognize that the breed standards are completely subjective and have created genetic disorders in many of the dog breeds. The dog breeders have also realized that the modern urban society needs different kinds of dogs. With less than 3% of the U.S. population living in rural areas, dogs are no longer needed to chase, herd, and pull for their owners. However, with their loyalty, desire for human contact, and their playfulness, dogs are still wonderful companions for children, young adults, and the elderly. Even though modern dogs function primarily as companions, there are still instances where the dog's predatory instincts and skills have been put to service for their human owners. Recently, with their exceptional sense of smell, dogs have been recruited to detect illicit drugs, explosives, and even cancer.

With their extraordinary adaptability after they chose self-domestication, dogs have continued to shape human society and culture. They have extended human capability in conquering some of the most difficult terrains on the planet. Furthermore, through the misfortune of "fancy" or "designer" breeding, we have learned the harm of inbreeding.

II.3. Why is inbreeding bad for dogs and humans?

To achieve the breed standard, dog breeders have introduced inbreeding into the dog population by arranging brother-sister mating for generation after generation. Inbreeding, however, reduces the genetic variation in the population. Using this approach, dog breeders have narrowed the gene pool within the breed. This narrowing constitutes an evolutionary phenomenon known as the founder effect. Breeders selectively mate a small group of individuals that share similar traits to "fit" the breed standards. In effect, the breeders are reducing the variability of the breed, making the distribution of the desirable traits more predictable. To achieve this goal, only a few founders are used in creating the population. Without access to the gene pool of the larger dog population, the breed reduces its genetic diversity within only a few generations.

Unbeknownst to the breeders, as they have selected for certain morphological traits, they have also selected for traits that have led to severe genetic disorders in the dog breed. This is a genetic phenomenon known as inbreeding depression. Inbreeding inevitably leads to homozygosity, where the two alleles for a gene are identical. In normal individuals, the two alleles of most genes are different, a condition known as heterozygosity. Many human individuals are carriers of recessive disease traits, such as cystic fibrosis and sickle cell disease. However, they are healthy because they are heterozygous, and their normal allele compensates for the defective allele. Inbreeding, however, increases the chance for homozygosity of the recessive genetic disorders and greatly exaggerates the prevalence of certain genetic disorders in an isolated breeding population.

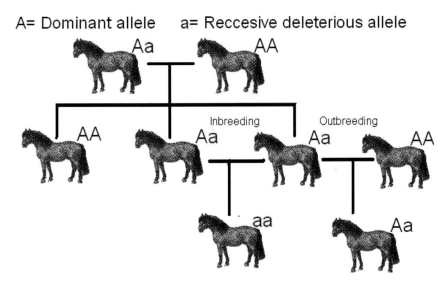

Inbreeding depression

Inbreeding can lead to an increased frequency of homozygosity of recessive traits that cause genetic disorders. *(Public Domain)*

Genetic diversity is essential for the adaptability and survival of the species, but it also has a hidden cost, which is the generation of "bad" as well as "good" genes. Genes consist of a strand of DNA nucleotides, a string of letters represented by the four nucleotides of ATGC. As in a string of words, randomly changing the words can make a sentence meaningless. Therefore, a mutation in a gene often destroys or severely affects the structure and the function of the protein that it encodes. Mutations can create defective genes, leading to genetic disorders, such as Tay-Sachs disease, cystic fibrosis, and sickle cell anemia. Some mutations affect genes that are critical during development resulting in the halting of an embryo's development in its early stages.

Detrimental mutations are randomly distributed in the population. However, these mutations can become concentrated in a population through inbreeding. Many dog breeds are now experiencing inbreeding depression, because they have been subjected to inbreeding by the dog breeders. However, with a better understanding of population genetics, breeders have found ways to bring genetic diversity back into the gene pool while still selecting for the desired traits.

The founder effect also affects the human population. For example, during the early settlement of the New World, a small population of people established a settlement that had a high level of inbreeding. The original population that settled in Quebec, Canada, numbered around 2,600 individuals. The resulting population after 15 generations exhibited a low genetic variation and a high prevalence of certain inheritable diseases that had been brought over by the founder population.

Another example of the founder effect is the high prevalence of total color-blindness among the inhabitants of the Micronesian island of Pingelap. In 1775, a devastating storm reduced the population of the island to only 20 people. One of the survivors was a carrier for total color blindness. After a few generations, the prevalence of total color blindness was 5% of the population, and the carrier rate was 30%. This is in contrast to the prevalence of total color blindness, which is 0.003%, in the general population.

III. WHY ARE WE DIFFERENT?

III.1. *Why are there different sizes of dogs and humans?*

Largest and smallest dogs

The Great Dane and the Chihuahua. (*Creative Commons Attribution*)

Dogs have been developed into hundreds of breeds, and there are now more than 400 internationally recognized breeds. It is amazing to find such morphological diversity in a single species. One of the most striking features of different dog breeds is their size. An average dog has about 25 inches in shoulder height and weighs about 50 lb. However, the range in the size of dog breeds is extraordinary. The smallest dog breed is the Chihuahua, which originated from the state of Chihuahua in Mexico. A Chihuahua can weight as little as 2 lb and have a height of only 6 inches. The largest dog is the Great Dane, which can weigh up to 200 lb and have a height of 42 inches at the shoulder. How can members of the same species have such a great size difference? Why do these differences not exist in the wild wolf population?

By studying the human population, the biological basis for size differences in dogs can be better understood. In the human population, there exists a bell shape distribution for body size, but the difference between the two extremes is remarkably large. Across different ethnic groups, there are variations of the average height and weight, but their ranges often overlap and form a continuum from one end to the other of the entire human species. When taking into account the entire human population, the average heights for a human male and female are 5 ft 10 in, and 5 ft 6 in, respectively.

Robert Wadlow

The tallest man in history, standing with his father. (*Public Domain*)

The tallest person in human history was Robert Wadlow, a man from Alton, Illinois. Wadlow reached a height of 8 ft 11 in, and weighed 440 lb. He was born a normal size, but he started to grow rapidly at four years of age. He was 6 ft 6 in tall and weighed 220 lb at age ten. He continued to grow until he was 22 when he reached a height of 8 ft 11 in. He was of normal intelligence and lived an ordinary life. His large size resulted from a hormonal condition known as gigantism. This condition results from an excessive growth (hypertrophy) of the pituitary gland. The pituitary gland is located in the center of the brain and is responsible for producing the human growth hormone. In Wadlow's case, the excessive production of the growth hormone was responsible for his great height. The cause for the hypertrophy of his pituitary gland was a benign pituitary tumor.

Many individuals are taller and bigger than others because of inheritable traits. In these individuals, tallness runs in the family. In the case of different dog sizes, researchers have discovered that the different body sizes of dogs are due to mutations in a gene that encodes for a growth factor receptor protein. Both in humans and in dogs, there is a range of body size that is optimum. Dogs and humans that exceed this size range suffer from physiological difficulties. Therefore, very large or very small individuals do not leave many offspring, and their traits are not passed onto future generations.

Human dwarfism is the opposite of human gigantism. Individuals who have an adult height less than 4 ft 10 in are defined by the Little People of America (LPA) as dwarfs. There are two major types of dwarfism: disproportional and proportional dwarfism. The disproportional dwarfism is the most common type, accounting for nearly 90% of all cases. Individuals who have this type of dwarfism have short limbs that are disproportional to their bodies. This type of dwarfism is usually caused by an inheritable disorder in bone and cartilage development. There are over 100 different types of disproportional dwarfism due to different mutations in genes that are involved in skeletal and cartilage formation.

Queen Henrietta Maria
With the dwarf Sir Jeffrey Hudson. *(Public Domain)*

The most extraordinary form of dwarfism is primordial dwarfism, an extremely rare condition that affects less than 100 people in North America. Individuals with primordial dwarfism are small but proportional; the smallest human ever recorded was Lucia Zarate at 1 ft 8 in, weighing 5.5 lb. She became the highest paid little person of all time when she toured with P.T. Barnum's circus, earning 20 dollars per hour in the 1870s. She had normal intelligence and had a "bright and animated" personality. In 2008, researchers discovered the genetic mutation that causes primordial dwarfism. Primordial dwarfism offers insights into the remarkable variations that are possible among fully functioning individuals of a species.

III.2. *Why do dogs have so many different types of hair?*

We are familiar with dogs that have different hair colors, textures, and thicknesses. These variations are special features of different breeds. Most dogs have two coats of hair, which includes a soft undercoat and a coarser topcoat. Some dog breeds have only one type of coat or the other, more often only the topcoat. Dogs with two coats shed their undercoats each spring and

Mexican hairless dogs
A genetic mutation is responisble for the hairless phenotype. *(Creative Commons Attribution)*

regrow them in the fall in preparation for colder weather. Some dog breeds have coats that grow continuously. The poodles are examples, and they require regular trimming. One species of dog, the Mexican hairless dog, has lost its hair due to a genetic mutation. Through artificial breeding, humans have intentionally selected dogs to have different types of coats. The genes for various coat characteristics, however, were already present in the dog gene pools. They are expressed randomly and can be selected through breeding.

Human hair also exhibits wide variations. Hair is one of the most identifiable features of an individual. In its natural stage, human hair exhibits many variations in terms of color, texture, thickness, and luster. Furthermore, there are distinct

Hirsutism

It is a form of male-pattern hair growth in women. *(Public Domain)*

Hypertrichosis

Also known as the werewolf syndrome. Lionel the Lion-Faced Man - Stephan Bibrowski. *(Public Domain)*

sexual differences in the hair distribution for various regions of the body. The human species is often referred to as the naked ape, but in fact, nearly all skin of the human body is covered with hair. The only exception to this is the palms of the hands and the soles of the feet. During fetal development, the entire fetus is covered with a fine coat of downy white hairs known as lanugo. As the fetus reaches full term, the hair follicles of the skin replace the lanugo with an even finer coat of microscopic hair, giving the newborn an appearance of having hairless skin. This coat of fine hair is known as the vellus hairs, and they are only visible under microscopic examination. In addition, these hairs lack pigmentation, making them even less conspicuous.

For reasons that are not fully understood, the scalp hairs are thick, pigmented, and are present at birth. During development, the vellus hairs at certain regions of the body are transformed into hairs, known as androgenic (terminal) hairs, that are similar to the scalp hair. This transformation occurs because of testosterone and other androgens. This explains why taking anabolic steroids leads to hair growth in the chin, beard, and sideburn areas, as well as other parts of the body where the vellus hairs respond to the stimulatory effects of androgens. Furthermore, the scalp and the androgenic hairs are pigmented due to the presence of pheomelanin and eumelanin, the same pigments that are responsible for skin color.

Human hair, as is the case for all mammalian hair, is an outgrowth of protein fiber from a hair follicle deep in the dermis. The protein is known as keratin. Keratin polymerizes with embedded melanin pigments to form the shaft of the hair. Researchers have suggested that only four genes are responsible for the entire spectrum of human hair color. The genetic variations of the keratin gene are also responsible for the texture of the hair. Altogether, the number of genes that control the physical properties of the complete range of human hair is likely only six or seven.

In addition, there are tremendous variations in the growth patterns of human hairs. Some are subtle, whereas others are quite extreme. During puberty, hormonal production contributes to the individual differences in hair growth. One common variation, known as hirsutism, occurs in women in the form of male-pattern hair growth of the androgenic type. Hirsutism is caused by genetic factors, but it can also be caused by medical conditions such as polycystic ovarian syndrome and medications, including some forms of oral contraceptives.

Many women find that inappropriate hair growth affects their femininity. Extreme disruption of normal hair growth causes profound social difficulties for the affected individuals. Hypertrichosis, also known as the werewolf syndrome, is a genetic disorder that results in the conversion of the vellus hair in parts of the body, or in the whole body, into terminal (androgenic) hair. Hypertrichosis was first described in 1648 near Innsbruck, Germany; the condition was found in a man, his daughters, a son, and a grandchild. They had been shunned from society and had been considered to be freaks and even devils. Over the next 300 years, only 50 similar cases have been described. However, the studies of hypertrichosis have brought insights to the extraordinary variations of human traits and have helped us to realize that only a few genes can lead to exceptional deviations from the norm.

III.3. *Why are there so many genetic variations?*

Dogs have provided an example of biological evolution in action that is under the powerful selective force of humans. When Darwin argued in favor of his theory of natural selection, he used the example from the hobby of breeding odd and bizarre pigeons in the 19th century. He called it artificial selection and suggested that by controlling the mating partners, humans can shape the biological traits of future generations. The evolution of the dog is a remarkable evolutionary process that occurred directly under our watch. Furthermore, humans are playing an increasingly greater role in shaping their appearances and behaviors. However, the selective process is only made possible by the diversity that already existed in the dog genome.

This genetic diversity exists in several levels, and the understanding of how these different levels occur in the dog will also provide an appreciation of human genetic diversity. With every single human individual possessing a unique set of genetic combinations, and with a population that is nearly 15 times greater, the potential for adaptation is significantly greater in humans than in the dogs. What is the source of genetic diversity in a species?

One can compare the human genetic diversity to a painter's palette that has 23,000 basic colors (genes). Each of the colors can take on different hues, and new hues are created continuously. The creation of the hues is completely random, and the end result is that each palette has a unique combination of the various hues for each color. Furthermore, during sexual reproduction, both parents contribute their colors in order to produce a unique palette for each of their children. Each of these new combinations of genes may have no significance other than just being a new and different combination that has never existed before in the universe. However, with 6.6 billion different color palettes that have already been selected by particular environmental factors, the odds for one or two individuals from this vast ocean of genetic combinations to fit any possible condition is good.

Individual uniqueness
The chance for two sisters to be genetically identical is 1 in 70 trillion. (*Creative Commons Attribution*)

The human condition of hypertrichosis might seem bizarre under the current climatic conditions. However, the situation would be different if the climate suddenly turns cold. The extra hair might be a key factor for survival. Similarly, the variations of different human body sizes could be of significant survival value when food is scarce. In addition, we have yet to understand the significance of human variations in intellectual skills. It is conceivable that the visual cortex of some individuals might be better suited for reading text on the computer than others. If reading computer text becomes the only reading option, some individuals will be more likely to succeed than others.

The human species is not unlike any other species in regards to the possibility of its continuing existence. About 140,000 years ago, the human species was at the brink of extinction, but somehow, certain individuals survived and perpetuated the species.

In this particular episode of near extinction, some of these individuals possessed the genetic variations that allowed them to survive. In addition, during the Middle Ages, the human species was threatened by the bubonic plague, but the species persevered, because some members of the species harbored genetic variations that provided them protection against the disease.

Genetic variations

Through sexual reproduction, this extended family has contributed genetic variations to ensure the survival of the species. (*Creative Commons Attribution*)

From a biological standpoint, individual humans are agents for the survival of the species. When we take away our culture and place the human species at the biological level, our individual lives serve solely to perpetuate the species and to protect the human genome from extinction. Through mutation and sexual reproduction, all living organisms possess the basic biological tools that are needed to create individuals who have infinite variations. Diversity among members of a species has proven to be an important winning strategy. Low diversity within a species that occurs through a population bottleneck or a founder effect inevitably places the species in danger of biological extinction.

Chapter 20

Arms Race

Who are our enemies?

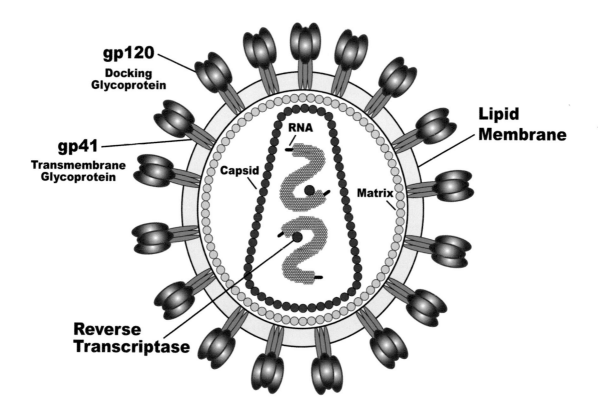

gp120
Docking
Glycoprotein

gp41
Transmembrane
Glycoprotein

Capsid

RNA

Matrix

Lipid
Membrane

Reverse
Transcriptase

Why can something so simple be so deadly?

The HIV virus has killed over 25 million people since the 1980s. Why can such a simple creature be so deadly?

(Public Domain)

CHAPTER 20. ARMS RACE

I. WHY DON'T WE GET SICK MORE OFTEN?

I.1. What would happen if we did not have an immune system?

When we get old, we become sick more often, and eventually, we succumb to infectious diseases such as pneumonia. However, a healthy adult rarely gets sick, because the human body possesses an exceptionally effective ability to defend itself against the invasion of infectious agents. This defensive ability, known as the immune system, is composed of a complex set of cells and organs that are spread throughout the body. The critical importance of the immune system is best illustrated in individuals who are born without an immune system because of a genetic disorder.

The most famous case is David Vetter, famously known as the "boy in the plastic bubble." David was born in 1971 with a rare genetic disorder known as SCID (severe combined immune deficiency syndrome). His older brother had been born with the same syndrome and had lived for only seven months before succumbing to a bacterial infection. SCID occurs because of a mutation in a gene that is critical for the normal development of the immune system. Most children who have SCID die before their first birthday. Because of this, David's doctors and parents decided to isolate him immediately after his birth in a sterile inflated plastic bubble.

David made worldwide headline news as the boy in the plastic bubble. David's doctors intended to keep him in isolation until they could give him a bone marrow transplant to reconstitute his immune system. However, he could only receive bone marrow from someone who matched his tissue type. Unfortunately, they failed to find a match, and for the next 12 years, David grew up inside the plastic bubble. Finally, David received a bone marrow transplant from his sister. Sadly, the pre-screening testing missed a dormant virus that was present in her blood, and without a protective immune system, David died from a viral infection at the age of 13. This story demonstrates how important the immune system is to human survival.

Without his immune system, David was confined inside the sterile, germ-free environment. Even though humans are the top predators in the bigger world, we are the prey in the microbial world, and the microorganisms are our predators. In situations where the prey is much larger than the predator, the prey is referred to as the host, and the predator is known as the parasite. To protect the body against parasites, the human immune system must defend it against an array of microbial organisms. Consequently, the human immune system is the most complex organ system next to the central nervous system.

Various components of the immune system are specialized to defend against different types of microbial predators, which include bacteria, fungi, protozoa, small multicellular animals, and viruses. David's condition was one of the most severe forms of an immunodeficiency. There are over 150 known immunodeficiency disorders that are caused by mutations in genes which affect the development of various components of the immune system. These disorders are collectively known as primary immunodeficiencies. They vary in severity, and most are diagnosed before one year of age, because the affected individuals have persistent and repeated infections. Many of these children die in early childhood from infections that normally do not severely affect children.

Immunodeficiency also can be acquired through other infectious diseases, such as acquired immunodeficiency syndrome (AIDS). In this case, the HIV virus infects and destroys the cells of a component of the immune system known as cell-mediated

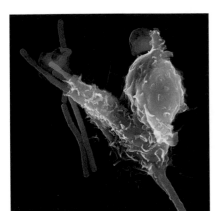

Defense against invaders

A white blood cell (neutrophil) is in the process of "eating" some anthrax bacteria. *(GNU Free Documentation License)*

Blood cells

Blood contains a mixture of cells of the immune system in addition to red blood cells. The lack of some of these cells leads to immunodeficiency. *(Public Domain)*

immunity. This renders the individuals susceptible to common infections. Other medical conditions, such as cancer, diabetes, heart diseases, and clinical depression, also lead to immune suppression. In addition, immunodeficiency can be caused by drugs that either suppress or destroy the immune system. For example, the use of corticosteroids can cause profound suppression of the immune system. Chemotherapeutic drugs that are used in cancer treatment also suppress the immune system because of their toxic effects on the bone marrow, the source of all cells of the immune system. Immunodeficiency also occurs during the aging process, making the elderly more vulnerable to infectious diseases.

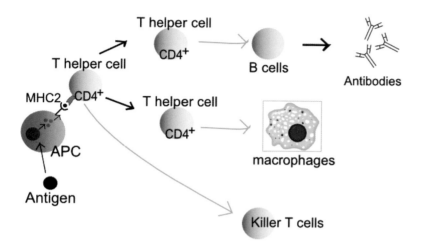

The immune system

The immune system contains various cells that interact with each other to generate antibodies, macrophages, and killer T cells to fight invading microorganisms. *(Public Domain)*

I.2. What is immunity?

There are many diseases such as smallpox, chickenpox, measles, polio, and whooping cough that infect individuals only once in their lifetime. Even if individuals are repeatedly exposed to these infectious agents, they cannot contract the disease again. Many of these diseases are known as childhood diseases, because once children survive the initial disease, they are protected from it for life. The mechanism of this protection is due to a phenomenon known as immunological memory. Immunological memory results from the development of memory lymphocytes. Lymphocytes are cells that are found in the blood, lymph nodes, spleen, and other part of the body. When a body is attacked by infectious agents, the lymphocytes respond by proliferating to create more lymphocytes to defend the body. The swollen lymph nodes that occur during an infection result from the activity of lymphocytes.

After recovery from a disease, 95% of the lymphocytes die, but a small percentage of these lymphocytes are transformed into long-living memory lymphocytes, which can remain in the circulation for 20 to 30 years. When these memory lymphocytes encounter the same infectious agent, they mount a faster and more vigorous immune response, known as a secondary immune response. This is in contrast to the primary immune response, which occurs when the body encounters the infectious agent for the first time. The secondary response is commonly underway in less than 24 hours after coming into contact with the infectious agent. The primary immune response, however, can take as long as five to six days before reaching the same level as the secondary response. The reasons for this delay are that the number of reactive lymphocytes in the primary response is much smaller and that a longer time period is required for their activation.

The secondary immune response forms the biological basis of immunity. In the case of measles or chickenpox infection, the viruses never take hold, because the memory lymphocytes mount a rapid response and destroy them before they can cause an infection. Since the secondary immune response lasts for a lifetime, it provides protection even if individuals are repeatedly infected. However, some diseases are

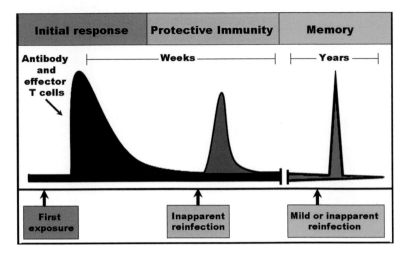

Biological basis of immunity

The time of immune response is the fastest in protective immunity and the body shows no clinical symptoms due to the rapidity of the immunological reaction. *(Public Domain)*

unaffected by this immunological memory, and individuals can become sick with these repeatedly. Examples include the common cold, influenza, and strep throat. These are the types of diseases that infect children and adults alike.

Why do people get the flu year after year, and why do some people have several colds during the same winter? There are two distinct biological processes that are responsible for the ineffectiveness of immunological memory in these diseases. In the case of the common cold, the number of different viruses that can cause the common cold is very high, as many as several hundred. The viruses are different enough from each other that immunity against one virus will not provide protection against the other viruses. Even though the symptoms of infection are similar, the infections are caused by distinct viruses. Therefore, each time an individual recovers and gains immunity against one common cold virus, they remain susceptible to many other common cold viruses.

The other biological mechanism that results in the ineffectiveness of immunological memory is the ability of a virus to mutate and change its surface proteins. If these proteins are the target of immunological protection, then the change in the structure of the proteins renders the immunological memory ineffective. The best known example of such a mutation is the influenza viruses. Even though the human influenza viruses have only a limited number of strains, they are highly mutable. Mutations of the influenza viral genes occur frequently.

On the surface of the influenza viruses, there are two proteins that are targeted by the immune system. These proteins are important for the entry of the viruses into host cells. The immune system produces antibodies that block these proteins and prevent the viruses from infecting the cells. However, these proteins are often changed by mutations in the genes that encode them. Consequently, the secondary immune response fails to recognize the new protein variants. Instead, the immune system responds as if this is the first exposure and mounts a primary response or a weak secondary response. Minor changes to the viruses are known as antigenic drift; large changes are known as antigenic shift.

I.3. How effective is immunization?

The ability of the immune system to form immunological memory is the biological principle behind vaccinations. Rather than having the infectious disease to acquire immunological memory, vaccination is used to elicit an immunological memory in the body. Vaccinations (against smallpox) were developed as early as 200 BC in China, long before the biological principle of immunological memory was known. The basis of vaccination is to induce immunological memory by eliciting a protective immune response without causing a serious disease.

Edward Jenner

He was credited to be the first to develop a vaccination against smallpox in 1796. *(Public Domain)*

Vaccinations were first developed to prevent smallpox, which was a deadly and common disease in the Old World. Smallpox was dreaded because of its 20% to 30% mortality rate, and it was responsible for 8% to 20% of all deaths in several European countries in the 18th century. Finding a way to prevent smallpox was one of the highest priorities during that period. In 1796, Edward Jenner, an English physician, developed the first effective and safe vaccine against smallpox. He used a similar virus, the cowpox virus, to develop his vaccine. Vaccination (Latin: *vacca—cow*) is named after the cowpox virus that was used to provide protection against smallpox. In Jenner's vaccine, cowpox viruses were inoculated into humans to elicit an immune response. Due to the similarities between the smallpox and cowpox viruses, a mild cowpox infection elicits immunity against a later smallpox infection. The word vaccination was used originally to describe the inoculation of the smallpox vaccine, but today, the terms immunization and vaccination are used interchangeably.

Currently, there are three approaches that are used for the preparation of materials for vaccines. The first approach is to develop a live but weakened form of the infectious agent. The second approach is to kill the infectious agents using methods that do not destroy their ability to generate an appropriate immunological response. Examples of these two types of vaccines are found in the polio vaccine. Each has advantages and disadvantages. The live and killed polio vaccines are known as the Sabine vaccine and the Salk vaccine, respectively. The last approach is to isolate the proteins from the infectious agents and use those proteins to generate a protective immune response.

Worldwide vaccination against smallpox

Over a period of 25 years, the WHO set out to vaccinate every person on Earth, leading to the eradication of smallpox. *(Public Domain)*

Vaccinations have unequivocally been the most cost-effective method for preventing infectious diseases. Over the past two hundred years, vaccinations have saved as many as two billion lives, with most of them being children. The greatest success was the vaccination against smallpox. Over a 25 year period, the World Health Organization set out to vaccinate every person on Earth. Since smallpox is strictly a human disease, the global vaccination project completely eliminated the disease from the human population. In 1977, the WHO pronounced that smallpox had been eradicated. Since then, there has not been a case of naturally occurring smallpox in the world. Consequently, the smallpox vaccination has also faded into history.

Many of the childhood diseases, such as whooping cough, diphtheria, measles, polio, and chickenpox, can be prevented by vaccination. However, vaccination has not worked for some of the worst human diseases, such as malaria, AIDS, and influenza. For some of these diseases, the failure of vaccination is because of the high rate of mutation in these viruses. For influenza, the high mutation rate of the virus necessitates the development of new vaccines each flu season. For HIV, a suitable vaccine has yet to be found for the same reason.

Despite their effectiveness in eliciting immunity, almost all vaccines have negative side effects. In the United States and other countries, where vaccination is a requirement for enrollment in public schools, these negative side effects have caused social and political controversies. Since the time of Edward Jenner, there have been continuing debates on the morality, ethics, effectiveness, and safety of vaccinations among the general public. Some of the controversy stems from the rare occasion when an immunocompromised individual succumbs to a live attenuated vaccine. In other cases, the vaccines can trigger autoimmune disorders.

In a recent claim, thiomersal, an organomercury compound that was used as a vaccine preservative, was alleged by more than 5,000 U.S. families to have caused autism.

After an exhausting investigation by researchers, such claims remain unsubstantiated. Unfortunately, such controversies can have negative effects. If many members of a community decide not to vaccinate their children, then recurrent epidemics of many childhood diseases could occur. Therefore, the medical community has offered unequivocal support for mandatory vaccination, as the benefits far outweigh the risks.

II. WHAT HAPPENS WHEN YOU GET SICK?

II.1. Why do bacteria make you sick?

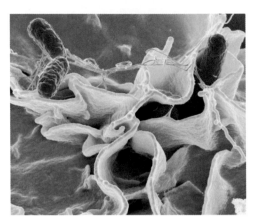

Bacterial invasion

Bacteria in the process of penetrating the mucosal lining of the intestinal tract. *(Public Domain)*

How do you get sick? How do microorganisms, such as bacteria, get into your body? Why do you develop a fever? These are questions important for you to answer, so that you can avoid getting the diseases as well as helping yourself to recuperate after becoming sick. To understand how we become infected, we need to first understand the different defense systems of our body. The human body has several layers of defense mechanisms against the invasion of bacteria. The most basic form of defense is the physical barrier which prevents the bacteria from entering into the underlying tissues. The human skin has evolved into a barrier containing layers of dead tissue on its surface. However, the sweat glands and the hair follicles provide gaps for bacteria to enter. The bacteria can enter the follicles and invade the adjacent tissues. The consequences of these infections are pimples and other skin infections.

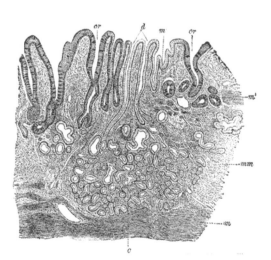

Mucosal lining of the esophagus

The lining is a complex structure with many cell layers to protect against microbial invasion. *(Public Domain)*

The main weakness of the human body surface is the mucosal linings, which are cells that cover the surfaces of our lungs, gastrointestinal, and urogenital tracts. These surface layers are permeable to the external environment because of the need for gaseous exchange, nutrient absorption, and excretion. Bacteria have evolved invasive strategies to penetrate the mucous linings. However, the human body has also evolved several mechanisms to prevent bacteria from colonizing the mucosal linings. This interplay between bacteria and the human immune system is also an example of an evolutionary arms race.

The mechanisms by which mucosal linings mount a defense can also cause symptoms which are familiar to us. The first mechanism is the production of mucous fluid that contains antimicrobial chemicals to inhibit the growth of bacteria or to kill them. The second mechanism involves specialized cells, known as cilia cells, which are found on the surface of the mucosal ling. These cells possess small cilia that, through their constant beating, generate enough local current to prevent bacteria from colonizing the mucosal surface. The third mechanism is coughing, which is a mechanical process that expels excessive mucous fluid that has become lodged in the lungs. The fourth mechanism is sneezing, which serves a similar purpose as coughing, but functions at the level of the nasal cavity. The last, but related, mechanism is rhinnorhea (a runny nose), which also serves to remove excess mucous fluid. Many of the clinical symptoms that we experience because of an infection directly result from our body's defense.

Our first line of defense works well most of the time in keeping bacteria from entering our tissues. Occasionally however, physical injuries allow bacteria to bridge these defense mechanisms. In these cases, the body's next response is inflammation, which is a rapid and intense response to the microbial intruders. We are familiar with inflammation, because we experience it every time we cut our skin or have a pimple. For many years, the purpose of inflammation was unclear, even though it had been recognized by the ancient Greek physician, Hippocrates, in 400 BC. He described the four classic symptoms of pain, redness, swelling,

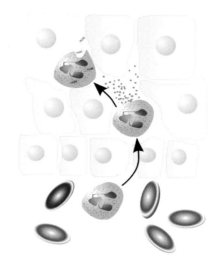

Inflammation

Neutrophils (white blood cells) migrate from the blood into tissue space in response to inflammatory mediators. *(Public Domain)*

and heat. Today, the biological mechanism of inflammation is well understood, and the mediators that trigger inflammation have been determined.

The main purpose of inflammation is to increase blood flow to the affected tissues. This blood flow is then followed by a fluid infiltration from the blood into the surrounding tissue, which causes swelling. This tissue fluid contains defensive molecules that can either kill or block further advancement of the bacteria. If this does not stem the advancement of the bacteria, then white blood cells are directed to leave the blood vessels and migrate toward the sites of infection. The chemicals that direct the inflammatory process are known as inflammatory mediators. One of the most important inflammatory mediators is histamine.

Inflammation is highly destructive to our tissues, and nearly all the clinical symptoms that we experience when we are sick are caused by inflammation. Inflammation is also caused by allergens, which can be pollen, chemicals, and food. The inflammation that is induced by allergens is indistinguishable from that which is induced by infectious agents. In a severe inflammatory response, known as anaphylaxis, the entire body is affected, leading to respiratory failure, cardiac arrest, and death. Some antibiotics, such as penicillin, can cause anaphylaxis, and individuals who are penicillin allergic wear a tag or bracelet to inform others that they should not be given penicillin in an emergency situation.

II.2. *What happens when bacteria enter the tissues?*

Once bacteria enter our tissues, our body's defense mechanism immediately springs to action. This response is vital. Because our tissues are rich in nutrients, bacteria can grow at an alarming speed if they remain unchecked. The human body has evolved complex mechanisms to destroy the invading bacteria. Inflammation is the first step in initiating this response because during inflammation, cells of the immune system are recruited to the site of bacterial infection. In a series of biochemical steps, the injured tissue cells produce chemical signals, known as chemotactic factors, to attract white bloods to leave the blood vessels and enter the sites of infection. The formation of pus in the wound is an indication of the presence of these white blood cells.

The first wave of white blood cells that enter into the infected tissues is the phagocytes. The most important phagocytes are the neutrophils and the monocytes.

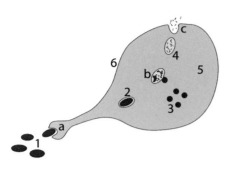

Phagocytosis

White blood cells, such as neutrophils and macrophages, engulf bacteria and kill them. *(Public Domain)*

Normal lung

The dark area is air space. *(Public Domain)*

Lung with pneumonia

The white area is fluid-filled due to inflammation. *(Public Domain)*

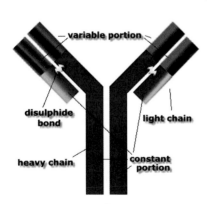

Antibody

It is a defensive protein molecule produced by B lymphocytes to bind specifically to foreign substances. *(Creative Commons Attribution)*

The former are highly active in the beginning of the infection, whereas the latter are important for cleaning up the cellular debris once the initial infection has subsided. These cells share many similarities with free-living unicellular organisms, such as amoeba. They have a voracious appetite for bacteria, and they engulf the bacteria in a process known as phagocytosis. During phagocytosis, the cells extend their cell membrane, like an embracing arm, to take in the bacteria. However, to prevent the cells from destroying the body's own cells, bacteria are tagged by special proteins in the tissue fluid to mark them for destruction. Occasionally, mistakes are made, leading to the destruction of the body's own tissues by the phagocytes.

Once the bacteria are engulfed by the phagocytes, they are destroyed by a process known as intracellular killing. This killing, however, can also be damaging to the tissues. Most bacteria have thick and resistant cell walls, and because of this, their destruction requires powerful digestive enzymes that are also damaging to the phagocytes. Often, the digestive enzymes leak out from the phagocytes and cause extensive damage to the surrounding tissues. The phagocytes also die in the process, leading to further release of these digestive enzymes. Depending on the severity of the infection, the damage to the surrounding tissues can be extensive, leading to pus formation. The whitish pus contains debris of both bacteria and phagocytes. In some cases, the

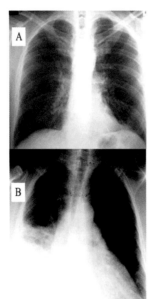

pus also contains live bacteria. Common skin infections, such as pimples, form pus that is surrounded by a thick layer of connective tissue to prevent the bacteria from spreading. Breaking the pus pocket can lead to spreading of the bacteria to other parts of the body.

Inflammation is a damaging tissue response and severe inflammation, such as those that occur in response to a severe infection, can lead to permanent tissue damage and scar formation. One example of how permanent tissue damage can compromise the function of an organ is pneumonia. Pneumonia is caused by different types of bacteria, but the most severe form of pneumonia is caused by the bacteria, pneumococcus. These bacteria possess capsules on their surface that protect them from phagocytosis by the white blood cells. However, as they multiply in the air sacs of the lung, they attract large numbers of white blood cells. These white blood cells block gaseous exchange and cause extensive damage to the lung tissues. This leads to impairment of lung function and can result in respiratory failure and death.

Pneumonia is a serious disease that can cause death unless the immune system can rapidly destroy the pneumococci. In an individual who has a normal immune system, the disease subsides after five to six days. The bacteria in the lung tissues are cleared by the phagocytes, and an infected individual recovers rapidly in the following several days. The reason for this recovery is also because of the development of a specific immune response. The cells that are responsible for this response are a group of white blood cells known as lymphocytes. Lymphocytes identify the invading microorganisms and then produce specific proteins that tag the capsules of the bacteria. These proteins are known as antibodies, and they are produced by a group of lymphocytes, known as B lymphocytes.

Antibodies guide the phagocytes to the targets and mark them for phagocytosis and destruction. In rare instances, these antibodies accidentally recognize proteins that are on normal tissues and organs. This is a phenomenon known as crossreactivity. For example, certain bacterial infections, such as strep throat, can result in a person developing kidney failure years later. The kidney failure results from the immune system attacking cells of the kidney. This occurs because the antibodies that were originally produced against the bacteria crossreact with proteins on the surface of the kidney cells. This is a biological phenomenon known as autoimmunity. The kidneys are gradually destroyed by the body's own immune system, and eventually, the kidneys fail to function.

II.3. *What happens when viruses attack the body?*

Viruses differ from bacteria in how they cause diseases in humans. Viruses are obligate intracellular parasites, meaning that they must live inside a cell. They cannot make proteins or produce energy. In other words, viruses rely on the host's biosynthetic machinery for their reproduction. Viruses are among the simplest living organisms (some scientists consider them not to be alive), and they are the ultimate parasites. Despite their simplicity, viruses are highly specialized and they have evolved to target one or just a few species, giving them perfect adaptations to certain biological niches.

To understand how the human immune system combats viruses, it is important to study the life cycles of viruses. The viral infectious cycle begins with the attachment of viruses to their host cells through highly specific interactions between the viral coat proteins and the host cell surface proteins. This step is critical for viral infections to take place. Through natural selection, the viruses have evolved an ingenious mechanism to trick the cells into accepting the viral genes as their own. Instead of using just DNA as their genetic material, some viruses also use RNA for their genes. Two well-known RNA viruses are influenza viruses and HIV. The highly mutable nature of these viruses is related to their use of RNA as their genetic material.

Once the viruses enter their host cells, they behave exactly like computer viruses. They reprogram the host cells to synthesize viral DNA or RNA, viral proteins, and other viral components. The host cells, however, have evolved some counter measures. One strategy that is commonly used by many species is self-destruction. Once the host cells detect signs of a viral invasion, they produce degradation enzymes and begin the biochemical process of cellular suicide, known as apoptosis. However, some viruses have evolved genes that encode proteins to prevent apoptosis. Despite their simplicity, viruses have evolved over millions of years to attack their host cells. In fact, every living organism on Earth can be infected by viruses.

Nucleus

Nucleus condensing (pyknosis)

Blebs

Cell shrinkage

Nucleus fragmenting (karyorrhexis)

Apoptotic body

Phagocyte engulfs apoptotic bodies

Programmed cell death

Also known as apoptosis. Cells undergo self-initiated destruction in response to viral infection. *(Public Domain)*

When we have the flu, antibiotics are ineffective, even though antibiotics are miracle drugs for bacterial diseases. Antibiotics target characteristics of bacteria that are absent or are different in human cells. For example, all bacteria possess cell walls on their outsides, and bacteria require their cell walls to survive. Some antibiotics, such as penicillin, block the construction of the cell wall, and without it, the bacteria die. Since the propagation of viruses rely entirely on the biosynthetic and metabolic machineries of the host cells, any drug that blocks viral replication also blocks normal cellular functions. There are some drugs, however, that can affect specific aspects of viral replication, but they also cause many side effects. One of the most active research areas for anti-viral drugs is for the treatment of HIV. Many of the drugs that are in current use for HIV have severe side effects. Furthermore, their effectiveness is limited because of the high mutation rate of HIV.

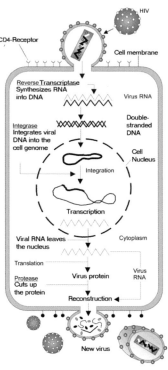

HIV replication cycle

The infection begins by binding to cell surface proteins including CD-4 receptor and CCR5. *(GNU Free Documentation License)*

Viruses and their host cells undergo a continuous evolutionary arms race. One of the most interesting examples of this is the emergence of a mutation known as CCR5Δ32; this mutation is significant because it provides protection against HIV infection. CCR5 is a receptor protein on the surface of cells that HIV uses to gain entry into their target cells, the T lymphocytes. A deletion mutation in the CCR5 gene creates the CCR5Δ32 version of the gene. This gene encodes for a protein that no longer binds to the HIV surface protein.

The immune system defends against viral infections by killing the virally-infected cells. A group of lymphocytes, known as the cytotoxic T lymphocytes, search out the virally-infected cells. These infected cells are destroyed before the viruses complete the replication cycle inside them. Similar to bacterial-induced immunity, anti-viral immunity can also lead to crossreactivity, resulting in autoimmunity. Type 1 diabetes is an autoimmune disease that occurs when the insulin-producing cells in the pancreas are destroyed by the body's own immune system. Researchers have found evidence that early viral infection is responsible for eliciting the autoimmunity.

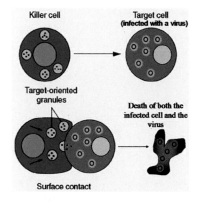

Killer cell

Cytotoxic T lymphocytes are responsible for destroying virally-infected cells. *(Public Domain)*

III. WHY ARE SOME INFECTIOUS DISEASES SO DEADLY?

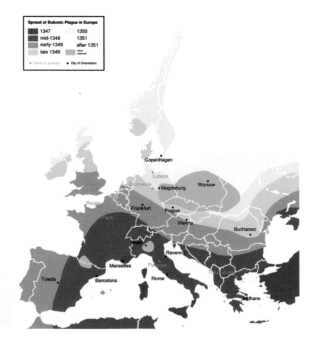

The Black Death

The spread of bubonic plaque in the 14th century in Europe. *(Creative Commons Attribution)*

III.1. Why are we afraid of a flu pandemic?

Over the last one thousand years, human society has been repeatedly devastated by the spread of infectious diseases. The bubonic plague of the late 1340s decimated the European population, killing as many as two out of three people in some parts of Europe. Such widespread infectious diseases are known as pandemics. Pandemics can affect populations that are located over many geographical regions and can sometimes affect the entire world. In the past several hundred years, influenza has been one of the most feared pandemics, because of its rapid spread, high rate of mortality, and lack of treatment.

The first global influenza pandemic was the 1918 Spanish flu. It began on a hog farm in the U.S. and crossed the ocean with U.S. troops to the European battlefields of World War I. In the first 25 weeks of the pandemic, 25 million people succumbed to this devastating disease. Over the next two years, it swept across the world in three waves, reaching even the Artic and remote Pacific Islands. When the disease finally subsided, it had taken an estimated 50 to 100 million lives. Approximately one quarter of the world population was infected, and 5 out of every 100 people around the world were killed. The Spanish flu left an indelible mark on the history of infectious diseases.

1918 Spanish flu
American Red Cross nurses tend to flu patients in temporary wards. *(Public Domain)*

Pandemics, such as the 1918 Spanish flu, are of great interest to epidemiologists (epidemiology is the study of how diseases spread) because of their widespread effect on the population across wide geographical areas. The spread of infectious diseases is grouped into three types. The first type is endemic diseases, which are always present in the population, such as the common cold, strep throat, and chickenpox. They are generally mild when contracted by healthy individuals, but they could be serious for the young and elderly. They also generally occur in isolated incidents. An epidemic is when an endemic disease reaches an unusually high caseload. For example, rabies is extremely rare and has an annual caseload of less than ten in the United States. If, however, the caseload jumps to 50, a rabies epidemic is declared by the local health authority. Another example of an epidemic is an unexpected rise of intestinal ailments on a college campus, leading to the declaration of an epidemic of bacterial food poisoning. An epidemic can be widespread in its location, and it can be severe; however, the causative agents of epidemics are generally familiar infectious agents.

A pandemic is defined as an epidemic that has spread to all human populations in a large region or even worldwide. Often a pandemic disease is new to the population of a particular geographical area. Due to the lack of past exposure, the population lacks immunity to the disease. Without immunity, the population is highly susceptible to the disease, and the disease course is often more severe. Throughout history, such pandemics have decimated human populations in different parts of the world. The bubonic plague of the late 1340s is the first pandemic on record.

The exposure of the native inhabitants of the Americas to Old World diseases are additional examples of pandemics that are caused by new diseases. Before the arrival of the European colonists, diseases such as smallpox, measles, influenza, and whooping cough were unknown to the local American population. In the 16th century, diseases that had been brought by the Europeans killed the entire native population of the Canary Islands. In 1518, over 50% of the native population of Hispaniola was killed by smallpox. In 1520, smallpox decimated Mexico, killing approximately 150,000 people, including the Emperor. A similar devastation of the native population occurred in Peru in 1530. Measles caused another wave of deaths in Mexico, killing another two million people. In North America, some historians have estimated that as many 90% to 95% of the Native American population died from Old World diseases.

III.2. *Why are some infectious diseases more severe?*

During the past several years, the World Public Health Organization has been concerned about the possible spread of a new strain of influenza virus, known as the avian flu, which thus far, has infected primarily birds. Avian flu has also been given the designation H5N1, which is based on its cell surface protein markers. Since the first outbreak in 1997, millions of birds have been killed by the avian flu. Until now, the avian flu has only been occasionally transmitted from birds to humans and only slightly more than 200 people have been killed by this flu virus. All the victims had been in close contact with infected domesticated fowls. To date, the virus has not been transmitted between humans.

There are two concerns about the avian flu from the public health and medical standpoints. From the public health standpoint, the avian flu virus has many similarities with the virus that caused the 1918 Spanish flu. First, both the Spanish flu and the avian flu viruses originated from another species. The Spanish flu crossed from pigs to humans. The second concern is the high mortality rate. The mortality rate for the Spanish flu was as high as 20%, a rate that is similar to the mortality caused by the avian flu. The mortality rate for annual influenza is less 0.1%. This high mortality rate indicates that the Spanish and the avian flues are far more deadlier than the regular flu.

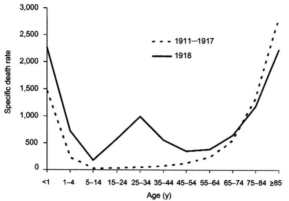

Different mortality rates
The 1918 Spanish flu killed more healthy adults than the annual flu.
(Public Domain)

There are several differences between the regular flu and the flues that can cause pandemics. The Spanish flu and the avian flu both progress rapidly; the time from the first sign of clinical symptoms to death could be as short as 24 hours. More surprisingly, the Spanish flu, as well as the avian flu, extracted the greatest toll in young and healthy adults between the ages of 20 and 40. In contrast, the mortality that is caused by general influenza is limited to the very young and the very old, and the death of these patients is often caused by bacterial infections such as pneumonia. This type of bacterial infection is known as a secondary infection, because the bacteria take advantage of the weakened immune response that is caused by the "primary" influenza infection. The Spanish and avian flues, however, directly kill the patients. Why do such differences exist between these essentially identical infectious agents?

The differences in disease severity result from the ways in which the immune system responds to these two viruses. An infection by the annual influenza viral strain is often brought under control within a few days after the onset of the disease. In fact, those who have been vaccinated against the viral strain might not develop any clinical symptoms. Furthermore, in most cases, the inflammation is localized to the respiratory tract. The disease processes of the Spanish and avian flues, however, are very different. These viruses stimulate a large number of lymphocytes, which then produce a copious amount of immunologically-reactive proteins, known as cytokines. These cytokines are powerful stimulants of inflammation. The inflammation is body-wide and can lead to severe tissue damage and fluid infiltration into tissue spaces. In other words, the severity of the Spanish and avian flues is caused by the body's own immune system. This phenomenon is known as a cytokine storm.

The biological process of the cytokine storm has only recently been understood. Since the immune system of young adults is the most vigorous, the magnitude of their cytokine storm is the greatest. This explains the high mortality of the Spanish flu in young and healthy adults. Some of the most lethal infectious diseases, such as SARS, Ebola viral disease, Hanta viral disease, and meningococcal sepsis, inflict their damage on the human body through the development of the cytokine storm. For example, during meningococcal sepsis, the meningococcal bacteria enter into the blood vessels and trigger a cytokine storm. The resulting damage to the blood vessel walls by the immune system leads to shock, cardiac arrest, and death within a matter of hours. The understanding of the cytokine storm has led to insights into the pathological mechanisms of these serious and often fatal diseases.

III.3. *What are the causes of pandemics?*

Throughout human history, some of the most severe infectious diseases have been the result of infectious agents crossing the species barrier from either domesticated or wild animals to humans. This process for infectious agents moving from one species to another is known as zoonosis. Many of the most deadly human diseases jumped from domesticated animals to humans. Smallpox, for example, was originally found in cattle as cowpox. Humans first contracted a virulent strain of cowpox, which then evolved into smallpox.

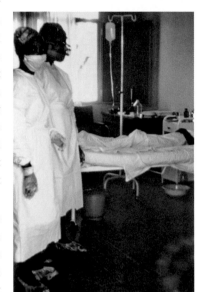

Ebola virus
A deadly zoonotic disease.
(Public Domain)

Since cattle were not found in the New World, smallpox was absent until the Spaniards brought the disease to the New World and infected the native population. Another example is tuberculosis, which is also a zoonotic disease that originated in cattle. In the 20th century, SIV (simian immunodeficiency virus) crossed the species barrier from wild chimpanzees into humans to become HIV. Similarly, the deadly Ebola virus also crossed the species barrier from wild chimpanzees to infect humans. The list of zoonotic diseases is long, but only a few have reached pandemic proportions.

The bubonic plague is a classical zoonotic disease that reached pandemic proportions. The causative agent of the bubonic plague is the bacterium, *Yersinia pestis*, which is primarily found in rats. The bacteria also infect the fleas that infest the rats. The fleas serve as the vector for transmitting the bacteria from rat to rat. The disease spreads to humans after rats infest human dwellings in large numbers. Under poor sanitary conditions, the fleas from the dead rats transmit the bacteria to humans. The development of the bubonic plague in human dwellings creates a further deterioration of sanitary conditions. This deterioration results in the flea infestation becoming even more severe and in accelerating the disease transmission.

Flea
Fleas are frequent transmitters of zoonotic diseases. *(Public Domain)*

The plague becomes a pandemic when the bacteria are transmitted from human to human. This stage of the disease is known as the pneumonic plague. In this stage, the bacteria infect the lungs and cause pneumonia. It is also during this stage that the disease becomes highly contagious because it is spread through contaminated respiratory secretions. The pandemic subsides when the number of susceptible individuals decreases through death, and immunity is developed in the surviving population. However, the bacteria remain in the animal reservoirs of rats and fleas. When conditions are right, the plague can reemerge and unleash the next devastating pandemic.

The Spanish flu is another example of a zoonotic disease. The predecessor of the Spanish flu was a swine flu, and its host range did not include humans. However, when humans and pigs live in close contact, it is possible for the human and the swine influenza viruses to mix together. When this occurs, the two viruses can exchange genetic information and create a new influenza virus that has the properties of both viruses. In the case of the Spanish flu, the mixed virus was basically a swine flu virus that had obtained the capability of infecting human cells and of being transmitted between humans.

Throughout history, human populations around the world had endured many cycles of pandemics. These infectious agents have jumped the species barrier from animals to humans and have caused severe and fatal diseases. However, the human species survived, because of variations in the human population. Some individuals had the proper genetic combinations to defend themselves against the infectious agents. These traits were then passed onto the next generation, and the cycle of infection was broken. From the biological perspective, mutation and sexual reproduction are critical for the survival of the human species.

Chapter 21

Coexistence

Who are our friends?

St Bernard's Lily *(Anthericum illiago)* — Bermuda Buttercup *(Oxalis pes-caprae)* — Oleander *(Nerium oleander)*

Lantana *(Lantana camara)* — Scarlet Pimpernel *(Anagallis arvensis)* — Verbascum *(Verbascum sinuatum)*

Common Mallow *(Malva sylvestris)* — Spanish Oyster *(Scolymus hispanicum)* — Stork's bill *(Erodium malacoides)*

Bindweed *(Convolvulus arvensis)* — Blue Gem *(Hebes x franciscana)* — Calla Lily *(Zantedeschia aethiopica)*

Why do flowers delight our senses?
Flowers are the most beautiful creations of nature. Why do they exist?
(GNU Free Documentation License)

CHAPTER 21. COEXISTENCE

I. WHY DO LIVING ORGANISMS COOPERATE?

I.1. Why are there flowers?

Flowers are among the most beautiful creations of nature, and humans take great pleasure in them. However, flowers are also an ingenious biological device that plants have created to manipulate animals, including humans. Flowers are the sexual organs of plants, even though most people do not consider plants as sexual organisms. The ancestors of plants released their gametes directly into an aquatic environment in a manner that is similar to that of corals and fish. About 450 million years ago, plants moved onto land and took advantage of the greater intensity of solar radiation. Since plants lack mobility, a different solution was required to transfer gametes from plant to plant to ensure cross-fertilization.

Seaweed

The ancestors of land plants have no flowers. Flowers are resource intensive to produce.
(GNU Free Documentation License)

Moss

Land plants, such as these mosses in a cool coastal forest, also do not produce flowers.
(Public Domain)

The primitive land plants lived in a swampy environment, and they released their gametes into pools of water. This strategy, however, limited the ability of land plants to extend their territories. To solve this, some plants evolved gametes in the form of pollen that could be swept away by wind upon release. These windblown pollens were destined to fertilize the female reproductive structures on other plants. For this strategy to be successful, however, the plants must meet two requirements. First, they must produce a large amount of pollen, and second, the other plants must be located in close enough proximity for the wind to carry the pollen to fertilize the egg. Wind pollination was the most successful form of pollination until about 130 million years ago, when flowering plants started to evolve. Instead of using wind, the flowering plants used animal couriers to ferry pollen from plant to plant. By 100 million years ago, flowering plants became the dominant land plants.

Basic structure of flowers

All flowers are reproductive organs. *(Public Domain)*

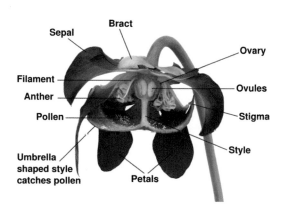

Sepal • Bract • Ovary • Filament • Anther • Ovules • Pollen • Stigma • Style • Umbrella shaped style catches pollen • Petals

Flowers are the reproductive organs of plants. All flowers share the same basic design for sexual reproduction. Every flower is structured to carry out three functions. The first function is to deliver pollen, which is the equivalent of sperm in animals. The pollen must be carried by wind, water, or animals to another flower. The second function is to receive pollen from another flower. Flowers contain ovules (egg equivalent) in an ovary that is connected to a structure known as the stigma, which functions to collect the pollen. Therefore, nearly all flowers are bisexual, because they have both male and female reproductive organs.

Flowers have evolved elaborate mechanisms to prevent self-fertilization. This is important because self-fertilization can lead to inbreeding depression. To prevent self-fertilization, flowers have evolved at least two strategies to ensure cross-fertilization. The first strategy is to release all the pollen before the stigma has matured to be able to accept pollen. In many flowers, the stigma unfolds to receive pollen only after all of their pollen has been released. The second strategy is based on anatomical positioning; the stigma is much taller than the anthers (structures containing the pollen); this prevents any pollen from falling back onto the stigma.

Preventing self-fertilization
The stamens are located away from the stigma. *(GNU Free Documentation License)*

The third function of the flower is to attract animals. This is important because animals often function as pollen couriers. To encourage the animals to visit, flowers contain nectar. As the animals drink the nectar, they inadvertently carry away pollen or deposit pollen from other flowers. To attract insect couriers, the flowers that open during the daylight hours have bright colors so that they are highly visible to the insects. Flowers that open at night produce scents to attract their animal couriers. Humans also enjoy the beauty and scents of flowers, because we still have the genes from our early ancestors who were attracted to flowers.

Pollination
The beauty of flowers is to attract pollinators. *(Public Domain)*

Flowering plants are relatively new in evolutionary time. About 100 million years ago, some plants evolved flowers, which were a minor modification of existing reproductive structures and leaves. It was immediately and spectacularly successful, because over only several million years, flowering plants became the dominant form of plants on land. Today, there are over 450,000 species of plants, and nearly 90% of them are flowering plants. How did the flowering plants achieve such great success?

I.2. *Why do humans need honey bees?*

Plants use insects as their pollen couriers, and insects rely on plants for their survival. Humans also rely on this relationship for agricultural production. The honey bees, for example, are needed to pollinate the agricultural plants, such as fruit trees and vegetables, which humans heavily rely on. However, over the past several years, the honey bees have started to disappear in what scientists call the colony collapse disorder. The exact reasons for this disappearance are not clear. Nevertheless, this disorder has highlighted the interdependence of life on Earth and has demonstrated that humans are only one part of this complex web of life.

Of all the insect pollinators, the honey bee is among the most effective and abundant pollinators for three reasons. First, they have a highly organized and complex social structure, which gives them a competitive edge over other pollinators. Second, honey bees are general pollinators because they pollinate a wide variety of flowers. Third, honey bee foragers are highly intelligent. These bees have an excellent navigational system, which consists of memory and mental maps. As eusocial insects, honey bees perform various hive duties until the last several weeks of their lives. Before they become foragers, their brains expand because of the addition of several hundred thousand neurons. This increase in neural circuitry makes them one of the most intelligent insects.

Honey bees are valuable for human agriculture. Up to one third of plants that are grown for human consumption rely on pollination by honey bees. However, as human agriculture has grown, the honey bees' natural habitats have been gradually destroyed. There are currently not enough bees living in their natural habitats to pollinate the large concentration of crops. To pollinate the millions of acres of fruits and vegetables that are grown for human consumption, honey bee pollination has become a service for hire.

Bee migration

Moving spring bees from South Carolina to Maine for blueberry pollination. *(Public Domain)*

In the U.S., commercial bee keepers transport hives of honey bees from farm to farm. On a 3,000 acre blueberry farm in Vermont, for example, beekeepers bring in several hundred hives and set them up in the fields for several weeks. The rental fee is as much as $150 per hive for a two-week period. When the pollination is completed, the hives are loaded onto semi trucks and are set up again on another farm. These bee keepers transport their beehives around the country. Some bees travel as far as 8,000 miles annually.

In 2006, honey bees made headline news around the world due to their mysterious disappearance. The disappearance was first reported in certain regions in the U.S., but was also soon observed around the world. This first appeared to be a global pandemic of an unidentified honey bee disease. Over the years, commercial hives have suffered from infectious diseases that sweep through honey bee colonies. In the 1990s, for example, half of the honey bee hives in the U.S. were destroyed by a parasitic mite that infested the honey bee colonies. However, the current epidemic is more difficult to understand. It began when beekeepers found that the worker bees were not returning to their hives. In some instances, almost the entire colony collapsed with no workers left. Only the queen and her attendants remained in the hive. It was also observed that a hive of 30,000 bees can collapse within one to two days. This syndrome was named colony collapse disorder (CCD). In 2006 and 2007, nearly one third of the U.S. honey bee colonies had collapsed. Similar occurrences were reported around the world from Europe to Asia. The consequences of CCD are serious, and researchers are striving to determine its cause. Only by finding the causal agents of CCD can researchers hope to prevent further loss of the honey bee colonies.

Dead bees

In recent years, bee colonies have been highly susceptible to diseases, including CCD. *(GNU Free Documentation License)*

Recent studies on the honey bees have discovered that the health status of the honey bees is poor. Autopsies of bees from CCD colonies have shown that the bees have many abnormalities in their intestines and in other anatomical structures. In addition, many honey bees had been infected by microorganisms that are usually part of their normal flora. This result has suggested that the bees' immune systems have declined. The reasons for these observations are not clear, but researchers have suggested that CCD could have resulted because of changes that human agriculture and technology have imposed on the environment.

The creation of large cultivated areas, extensive monoculture (planting only one type of crop), industrial scale farming, mass application of insecticides and herbicides, and the use of genetically-modified crops all have had unpredictable consequences on the environment. It is possible that these changes could have weakened the honey bees' immune defense and made them more susceptible to diseases. If robust organisms such as the honey bees can be so severely affected, then it is highly likely that many other organisms in this complex ecosystem are being displaced or killed. To prevent further problems, the general public must become more aware of the actions that are taken by multi national corporations on the farming and management of our land. It is also important that the interactions between animals and plants are understood so that appropriate decisions can be made regarding the future of our environment.

I.3. Why are there so many insects?

Even though the honey bee numbers are in decline, the world remains full of insects. A famous entomologist was once quoted saying, "if there was a creator, beetles would be his favorite creation." There are over 300,000 species of beetles, more than any other group of animals living on Earth. From the biological standpoint, the dominant living organisms on Earth are not humans or even mammals. It is the beetles and the other insects that can make the rightful claim as masters of this planet. Biologists have cataloged approximately 1.5 million living species (also known as extant species), and as many as 60% of these species are insects. In addition, new insect species are constantly being discovered, particularly in the tropical rainforests. Researchers have estimated that the unknown insect species could be as high as 30 million. This suggests that insects potentially represent over 90% of all life forms on Earth. They account for over 80% of all the animal biomass.

Insect diversity

Evolution has produced astonishing variety in insects. These are some of the possible shapes of antennae.
(Public Domain)

Biologists have always been puzzled by the extraordinary diversity of insects. During the 19th century, most biologists attributed insect diversity to the tendency for them to form small isolated populations. If two populations, for example, remained separate and did not have any genetic exchange, then in time, the populations could have evolved into two different species. This idea, however, was found to be only partially correct. The main cause of insect diversity was the evolution of flowers. During the 20th century, biologists discovered that the explosive evolution of insect species coincided with a dramatic increase in the diversity of flowing plants. These observations have led to the concept of co-evolution, which is defined as the adaptation of two species to each other for their mutual survival. The insect-flower co-evolution is an extraordinary example of how the mutual selection of two organisms affects their physical and behavior characteristics.

The most notable example of the co-evolution of insects and flowers was first described by Charles Darwin in the 19th century. In 1822, naturalists who were returning from Madagascar brought specimens of an unusual orchid (known as the comet orchid) that had a nectar tube that was nearly 12 in long. In this flower, nectar is located only in the bottom of the tube. The reason for this long nectar tube was not immediately clear. However, similar orchids that had much shorter nectar tubes had been described and observed to be pollinated by moths. To pollinate the orchids, the moths had evolved a tongue-like structure, known as a proboscis, that function like a straw to drink nectar at the bottom of the nectar tube. When a proboscis is not in use, it is rolled up like a coil spring. When a moth approaches a flower, it uncoils and inserts its proboscis into the nectar tube. As the

Comet orchid and Darwin's hawk moth

This is an excellent example of the co-evolution of two species.
(Creative Commons Attribution)

moth pushes its proboscis into the nectar tube, its head is pushed against the anthers of the orchid. Because of this, the moth collects the pollen as it drinks nectar.

With a nectar tube nearly 12 in long, the comet orchid must be pollinated by a moth that has an incredibly long proboscis. Darwin predicted that there must be some specialized animal (most likely a species of moth) that could feed from it. Darwin wrote: "in Madagascar there must be moths with proboscises capable of extension to a length of between 10 and 12 inches!" Darwin was ridiculed by his colleagues for this claim, but 21 years later, the insect in question was found and described. The moth is a hawk moth, later known as Darwin's hawk moth, and when it feeds on the orchid, it unrolls a proboscis that is five times the length of its body.

The partnership between the comet orchid and Darwin's hawk moth is an example of co-evolution. In this case, the traits of both are matched so that successful pollination (for the orchids) and feeding (for the moths) can occur. The length of the nectar tube must be just right for the moth to drink from it but still be able to get a head-load of pollen. If the nectar tube was too long, then the moths could not reach the nectar and would starve. However, if the nectar tube was too short, the moths would drink but fail to bump their heads against the anthers to pick up pollen. Without pollination, the orchids could not reproduce and would die out. Each generation of both species are genetically selected to have the proper length of proboscis or nectar tube. If, however, a genetic variation occurs and a nectar tube becomes longer, then only the moths that also have a genetic variation of a longer proboscis can feed from that orchid. It is through many generations of this type of mutual selection, that bizarre features can evolve.

The comet orchid and Darwin's hawk moth are examples of mutual dependence. In the tropical rainforests, many flowers and their insect pollinators have formed specialized pairs. Through natural selection, these flowers and insects have evolved remarkable features to ensure their mutual survival. Humans can enjoy and admire the exquisite beauty of flowers, but it should also be remembered that the beauty of flowers has evolved for attracting their pollinators so that they can ensure their own survival.

II. How do living organisms coexist?

II.1. Could ants be farmers?

Modern human society is built on a strong agricultural production system. For nearly 10,000 years, humans have used domesticated plants to create large scale farming that occurs on nearly all arable land on Earth. We often think of ourselves as the masters of the environment and the only biological species that can control the growth of other organisms solely for our benefit. Until recently, it appeared that humans were the only species with this capability, but this perception changed when scientists discovered that other species, particularly the eusocial insects, have also used farming to provide food for a large population.

One such group of "farming" insects is the leafcutter ants. There are 39 species of leafcutter ants that are found in the forests of Central and South America. They are the most dominant animals in their ecosystem. In the forests, it is common to see a long column of these ants ferrying cut leaves from trees to their underground nests, which can contain more than eight million individuals. They are eusocial organisms that are related to the bees, and their members are divided into castes. The largest group is the sterile female workers. In addition, the leafcutter ants have extraordinary size variations; for example, the queen can grow larger than a mouse. The workers are divided into four groups by body size: minims (smallest), minors, mediae, and majors (largest) size. The minims and the minors work around the colony. The mediae are the generalized foragers, and they have a pair of powerful mandibles

Leafcutter ants

Workers transporting leaves back to their nest. (*Creative Commons Attribution*)

for cutting leaves. The majors are the soldiers, which defend the nests from intruders.

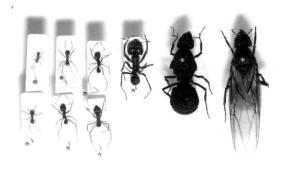

The leafcutter ants behave as a super-organism in the tropical rainforest. A colony of leafcutter ants can consume twice the vegetation that is consumed by a cow on a pasture. When they find a suitable tree, the worker ants use their sharp mandibles to cut the leaves into appropriate sizes and carry them back to their nest. They work with extreme efficiency, and they can defoliate a tree in one to two days. However, they do not focus on trees in a single area. They select trees over a wide area to minimize their impact on the ecosystem. In other words, leafcutter ants have evolved a mechanism by which to maintain the health of the forest.

Leafcutter ant castes
The caste members are highly varied in size, even though they are members of the same species. (*Creative Commons Attribution*)

After the worker ants bring the leaves back to their underground nest, they do not immediately consume the leaves. This occurs because most trees in the tropical rainforests produce toxic chemicals in their leaves to deter plant-eating animals. Many animals have evolved biochemical mechanisms to detoxify the chemicals, but they must limit their consumption to avoid toxicity. Furthermore, plant fibers are difficult for the animal digestive system to degrade. Most ant species are carnivores, and plants are not part of their natural diet. Therefore, it is not surprising that the leafcutter ants do not directly consume the leaves. However, they have evolved an ingenious way to prepare the leaves for their use.

In the vast underground nest of the leafcutter ants, an extensive fungus garden is prepared in carefully constructed chambers that have ideal humidity and temperature. The minims take the leaves from the foragers and chew them into mulch. Even though the leaves are indigestible for the ants, they can be used as nutrients for the growth of the fungus. Just like human farmers, the ants practice monoculture with only a single cultivated fungal species. All colonies of the same ant species use the same fungal species for cultivation. The worker ants harvest the fungal fruiting body, which is similar to mushrooms but at a smaller scale, and use them as food to feed the entire colony.

Queen of leafcutter ants
The fungal substrate is mixed by the workers. (*Creative Commons Attribution*)

For many years, researchers were surprised by the lack of microbial contamination of the fungal farms. Human farmers must relentlessly control weeds and pests in their farms. At first, researchers suspected that the ants were very skillful in "weeding." However, they discovered that as soon as they removed the worker ants from the colony, foreign fungal growths took over the culture. This observation indicated that the contaminating organisms were already present. Somehow, however, these organisms had been prevented from growing. The reason for this growth inhibition remained unclear until it was discovered that the worker ants in the farm had whitish materials on their backs. Interestingly, analyses of this material revealed that it was bacteria. These bacteria were also found to produce antibiotics. It was then observed that antibiotics were applied by the worker ants on the fungal gardens to suppress the growth of any contaminating microorganisms. This remarkable example of coexistence between plants, animals, fungi, and bacteria demonstrates that the biological world has become a complex web of cooperation through millions of years of evolution.

II.2. Why can cows eat grass?

Over millions of years of evolution, plants and plant eaters have been involved in an evolutionary arms race. Plants have evolved indigestible fibers and toxic chemicals to deter plant eaters from consuming them. In turn, plant eaters have evolved ways to circumvent these obstacles. Some plants, such as grasses, defend themselves by producing the toughest fibers in the biological world. This works for the plants because there is no animal digestive system that can destroy them. Even the most ferocious insect herbivores cannot digest these plants. Only when the grass leaves have been cut and allowed to rot can bacteria break them down. However, why is it possible for some herbivores to consume these plants?

The mammalian herbivores are some of the best examples of how coexistence is mutually beneficial. This type of relationship is known as mutualism. The mammalian herbivores are one of the greatest success stories of the evolution of coexistence. They feed on grasses, which are some of the most abundant plant species on Earth. Furthermore, grasses are nearly impossible for most animals to digest, and the mammalian herbivores have few competitors for this vast resource. These animals can use the grasses because of a special adaptation of their anatomy, which allows for a mutualistic cooperation between the animals and certain microorganisms to take place.

The mammalian herbivores, such as cows and sheep, are among the most important farm animals. They eat grass and convert it into protein with extraordinary efficiency. Since grass is highly resilient to the animal digestive system, how do the mammalian herbivores overcome this biochemical challenge? The answer is a specially constructed digestive system that uses resident microorganisms to breakdown the cellulose of the plants. The herbivores then absorb the nutrients that have been released by the microorganisms. However, the microorganisms cannot penetrate the intact cellulose without the help of the herbivores. They work as collaborators, with each contributing in different ways.

The herbivore serves as a delivery system by harvesting the grass with its mouth. The grass leaves are chopped into small pieces by the herbivore's teeth, swallowed, and then placed in a specially designed four compartment digestive system, which is collectively referred to as the stomach. The four compartments are the rumen, reticulum, omasum, and abomasum. The rumen is the largest compartment, and it serves as the primary site for digesting the grass. The digestive process in the rumen is carried out by microorganisms, which includes bacteria, fungi, and unicellular eukaryotic organisms. These microorganisms are normally found in decaying plant vegetation, and they are important for recycling dead plant materials. Somehow, these microorganisms were introduced into the stomachs of the ancestors of mammalian herbivores. In time, they established a mutualistic existence in the rumen.

To digest the grass leaves, the plant fibers must be physically broken down to allow the microorganisms to penetrate the plant tissues. The jaws of the mammalian herbivores perform this function by rumination, a process in which the herbivores repeatedly regurgitate the food from the rumen and repeatedly chew it until they form a cud. Without this action, the microorganisms would be unable to penetrate the plant fibers. The cud is re-swallowed and is further decomposed by the rumen bacteria, which convert the cellulose into sugar and fatty acids that are absorbed in the omasum and abomasum.

The microorganisms also provide all the other nutrients that the mammalian herbivores need. These include amino acids, nucleotides, vitamins, and ions. Therefore, eating grass is all the mammalian herbivores need to do. This collaboration has achieved remarkable results, making the mammalian herbivores one of the most successful animals on Earth. Another example of a mutualistic cooperation between an animal and microorganisms is the relationship between termites and

Mammalian herbivores

They are one of the most successful mammals because they eat grass that is indigestible for nearly all other animals. (*Creative Commons Attribution*)

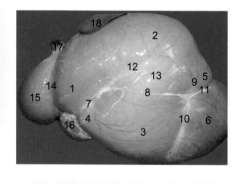

Stomach of sheep

The mammalian herbivore stomach (also known as rumen) is a fermentation incubator. (*Creative Commons Attribution*)

microorganisms. This collaboration allows termites to consume wood, something that very few other organisms can do. Wood has a highly specialized fiber structure, making it indigestible. The termites also cannot digest it, but they have microorganisms that have taken up residence in their gut to break down the wood. This arrangement is similar to that of the mammalian herbivores.

Termites
They harbor gut microbes to help break down wood. *(GNU Free Documentation License)*

II.3. *Why do organisms associate with each other?*

All living organisms are associated with each other in one form or another. They rely on each other in many different ways, and the human species is no exception. We rely on other organisms for our existence, and many other organisms rely on us for their existence. The richness and diversity of the biological world is the result of these interactions. When we look at nature, we can find it more interesting and insightful when we search for the connections between the different living organisms. There are three main types of biological relationships that link together all living organisms in the complex web of life.

The first type of relationship is mutualism. The relationship between the leafcutter ants and the fungus they cultivate is a mutualistic relationship. They need each other for their survival. If one of them became extinct, it is likely that the other species would also become extinct. The relationship between flowers and their pollinators is another example of mutualism. Similarly, the microbes and their mammalian herbivore hosts rely on each other for their survival. In many of these relationships, the two species have an absolute dependence on each other, and the extinction of one species would inevitably lead to the extinction of the other species.

How did these relationships evolve? Recent studies on a group of fish that live in the coral reef has offered an explanation to the evolution of the mutualistic relationship. There is a group of small fish found in the coral reef known as cleaner fish. They have developed an interesting behavior that at first seemed difficult to understand. These fish routinely swim into the mouths of much larger fish to pick parasites and dead skin from their jaws and teeth without being eaten. These cleaner fish provide a "dental" service for the large fish. In turn, they feed on the parasites and the dead tissues. Why would the large fish allow the small fish to enter their mouths? Shouldn't their predatory instinct make them want to eat these fish? Since fish have low intelligence, they would not "think" that this is good for their health. Similarly, how do the small fish overcome their instinctual fear of being eaten?

Cleaner fish
Cleaner fish are shown to set up cleaning stations waiting for fish "customers" to pay them a visit. (*Creative Commons Attribution*)

The results from these studies provide an insight into how mutualism is developed. In this case, the cleaner fish benefit from the food that they pick out of the mouths of the large fish. The large fish benefit in two ways from this relationship. The first one is that they are healthier by having parasites and dead tissues removed from their mouths. Researchers have also found that the large fish actually enjoy this experience. By examining their endorphin (the neurotransmitter for pleasure) levels in the blood, they discovered that when the large fish are being "cleaned," their blood endorphin level increases, suggesting that they are having a pleasant experience.

The second type of relationship is parasitism. The relationship between the cheetahs and the gazelles is an example of parasitism. In this relationship, one species survives at the expense of another species. In the relationship between the cheetahs and gazelles, the cheetahs are the predators, and the gazelles are the prey. The cheetahs also have a permanent relationship with the gazelles, because the cheetahs have become specialized gazelle hunters. If the gazelles became extinct, it is likely that the cheetah would also become extinct. In addition, the gazelles have a relationship with the grass that they eat. In this case, the gazelles are the predators, and the grass is the prey.

The third type of relationship is commensalism. This relationship is a transition between mutualism and parasitism. In other words, in this relationship one member benefits whereas the other is not affected. One example is the relationship that exists between the barnacles and whales. Barnacles are related to crabs and lobsters, but they lack mobility. They attach themselves permanently to rocks, boats, and sometimes to other animals. They filter feed on small creatures in the water using similar mechanisms that are used by the clams and mussels. Occasionally, they attach to large whales, such as the humpbacks or the blue whales. The whales give the barnacles a free ride, allowing them to feed in different environments. However, the whales receive neither benefit nor harm from this association.

When the various relationships between organisms are considered, we can see how different species are related to each other to form a complex web of interactions. These interactions are also affected by environmental factors such as temperature, sunlight, and moisture. All these interactions together form the ecosystem, which is defined as the summation of the biological and physical interactions of life. Understanding the structure and function of the ecosystem is critical for us to assess our impact on the environment.

III. IS THE HUMAN BODY AN ECOSYSTEM?

III.1. Why do we have microorganisms living on our body?

In the human body, the amount of microorganisms far outnumbers the body's own cells. Without the immune system, the human body would be overwhelmed by these microorganisms and would quickly die. One of the greatest dangers, for example, to severe burn patients is the invasion of their bodies by the normally harmless microorganisms that live on the skin. Once the protective layer of the skin is destroyed by the burn, these microorganisms invade the tissues and cause serious damage and even death. Where did we acquire these microorganisms?

When a baby is inside the mother's uterus, the baby is germ free. However, as soon as the baby passes through the cervix and enters the vagina, it immediately comes into contact with vaginal microorganisms, which include mainly bacteria, but also some fungi and unicellular eukaryotic organisms. These organisms immediately attach to the baby's skin, and they promptly establish their permanent residency among the crevices of the skin. When the baby breathes in the outside air, airborne microorganisms enter the upper respiratory tract and establish long-term colonies in the oral cavity, sinuses, and occasionally, the lower respiratory tract of the lungs. When the baby suckles milk from his or her mother's nipples, the microorganisms on the mother's skin enter into the gastrointestinal tract and establish residence in the lining of the intestines. In less than a few weeks after birth, every square inch of the exposed body surface is covered with microorganisms. By the time babies reach

Cheetah with kill
This is a prey-predator relationship. However, predators can also be microorganisms. *(GNU Free Documentation License)*

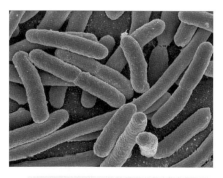

E. coli
It is one of the most common bacteria that live on the surface of our bodies. *(Public Domain)*

adulthood, they will carry one quadrillion microorganisms, ten times more than the 100 trillion cells in the human body.

One of the most important functions of the human immune system is to destroy these microorganisms if they enter the tissues. The skin and the mucosal linings serve as the first line of defense. Physical or chemical injuries can damage these barriers and allow these resident microorganisms to enter the tissues. Once the microorganisms have gained entry into the body, inflammation begins. This defensive measure is generally effective in eliminating these microorganisms while the body repairs the damage to the outer protective layers. Many factors can reduce the normal protective functions of our skin. Drying of the skin, for example, can result in cracks forming in the skin. These cracks can then lead to skin infections.

We harbor many disease-causing agents on our skin and on our mucosal linings. These microorganisms normally do not cause disease, because our body's defense keeps them in check. It is not clear where these microorganisms first originated, but it is likely they were once devastating pathogens. Instead of killing the host animal, these microorganisms established a co-existence with the host. This situation likely occurred because of two processes. First, the host had evolved more effective defensive mechanisms to keep the microorganisms in check. Second, the infectious agents likely evolved to be less virulent.

A majority of the common infectious diseases, such as skin infections, strep throat, meningitis, gonorrhea, and pneumonia, are caused by bacteria that normally reside on the skin or the mucosal linings. In a healthy individual, these organisms are kept in check by the body's immune defense. In the case of SCID (as represented by the boy in the plastic bubble), the lack of a functional immunological defense results in the invasion of these infectious agents. Without a functional immune system, the microorganisms can take advantage of any defects or weaknesses of the host defense. This type of infection is known as an opportunistic infection.

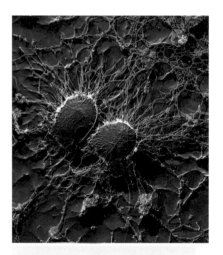

Staphylococcus aureus
Electromicrograph of two staphylococci. *(Public Domain)*

One type of opportunistic infection is a nosocomial infection. These infections occur in hospital or nursing home patients who have weakened immune systems that are caused by a medical condition. As many as one in ten hospital patients in the United States contract a nosocomial infection. Each year, as many as 80,000 deaths are attributed to nosocomial infections. In 2007, the common skin bacterium *Staphylococcus aureus* attracted attention from the general public because of its role in causing serious nosocomial infections. In fact, some consider this bacterium as the next major infectious killer.

III.2 What is MRSA?

S. aureus is an interesting example that illustrates the interactions between the human body and its microbial residents. These microorganisms and the human body have evolved to coexist, but this is only a temporary truce. Whenever there is an opportunity, the human body will try to eliminate the microorganisms, or the microorganisms will try to expand their area. This balance can be easily tipped, leading to serious consequences. In the past several years, *S. aureus* has tipped this balance because it has acquired an ability to resist antibiotic treatments.

Methicillin resistant *Staphylococcus aureus,* also known as MRSA, is an opportunistic infectious agent that rarely causes serious disease in healthy individuals. It is frequently found in the crevices of the skin and is the most common causative agent of skin boils and cellulitis. It also forms colonies in the anterior nares (the nostrils), and occasionally, it can cause respiratory disease. Approximately 20%-30% of the population is a carrier for MRSA. However, it is also a very aggressive opportunistic infectious agent. Hospital patients who have weakened immune systems are highly susceptible to *S. aureus* infections. Every year, nearly a half million patients acquire a staphylococcal infection in U.S. hospitals. A recent study has indicated that in 2005,

Alexander Fleming
Discovered penicillin in 1928.
(Public Domain)

staphylococcal-induced deaths in the U.S. numbered 19,000, which was higher than AIDS-related deaths. The problem made national headlines when, in October 2007, a 17-year-old healthy high school football player in Virginia contracted a staphylococcal infection and died shortly after. This and other incidents have created a fear that staphylococcal infections could become the next epidemic.

The concern about staphylococcal infection stems from its remarkable ability to become resistant to antibiotics. Antibiotics are one of the greatest medical innovations in modern medicine. In 1928, penicillin was the first antibiotic discovered. During World War II, penicillin saved many lives of soldiers who would have died from wound infections. At that time, penicillin was considered a magic bullet that could destroy infectious bacteria without causing any side effects. Diseases caused by *S. aureus* were among the first to be treated successfully by penicillin.

However, because of the broad use of penicillin, *S. aureus* soon developed resistance to penicillin. Its resistance was first reported in 1947, less than four years after penicillin was first introduced. At the time, researchers could not understand the rapidity of the emergence of antibiotic-resistant *S. aureus*. Shortly after, however, other bacteria that had been sensitive to penicillin also developed antibiotic resistance. To treat these penicillin-resistant bacteria, new antibiotics had to be developed. A race between the emergence of resistance and the search for new antibiotics had begun. The emergence of the MRSA strain suggests that human technology has yet to match the process of natural selection.

The development of antibiotic resistance is a form of natural selection. With generation times as short as 20 minutes, several billion bacteria are produced within days, with each carrying different traits as a result of mutation. Some of these traits provide the bacteria with the ability to block the biochemical action of penicillin. These mutations cause a minor change in an enzyme that would normally have been inhibited by penicillin. Antibiotic resistance most likely starts with a single bacterium that possesses the mutation. In the absence of antibiotics, this mutation has no

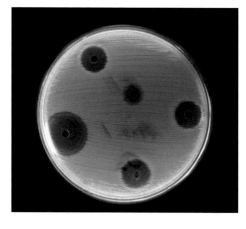

Test for antibiotic resistance
Antibiotics are incorporated into filter paper disks and placed on a plate with growing bacteria. Antibiotics diffuse out from the disks and inhibit the growth of bacteria resulting in a zone of clearing. *(Public Domain)*

advantage and eventually will be displaced by other more useful variations of the gene. However, when the antibiotic becomes a selective force, the antibiotic-resistant mutation is selected and propagated in the population.

The danger of MRSA is its ability to resist multiple antibiotics, including methicillin, which is one of the newer derivatives of penicillin. Methicillin was once effective against *S. aureus* that were resistant to other antibiotics. Because of its resistance to methicillin, MRSA is susceptible to only a few antibiotics. MRSA became known as the superbug because of its resistance to nearly all antibiotics on the market. This is only one of many examples of natural selection that occurs when human technologies drive the process of evolution. The development of multiple antibiotic resistance provides further evidence of the importance of mutation and individual variation. The understanding of the evolutionary process of antibiotic resistance has provided insight into the need for judicial use of antibiotics.

III.3. Is our body a microbial ecosystem?

Why does 20%-30% of the human population harbor MRSA? Why do the vast majority of them show no clinical symptoms? Where are these bacteria living on our body? Why does the immune system not get rid of them? The answers to these questions provide important insights into humans' place in the biological world. If we think that we are somehow apart from the biological world, we should think again, particularly when we consider our relationship with microorganisms.

For every human cell, there are ten microorganisms living on our body. On a healthy individual, the microorganisms live on the surface of the body, which includes the skin, the mucosal linings of the respiratory, digestive, and urogenital tracts, and any areas that are exposed to the outside world. These microorganisms are colonizers which are similar to human colonizers. Once they land on our body, they find the most habitable regions to establish colonies and reproduce. The microorganisms also compete with each other. For them, the human body is a vast resource for food, shelter, and protection. Over 1,000 species of microorganisms have been identified on the human body, and researchers have estimated that as many as 10,000 species might actually be present.

Different biological organisms living together in a complex system is known as an ecosystem. The microorganisms living on the surface of the human body can be described as a microbial ecosystem. The human body surface provides the microorganisms with a wide range of environments. The human colon, for example, resembles a tropical rainforest in that it can support trillions of bacteria and other microorganisms. The human upper respiratory tract, the oral cavity, and the vagina are also desirable microbial habitats. The human skin also supports microbial communities, but it is harsh and desert-like; only a few microbial species have adapted to this environment. The human microbial ecosystem is finely tuned, and a delicate balance is maintained between the different species. These microorganisms compete against each other for resources in a phenomenon known as microbial antagonism.

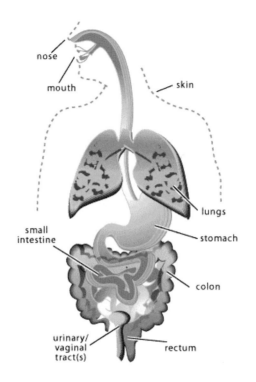

Normal flora

Microorganisms are found on all the surfaces of the organs that come into contact with the outside world. *(Public Domain)*

The colonization of the human body shares many similarities with the colonization of newly-created volcanic islands. Islands, such as the Hawaiian Islands, are created from underwater volcanoes. When these islands first emerge, they are entirely devoid of life. Similarly, a fetus in utero is germ free and has no microbial colonization. The first encounter of the microbial world occurs when the baby passes through the birth canal. Within a few hours, microorganisms are introduced onto the baby through human contact and feeding. It is remarkable that all human beings are colonized by a set of similar microorganisms in the same locations. Collectively, this assortment of microorganisms is known as the human microbial flora.

There are three major groups of organisms that are found in the microbial flora. Bacteria are the most dominant, accounting for 85% of the flora. The next group is fungi, and they are mostly found on skin. The last group is comprised of unicellular eukaryotic cells and small multicellular animals. One example is the hair follicle mites, which are microscopic invertebrates that live within hair follicles, such as the eyelash follicles. They feed on the oily secretions of the hair follicles, and some have even been shown to feed on mascara. Humans are not aware of their presence because their minute size allows them to escape the detection of the sensory neurons.

Microorganisms have been living on the surface of multicellular organisms for millions of years, ever since the evolution of multicellular organisms. Multicellular organisms provide shelter and nutritional resources. However, it is important for the microorganisms not to overwhelm the multicellular organisms and cause their demise. Those microorganisms that cause their host serious harm or even death are classified as parasites. The perfect parasites are those that have a commensalistic relationship with their hosts. They do little or no harm to their hosts, and they can pass onto the offspring of the hosts. This is the type of relationship that exists between the normal flora and the human host. Occasionally, commensalistic relationships can turn into a mutualistic relationship as in the case of the rumen bacteria of the mammalian herbivores. We are indeed a part of the complex network of the biological world.

Chapter 22

Energy

What keeps you alive?

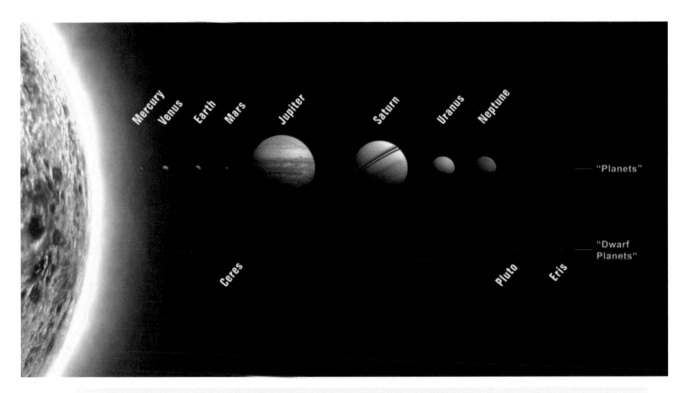

How do we fit into the solar system?

Notice that the size of the sun dwarfs all the planets. The sizes of the planets and dwarf planets are to scale. The relative distance from the sun are not.

(Public Domain)

CHAPTER 22. ENERGY

I. ENERGY AND YOU

I.1. What is your ideal body weight?

Our body weight is important to our self-image for many reasons. Most people feel that their body weight is under their conscious control and that they can manipulate their body weight through dieting. Nevertheless, most dieters know that to dramatically alter one's body weight is difficult. This difficulty has arisen because human body weight is regulated by many genes that control appetite, metabolism, and adipose (fat) tissue formation. The strongest evidence for the role of genes in determining body weight came from studies on 5,000 identical twins. From these studies, it was concluded that childhood obesity has a strong (approximately 80%) genetic component. In addition, the genetic role in obesity was further supported by studies which demonstrated that certain ethnic groups were more prone to obesity than others. The observation that genes are important in determining body weight has led to a hypothesis called the thrifty gene hypothesis. In this hypothesis it is suggested that individuals who live in environments that have fluctuating food availabilities are more likely to survive if they can accumulate greater fat. Unfortunately, this genetic disposition to store fat has led to obesity in those countries that have stable food supplies.

Obese mice
Studies with animal models have provided a better understanding of factors that cause obesity in humans. *(Public Domain)*

Until about 100 years ago, obesity was neither a health nor a social issue. Prior to that time, the food supply was not sufficient to feed the entire population, and famines frequently occurred. Today, even with a robust structure for food security, there are still occasional episodes of famine. However, in affluent societies, such as the United States, there is an overabundance of food, and the result of this overabundance is obesity. The incidence of obesity has gradually increased in the U.S. over the past 50 years and has now become a national health crisis. Furthermore, this increase in obesity has been correlated to a 400% increase in caloric intake over the same time period. One of the main causes for this elevated caloric intake is an increased consumption of energy-dense fast food. From 1977 to 1995, Americans tripled their intake of fast food. Furthermore, with advances in technology, the American population has shifted to a sedentary lifestyle for both work and leisure. In other words, the amount of calories that is spent doing physical activities has markedly decreased.

As obesity was gradually becoming a major health issue, it became important to quantify the changes that were caused by weight gain. To accomplish this, the body mass index (BMI) was used. The body mass index was invented in the 1840s by a Belgian statistician as a simple measure for classifying people's weight relative to an ideal weight for their height. He developed a simple equation in which the individual's body weight is divided by the square of their height. His intention was to make statistical comparisons between different populations. The BMI was rediscovered in the 1970s due to the increase in obesity. Since that time it has been used as a quick measure for deciding whether an individual's weight is appropriate for their height. BMI has become a measure of a person's fatness or thinness, and it is now widely used by the general public. Having a BMI of 18.5 to 25 is considered normal; having a BMI below 18.5 is considered underweight; and having a BMI over 25 is considered overweight. Anyone having a BMI exceeding 30 is considered obese. In the U.S., nearly 33% of individuals have a BMI above 30. Unfortunately, the simplicity of the BMI equation fails to take into consideration the variations in body frame of different ethnic groups. Southeast Asians, for example, who have small body frames, are inaccurately represented by the BMI.

Weight [pounds]

BMI chart

The dashed lines represent subdivisions within a major class. The underweight classification is further divided into severe, moderate, and mild subclasses. *(Public Domain)*

Humans vary in bodyweight in the same manner that they vary in many other traits. Both genetic and behavioral factors contribute to causing obesity. The thrifty gene hypothesis, for example, offers one explanation for why certain ethnic groups are more prone to obesity than others. In the past, having additional energy reserves enhanced the chances for survival. Today however, an excessive accumulation of fatty tissues leads to physical and physiological burdens for the body. Individuals who are obese are predisposed to various diseases, including cardiovascular diseases, type II diabetes, sleep apnea, osteoarthritis, and cancer. Currently, these diseases occur at a high frequency in the U.S.

I.2. *Why does hunger occur?*

To understand how obesity occurs, it is important to study the biological basis of energy metabolism. One cell type that is particularly useful for studying the mechanisms by which a cell uses energy is the neuron. Neurons are the only cells in the human body that need a constant supply of energy. Their energy comes from glucose, a simple sugar. During times when the blood glucose level is too low, a condition known as hypoglycemia, the neurons cease to function. Glucose is important because it is the main molecule that is used for generating energy. All cells have a set of biochemical pathways that break down glucose into water and carbon dioxide. During this process, the cell produces an intermediate energy carrier molecule called ATP, also known as the energy currency. Each cell produces its own ATP, because ATP cannot leave the cell. ATP functions like monetary currency, because it provides energy for all the cellular activities, from DNA synthesis to muscle contraction. To generate the maximum amount of ATP, oxygen must be present to form water, one of the final products. Cells die in the absence of oxygen, because ATP production shuts down.

Humans obtain glucose from their diets, usually in the form of sucrose (sugar) or in starch from plants. When these complex sugars enter the digestive tract, they are converted into glucose by enzymes in the small intestine. After passing through the intestinal wall, glucose enters the blood circulation and is transported to every cell in the body to provide energy. Cells will either use the glucose to produce ATP, or they will convert the excess glucose into glycogen, a polymer of glucose for storage. When the amount of glucose exceeds its cell storage capacity, the excess is picked up by the fat cells that are abundant under the skin. Fat or fatty acids have two important functions. First is their heat insulation property; many animals living in

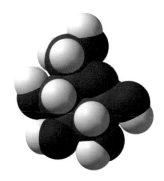

Glucose

It is a simple carbohydrate used as the primary source for energy production.

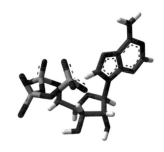

ATP

Adenosine triphosphate is the energy currency of the cell.

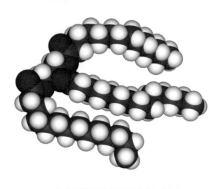

Triglyceride

This is the basic building block for fat and fatty acid.

Hypothalamus

The region of the brain that controls hunger and appetite. *(Public Domain)*

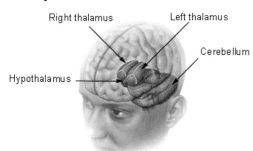

Diencephalon

Right thalamus   Left thalamus

Cerebellum

Hypothalamus

cold climates use a layer of fatty tissues to protect them from the freezing weather. The second function is their property as energy storage molecules. Fat molecules contain more calories per unit weight than any other class of biological molecules. Many migrating animals can store enough fat to provide them with the energy to fly for several hundred miles without eating any food. However, humans put on fat without the need for using it. This process of acquiring extra energy, even though it is not required, is controlled by appetite.

Why do you get hungry? Why do some people have better appetites than others? What controls your appetite? Recent studies have revealed that appetite has a complex control system. When any component of this system fails, a change in appetite results, which then leads to an alteration of body weight. The system involves an interplay between the digestive tract, the fat tissue (also known as adipose tissue), and the brain. Several hormones that are produced by the digestive tract and the adipose tissue are important in regulating appetite. These hormones travel to the brain and bind to receptors in the hypothalamus. The hypothalamus then further communicates with the limbic system and the cerebral cortex. Leptin was the first hormone discovered to suppress appetite. Shortly after, another hormone, ghrelin, was discovered to stimulate appetite. At first, these discoveries suggested the possibility of treating obesity by using these hormones as drugs to control appetite. However, more appetite regulatory hormones were soon discovered, and multiple pathways are now known to be involved in controlling appetite.

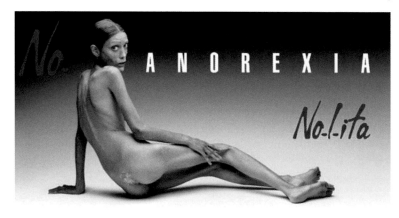

Anorexia nervosa

An anti-anorexia nervosa billboard featuring recovering anorexic actress Isabelle Caro. *(Education Fair Use)*

Some individuals have better appetites than others, and both genetic and environmental factors regulate appetite. Infectious diseases, autoimmune disorders, and cancers often cause a marked decline in appetite, leading to a rapid weight loss. However, the most profound changes in appetite are caused by psychological disorders, such as anorexia nervosa, bulimia nervosa, and binge eating disorder. The treatments for these severe eating disorders involve the use of psychiatric drugs and counseling to treat the anxiety and depression that often underlie these disorders. There are also conditions that result in an increased appetite. There are hereditary forms of obesity that are caused by mutations in the genes for receptors that respond to leptin, ghrelin, and other appetite controlling hormones. Therefore, it is important to understand that both genes and the environment are important for the acquisition of energy.

I.3. How does the body manage energy?

In the early 20th century, it was terrifying when parents learned that their child had diabetes mellitus. Diabetes mellitus is an ancient disease that was first described by a Greek physician nearly 2,000 years ago. The disease was also named the sugar urine disease in ancient China, because of the sweet taste of a patient's urine. The sweetness of the urine can also attract ants, and this was one way to diagnose diabetes in ancient India. The sweetness results because of a dysregulation in glucose uptake. The diagnosis was a death sentence until the 1920s when insulin was discovered to treat the disease. The symptoms of the disease include excessive urine production, constant thirst and fluid intake, weight loss, lethargy, and blurred vision. Before the availability of insulin, diabetic patients experienced a severe and often fatal condition known as diabetic ketoacidosis (DKA). In DKA, the patients experience difficulties in breathing, nausea, vomiting, agitation, confusion, and gradual loss of consciousness. If left untreated, a patient rapidly enters into a coma, and death soon follows. DKA rarely occurs now because most diabetic patients are diagnosed in the early stage of the disease. However, if DKA occurs, it is a medical emergency that requires immediate hospitalization.

Diabetes is nature's experiment to demonstrate the importance of glucose in energy metabolism. In the 1920s, researchers discovered that glucose in the blood is not taken up automatically by cells of the body. Instead, when the blood glucose level becomes high after a meal, the pancreas produces the hormone insulin, which serves as a signal for the body cells to take up glucose. This regulation is important so that a sufficiently high blood glucose level is maintained for the neurons that rely on a constant supply of glucose. The pancreas monitors the blood glucose level, and when it drops below a certain level, it shuts off the production of insulin. In type I diabetes, the insulin-producing cells in the pancreas are gradually destroyed by autoimmunity to the point that no insulin is produced. Without insulin, the glucose levels in the blood remain high because the cells are unable to take it up. In other words, the cells starve even though there is plenty of glucose in the blood. The high sugar concentration in the blood overwhelms the kidney, and the sugar is excreted

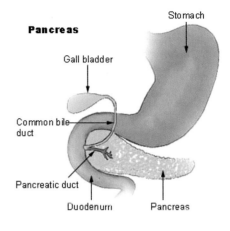

Pancreas

In addition to producing insulin, the pancreas also produces digestive enzymes for the small intestine. *(Public Domain)*

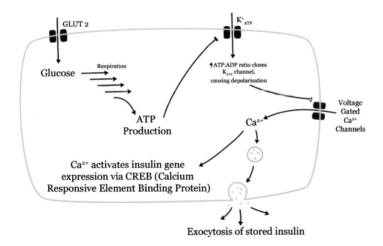

Mechanism of insulin release

Insulin is produced and stored in granules of pancreatic beta cells. It is released when there is a rise in the blood glucose level. *(GNU Free Documentation License)*

into the urine. In many ways, untreated diabetes is akin to starvation amidst an ocean of glucose.

Starvation is the most extreme form of malnutrition that results from a severe or a complete reduction in the intake of energy, nutrients, and vitamins. Without any food, humans can live for about one to two months, depending on fat storage, before permanent organ damage occurs. During starvation, the adipose tissues are the first to be converted into glucose to meet the cell's energy needs. If starvation continues, muscle mass is reduced, because muscle proteins are the next to be converted to glucose. These biochemical processes occur during both starvation and diabetes. In starvation, insulin production ceases because there is no glucose in the blood circulation. This situation forces the cells to utilize all non essential molecules for the production of glucose. This is similar to burning everything inside the house to keep warm when there is a severe fuel shortage. In diabetes, the fuel (glucose) is outside the house, but the inhabitants fail to realize that it is there (no insulin).

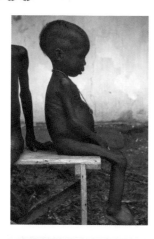

Starvation

A child suffers from severe mulnutrition and hunger.
(Public Domain)

One of the most serious global problems is starvation, even though the news reports on it are rare and infrequent. The Food and Agriculture Organization of the United Nations reported that more than 25,000 people die of starvation every day. Around the world, over 800 million people are chronically undernourished. When starvation becomes widespread, a famine occurs. Most famines are caused by food shortages because of drought, crop failure, pestilence, and man-made causes, such as war or failed economic polices. Famines have claimed nearly 70 million lives during the 20th century. An estimated 30 million people died from starvation during the famine of 1958-1961 in China. For citizens of industrialized nations, famines are a vestige of the distant past. However, in many parts of the world, where agricultural technology is primitive and food reserves are non-existent, a crop failure can put a population in severe danger of famine. Why should this happen in a modern world that has rapid transportation and vast food reserves? The understanding of the flow of energy in the biological world is essential for solving these problems at the global level.

II. Humans in the Ecological Energy Pyramid

Humans depend on the energy of the biological world through the food that they consume. Without the diversity of other living organisms, humans would cease to exist. This provides the strongest evidence that humans are an integral part of the ecosystem and are only one of the many threads that form the complex web of life.

II.1. What is the biological basis of the human diet?

Across the world, there are many different cuisines, from French to Indonesian. How do these cuisines, or cooking styles, differ from each other? How different are the diets between humans who lived 100,000 years ago and 21st century humans?

Chinese barbeque

Roast ducks and chicken hang in a shop window. *(Public Domain)*

Answers to these questions can help us understand how to formulate a diet that is suitable for modern society and its life style.

Despite the great differences in food preparation and cooking styles across the world, there is an amazing consistency in food preference of humans from different cultures. Sugar, for example, is universally preferred, and high carbohydrate foods, such as bread and rice, are staples for all human populations. Furthermore, food that is high in fat content is also a favorite in every culture. The reason why humans crave sweet and fatty food can be explained from an evolutionary standpoint. It is no coincidence that glucose is sweet and desirable for human taste, because energy production begins with glucose. Therefore, having a "sweet tooth" propels humans to seek food that provides energy. In fact, all animals have a predilection toward sweetness. Even though potatoes, rice, and breads are not sweet, they consist of complex carbohydrates, which can be converted to glucose. Therefore, we have a craving for them as well. Fat is the best energy source for biological organisms, and consuming fat provides a high energy supply. In summary, humans like sugar and fat, because they provide the energy that is necessary for survival. Both complex carbohydrates and fat are readily converted to glucose, which is the central molecule

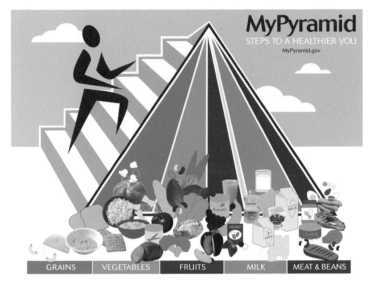

Food guide pyramid

This is the latest food pyramid recommended by the USDA.
(Public Domain)

for generating ATP. Therefore, it is not surprising that sugar and fat appeal strongly to human tastes.

Humans like to eat meat as well, although it does not appear that meat is essential in their diet. Vegetarians lead healthy lives without eating meat. Why do humans like to eat meat? Other great apes, such as the orangutans, gorillas, and chimpanzees, consume a diet very low in meat. The reason that humans have a desire for meat has an evolutionary root. When early humans left the forest for savanna living, they started to supplement their vegetarian diet with meat. The reason for this comes from a need to acquire all the necessary amino acids. There are 20 amino acids that are required for protein synthesis; human cells can synthesize 11 of the amino cells from precursor molecules. The other nine amino acids, also known as the essential amino acids, must come from dietary sources. Vegetation alone does not provide a sufficient quantity of the essential amino acids. Therefore, humans have a craving for meat, which is protein rich, to acquire these amino acids. Most vegetarians pay close attention to the possibility of protein deficiency, which is a cause of serious malnutrition. To prevent this, they supplement their diet with beans, which are high in protein.

The biochemical processes in the body that require vitamins also have a deep evolutionary root. Some of the biochemical reactions cannot proceed solely with enzymes; they need some additional "helper" molecules, known as vitamins. The best known example is vitamin C. The deficiency of vitamin C was first discovered by those who took long sea voyages and had no access to citrus food. Sailors who had no vitamin C often died. Vitamin C is critical for many biochemical reactions because it serves as a co-factor to assist the enzymes in carrying out their functions. Most organisms can synthesize the vitamins that they need, but humans and some other primates have lost this ability and therefore rely on dietary sources. In humans, vitamin C deficiency causes scurvy, a deadly disease that causes the breakdown of mucous membranes and skin. Humans must obtain 13 vitamins in their diet. Vitamin deficiencies lead to serious and often deadly diseases. Until the modern era, humans had consumed a broad spectrum of food, which included all the necessary vitamins. Their diet included primarily plants, with an occasional protein supplement from meat. Human diets have changed significantly from our evolutionary past and

Vitamins

Fruits are an excellent source of vitamins. *(Public Domain)*

have become more restricted in variety. Today, vitamin supplements have become essential for achieving a balanced diet.

There are many ways to achieve a balanced diet, and research has provided a better understanding of our nutritional needs. However, it is important to understand that the social and technological changes take place much faster than evolutionary changes. Human's requirements are still based on the hunter-gatherer life style, and humans have yet to evolve the digestive and physiological systems for consumption of the modern diet (i.e., regular fast food consumption). This is an important area of research: the design of a modern diet for the prehistorically-evolved human body.

II.2. *Why are there different animal diets?*

Why does the human diet contain both vegetation and meat? Why do some animals subsist entirely on vegetation, whereas other animals eat only meat? Why are the meat eaters rare, whereas the plant eaters are abundant? These questions have led to the formation of the ecological energy pyramid. The human species is a member of this pyramid.

Humans are omnivores, because the human diet includes both vegetation and meat. However, most other animals have highly specific dietary requirements. Among the great apes, the orangutans are the most strict plant eaters. The gorillas are the next most strict plant eaters, and the chimpanzees are less strict. By studying the evolutionary history and the modern daily habits of animals, researchers have concluded that environment and food availabilities were important to dietary development. The omnivores most likely evolved in environments that had unstable but varied food resources. Some of the most successful wildlife organisms, such as the rats, foxes, raccoons, and opossums, are omnivorous in the wild. Their ability to eat a wide variety of food allows them to make easy transitions into urban settings, where they can feed on human refuse. The human species is one of the most omnivorous species because of the hunter-gatherer lifestyle that was lived first in the savanna and later in northern regions of the world during the ice age.

The animal world is dominated by herbivores, both large and small. Their dominance is exemplified by the millions of wildebeests, gazelles, buffaloes, and zebras that graze on the Serengeti during the annual breeding season. However, the real force of the herbivores is the insects. The immense biological diversity in the tropical rainforest has resulted from the availability of food for the insect herbivores. The abundance of plants provides an endless feast for animals, as long as they can digest the plant materials and withstand the toxic chemicals that are produced by the plants. To digest plant fibers, most animals have established mutualistic relationships with microorganisms (these organisms have specialized enzymes that can digest rough plant material). The spread and growth of the herbivore species is a testimony of their success. However, the continuing evolution of plant defenses maintains a balance between the animals and plants. Herbivores were most likely the first animals to leave the sea and adapt to terrestrial life. However, in time, some herbivores evolved into carnivores that prey on herbivores.

In comparison to the herbivores, carnivores are significantly fewer in number. On the Serengeti savanna, spotting a pride of lions, a leopard, or a cheetah is far more difficult than spotting the wildebeests, zebras, or gazelles. To explain why the prey significantly outnumber the predators, the ecological pyramid of productivity was developed. In this pyramid, the plants are located at the broad base and serve as the foundation of the system. The plants are known as the producers, because they create the organic matter that is consumed by the herbivores, which are also known as the primary consumers. The herbivores then serve as the organic matter for the carnivores, which are also known as the secondary consumers. Some of these carnivores, however, serve as prey for other carnivores, which are known as

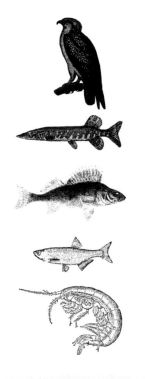

Food chain

The number of individuals is lower at each higher trophic level in the food chain. *(GNU Free Documentation License)*

the tertiary consumers. This pyramid also describes how energy flows through the ecosystem, and each level of the pyramid is known as a trophic level. The pyramidal shape of the system reflects the idea that in order for the ecosystem to sustain itself, there must be more energy at lower trophic levels than there is at the higher trophic levels.

All animal diets have evolved through the selective pressure of the environment. The abundance of an animal species is directly related to its trophic level. In other words, species that are located on the lower trophic levels are more abundant. This has resulted because from one trophic level to the next there is a ten-fold difference in energy content. For example, it requires ten units of plant energy to make one equivalent unit of animal energy. Consequently, in the pyramid of productivity, every trophic level is 10% the size of the previous level (100, 10, 1, 0.1, 0.01, 0.001, etc). Therefore, the diet of an animal is reflective of its position in the ecosystem.

II.3. How do plants produce energy?

Every day, the earth receives energy from the sun, and the energy is absorbed as heat. At night, this heat radiates into space. Without the biochemical "talents" of the plants, none of the sun's energy could be captured for biological use, and no life would have ever existed. How do plants capture energy from the sun? How does this energy flow through the ecological system? What happens to this energy at the end? Answers to these questions provide an appreciation of how humans fit into the ecosystem.

Leaf harvesting solar energy

Plants convert solar energy into chemical energy in the form of organic molecules. *(Public Domain)*

It is well-known that plants use photosynthesis to capture the sun's energy. The ingredients for photosynthesis are simple: water and carbon dioxide, both of which are abundant in the environment. The main product of photosynthesis is glucose, and its main byproduct is oxygen. In plants, the glucose that is produced is immediately used by the cells to generate ATP, which is then used to provide the energy for all the cellular processes. The process of photosynthesis occurs in two simple steps. In the first step, plants use a dark pigment (chlorophyll) to absorb energy. This energy is used to split water into hydrogen and oxygen atoms. In the second step, the free hydrogen atoms are joined with carbon dioxide to form glucose. The principle of photosynthesis is simple, but the chemistry is complex. Researchers have yet to be successful in duplicating this process. The application of this knowledge would allow for the production of renewable energy in the future.

Not all plant growth requires fertilization. Plants growing in the tropical rainforest have no need for fertilizers. Fertilization is only required for human agriculture. However, understanding the principle of fertilization provides insight into the biological process of plant growth. Fertilizers do not provide plants with energy or even building materials, because 98% of the biomass of the plant comes from water and carbon dioxide. However, plants need nitrogen for synthesizing amino acids and phosphorus for synthesizing nucleic acids. Together, nitrogen and phosphorous

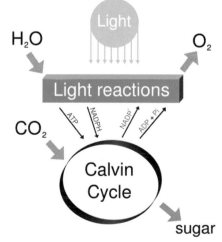

Photosynthesis

Light, water, and carbon dioxide are all that are required for creating biological energy. *(GNU Free Documentation License)*

contribute less than 1.5% to the plant's biomass. In a natural habitat, plants absorb various chemical forms of nitrogen and phosphorous which have been left by dead vegetation, microorganisms, and animals. In human agriculture, the intensive farming depletes the nitrogen and phosphorous reserves in the soil. Because of this, farmers could not grow a good crop without regularly fertilizing the fields. The development and application of chemical fertilizers were responsible for the Green Revolution around the world. Consequently, many previously impoverished land areas have become productive.

In addition to producing energy for the entire biological world, photosynthesis has transformed Earth's atmosphere by making life possible. Researchers have now accurately determined that the earth was formed 4.55 billion years ago based on radiometric dating. Fossil records have suggested that during the first billion years, Earth either supported very primitive life or no life at all. In time, simple prokaryotic cells evolved and existed in the bottom of the ocean by drawing energy from undersea volcanic activity. About 2.5 billion years ago, a group of blue-green bacteria, known as cyanobacteria, started to inhabit the surface of the ocean and evolve into the first photosynthetic organisms. These tiny microorganisms began a transformation of the world that made it possible for complex animals, including humans, to evolve. Over the next two billion years, the cyanobacteria released oxygen as a byproduct of their photosynthesis. This raised the oxygen concentration from 0% to 21% by 550 million years ago. The elevated atmospheric oxygen allowed animals to have a higher metabolic rate. Higher animals would not have evolved without this change in Earth's atmosphere.

The existence of life on Earth is based on the utilization of solar energy. Our individual existence can be traced back to 3.6 billion years of evolution that created the complex biochemical processes that allowed plants to store energy as glucose. Life on Earth is unified by these biochemical processes which harvest energy from the sun. Today, in addition to extracting energy from glucose, humans use another form of biological energy that is buried deep below the earth: the fossil fuels.

Cyanobacteria
The most primitive photosynthetic organisms. *(Public Domain)*

III. ENERGY IN THE PHYSICAL WORLD

In the 20th century, physics, chemistry, and biology have joined forces in the study of energy. Physicists have split the atom and have discovered that a vast amount of energy is released from this process. Chemists have discovered the chemical process that is involved in combustion and have revealed the chemical changes in molecules that are responsible for energy release. Biologists have uncovered the secret of how biological organisms derive energy from organic molecules. By the mid-20th century, a synthesis of these three forms of energy has provided a complete picture of how humans fit into the physical world.

III.1. What is the chemical basis of biological energy?

Do you know how your body converts the food that you consume into physical action? Do you know how food keeps your body warm? Have you ever considered the connection between wood burning in the fireplace and your energy metabolism? It was not until the 1780s when the link between combustion and biological energy metabolism was discovered. These findings were instrumental to the understanding that biological energy is nothing more than an extension of physical energy.

When the first humans learned how to control fire, the phenomenon must have seemed magical to them. The ability to master fire was one of the most important milestones in human evolution. Over nearly 1.2 million years, humans had pondered the mystery of fire. In the 18th century, several chemists observed that oxygen is required for keeping an animal alive as well as for keeping a fire alight. Later studies discovered that the products of burning wood and of animal respiration are the same: water and carbon dioxide. Since both wood and glucose are carbohydrates, the chemical processes of burning wood and animal respiration must be the same. Chemists discovered that burning wood is a chemical process, in which the hydrogen in the carbohydrate is joined with oxygen to form water. The carbon is then released as carbon dioxide. It is the chemical reaction between hydrogen and oxygen that produces the heat and light energy in wood burning, a process also known as

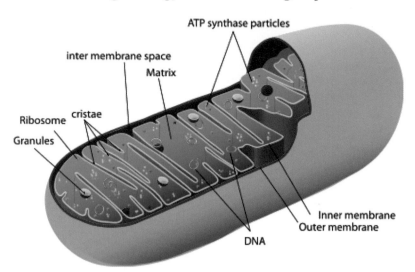

Mitochondrion

This is the organelle where hydrogen is joined with oxygen to form water with the release of energy to make ATP. *(Public Domain)*

combustion.

Respiration consists of the same chemical reaction as wood combustion, except that it occurs slowly. Imagine combustion as Niagara Falls, where water falls from a great height creating the splashing and thunderous roar. Respiration is like the Hoover Dam, where water falls in a more controlled manner. In respiration, cellular enzymes control the interaction between oxygen and the hydrogen that is extracted from glucose. Through a series of intricate biochemical processes, the same amount of energy that would have been instantaneously released is used to synthesize ATP. A total of 36 ATP is produced by one molecule of glucose, and on average, our cells produce thousands of ATP per second. In photosynthesis, solar energy is used to split water into oxygen and hydrogen; hydrogen is then joined with carbon dioxide to form carbohydrates. Respiration, however, is the reverse of photosynthesis.

Every time you enjoy your favorite beer, you are drinking a form of biofuel. Ethanol is produced by yeasts and some other microorganisms in a process known as fermentation. In the absence of oxygen, glucose is converted by yeast to ethanol to generate only two molecules of ATP, an amount of energy that is barely able to support the yeast. Ethanol is rich in energy, and because of this property, it can be used as an automobile fuel. Biofuel is the name given to the ethanol fuel that is produced by fermentation. To develop self-reliance in energy production, the U.S. government has invested billions in research projects to develop biofuels.

III.2. *What are the alternatives to fossil fuels?*

Fossil fuels are vital to modern society, and their role in fueling the industrial complex is central to today's world. The worldwide use of fossil fuels in 2005 accounted for 86% of the primary energy use. The remaining percentage of energy use was from non-fossil fuel sources. These include hydroelectric (6.3%), nuclear (6%), and other (geothermal, solar, wind, wood, and waste - 0.9%). With recent oil prices at over $100 per barrel, many countries are looking for alternative energy sources. However, this effort has not been easy because of economical, political and scientific reasons.

Fossil fuels, such as coal, have been used as energy sources by humans since prehistoric times. Fossil fuels range from volatile gas, such as methane, to liquid petroleum, to solid coal. There are two theories for the formation of fossil fuels. The first theory is known as the biogenic theory. In this theory, it was proposed that all fossil fuels are formed from the fossilized remains of dead planktons, plants, and animals that had been subjected to heat and pressure in Earth's crust for hundreds of millions of years. The second theory is known as the abiogenic theory. This theory proposes that more volatile materials, such as natural gas, were formed by volcanic activities. The most sought after fossil fuel is petroleum, which is formed by plankton remains that have settled in sea or lake bottoms and have been buried under heavy layers of sediment. In time, these buried materials are transformed into petroleum because of high levels of heat and pressure. Large quantities of plankton materials are needed for the production of fossil fuels. For example, 23.5 metric tons are required to yield 1 liter of gasoline. The current use of fossil fuels is immensely faster than their formation, making fossil fuels a non-renewable resource.

Modern society depends heavily on petroleum, and all current modes of transportation would be severely affected without petroleum. Is it possible to replace petroleum with a fuel that is simple to produce and creates no pollution? Biofuel is a potential candidate, but it is complicated to create. Furthermore, it causes pollution by releasing carbon dioxide into the atmosphere in the same way as fossil fuels do. Recently, another alternative fuel source has been suggested. Interestingly, this energy source is derived from the same process that living organisms use to generate energy (i.e., joining hydrogen with oxygen to form water). This energy source is called the hydrogen fuel cell. In a process that is almost identical to the cellular process of producing energy, the hydrogen fuel cell creates electrical energy by controlling the interaction between hydrogen and oxygen to form water. Instead of producing ATP, hydrogen fuel cells create electricity that can be used for powering various vehicles. Since the product of the reaction is water, pollution is not a concern. However, the fuel cells rely on the splitting of water into hydrogen and oxygen by electricity, a process that is currently expensive to perform. Currently, the production of hydrogen fuels is economically infeasible.

Since its formation 4.55 billion years ago, the sun has released enormous amounts of energy. The ultimate solution for solving the energy crisis on Earth is to harness solar energy. Cyanobacteria have harnessed energy from the sun by photosynthesis for billions of years. Researchers are confident that technology similar to this process will be developed in the foreseeable future to create hydrogen fuel. From a human standpoint, the energy that the sun creates is beyond comprehension. The temperature on the surface of the sun is nearly 6,000°C, and the temperature in the core of the sun is 13,000,000°C. Hydrogen is also the source of the sun's energy, but it is produced in an entirely different way. Instead of generating energy by combining with oxygen to form water, the hydrogen atoms in the sun undergo nuclear fusion to form helium. The power of nuclear fusion was also evident in the development of the hydrogen bomb.

The discovery of petroleum has been a major impetus in the industrialization of western societies. As other countries around world begin their industrial development, the depletion of this non-renewable resource poses a major threat to global stability. However, these problems may be solved with the development of hydrogen fuel and ultimately, the development of nuclear fusion.

III.3. Why does the sun have infinite energy?

The sun is the giver of life, and it dominates every aspect of life on Earth. We often take it for granted and forget about its central role in the biological world. To understand your place in the physical world, some understanding of the physical and chemical properties of the sun is essential.

Our sun is one of several billion stars in the Milky Way galaxy. It was formed about 4.57 billion years ago, which is less than half of the age of our galaxy. It is known as a second generation star, because it was formed from the remnants of

Hydrogen fuel cell

In this fuel cell, hydrogen combines with oxygen to form water and energy. It is based on the same principle as the mitochondrion.
(Public Domain)

dead stars. The formation of the sun is based on the nebular hypothesis. In this hypothesis, it is proposed that after the death of a star, its remains form a massive luminous cloud known as the nebula. Astronomers have used the Orion Nebula as an example for such a stellar cloud. As the gravitational force pulls the molecular cloud together, they first form plasma, which eventually collapses to form a star.

The Milky Way galaxy

Our sun is one of 20 billion stars in the Milky Way galaxy. *(Public Domain)*

Albert Einstein

His memorial located outside the U.S. National Academy of Sciences, Washington, D.C. *(Public Domain)*

A star contains only hydrogen atoms, and as the gravitational force squeezes the hydrogen atoms together, nuclear fusion is started in the core of the star.

Until the 20th century, the source of the sun's energy was a mystery. Without the knowledge of atomic energy, most observers believed that the sun's energy was derived from combustion. By the 19th century, however, many scientists recognized that the sun puts out far more energy than what could be explained by combustion. The mystery was solved in 1905 when Albert Einstein derived his famous equation of $E=mc^2$. One of the ramifications of this equation is that mass can be converted to energy. This equation predicted that if hydrogen is converted into helium, a tiny amount of mass can be transformed into a prodigious amount of energy (billion times greater than combustion). The difference is that during the combustion of wood, the atoms are rearranged, but the nature of the atoms remains unchanged. Hydrogen remains hydrogen, and it binds with oxygen to form water. During the nuclear fusion that occurs in the sun's core, hydrogen atoms are fused together to form helium, an entirely different element. During this process, a small amount of matter is converted into energy.

All stars have a life cycle. Our sun is in the mid-stage of its life cycle, and it is predicted that it will remain relatively the same for the next five billion years. Currently, the sun still has abundant fuel; it is composed of 74% hydrogen, 25% helium, and 1% of other elements. This hydrogen fuel will sustain the sun's fusion reactor for another 4.5 billion years. Once the hydrogen fuel drops below a certain level, the nuclear activities in the core will accelerate and cause the sun to expand dramatically, increasing its size as much as five fold. At this point, the sun will turn bright red and be called a red giant, and life on Earth will end. The sun will then collapse when its gravitational pull exceeds the expansion force. The collapse will

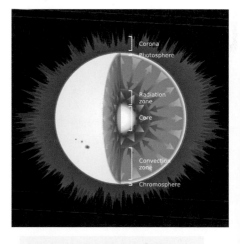

Internal structure of the sun

The sun is a nuclear thermal reactor, fusing hydrogen into helium. *(Public Domain)*

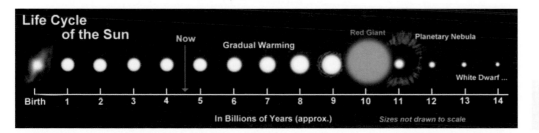

Life cycle of the sun

Sizes are not drawn to scale. *(Public Domain)*

result in the sun becoming a white dwarf, and its size will decrease to one tenth of its current size.

It is remarkable that the human species has gained this knowledge about the sun, the giver of life in our solar system. However, life probably began in the bottom of the ocean relying on the energy from the center of the earth. Recently, researchers in deep sea diving vehicles have discovered thriving communities of life on the ocean floor in total darkness. These discoveries suggest that life did not rise from the surface of the earth with energy from the sun. Nevertheless, it is through the energy of the sun that the diversity of life has evolved in the last 3.6 billion years. Humans are only one of the members of this long chain of beings, but we are the only species that has discovered the process.

Our existence relies on energy, and when a living organism is no longer extracting energy from the environment, its life comes to an end. Energy is mysterious, and it is often difficult to explain. The unification of energy provides important insights into human's place in the physical world, and this knowledge has both practical and philosophical significance in developing our worldview.

Chapter 23

Water

Why do you need water to survive?

Will we ever run out of water?
With the abundance of water, as seen in this photo of Niagara Falls, it seems that we will never run out of water.

(Creative Commons Attribution)

CHAPTER 23. WATER

Even though water is critical to sustain our lives, we often take it for granted. Do you know why water is essential for your survival? Do you know how water keeps your body functioning normally? How can severe dehydration kill a person in less than a few hours? Do you know that you can be poisoned by water? This information is important to your personal well-being, but there are also other ways in which water is important to our society and to the entire biological world.

I. WATER AND YOU

Humans cannot survive without water for more than two to three days. Why do humans need water for survival? How much water do they need? What are the causes of dehydration? The answers to these questions can provide insights into the biochemical and physiological significance of water.

I.1. What is dehydration?

The study of dehydration has provided an understanding of the role of water in various biological processes. Dehydration is a medical condition that results when the volume of water in the body is insufficient for normal functioning. Dehydration is caused by environmental factors or diseases. The severity of the dehydration, however, depends on how quickly the fluid balance is restored. Dehydration is often associated with electrolyte imbalances, such as abnormalities in sodium, potassium, and chloride. If the dehydration becomes severe enough, many of the body's organs fail.

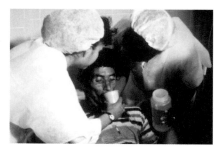

Oral rehydration
Nurses encourage a patient with cholera to drink an oral rehydration solution for his dehydration condition. *(Public Domain)*

The many causes of dehydration are divided into three broad categories: 1) external or stress-related causes, 2) infectious diseases, and 3) malnutrition. One of the most common causes of dehydration is prolonged exposure to dry air. Anyone who has taken a long flight from the U.S. to Europe or Asia has experienced this type of dehydration. Another common cause of dehydration is prolonged physical activity that occurs without drinking adequate water. Physical trauma that results in a large amount of blood loss can also cause dehydration. Infectious diseases are also among the main causes of dehydration. Cholera, a gastrointestinal disease that is caused by the bacterium *Vibrio cholerae*, is a common worldwide cause of severe dehydration. The cholera bacteria infect the small intestine and produces the cholera toxin. This toxin then quickly causes a large fluid loss across the intestinal wall. The result is massive diarrhea. From the first onset of symptoms, an infected person can progress to death in as short as four hours.

Dehydration occurs in several stages, ranging from mild to severe. The symptoms of dehydration are first noticeable at 2% volume loss in body fluid. At this low level of dehydration, a person feels thirst and has other symptoms such as irritability, flushing, elevated heart rate, loss of appetite, dry skin, and elevated body temperature. By about 5%-6% volume loss in body fluid, individuals experience headaches, visual disorientation, dizziness, and fainting when standing up. In addition, the urine output ceases, and in infants, seizures and a sunken fontanel can occur. With a loss of 10%-15% of body fluid, muscles spasm, skin shrivels, vision dims, and delirium sets in. Death occurs when the fluid loss is greater than 15%. An example of how severe dehydration can cause death was seen in a man who was hiking in Death Valley. The temperature that day reached 120°F, and at this temperature, the body loses up to 3 quarts of water every hour. This hiker needed at least four gallons of water. He carried with him, however, far too little water. When he was discovered dead less then a half mile from his vehicle, his skin had been completely parched, his face had been mummified, and his body weight had been reduced by half.

Water is lost from the body through three main routes: 1) escaping from the lungs as water vapor, 2) evaporating from the skin as sweat, and 3) excretion from the kidneys as urine. Under sedentary conditions, a person loses approximately 2.5 to 5 liters of water a day. One easy method by which to monitor a person's hydration level is by observing the color of the urine. A normally-hydrated person excretes a full bladder of clear urine every three to five hours. In contrast, if someone excretes darkly colored urine every 7-8 hours, then they are in a state of dehydration. To reverse mild dehydration, all that is needed is for that person to drink water. However, if a person is involved in extreme physical activities that cause excessive fluid loss, it is preferable for them to have a sports drink or a commercial rehydration fluid.

Death Valley

The heat in Death Valley poses a great danger of dehydration. *(Public Domain)*

I.2. Why can you not survive without water?

The human body essentially exists in an aquatic environment. Although we live a terrestrial life, the human body is composed of 60%-70% water. All our body cells can function solely in an aqueous environment because all cellular activities can only proceed in the presence of water. Furthermore, this high percentage of body water is shared by many other organisms, such as plants, which are made up of 90% water, and jellyfish, which are composed of nearly 98% water.

Water is considered the universal solvent because it can dissolve many types of molecules. This property allows us to use water to clean almost anything. In fact, we would find it difficult to clean most things without water. The ability to dissolve different molecules also makes water useful for allowing molecular interactions to occur that would not otherwise be possible. For example, adding sugar and lemon juice to a glass of ice tea allows for a new mixture of chemicals. Furthermore, chemical reactions can take place by adding reactants together in the presence of water to produce new products. In addition, cellular chemical reactions are only possible when water is present. Photosynthesis, for example, requires water to produce the hydrogen and oxygen that is used for forming glucose. In fact, all the basic chemical processes take place in water.

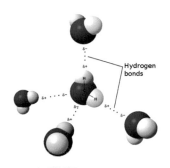

Chemical structure of water

Water molecules form weak hydrogen bonds with each other. (*Creative Commons Attribution*)

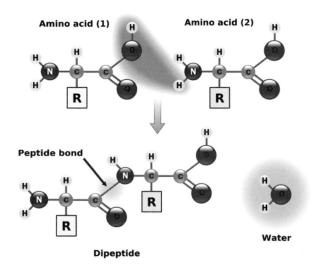

Water in biochemical reactions

Water takes part in all biochemical reactions, including synthesis and degradation. (*Creative Commons Attribution*)

The human body maintains a proper balance between the uptake and the excretion of water. This function occurs in the kidneys, which are also responsible for maintaining a constant chemical composition of the body fluid. The kidneys function by acting as a filtration system which removes waste products from the blood circulation, combines them with water, and secretes them as urine. When kidneys fail, water accumulates in the body, leading to high blood pressure and a generalized swelling of the body. In addition to regulating body water content, the kidneys also excrete nitrogenous waste products in the form of urea and removes excess electrolytes. Imbalances of electrolytes in the blood and in the tissue fluid often lead to serious heath problems.

Even though we must drink water to survive, it is possible to drink too much water. Several years ago, some individuals died after drinking excessive amounts of water during a water drinking contest. These individuals consumed up to ten liters of water in a course of just a few minutes. In addition, it is possible to consume too much water after a long bout of intensive exercise, especially if the electrolytes are not replenished. The condition in which too much water is consumed is known as water intoxication. In this condition, the blood electrolyte levels are rapidly decreased beyond a safe limit by the drinking of an excessive amount of water. Under normal conditions, we do not drink an unsafe amount of water because of hormonal and neurological mechanisms.

I.3. When is water safe to drink?

Will the human population run out of water? This seems unlikely especially when considering that water covers 71% of Earth's surface. However, most of the water cannot be used by humans because 97% of the water consists of sea water, and 2.4% of the water is locked in glaciers and in polar ice caps. In other words, only 0.6% of the water is available to humans and to other terrestrial organisms. Because of our expanding population, we are already experiencing problems with shortages in the supply of freshwater. In addition, there are many concerns regarding the pollution of our drinking water.

Availability of water

Ocean water accounts for 97% of all water on Earth. Polar ice caps lock up another 2.4% of Earth's water. Only 0.6% of water is available to terrestrial organisms. (*Creative Commons Attribution*)

Water that is contaminated with microorganisms is a great threat to human health. In the past, water-borne epidemics were common around the world. The incidence of these diseases has been decreased because of improvements in sanitation. One of the most serious water-borne infectious diseases is cholera. Even though epidemics of cholera have markedly decreased, it can still pose a serious threat, especially when sewage systems break down. The causative agent of cholera is *Vibrio cholerae*. This bacteria produces a powerful toxin that induces a massive fluid loss in the intestines, which leads to acute and uncontrollable diarrhea. The resulting diarrhea rapidly causes severe dehydration that almost inevitably results in death. Without proper treatment of the infected excrement, the bacteria can contaminate the water supply. A contaminated water supply can also occur during times of major natural disasters, such hurricanes and earthquakes. After these events, the urban infrastructure often breaks down, a situation that can lead to contaminated water supplies. Therefore, securing a safe water supply is critical during any major natural disaster. One of the highest priorities after the 2004 Indian Ocean earthquake was to provide safe drinking water in the afflicted areas around the world.

Water pollution poses a serious danger to the population on a continuous basis. Because of the use of large quantities of agricultural herbicides and pesticides, the water supplies in some areas are polluted to the level that causes serious health hazards. The effect of this water pollution is not yet clearly known, but the results from some studies have indicated that there have already been some serious consequences. During the early 2000s, for example, a series of studies were conducted to determine the incidence of male infertility around the country.

Water pollution
Sewage and industrial wastes have threatened water supplies around the world, causing public health problems. *(Public Domain)*

The initial intent was to determine what effect air quality has on male sperm quality. Samples were collected from large cities and from rural areas around the country to make appropriate comparisons. Researchers were surprised to find a low sperm quality in men living in rural agricultural areas. The cause was traced to the drinking water, which had been polluted by a cornucopia of agricultural chemicals. Water pollution also results from depositing industrial wastes in landfills. These chemicals gradually decompose and become present in the groundwater that provides the major source of water for many parts of the countries.

The incidents of water contamination and pollution have reduced the trust that the general public has in their drinking water supply. Many city and rural residents complain about the bad taste of their water, and many are concerned about the potential health hazards. Safe drinking water is also known as potable water, and in many parts of the world, potable water is not available. According to the World Health Organization (WHO) nearly one in six people living on Earth does not have access to potable water. Instead, these people are drinking contaminated water and face serious threats of water-borne infectious diseases. In many parts of the world, water must be boiled before it is safe for drinking. The main cause of contaminated water is the lack of basic sanitation and sewage treatment facilities. Many poor countries lack the resources and infrastructures to provide these basic public health measures.

There currently exists a serious worldwide water crisis that could lead to great economic and political instabilities. In the future, it is conceivable that nations could wage war for water. Even in the U.S., there are disagreements regarding water supply. In North America, there is a continuing dispute over the water flow through the Colorado River. Because the flow of the river is diverted for agricultural irrigation in California, water is no longer reliably reaching areas in Mexico, leading to an agricultural decline in that area. Such man-made river diversions have occurred around the world as new irrigation engineering projects have been developed. One of the most extreme examples is the diversion of rivers that flow into the Aral Sea, once the world's fourth largest lake in Central Asia. By 2004, the Aral Sea had shrunk to 25% of its original size.

II. Water in the Biological World

II.1. How does life thrive in the ocean?

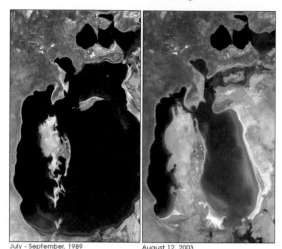

July - September, 1989   August 12, 2003

Aral Sea

The Aral Sea has shrunk dramatically due to the diversion of water for irrigation.

After Earth was formed about 4.55 billion years ago, its surface was completely inhabitable because of numerous meteor bombardments. In fact, at one point, the surface of Earth was completely molten and consisted of a huge lava ocean with temperatures as high as 5,000°C. In time, the surface of Earth gradually cooled, and a watery world was formed during the next 100 million years. Today, researchers have unequivocal evidence that life originated in this watery world (oceans). Furthermore, the colonization of land did not occur until nearly three billion years later. Why was the ocean so hospitable for living organisms over this long time period?

By examining the compositions of body fluids, researchers have traced the origin of all terrestrial plants and animals back to the ocean. Both the cell cytoplasm of all biological organisms and the ocean consist of a sodium chloride (table salt) solution. This similarity between the cellular and the ocean environments suggests that early life originated in the ocean. Even after migrating to a terrestrial environment, the land plants and animals have still retained their sodium chloride cellular environment. In seawater, however, the sodium chloride concentration is 3.5%, whereas the sodium chloride concentration inside living cells is 0.9%. This difference suggests that the sodium chloride concentration in seawater gradually accumulated over billions of years after the formation of life. The source of the sodium chloride in the ocean is thought to have come from the weathering process of terrestrial rocks. The salts from the rocks were most likely transported to the ocean by rivers and streams.

Formation of new ocean floor

New ocean floor is forming continuously, resulting in the formation of hydrothermal vents.
(*Creative Commons Attribution*)

The ocean is not static because the positions of the continents and the oceans undergo continual changes. The ocean floor is composed of giant geological plates that ride on top of the semi-molten upper mantle. The ocean floor undergoes movement, which forces the geological plates to interact with each other. These interactions destroy the old ocean floor and create a new one. Occasionally, these interactions cause violent earthquakes that create huge tsunamis. In the 1980s, deep sea research submarines reached an area where two geological plates come into contact. At these contact points, it was observed that hot lava pours out from the junctions forming overheated water and producing methane gas. These laval structures are known as deep sea hydrothermal vents. In these vents, researchers were surprised to find thriving biological communities consisting of many different species. The foundation of this community is bacteria that are capable of extracting energy from methane. From the bacteria, an ecological energy pyramid is created resulting in a diverse community. These observations indicate that life can exist without sunlight and that life most likely first began in this environment at the bottom of the sea.

During the first several hundred million years after Earth's creation, life most likely remained at the bottom of the ocean. Meteorites continued to bombard the surface, creating an extreme climate. In comparison to Earth's surface, the ocean floor was far more hospitable for life. By about one billion years after Earth's formation, the solar system became more stabilized as the planets settled into their orbits. Around this time, some of the simple prokaryotic cells ventured near the surface of the ocean and discovered that the sun could function as another source of energy. These cells then evolved the ability to capture the sun's energy in a process now known as photosynthesis. These organisms were the ancestors of the modern photosynthetic bacteria known as cyanobacteria. These simple organisms evolved to have a green color because this color works best in an aquatic environment. The cyanobateria eventually evolved into unicellular eukaryotic organisms, which later became the blue-green algae, the dominant form of aquatic multicellular photosynthetic organisms.

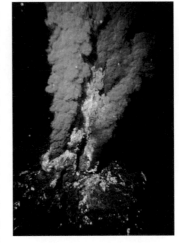

Hydrothermal vents
Also known as the black smoker. *(Public Domain)*

The migration of living organisms from an aquatic environment to a terrestrial one began about 500 million years ago. The evolution of plants was the first step of this migration. Some primitive plant-like organisms discovered that there were advantages to living in the terrestrial environment. In this environment, there was a greater intensity of solar radiation and less competition for space and nutrients. The first group of land plants was simple, including the ancestors of green algae, ferns, and mosses. They were small and were restricted to habitats that had high humidity and moisture. These plants can still be found in tropical rainforests, but they are rare. Nearly 50 million years after the plants started to live on land, animals started to evolve and to adapt to terrestrial life.

Tube worms
Located at the base of a black smoker. *(Public Domain)*

II.2. How does life adapt to land?

There were numerous challenges to living on land, but the most significant was how to acquire oxygen from the environment. Aquatic organisms used the oxygen that was dissolved in the water. Unicellular and simple multicellular organisms acquired their oxygen by diffusing it directly across the cell membrane from the surrounding solution into the cytoplasm. Complex aquatic organisms evolved specialized structures, such as gills, to absorb oxygen. However, none of these processes were sufficient for the terrestrial organisms to use. Instead, specialized organs, such as the lungs, were evolved.

In the lungs, large aqueous surface areas are exposed to air, and to prevent drying, this surface is constantly bathed with mucous secretions. Oxygen is then dissolved in the mucous fluid and transported.

Lungfish
They are freshwater fish that possess primitive lungs to breathe air. *(GNU Free Documentation License)*

Water is also used for controlling body temperature. The mechanism by which water is used to accomplish this varies depending on the animal species. Some Australian kangaroos, for example, use water to keep cool during the hot days. The water the kangaroos use is in the form of their own saliva. The animals apply their saliva to a patch of bare skin on their forearms. This saliva is then evaporated and, in doing so, cools the body. Humans also use the evaporation of water to keep cool, but in this case, the water is in the form of sweat. For both forms of evaporation, the

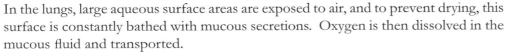

faster the evaporation, the greater the cooling effect. This is why fans are effective in keeping a body cooler. The moving air that is caused by a fan results in quicker evaporation.

Giant sequoia

It is major mechanical challenge to bring water up to the top of the tree, which can be as high as 300 ft above ground level. *(GNU Free Documentation License)*

The management of water is particularly important for plants, because plants must acquire sufficient water to use for photosynthesis. Plants also face another problem of transporting the water to the leaves, which are usually located on the top of the plants. Some of the tallest trees in the world, such as the giant sequoias, can reach a height of 300 ft, nearly as tall as a 30-story building. To transport water to such heights requires an amazing engineering feat. To accomplish this, plants have evolved a water transportation mechanism, known as transpiration, which utilizes a transport tissue known as xylem. Xylems are long tubular structures that connect the leaves on the top of the trees to the roots in the soil. Water is pulled up from the soil to the leaves by evaporation through the stomata, which are pores in the leaves. The amount of water that evaporates from a fully grown tree, such as a maple, is as much as several hundred gallons a day. Only a small fraction of the water, however, is actually used for photosynthesis; the rest of the water (over 90%) is used solely for transpiration.

Interestingly, during evolution some land mammals returned to the ocean, and because of the buoyancy of water, became the largest animals that have ever lived on Earth. These animals include the dolphins, whales, and porpoises. The closest relatives of the whales are the hippos. These two species shared a common ancestor before they diverged from each other about 50 million years ago. The ancestors of the whales entered the water and evolved a fish-like body with fins and flukes. However, the whales and the other sea mammals have retained many of their terrestrial adaptations. The most notable example is the inability of whales to breathe in water because they lack gills. Instead, they use lungs that are similar in structure to terrestrial mammals. The dolphins, whales, and porpoises also have intelligence that is comparable to the primates. The dolphins are highly social, and by passing the mirror test, they appear to have self-awareness. The return of the mammals to the sea is one of the most impressive examples of how natural selection can lead to the evolution of some remarkable creatures.

Humpback whale

Humpback whales are mammals that returned back to the sea. They do not have gills and must breathe air with their lungs. *(Creative Commons Attribution)*

II.3. How does life survive in extreme conditions?

Cactus

They adapt to desert climates by storing water in their stems and roots. *(Public Domain)*

The Sahara desert and Death Valley provide reminders that there are places on Earth that are inhabitable for humans. However, many plants and animals make the deserts their homes. Cacti provide an example of how life can solve the problem of water shortage by developing adaptive structures. To prevent water loss in a hot and dry climate, cacti have lost most of their leaves or have reduced them to needles. For photosynthesis, the cacti use their stems, which have been coated with a waxy substance to prevent water loss. For their existence in a dry and hot climate, the cacti have developed many mechanisms by which to store, conserve, and absorb water. Cacti, however, cannot grow in a completely dry environment because they still need water for photosynthesis and for carrying out crucial biochemical processes. In most of the habitats where cacti live there are less than ten inches of rainfall per year. In addition, in many desert areas, the rainfall comes suddenly and is often limited to once or twice each year. To maximize their water storage capacity, cacti have developed succulent stems for water storage. Immediately after a rain, a cactus can absorb up to 3,000 liters of water within a few days.

Another extreme environment where life has been observed is in one of the deepest mines in the world. In this mine, researchers have discovered unusual microorganisms that live inside minute water pockets inside volcanic rocks. Some of these rocks are buried up to two miles beneath Earth's surface. The microorganisms that were found in these rocks belong to a group of bacteria known as the archeabacteria. When researchers first found these organisms, it was discovered that these bacteria are killed by exposure to oxygen. In addition, when the rocks containing the bacteria were dated, it was observed that some of the bacteria were over several thousand years old. Researchers, however, were unsure as to how the bacteria became trapped in the rocks. From further studies, it was determined that these bacteria use methane gas that is found in the rocks for growth. Furthermore, it was discovered that the bacteria divide only once every 1,000 years, making them the slowest growing biological organisms. The discovery of these rock-loving bacteria provides further evidence for the diversity and complexity of life as long as there is water.

For many years, scientists believed that life could only survive in a very narrow range of physical conditions. This is certainly true for humans, and our experience has informed us that without the aid of technology, we could not survive for any length of time in temperatures beyond our normal comfort zone. However, recent discoveries of living organisms in the hydrothermal vents indicate that as long as there is water, living organisms can live in temperatures as high as 121°C, a temperature that is higher than the boiling point of water on Earth's surface. These organisms are known as hyperthermophiles, meaning the love of high temperature. In addition, organisms have also been found thriving at the bottom of the ocean, an area that is under immense pressure. Yet another extreme environment where organisms have been found is in the Antarctica ice core as deep as two miles below the surface. Under the heavy layers of ice, researchers have discovered lakes, such as Lake Vostok, where microorganisms, known as psychrophiles, thrive in the near freezing temperatures.

In addition to extreme temperatures and pressures, there are other inhospitable environments that can support life, as long as there is a source of energy and water. About ten years ago, researchers discovered caves in Mexico that contained large

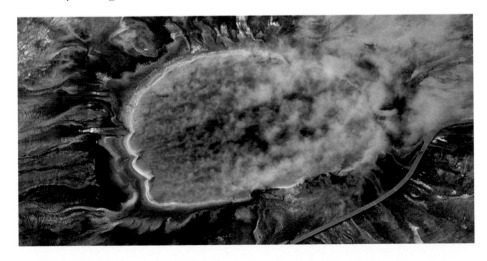

Thermophiles
A type of extremophile; they are responsible for producing the bright colors of the Grand Prismatic Spring, Yellowstone National Park. *(Public Domain)*

amounts of sulfuric acid. The sulfuric acid in these caves had been formed from hydrogen sulfide (which had leaked in from deep fissures within the earth's crust) and water. To the researchers' great surprise, they found life within these caves. The life that was discovered consisted of microorganisms that can utilize hydrogen sulfide as an energy source. These microorganisms are also known as acidophiles, because they have developed a tolerance for acidic environments. There are other organisms that have adapted to live in other extreme conditions, such as alkaline conditions and high salt conditions. Collectively, the organisms that can thrive in extreme environments are known as extremophiles. They belong to a group of prokaryotic cells known as archeabacteria.

Acidophiles
A new group of extremophiles was discovered in acid mine drainage.
(Public Domain)

It has become clear that the two most important requirements for life are energy and water. From the studies of extremophiles, researchers have gained a new appreciation that the conditions for life are not limited to Earth's surface. This recognition further confirms the narrow range of human existence and our place in the biological world. We live in a far more complex ecosystem than we have ever realized.

III. Water in the Physical World

III.1. *What is the water cycle?*

In addition to its critical role in biological organisms, water is also vital in shaping Earth's physical environment. Without water, Earth would be a very different place. Water is a remarkable molecule that has unique physical and chemical properties. Water, for example, is the only molecule on Earth that exists in all three of its chemical forms: steam, water, and ice. In addition, water has the second highest capacity to absorb heat, second only to ammonia. It also has a high index of heat of vaporization. These two properties allow water to moderate Earth's temperature by preventing large temperature fluctuations between day and night and between the various seasons. Because of the ability of water to change its chemical forms in Earth's environment, water is continuously recycled through the physical world. Everyday, water is evaporated by heat along the equator as well as through the transpiration of trees. This water enters the atmosphere as water vapor. When this vapor comes into contact with small particulate matter, it condenses around the matter to form clouds. Eventually, the droplets enlarge, and the water returns to the earth as rain. This process provides a natural system of water purification for supplying fresh water.

All living organisms are part of the continuous cycle of water, even though life occupies only a small portion of the water cycle. Without this cycle, life would not be possible on Earth. Water first enters the biological system through photosynthesis, which uses water as a source to generate hydrogen for the construction of glucose. However, only freshwater can support plant growth on land. Therefore, the water cycle that generates rain water is vital for life to survive on land. To complete the biological cycle, water is formed during respiration, which essentially reverses the chemical reaction of photosynthesis. This role of water makes it essential to the energy metabolism of living organisms.

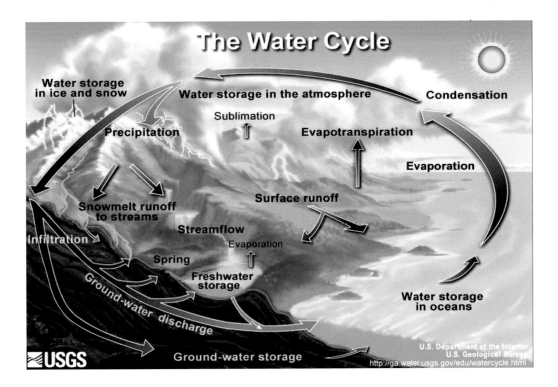

Water cycle

The water cycle plays a critical role in providing freshwater for living organisms and maintaining a stable climate on Earth. *(Public Domain)*

The influence of water on the biological world is also affected by the global climate. The heat absorbing capacity of water, for example, has profound effects on temperatures around the world. The differences in temperatures between ocean waters create ocean currents, which are akin to great rivers of hot and cold water flowing around the world. These ocean currents are caused by many factors, such as the rotation of the earth, wind, temperature and salinity differences, and gravitational forces of the moon. One of the great ocean currents is the Gulf Stream, which is a powerful, warm, and swift Atlantic ocean current that originates in the Gulf of Mexico. The Gulf Stream brings warm water to the East Coast of the United States and all the way to Northern Europe. The weather in both these areas would be much cooler without this important "river" of ocean current. There are over 20 major ocean currents around the world, with the water bringing either warm or cold temperatures to these regions.

Across the world, the ocean water temperature has had a profound impact on the global climate. However, its greatest impact is on life in the ocean. One area where the ocean temperature is vital for the biological diversity in the ocean is the tropical coral reefs. These reefs are akin to tropical rainforests in both the quantity of living organisms that are found and in the large number of species. The coral reefs are immense structures that are built from the calcium carbonate skeletons of corals. They are generally found in shallow, tropical marine waters. The corals provide shelter to an extraordinary number of species, from fish to microorganisms. The corals are filter-feeding organisms which capture microscopic plankton during the night. The varied colors of the corals that are observed are the result of a mutualistic relationship between the corals and the photosynthetic algae that live inside the coral. This symbiotic co-existence is critical for the entire ecosystem of the coral reefs. Unfortunately, above normal temperatures that have been caused by global warming and by abnormal ocean current flows have led to the destruction of nearly 70% of the world's coral reefs.

III.2. *How did the earth get its water?*

The history of Earth was determined using radiometric dating. This technique relies on the atomic decay of radioactive elements; for example, some forms of the element uranium lose energy and gradually transform into the element lead. This process is known as radioactive decay, and it occurs in a constant rate akin to the flow of sand in an hour glass. By measuring the ratio between the original element (e.g., uranium) and the daughter element, the age of a rock is determined. After nearly 100 years of development, researchers have perfected the techniques for determining the age of rocks and can now date rocks at a high degree of accuracy. Using radiometric dating, geologists have determined the age of rocks that are associated with the time when water first appeared on Earth. From this information, it has been concluded that as soon as the primordial Earth began to cool, water started to accumulate on its surface. However, where did the water come from?

Mount Cleveland, Alaska
Volcanic eruption photographed from the International Space Station. *(Public Domain)*

One possible source for Earth's water was the violent volcanic activity that occurred on the primordial Earth. In the middle of Earth is the core, which is made up of a solid inner core of iron and nickel that is surrounded by an outer core of liquefied lighter elements. The inner core has a temperature of over 6,000°C, as hot as the sun's surface. Earth's core is surrounded by the mantle, which is a highly viscous layer that is situated directly under the crust. Earth's crust is composed of a set of rocky plates (also known as tectonic plates) that undergoes constant destruction and renewal. At the borders of the plates, materials from the mantle emerge in the form of volcanic activity. A phenomenon known as outgassing is responsible for the emission of gases, such as water vapor, carbon dioxide, and ammonia, from the mantle. It is possible that these gases replaced Earth's original atmosphere of helium and hydrogen. As Earth continued to cool, the steam from the volcanoes condensed into rain and began to blanket Earth's surface with water.

Over 71% of Earth's surface is covered with water, with more than half of this area over 3,000 meters deep. Many researchers doubt that the volcanic activity could alone account for the entire provision of water on Earth. Instead, many scientists have suggested that Earth's water might have been delivered by an extraterrestrial source: comets. Comets are comprised of primarily ice, frozen gases (carbon dioxide, methane, and ammonia), rock, and dust. There have been over 3,500 comets reported as of January 2008, and new comets are continuingly being recorded. It has been estimated that there are over one trillion comets in the solar system. Also, it has

Comet
Comets could be responsible for bringing water to the primordial Earth. *(Public Domain)*

been suggested that the number of comets was much greater during the early stages of the solar system. Therefore, it is possible that millions of comets collided with Earth during the first 500 million years after its formation. Because the tails of these comets would have contained vast amounts of ice, it is likely that comets significantly contributed to the formation of Earth's oceans.

Another factor that was important for the formation of an aqueous environment on

Earth was the atmosphere. The atmosphere was important because it maintained temperatures on Earth that were conducive for liquid water. The temperate conditions that are necessary for an aqueous environment depend on the protection by the atmosphere. Earth is shielded from abrupt temperature changes by greenhouse gases, such as water vapor, carbon dioxide, and methane. These gases allow the UV light to pass through the atmosphere to heat up Earth's surface. In addition, these gases also prevent the release of the absorbed heat back into the atmosphere, leading to cooler temperatures. However, geologists have discovered evidence suggesting that about 850 to 630 million years ago, the entire surface of Earth was shrouded in ice, with the equator as frigid as Antarctica. This period is known as the Snowball Earth, or the Cryogenian geological period. Researchers have suggested that the cause of Snowball Earth was the extensive absorption of carbon dioxide and water by the continental rocks. In other words, the greenhouses gases that could have caused the warming of Earth were trapped on its surface. This cold period most likely abruptly ended when extensive volcanic activity resulted in the release of large quantities of greenhouse gases.

The accumulation of water on the surface of Earth began with volcanic activities and was further assisted by comets. This watery world was the most important ingredient for life to evolve. Why do none of the other planets in the solar system contain liquid water? What is special about Earth?

III.3. Why is Earth the only planet with liquid water?

Hydrogen is the most abundant element in the universe, and helium is the next. Helium is formed in the sun by the nuclear fusion of hydrogen molecules. Together, these elements account for over 98% of all the elements in the universe. The third most abundant element is oxygen, which is created in the sun by the nuclear fusion of helium. Oxygen readily reacts with hydrogen to form water, and there is evidence that water was common during the early formation of the solar system. However, many planets in the solar system are either too hot or too cold for the existence of liquid water. Therefore, it is predicted that water on the other planets exists as a gas or as a solid. Since liquid water is essential for life, the finding of liquid water on the other planets of the solar system would be a strong indication of the existence of life on these planets. However, only Earth has liquid water.

None of the planets in the solar system other than Earth have been shown to harbor liquid water. Mercury has extreme surface temperatures, ranging from -180° to 430°C from the equator to the poles. Venus has a surface temperature of 461°C, making it the hottest place in the solar system. Mars has high temperature fluctuations with a daytime temperature of -5°C and a -87°C nighttime temperature. For the gas giants (Jupiter, Mars, Uranus, and Neptune) that are farther away from the sun, their mean temperatures range from -100 °C to -250°C, which are far too cold for the existence of liquid water. Earth, however, is located at the ideal distance from the sun for the existence of liquid water. Researchers have identified this region as the circumstellar habitable zone. Within this region, Earth receives sufficient sunlight to prevent the water from freezing but is not too hot that liquid water is evaporated to form water vapor.

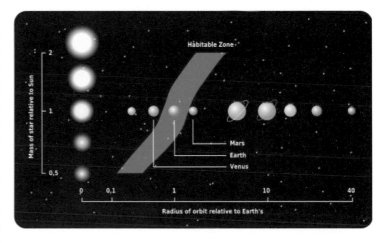

Circumstellar habitable zone

In this zone, the temperature is appropriate for liquid water to exist.
(GNU Free Documentation License)

The search for liquid water on Mars has been one of the most important space exploration objectives, because such a discovery would offer strong evidence for the existence of life on Mars. Many Mars exploration missions have been devoted to the search for liquid water. The latest mission was the twin Mars exploration rovers, Spirit and Opportunity. Even though there is an absence of liquid water on Mars, geological evidence has suggested that Mars had liquid water in its past. Geological surveys and mapping of the Mars' surface have discovered geological features that resemble river valleys, dried river beds, ocean floors, and deserts. Furthermore, Mars has polar ice caps which are similar to the polar ice caps on Earth. In addition, the Mars twin rovers have sent back convincing evidence of sedimentary rock formations. These formations are only made in the presence of water. In August 2007, the Phoenix Spacecraft was launched to land on one of the polar regions of Mars with the goal to study the geologic history of water on Mars and to examine the events that led to past climate changes.

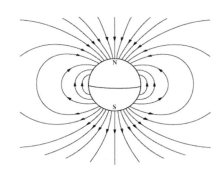

The magnetosphere

It protects Earth's atmosphere from the solar wind. *(Public Domain)*

The terrestrial planets

Mercury, Venus, Earth, and Mars. *(Public Domain)*

The evidence that Mars was once covered with liquid water is very strong, and the conditions that led to the loss of water on Mars have been gradually resolved. The primary cause was the lack of an atmosphere on Mars. Without an atmosphere, the Martian surface has large temperature fluctuations that cause the evaporation of liquid water. Researchers have also suggested that the Mars atmosphere was destroyed by solar wind, which is a stream of charged particles (electrons and protons) that is ejected from the upper atmosphere of the sun. Earth is also subjected to the damaging power of the solar wind, which is responsible for knocking out power grids and for triggering the Northern Lights (auroras). However, Earth's atmosphere is protected by the magnetic field (known as the magnetosphere) that is generated by the rotation of Earth's inner core. This rotation is possible because Earth's outer core remains molten, allowing the inner core to rotate to generate a magnetic field. This magnetic field deflects the solar wind and establishes the polarity of the poles. It has been proposed that Mars once had a similar magnetic field that protected its atmosphere. However, because Mars has only one tenth the mass of Earth, its core dissipated its heat, became solid, and Mars lost its protective magnetosphere. Without it, the solar wind stripped away most of its atmosphere, leaving it 100 times thinner than Earth's. Without an adequate atmosphere, Mars became waterless.

In summary, our existence relies on the water of the planet. The presence of water was also critical for life to evolve. However, there is far more than just knowing that we need water to survive, because an understanding of the origin and distribution of water on Earth will help each one of us gain an appreciation of our individual connection to the physical world.

Chapter 24

Carbon

What is your chemical makeup?

How do carbon atoms make both humans and diamonds?

Carbon is one of the most versatile elements. Carbon atoms join with hydrogen and oxygen atoms to form all the diversity of life on Earth.

(GNU Free Documentation License)

CHAPTER 24. CARBON

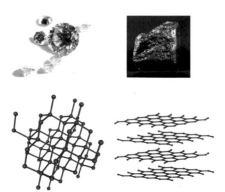

Diamond versus graphite

They are pure forms of the same element but differ in structure.
(*Creative Commons Attribution*)

Life on Earth is both simple and complex. It is simple because only four elements (hydrogen, oxygen, carbon, and nitrogen) account for 97%-99% of the matter in all biological organisms. It is complex, because from these four elements, living organisms can create several hundred thousand different molecules, with some being extraordinarily complex. These molecules, known as the organic molecules, are unique to living organisms. In other words, the organic molecules represent the signature of life. The central part of any organic molecule is the carbon atom. Carbon is the most remarkable atom because of its ability to form highly complex molecules in living organisms. Furthermore, carbon is returned to the physical world after an organism dies as the simple molecule, carbon dioxide. This carbon cycle is one of the most important cycles of nature.

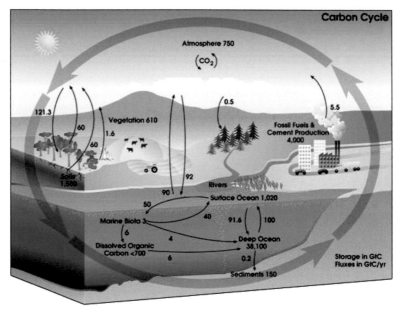

Carbon cycle

The carbon cycle involves both the biotic and abiotic pathways. (*Public Domain*)

I. LIFE AND DEATH

I.1. *What is life?*

Life and death are intertwined. To understand death, it is necessary to understand the property of life, and how death takes over when life comes to a halt. Humans are mystified by death, and only in the last several decades has human death been understood from the biological standpoint. This knowledge has provided an appreciation of how humans are part of the biological world, where life and death is the natural cycle of existence.

Carbon monoxide

With only one carbon atom and one oxygen atom, it is a poison with a very simple structure.

Life requires energy to survive. The energy is provided by the breakdown of glucose in the presence of oxygen to produce ATP, carbon dioxide, and water. ATP is a source of energy that is used by the cells to perform every cellular function. When there is a block in energy production, life processes stop, and the cells start to die. There are many steps along the energy pathway, and a blockage at any one can result in cellular death. Two examples of how death results from stopping energy production are asphyxiation (lack of oxygen) and carbon monoxide poisoning. One of the most striking examples of how the lack of oxygen can lead to a quick death is when the air supply is cut off, as in the cases of suffocation and drowning. Carbon monoxide poisoning occurs in about 40,000 people each year in the U.S. Nearly half of all fatal poisonings are caused by carbon monoxide. Sadly, more than 2,000 people commit suicide by intentionally poisoning themselves with carbon monoxide. Prior to the development of the modern catalytic converter, car exhausts contained high levels of carbon monoxide. The carbon monoxide in modern cars has been reduced by 99%; this has eliminated both intentional and unintentional carbon monoxide poisoning by automobile exhaust fumes.

The mechanism by which carbon monoxide is toxic is a good example to demonstrate that the human body is a complex machine that relies on the workings of intricate components. Carbon monoxide poisons by interfering with oxygen transportation. To transport oxygen to different parts of the body, the body produces the molecular transporter, hemoglobin. This molecular transporter is an engineering marvel: it binds and releases oxygen as part of its transport function. It can sense where oxygen is needed and release it with exquisite accuracy. Hemoglobin is a protein that has several thousand atoms, which are built on a carbon backbone, to form a self-running nano-machine. However, hemoglobin can be fooled by carbon monoxide, which acts as a competitor of oxygen. When hemoglobin binds with carbon monoxide, it loses the ability to bind oxygen. Without the service of the hemoglobin to transport oxygen, glucose cannot be metabolized and ATP cannot be produced. This is similar to cutting off gas to an engine.

In 1978, 913 people, including 287 children, were poisoned in a murder-suicide that had been orchestrated by the cult leader Jim Jones. This occurred in Jonestown, a short-lived settlement in northwestern Guyana that had been developed by the Peoples Temple, a cult from California. They were given a grape Flavor Aid that had been laced with cyanide, a simple molecule that consists of one nitrogen atom and one carbon atom. Victims of cyanide poisoning develop headaches and lose consciousness within minutes. They also usually die within two hours if no medical attention is provided. Cyanide also occurs in a gaseous form as hydrogen cyanide. Immediately upon inhalation, hydrogen cyanide gas causes seizures, cardiac arrest, and comas; death follows within a few minutes. During the Holocaust in the Second World War, the German SS used hydrogen cyanide to exterminate nearly one million innocent people.

Jonestown murder-suicide
The bucket in the picture contained grape Flavor Aid that was laced with cyanide. *(Education Fair Use)*

The toxic effect of cyanide provides another example of how the human body functions as a machine, with proteins forming the molecular components. ATP production is like the functioning of a hydroelectric dam and hydrogen (extracted from glucose) is like the water that flows through the dam. The water flows through the dam and turns the generators to produce electricity. Imagine that one of the generators is not working, preventing the flow of the water. Without water flow, there is a shut down in electricity production. A similar scenario is seen in ATP production: hydrogen drives the protein molecules to produce ATP. In cyanide poisoning, one of the ATP-producing molecules is jammed by the cyanide and stops the flow of the hydrogen, resulting in a shut down of the entire system. The ATP-producing protein behaves in the same manner as the electric generators in the hydroelectric plant. From these examples, it is clear that life depends on these small nano-machines to perform complex chemical reactions in extracting energy from glucose and to perform other complex tasks. What makes these biological nano-machines so effective?

I.2. How do organisms stay alive?

Life's nano-machines are largely built on four elements: carbon, hydrogen, oxygen, and a small amount of nitrogen. These nano-machines are proteins, a class of biological molecules that has an enormous amount of variation. Proteins are built from 20 different amino acids. The 20 amino acids join together in long chains to form different proteins based on the order of the amino acids and their lengths. The process is similar to the making of different sentences by joining different words in different orders. However, one major difference is that the length of proteins can be much longer than the length of sentences. The longest sentence is not likely to exceed 100 words, but the longest protein contains over ten thousand amino acids. Also, different proteins perform different functions in the same way as different sentences convey different meanings. What is the function of these different proteins? How do they perform their tasks? How do their structures allow them to carry out their functions?

Carbon makes proteins and other biological molecules successful. Without carbon, complex biological molecules could not be formed, and life would not exist. Carbon is central to the structure of proteins, because carbon's physical properties allow for the formation of four chemical bonds, allowing it to join with four different atoms. Like the hubs of a Tinkertoy, carbon atoms can join with multiple atoms to form highly complex molecules. Generally, the carbon atoms form the backbone and reside in the center of the molecules. On the outside of the molecules are hydrogen, oxygen, and nitrogen. The entire protein molecule can also be folded into a three-dimensional structure to assume different shapes, ranging from a rod-like shape to a globular shape. In addition, the individual protein molecules can aggregate with each other to form more complex structures, such as muscle fibers, hair strands, bones, and eye lenses. Furthermore, any change in the sequences of the amino acids can lead to a change in the three-dimensional structure of the protein. How do such changes affect the function of the protein?

Each protein molecule contains a unique structure that is specific for its function. The protein molecules can also bind and interact with other molecules in performing their functions. The muscle proteins are excellent examples of how the structures of proteins fulfill their functions. There are two muscle proteins (actin and myosin) that are involved in muscle contraction. Each protein joins together to form a fiber structure: actin forms actin fibers, and myosin forms myosin fibers. The alignment of these two fibers in the muscle cells is important for muscle contraction. When the muscle cells receive a signal from the neurons for muscle contraction, the myosin fiber is activated by ATP to pull back on the actin fiber, leading to muscle contraction. With millions of these units acting in concert, the muscle carries out its function on demand. Inside each of the body cells, there are millions of these protein nano-machines performing various functions, such as DNA replication, protein synthesis, secretion, mobility, and many others. The basic functions of proteins are known, but researchers are still searching for the reason why millions of different proteins can work in synchrony.

Each cell is a complex machine with different components constructed from many protein nano-machines. These machines draw their energy from ATP molecules that are produced by the metabolism of glucose. The ATP molecules supply energy to other nano-protein machines to carry out their functions. The entire cell operates in a seamless and orderly fashion without any external control. This type of self-organizing system is also found in the eusocial insects when the entire colony behaves as a super-organism. One goal of nanotechnology is to construct nano-machines that resemble the biological nano-machines. The long-term goal is to create nano-machines that can be used to work with the natural biological nano-machines to treat conditions such as diabetes, cancer, neurological injuries, joint diseases, and many other chronic diseases. These man-made nano-machines are likely to be carbon based and share many similarities with the biological nano-machines. In the near future, it will be possible to build and use biological-based components to supplement and enhance human body functions. These developments will have a major impact on medicine and healthcare.

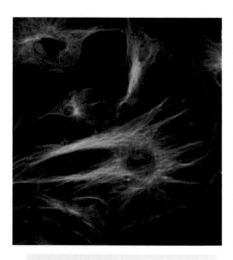

A cell as an intricate machine

Internal cellular structures are stained with special dyes to demonstrate their relationships to each other. *(Public Domain)*

I.3. Why do cells die?

Cells are the basic units of life, and each cell operates independently regarding its ability to acquire nutrients, synthesize biological molecules, metabolize energy, and export waste. However, cells in multicellular organisms must also work together. Cells are complex biological machines that contain many different protein nano-machines, which also must work in a coordinated and organized fashion. Cells evolved over 3.6 billion years ago to adapt to environmental changes and to survive in their biological niches. They are highly sophisticated, self-organizing entities, and researchers have only begun to understand the working of various cellular components. Cells also face many hazards in their microenvironments, and they have evolved many sophisticated mechanisms to manage any external or internal problems. However, all cells eventually die; there are many possible causes for their deaths. In multicellular organisms, cells are constantly dying and are being replaced. There are two ways that cells die: necrosis and programmed cell death. Understanding these two mechanisms will help us to appreciate the biological basis of death.

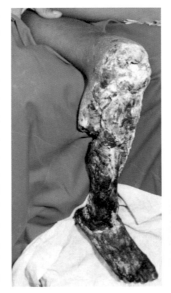

Cells can be injured by many different agents that can also cause cell death. Some of the most common causes of cell injury include oxygen deprivation, physical injury, chemical injury, inflammation, and infection. Some cells are more sensitive to certain types of injuries than others. For example, neurons are extremely sensitive to oxygen deprivation; cell death generally occurs within five minutes after the oxygen supply is cut off. In contrast, skin cells can survive without oxygen for up to an hour. Necrosis is usually caused by physical, chemical, or physiological disturbances of the normal function of the cells. Researchers have discovered that cells actively react to these damages. They begin by increasing the uptake of fluid, leading to swelling. As the cells gradually lose control of cellular functions, they start to release digestive enzymes that are normally sequestered in the lysosomes (specialized membrane bound granules filled with degradative enzymes). In addition to destroying the internal structure of the dying cells, these enzymes also cause damage to the neighboring cells. The most serious form of necrosis can result from the improper care of a wound or from the production of toxins by microorganisms in a gangrenous wound.

Necrosis

The victim was an 11-year-old boy who was bitten by a pitviper and was not properly treated. (*Creative Commons Attribution*)

Until twenty years ago, it was not realized that there is another form of cell death that is different from necrosis. This cell death does not result from the type of cellular damages that cause necrosis. Instead, this cell death is triggered by an internal program known as apoptosis. In contrast to necrosis, apoptosis takes place in a highly coordinated fashion with minimum disturbance to the neighboring cells. Why does a cell die through a self-induced destruction? The answer came from studies on the development of tadpoles, which go from tailed swimmers to tailless amphibians. Researchers discovered that when a tadpole is ready to develop into a frog, a set of special proteins are released into the appropriate region to trigger apoptosis of those cells. The resulting cell death in the tail region causes the cellular structures to become reorganized and reabsorbed into the body. Therefore, apoptosis benefits multicellular organisms by shaping the body structure during development. In humans, the formation of fingers and toes is the result of apoptosis in previously uninterrupted cellular regions, such as the tissue cells between the fingers.

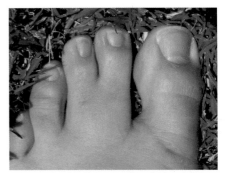

Importance of apoptosis

When apoptosis failed to occur properly during development, the two toes were not properly separated. (*GNU Free Documentation License*)

The two types of cell death, necrosis and apoptosis, have provided interesting insights into the life spans of living organisms. Life span is defined as the maximal

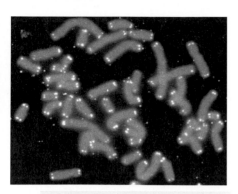

Telomere

Human chromosomes capped by telomeres at each end. *(Public Domain)*

length that members of a species can live. Species have different life spans; the human life span is very different from the life span of a mouse. Why do such differences exist, and what determines the life span of a species? The difference is related to the life history of the species, such as when sexual maturity is reached and when reproduction occurs. The controlling factor for life span is clearly genetic. In humans, longevity is a trait that has strong heritability. Researchers have discovered that apoptosis (programmed cell death) is related to the life span of a species. They found that the ability of cells to divide is linked to a region, known as the telomere, which is located at the end of the chromosome. This region becomes shorter after each cell division, and at a certain point when the telomere is exhausted, the cell dies from apoptosis. The life span of different species might be genetically controlled by apoptosis. It is now clear that cell death is a complex phenomenon, and how long an organism lives is related to genetically-determined factors as well as environmental factors.

II. END OF LIFE

II.1. *What is death?*

Death has historically been associated with the loss of the pulse and the stoppage of the beating heart. Stories abound in the 19th and the early 20th centuries that some people who were considered dead somehow "came back to life" days later in their coffins. With the development of CPR and prompt defibrillation, cardiac arrest is no longer an adequate definition of death, as patients are now routinely "brought back to life" after the heart ceases to beat for various lengths of time. In some conditions, such as electrocution, CPR for up to an hour can bring a "dead" person to life, apparently allowing the stunned nerves to recover. Another example is the returning to life of "dead" individuals who have been submerged under icy water for up to an hour. Their recovery is partially possible because of a remarkable physiological phenomenon known as the mammalian diving reflex, an adaptation that humans share with sea mammals. Upon exposure to a cold and oxygen-scarce environment, the body automatically shuts down most metabolic activities. With minimum energy requirements, the neurons can survive for up to 30 minutes without any significant damage. From these observations and others it can be concluded that the end of a human life is a complicated process, depending on many factors.

Dying is a slow and gradual process that begins with the breakdown of the cell's internal nano-machines, the proteins that are responsible for energy metabolism, biochemical synthesis, and other cellular functions. From the biological standpoint, death is not complete until every cell in the body is dead. The speed of cell death varies for different types of cells and tissues, and their rate of death is directly related to their rate of metabolism. Cells such as neurons and heart muscle cells have the highest metabolic rate and therefore, have the greatest demands for glucose and oxygen. They are first to die when the oxygen supply is cut off. When the oxygen supply drops below a certain threshold, the cells respond by triggering the biochemical steps for apoptosis, or programmed cell death. This is why dying tissues do not exhibit the extensive tissue damage that is evident in necrosis. Some cells types, such as the skin cells and intestinal mucosal cells, can survive for as long as 24 hours without oxygen. Therefore, for your favorite pet, it is possible to retrieve viable cells from the body even 12 hours after its death and use those cells to clone another pet. Because of this differential process of cell death, the human body does not lose all its heat until 24 hours after death.

Near death experiences have been reported by individuals who have lost consciousness due to a severe head injury, drowning, or heart attack. They report remarkable experiences of visual images, out-of-body sensations, and deep spiritual revelations. The descriptions of their experiences are consistent and often include traveling at high speeds in a tunnel toward a brilliantly illuminated opening. Some describe their entire life experience as zooming past in front of them. Others describe the sensation of floating outside and looking at their own bodies. Interestingly, the same experiences are described by fighter pilots during their training in human centrifuges. These are devices that help fighter pilots and astronauts acclimate to the high g-forces that occur during high-speed acceleration. At g-forces greater than eight, untrained individuals will experience blurred vision followed by the loss of consciousness. This is due to the gradual reduction of blood flow to the brain, as the g-force pushes the blood toward the peripheral of the body. These pilots describe the same sensation of traveling toward a lighted tunnel and a feeling of blissfulness just prior to the loss of consciousness. Based on these observations, researchers have suggested that the reduction of oxygen to the visual cortex is likely responsible for the visual tunneling and that the production of endorphins contributes to the euphoric sensations that are felt prior to brain death.

Near death experience
Visual perception of traveling down a tunnel toward a bright light.
(Public Domain)

Brain death of the cerebral cortex does not provide an adequate medical definition of death. An individual can still maintain nearly all organ functions at the physiological level as long as the brainstem remains viable. Because of this, the criteria for death must include the death of the brainstem. In most cases, the brain is the first part of the body to die. Many of the other organs, however, remain viable for as long as two hours, which allows the organs to be removed for transplantation. Organs such as the heart, liver, and kidneys can be kept viable in cold temperatures and protective solutions long enough for flights across the country. Over the next 24 hours after death, the body passes through the following stages of clinical signs: 1) pallor mortis: paleness, which occurs almost instantaneously due to the cessation of cardiac output; 2) algor mortis: the reduction in body temperature until matching that of the ambient temperature, usually taking more than 24 hours; 3) rigor mortis: the muscles become stiff making the limbs difficult to move or manipulate; 4) livor mortis: a settling of the blood in the lower portion of the body; and 5) decomposition.

II.2. How does the body decompose?

The understanding of biological decomposition was partially obtained by studying how humans have prevented decomposition. Over the centuries, human cultures in different parts of the world have developed techniques to preserve dead bodies for spiritual, religious, and cultural purposes. However, mummification also occurs naturally when corpses are exposed to extreme cold, low humidity, lack of air, or chemicals. These mummified corpses have been found around the world, and some have been remarkably preserved. In 1995, the mummified body of a 12 to 14-year-old Incan girl was discovered high in the Andes of southern Peru. Her body was over 500 years old, but her tissues have been remarkably well preserved. The cold climate of her burial site had prevented any decomposition. All her body organs and tissues were in excellent condition. In fact, DNA samples were easily extracted, and clinical diagnostic tests were performed on her lungs, liver, muscle tissues, and

A dead soldier on the battlefield
The body passed through various stages of physiological death.
(Public Domain)

Peruvian mummy

On display at the Carmo Convent, Lisbon. *(GNU Free Documentation License)*

Egyptian mummy

On display in the British Museum. *(GNU Free Documentation License)*

Embalming tools

These are used by modern funeral technicians for preparing the body.

Decomposition

Bacteria and insects immediately begin the process of decomposition. *(GNU Free Documentation License)*

kidneys to determine her cause of death. Analyses of her overall physical condition have provided valuable insights into Inca health and nutrition during this period.

In some cultures, the belief in an afterlife affects how a body is preserved. Such beliefs led to the practice of mummification in ancient Egypt. The ancient Egyptian mummies were prepared based on the principle of dehydration. By removing the source of water, no life can survive, including the microorganisms that would normally decompose the flesh. The ancient Egyptians used a salt-like substance, known as natron, to dry the flesh after the removal of all internal organs except the heart, which was treated by the ancient Egyptian as the seat of the soul. This practice of mummification was extended to other animals, including cats, which were deified by the ancient Egyptians. The practice of mummification lasted for nearly 3,000 years, until the fall of the Egyptian empire shortly after their conquest by the Roman Empire. Currently, embalming of the body is used by most western cultures as a way to delay decomposition for the purpose of display at a funeral. The discovery of the chemical formaldehyde as a biological preservative provided the impetus for embalming in the 19th and 20th centuries. Other chemicals, such as arsenic, have also been used in embalming, but they are too toxic for the embalmers to handle. The basic principle, however, is the same, which is to kill the microorganisms that would otherwise cause decomposition of the flesh.

After a body dies, biological decomposition takes over to recycle the biological molecules and other minerals for use by other living organisms. Decomposition is an important biological process; otherwise the surface of the earth would be quickly filled with dead plants and animals. The group of living organisms that are known as the decomposers is a vital part of the ecosystem. However, decomposition is a complex process that involves different species which "feast" on the corpse in succession. A certain species of insects, for example, is found on the corpse at a particular stage of decomposition. Forensic entomology is a discipline that can make an accurate estimation of the time of death by knowing when a particular species of decomposers is found on the corpse. It is even possible that this information can find a time of death that had occurred up to two years before the discovery of the body. By observing the types of species of insects that are associated with the body, the forensic entomologists can also provide accurate descriptions of the crime scene.

The human body decomposes in clear and defined steps. The first step is carried out by the bacteria that are part of the body's normal microbial ecosystem. Upon death, the body's defense no longer exists, allowing these microorganisms to invade the inner tissues. These massive microbial invasions lead to tissue putrefaction, giving rise to the characteristic odor of rotting flesh. This odor then attracts a large group of insects, which feed on the corpse. However, their main goal is to lay their eggs in the rotting flesh, which provide nutrients for the maggots as soon as they are hatched. In turn, the presence of the maggots attracts predatory insects, which use the maggots as a food source. A complex ecological community results from the interactions between bacteria, insects, and other animal scavengers. When nearly all the flesh on the corpse has been removed, several species of highly specialized beetles descend on the bones to strip off the residual proteins. At this point, nothing of nutritional value is left.

Maggots on flesh
They are very effective decomposers.
(Public Domain)

II.3. *What is the significance of death?*

Decomposers are important in the ecosystem for removing dead biological organisms. However, decomposers are also important in the removal of organic wastes. The contribution of these decomposers to the integrity of the ecosystem is absolutely vital. We might abhor the sight of decomposing animal flesh or of rotting vegetation, but it would be unimaginable if the decomposers were unable to perform their function. Every second, the lives of countless living organisms are ended, and their remains would have filled up all the space on Earth's surface in only a short time. Humans, for example, have 60 million deaths every year. Furthermore, human waste has become increasingly problematic because of non-biodegradable man-made chemicals. Waste disposable has become a serious problem around the world and has been associated with the growth of industrial capacity. Landfills have been constructed all around the country, and they are filling up rapidly. Much of the human refuse that is deposited in the landfills is either non-biodegradable or requires as many as several hundred years to decompose. This situation will leave a negative legacy for future generations. The human society needs to take some quick actions: 1) developing a better understanding of the biological basis of the decomposers and 2) avoiding the use of materials that cannot be recycled.

Wedge-tailed eagle
Feeding on carrion (kangaroo) in Western Australia. *(GNU Free Documentation License)*

There are two major groups of decomposers: bacteria and fungi. Animal remains are effectively handled by bacteria, but plant remains require the service of both bacteria and fungi. Small animals also participate in the process of decomposition, but their role is small in comparison to the contributions that are made by bacteria and fungi. Small animals, such as termites, millipedes, and woodlice are important plant decomposers, but they would not be able to digest plant vegetation without first forming mutualistic relationships with bacteria, fungi, and protozoan in their digestive tracts. In addition to degrading dead organisms, the decomposers are also important in the degradation of human waste. Before the congregations of large urban populations, human waste was degraded by decomposers as part of the natural cycle of the ecosystem. The concentration of human habitation, however, has led to the production of large amounts of waste, especially human excrement. Cleansing the water is vital for preventing contaminated water from returning to the freshwater supply. Today's sewage treatment systems use the indigenous waterborne microbial decomposers to degrade organic materials before releasing the water back into the ecosystem. Modern cities would breakdown completely if these microbial decomposers were unable to carry out their functions.

Fungi
They are decomposers of dead plants. *(Creative Commons Attribution)*

Decomposers are biological organisms that have evolved to obtain energy that is stored in the cells and tissues of dead organisms. Through biochemical processes, the decomposers extract energy from carbohydrates, proteins, and lipids for their growth and reproduction. The processes of decomposition are similar to the biochemical processes that are used by other organisms. The decomposers form a complex microbial ecosystem that involves both competition and cooperation. Some of the microorganisms, however, have evolved highly specific enzymes that allow them to breakdown plant cell walls or other hard-to-degrade molecules. For example, there are some bacterial species that can breakdown petroleum, making them useful for cleaning up massive oil spills. Fungi are particularly adept in producing highly specific enzymes to breakdown cellulose in plant tissues. Without the contribution of fungi, the forest would be littered with dead trees and leaves, stifling future growth.

The decomposers play a central role in the ecosystem by releasing carbon dioxide back into the atmosphere. Researchers have estimated that the decomposers are responsible for approximately 40% of the carbon dioxide that is recycled. However, the decomposers play an even more important role in maintaining the integrity of the ecosystem by recycling other essential minerals, such as nitrogen, phosphorus, calcium, sodium, potassium, and other trace elements. Of these, nitrogen and phosphorus are especially important for plant growth. However, with the exception of legumes (beans and peas), plants cannot use nitrogen directly from the atmosphere (which contains 72% nitrogen). The decomposers solve this problem by releasing the nitrogen and phosphorus in the forms of ammonia and phosphates, respectively. Plants rely on the supply of these molecules in the soil for their growth. In agriculture, these compounds constitute the fertilizers that enrich the soil.

III. THE ORIGIN OF LIFE'S BUILDING BLOCKS

III.I. *What are the building blocks of life?*

All biological organisms contain proteins, carbohydrates, lipids, and nucleic acids, which are constructed from simpler subunits of amino acids, monosaccharides, fatty acids, and nucleotides, respectively. These subunits are composed of four elements: oxygen (65%), carbon (18%), hydrogen (10%), and nitrogen (3%). These four elements account for 97% of the mass of all the atoms in the human body. The body also contains a small amount of other elements: calcium, phosphorus, potassium, sulfur, chlorine, sodium, magnesium, iron, colbalt, copper, zinc, iodine, selenium, and fluorine. Why does life require these elements and not any of the other elements? One answer to this question is that hydrogen, oxygen, carbon, and nitrogen are the most abundant elements in the universe. Therefore, it is not surprising that life uses them for the basic building blocks. In addition, these elements are the simplest of all the elements. More importantly, these elements have the chemical properties to form organic molecules.

Organic molecules were first defined as molecules that can only be found in and produced by biological organisms. This definition was altered when a simple organic molecule, urea, was synthesized in the laboratory in the 19th century. The modern definition of an organic molecule is any molecule that uses carbon as its backbone and that primarily uses hydrogen and oxygen to complete the molecular structure. Organic molecules can be of either biological or non-biological origin. Methane, CH_4, is a good example; it is an organic molecule of non-biological origin that comes from Earth's geological processes. Living organisms construct organic molecules from carbon dioxide and water through photosynthesis. Glucose, the organic molecule that is formed by photosynthesis, is used to build other organic molecules, such as amino acids, fatty acids, and nucleotides. However, photosynthesis occurs because of the activity of organic molecules that function as enzymes and as other structural components. This observation raises an interesting question: Where was the source of the first organic molecules that carried out photosynthesis? In the current environment, only living organisms can produce complex organic molecules. This observation raises the issue of the origin of the organic molecules that are necessary for life.

Searching for the source of the early organic molecules is akin to the search for the origin of life, because life would not have existed without organic molecules. These organic molecules include life's building blocks, such as amino acids, fatty acids, and nucleotides. In the 1950s, Stanley Miller, a young graduate student at the University of Chicago, performed an experiment to test the idea that organic molecules

Compost bin

Bacteria and fungi work to decompose the dead plant material. *(GNU Free Documentation License)*

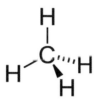

Methane

The simplest form of an organic compound that forms naturally.

could have been formed in Earth's primitive atmosphere. This atmosphere was thought to have contained water vapor, methane, ammonium, hydrogen, and carbon dioxide. Miller proposed the hypothesis that the extreme lightning that was present in the early atmosphere could have provided the necessary energy to form organic molecules for the evolution of the earliest life forms. He mixed water vapor, methane, ammonium, hydrogen, and carbon dioxide in a flask that was hooked up to two electrodes. These electrodes provided a source of continual electrical sparks to simulate lightning. Any chemical compounds that had been created in the flask were collected and analyzed. A week later, Miller analyzed the materials that had formed. He found amino acids as well as other organic molecules that are essential for life. This result was important because it demonstrated that life-sustaining organic molecules could have been created in conditions that were present on the early Earth.

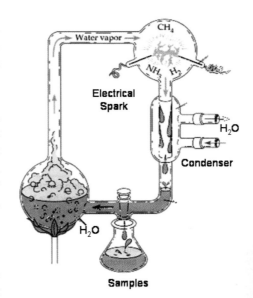

Abiogenesis

This experiment demonstrated the possibility that simple organic compounds spontaneously formed in Earth's early atmosphere. *(GNU Free Documentation License)*

Until 1969, Stanley Miller's experiment provided the only evidence that organic molecules could have been formed in Earth's primordial atmosphere. However, this was changed when a carbonaceous chondrite meteorite landed near Murchison, Victoria, in Australia. This type of meteorite was high in carbon content and was known to have struck the early Earth nearly 4.3 billion years ago. Upon chemical analyses of the Murchison meteorite, researchers were surprised to find that it was rich in organic molecules, including more than 40 different amino acids, as well as other organic molecules. These findings raised the possibility that life-sustaining organic molecules could have been delivered to Earth by meteorites during Earth's early formation. Furthermore, these observations suggested that the organic molecules that are necessary for creating life could have been abundant in the solar system. Today, researchers predict that both early atmospheric reactions and carbonaceous chondrite meteorites could have been responsible for providing Earth with the necessary ingredients for the evolution of the first life.

III.2. How do elements serve as life's building blocks?

Without an understanding of the physical nature of atoms, many modern technologies would not have been possible. The development of CT (computed tomography) scan and MRI (magnetic resonance imaging) would not have been possible without an appreciation of how atoms construct the human body. Through the understanding that biological organisms are made up of individual atoms, these techniques can examine the atoms that make up the molecules in the body. How is an MRI image created? The basic principle of the instrument relies on the manipulation of hydrogen atoms in the body. Using a powerful magnetic field, the magnetization of the hydrogen atoms are aligned in various ways, and the information is collected to reconstruct an image of the body. There are more hydrogen atoms in our bodies than any other atom, and most of the hydrogen atoms join with oxygen to form water. Through chemical reactions, the hydrogen atoms in water can be split up to join with carbon atoms. The chemical reactivity of atoms is inherent in their atomic structures. It was surprising when physicists discovered that all elements (from hydrogen to

Carbonaceous chondrite meteorite

It contains organic molecules such as amino acids. *(Public Domain)*

uranium) are built with the same basic building blocks of electrons, protons, and neutrons, collectively known as subatomic particles. Varying the number of these subatomic particles creates all elements on the periodic table.

When hydrogen is mixed with oxygen and then ignited, water is formed. This is an example of a chemical reaction that joins two atoms. The spark serves as a catalyst to trigger the chemical process, and the explosive reaction that results is a

Periodic Table of the Elements

■ hydrogen ■ poor metals
■ alkali metals □ nonmetals
■ alkali earth metals ■ noble gases
■ transition metals ■ rare earth metals

Building on the same plan

All elements are formed by the fusion of lighter elements. *(Public Domain)*

release of energy that occurs when the hydrogen atoms join with the oxygen atoms to form water. Biological organisms use enzymes as catalysts to facilitate the chemical reactions in joining hydrogen, oxygen, carbon, and nitrogen atoms together to form complex molecules. Some of these chemical reactions require the input of energy; for example, in photosynthesis, solar irradiation provides the source of energy. The energy is then stored in the chemical bonds of organic molecules, such as the carbohydrates. Other chemical reactions release energy; for example, in respiration, the breakdown of glucose releases the hydrogen atoms to join with oxygen atoms to form water. There are over ten thousand different chemical reactions that occur in the human body. Each of them is catalyzed by a specific enzyme. By arranging the atoms in different combinations and configurations, living organisms can create molecules with limitless variations and properties from only four basic elements: hydrogen, oxygen, carbon, and nitrogen.

All living organisms on Earth use hydrogen, oxygen, carbon, and nitrogen for the basic structure of life. With over 92 naturally-occurring elements, why do living organisms only use these four elements? One answer to this question comes from examining the elemental composition of Earth. When considering the elemental composition of the entire Earth, it is primarily composed of iron (32%), oxygen (30%), silicon (15%), and magnesium (14%); the remaining 9% includes all the other elements. Some elements, such as gold, are exceedingly rare. In addition, the elemental composition varies in different parts of the earth. For example, 60% of Earth's crust is made up of silica oxide. Many compounds on Earth are forms of oxides, including alumina, iron oxides, lime, magnesia, potash, and soda. However, the center of Earth is composed of iron (88.8%), with smaller amounts of nickel (5.8%), and sulfur (4.5%). It appears that the elemental composition of living organisms fails to match the elemental composition of Earth. Other than oxygen, none

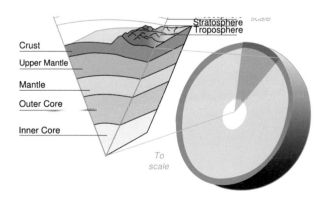

Earth cutaway

From the inner core to the exosphere. *(GNU Free Documentation License)*

of the basic elements of life are found in abundance on Earth. Why is this the case?

The sun accounts for more than 99.8% of the total mass of the solar system. Since the sun is composed of 74% hydrogen and 25% helium, the elemental composition of the solar system as a whole is predominantly hydrogen and helium. Compared to other stars in the Milky Way galaxy, our solar system is considered rich in the heavy elements. Researchers have discovered that in the Milky Way galaxy, there are differences in diversity of elements. In the center region of the galaxy, for example, elements other than hydrogen and helium are extremely rare. Since life requires the heavy elements for survival, the regions that harbor elements other than hydrogen and helium are known as galactic habitable zones. However, when considering the universe as a whole, the ten most common elements in the universe (by mass) are: 1) hydrogen – 74%, 2) helium – 24%, 3) oxygen – 1%, 4) carbon – 0.45%, 5) neon – 0.14%, 6) iron – 0.1%, 7) nitrogen – 0.09%, 8) silicon – 0.06%, 9) magnesium – 0.06%, 10) sulfur – 0.04%. Based on the elemental composition of the universe, it is not surprising that living organisms make use of hydrogen, oxygen, carbon, and nitrogen as the elemental building blocks of life.

III.3. How did the elements originate?

In 1980, a series known as *Cosmos: A Personal Voyage* was broadcast by the Public Broadcasting Service (PBS). The series was the second most widely watched series in the history of American Public Television, next to the 1990 series *The Civil War*. The *Cosmos* series introduced to the general public the idea that life on Earth is made up of stardust, because all the elements in biological organisms are remnants of deceased stars. What does this mean? What is the impact of this knowledge at the individual and societal levels? This knowledge changes both personal and societal perspectives of human's place in the universe. The universe is huge beyond imagination when one considers that there are more than several billion sun-like stars in the Milky Way galaxy and that there are over 20 billion galaxies in the universe. Many of these stars have planets that are similar to ours, making the total number of planets around several hundred quadrillion. The discovery of the dimension of the universe by Edwin Hubble represents one of the greatest astronomical discoveries of all time.

In addition to the discovery of the size of the universe, Hubble also discovered that the universe is constantly changing. He observed that the galaxies are moving away from each other, suggesting that the universe is expanding. This observation has led to the big bang theory, which postulated that the universe began approximately 13.6 billion years ago. Hydrogen atoms, the simplest elements, were formed from subatomic articles that were released during the big bang process. The hydrogen atoms eventually collapsed together by gravitational force to form the core of the star and to give off energy by nuclear fusion when the hydrogen atoms fused into helium atoms. The earlier stars completed their life cycle, from formation to destruction, when their hydrogen fuel became exhausted. Some of the large stars have shorter life cycles with one or two billion years, and their death is accompanied by a massive stellar explosion known as a supernova, which releases sufficient energy to outshine all the stars in the galaxy for a period of several weeks. Supernovae occur about once every 50 years in the Milky Way galaxy, and they can be seen by the naked eye at their peak luminosity.

All the elements known to physics and chemistry are created by nucleosynthesis, which is a process that combines subatomic particles to form elemental atoms. For example, one of the most common forms of nucleosynthesis is the fusion of hydrogen to form helium in the sun. This is known as stellar nucleosynthesis. As the sun uses up its hydrogen fuel, helium atoms start to fuse to form other elements, such as carbon, oxygen, and nitrogen; these are the first elements to form because they are among the smallest elements. During the final stage of the life cycle of the sun, other heavier elements, up to calcium, are formed. The fusion reactor, however, is not hot enough to create the heavier elements. At this point in the sun's life cycle, if the sun is of sufficient mass, it undergoes a supernova explosion, by first collapsing upon itself and creating enough pressure to form the rest of the elements before it explodes. This is known as the supernova nucleosynthesis. The fragments from this explosion are released to form a gigantic luminous cloud of matter known as a nebula. One of the most famous nebulae is the Orion nebula, which is visible with the naked eye.

The nebulae are the sites for the formation of new stars, and these stars are known as the second generation stars, which include our sun. Our sun is a condensation of the hydrogen atoms in the nebula cloud to gradually form a solid sphere of hydrogen and helium. As the gravitational force pulls the hydrogen atoms tighter together, the pressure reaches a critical point to begin the nuclear fusion reaction. It begins to shine, and a new star is born. The heavy elements in the nebula are found in very small quantities, and they also start to aggregate, first forming small microscopic particles and eventually, becoming planets. The terrestrial or rocky planets contain the largest amount of heavy elements, such as iron and nickel. Therefore, all elements other than hydrogen and helium began as stardust from the supernovae, and biological organisms, including humans, are built by elements created in stars.

Crab Nebula

It is the remnant of a supernova explosion. *(Public Domain)*

Chapter 25

Climate

How serious is global warming?

Does global warming cause more severe weather?
A hurricane, also known as a cyclone, viewed from the International Space Station.
(Public Domain)

CHAPTER 25. CLIMATE

Global warming has been in the news for the past several years, with former Vice President Al Gore receiving the 2007 Nobel Peace Prize (together with the Intergovernmental Panel of Climate Change) for their "efforts to build up and disseminate greater knowledge about man-made climate change, and to lay the foundations for the measures that are needed to counteract such change." His documentary, *An Inconvenient Truth*, won an Academy Award. In national surveys in the United States on issues of the greatest significance in the 21st century, global warming or climate change is ranked as one of the top issues by the general public. Global warming remains a topic of heated debate, despite the scientific community's consensus of the actuality and potential impact of it on Earth's climate. The general public often finds the evidence and arguments for and against global warming confusing and difficult to understand. It is important for all citizens to understand the scientific evidence and the potential impact that global warming will have in the ensuing decades. We all have a responsibility to maintain a habitable environment and leave a better world for future generations.

Al Gore

Receiving the 2007 Nobel Peace Prize. *(GNU Free Documentation License)*

I. EARTH'S ENVIRONMENT

I.1. *What is climate?*

Global warming is also referred to as climate change. What is climate change? If the climate does change, how often does this occur? What is the historical record for climate change? What were the consequences of those changes? These are some of the questions that need to be addressed before the significance and the concerns of the current climate change can be fully understood.

Heat waves are one form of climatic change that can have severe consequences on both the human and biological worlds. One of the worst heat waves that hit Chicago took place in 1995, when the temperature soared to a record high of 106°F on July 13. This year set the record for the warmest July since recordkeeping began in 1928. One elderly lady was found dead from heat-induced dehydration by her neighbor. By the time the heat wave had passed, over 600 heat-related deaths had been recorded over a five-day period. Another heat wave swept across Europe in 2003, leading to the hottest summer on record in Europe. This was one of the deadliest heat waves in modern history, affecting several European countries, and, when combined with a drought, created a crop shortage in Southern Europe. Over 35,000 deaths resulted from this devastating heat wave. France was one of the countries that was most severely affected, because France does not usually have very hot summers and was, therefore, unprepared. During this heat wave with temperatures exceeding 104°F and with extreme humidity, many failed to recognize the signs of dehydration. Nearly 15,000 people, mostly elderly, perished in heat-related deaths, creating one of the worst public health disasters in modern France.

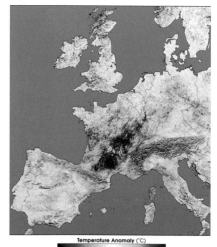

Temperature Anomaly (°C)

European heat wave of 2003

Average temperature difference in Europe during the heat wave. *(GNU Free Documentation License)*

The phenomenon of heat waves provide an example of how climates can abruptly change. A heat wave is a prolonged period of excessively hot weather lasting a day to several weeks. A heat wave is also relative to the climate in which it occurs; for example, a temperature of 100°F in Minnesota is a heat wave but would not be considered so in Arizona. Therefore, a heat wave is an abnormality of expected weather in a particular climatic region. In the 1995 Chicago and the 2003 European heat waves, the unexpected hot weather caught the citizens by surprise. Many elderly died from dehydration or hyperthermia. In addition, in large metropolitan areas, a heat wave increases the demand for electricity because of the heavy use of air conditioning. This situation strains the electrical system, leading to widespread power outages. However, heat waves also have a severe impact on agriculture, especially if they are associated with drought. In parts of the world where the population practices subsistence agriculture, protracted heat waves can lead to famine and starvation. Furthermore, a heat wave also leads to wildfires when it occurs during a drought because of dry vegetation.

Climate is defined as the weather averaged over a long period of time, with the standard average being 30 years. The distinction between climate and weather is frequently described by the adage: "Climate is what you expect, weather is what you get." Climates on Earth are classified according to three major factors: precipitation, temperature, and wind pattern. The climate most common in Illinois is known as humid continental, which is also found in large areas of central Europe and in some parts of China. The humid continental climate is characterized by a variable weather pattern and a large seasonal temperature variation. Another important and well-known climate is the tropical rainforest, a climate characterized by high rainfall and a relatively constant temperature over most of the year. With high precipitation and warm temperatures, the rainforests are the most productive climates on Earth, containing half of all living animal and plant species. The direct opposite of the rainforest is the desert, which accounts for nearly one third of Earth's land surface. Due to extreme low humidity, deserts have large temperature differences between day and night. This results because the dry desert air cannot block sunlight during the day or trap heat at night. Most deserts are formed by rain shadows, mountains that block the path of precipitation to the desert.

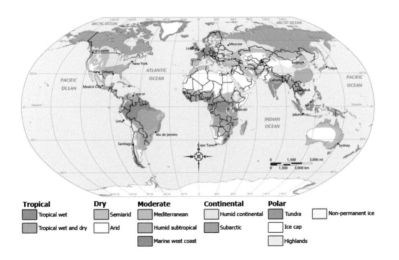

World climate classification

Based on precipitation, temperature, and wind pattern.
(GNU Free Documentation License)

Climates have a profound impact on living organisms because of temperature and water availability. Each climatic zone has a characteristic ecosystem that has distinct communities of plants, animals, and microorganisms. Similar climatic zones across the globe have similar ecosystems. The unique pairing of climate with its ecosystem is known as a biome, which is subdivided into two major categories: terrestrial biomes and aquatic biomes. Some biome examples are tundras, temperate glasslands, mangroves, and deserts. Living organisms have adapted to the physical conditions of the biomes that they live in, and together, they form a complex ecosystem. Furthermore, the biological diversity of the ecosystem is critical to the health of the ecosystem. The biological and physical worlds continually interact, and any changes in the abiotic factors (temperature, precipitation, and soil) can profoundly affect the biotic factors of the ecosystem. Biological organisms are absolutely dependant on the climatic conditions of their biome.

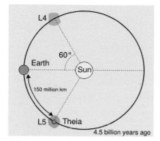

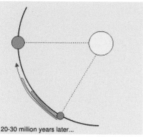

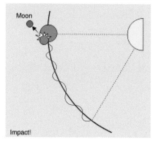

The Giant Impact hypothesis

The event that led to the formation of the moon. *(GNU Free Documentation License)*

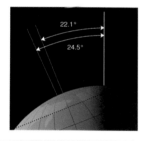

Axial tilt

This fluctuates over a 41,000 year cycle. *(Public Domain)*

Wobbles

This occurs over a 26,000 year cycle. *(Public Domain)*

I.2. What has shaped Earth's climate over geologic time?

Seasons are important to our lives, particularly in regions that are far away from the equator. All living organisms are affected by the seasons, and many exhibit physiological and behavioral adaptations to seasonal changes. These adaptations include reproductive timing, migration, and hibernation. Humans are also affected by seasons, even though modern technologies have provided protection against extreme weather conditions. The seasons of Earth are caused by the tilt of its axis in relationship to its orbital plane. Interestingly, the origin of Earth's tilt is the result of an impact between Earth and another planet. There is strong evidence that about 50 million years after the formation of the solar system, a planet that was similar in size to Mars, known as Theia, collided with the early Earth. The collision destroyed Theia and moved Earth's axis to 23.5°. In addition, enormous portions of Earth's crust were ejected into space, which eventually coalesced to form the moon. Without this event, Earth would not have developed seasons and, as a result, would not have developed the biological diversity that is based on seasonal differences.

The orbit and the rotation of Earth are important to its climate. The seasons of Earth are created by the annual orbit of Earth around the sun and the tilt of Earth's axis relative to the plane of rotation. At an angle of 23.5°, one part of the planet is more directly exposed to the rays of the sun, and the exposure alternates as Earth revolves in its orbit. In 1920, the Serbian geophysicist Milutin Milankovitch proposed the Milankovitch cycles to explain the long-term climatic changes that are caused by the cyclical fluctuations of Earth's orbit, tilt, and wobble. He proposed that Earth's orbit undergoes a cyclic change every 21,000 years from a nearly circular to an elliptical orbit. This change is known as eccentricity. The second cyclic phenomenon is the axial tilt, which fluctuates from 21.5° to 24.5° over a 41,000 year cycle. The 23.5° represents the average of the tilt. The last cyclic variation is the wobble, also known as the precession. Wobbles occur in Earth over a 26,000 year cycle. All these three aspects (eccentricity, axial tilt, and precession) are believed to have contributed to major climate changes in the history of Earth, including the ice ages and the most extreme case, the snowball Earth.

During expeditions to hunt for fossils, researchers were surprised to discover plant and animal fossils in exposed rock in the Antarctica continent. Earlier perceptions of the polar region had consisted of the continual presence of ice caps. These discoveries suggest that at one time, Earth was ice-free, even in the poles. In fact, recent evidence supports the conclusion that in the majority of the 4.56 billion years of Earth's history, the polar ice caps were either minimal or completely absent. However, at certain times, Earth experienced ice ages, which covered most of the planet in ice. Researchers propose that four major ice ages occurred in Earth's history, with the earliest occurring 2.7 to 2.3 billion years ago. The most severe ice age took place from 850 to 630 million years ago. During this ice age, in a period of several million years, the entire surface of Earth was blanketed with ice, a condition known as snowball Earth. It was likely that global ice cover would have destroyed ecosystems that were dependent on sunlight. Many factors contributed to the formation of the ice ages, and the Milankovitch cycles were likely the main contributors to global climate changes. Furthermore, the formation of ice ages highlights the importance of Earth's distance from the sun. In other words, a small variation in this distance has profound impact on an important aspect of life on Earth: the state of water.

The polar ice caps on today's Earth suggest that it is still in an ice age that started about 40 million years ago with the growth of an ice sheet in Antarctica. Over this cooling period, there have been cyclic periods of glaciations. During these glacial periods, Earth's average temperature dropped to between 5 to 10°C, resulting in an extension of the ice age in the form of glaciers. There are also periods, known as interglacial periods, when the ice sheets retreat to the polar region. The evidence for past glacial periods abounds. The plains of the Midwest, for example, were created by the enormous power of advancing glaciers. These glaciers act like a river of ice which smashes and pushes rocks out of the way to create the boundless flat plains. During the last glacial period, which ended about 10,000 years ago, the glaciers extended to Spain in Europe and to southern Illinois in North America. During this time, the world would have been very different, and the animals and plants would have evolved to adapt to this cold climate. However, when the glacier retreated and Earth started to warm, many species would have been unsuited for the new climate and would have become extinct.

Glacier
Perito Moreno Glacier in Patagonia, Argentina. *(Public Domain)*

I.3. What shapes Earth's short-term climate change?

For many years, climatologists considered Earth's climate to be relatively stable for up to thousands of years at a time. However, recent studies on global weather patterns have suggested that climate is a dynamic process. Many factors contribute to the long-term climatic conditions and to the short-term weather patterns. With the increasing complexity of human society and its dependence on technology, the ability to anticipate both short-term and long-term climatic trends is crucial to the survival of a large human population. Because of the need to feed a large population, any major crop failure that results because of adverse climatic conditions can create economical and social disasters that have global implications. In addition, modern society has a heavy reliance on technological infrastructures for communication, energy supply, and transportation. Adverse weather conditions, such as tornados, hurricanes, snowstorms, and heat waves, can seriously affect those infrastructures and pose serious threats to the well-being of the society. For these reasons, climatologists have begun to make long-term predictions of the climatic patterns for decades or even several hundred years into the future.

In 1991, Mount Pinatubo, which is located on the island of Luzon in the Philippines, produced the second largest terrestrial eruption in the 20th century. The volcano had remained relatively inactive for 500 to 1000 years after its last major eruption. The impact of the eruption was felt worldwide. During its eruption, over 10 billion metric tons of magma, and 20 million tons of SO_2 (sulfur dioxide) were spewed into the atmosphere. Vast quantities of minerals, metals, and gases were also showered on the environment and into the atmosphere.

Mount Pinatubo
The ash fall from the volcanic eruption. *(Public Domain)*

Fortunately, prediction of the eruption days in advance led to the evacuation of 40,000 people from the surrounding areas, saving many lives. The eruption had an impact on global weather because the small particulates and gases were ejected up to

15 miles above Earth's surface into the atmosphere. The dust cloud formed a shroud blocking sunlight from reaching Earth. Global temperatures dropped by as much as 0.5°C. In addition, the ozone layers around the world were substantially depleted, but have since recovered. The other major volcanic eruption was Krakatoa, a volcanic island in the Sunda Strait between Java and Sumatra, in 1883. It also affected the global weather for nearly a month. This eruption created the loudest sound that has been historically reported: the explosion was heard as far away as Perth in Australia, which is nearly 2,000 miles away. Because proper warning had not been given, 36,417 people died in this cataclysmic event.

Since the time of the Age of Sails (1571 to 1862), mariners have understood the importance of ocean currents. Ocean currents are akin to rivers in the ocean and are driven by differences in temperatures and in salt concentrations of the seawater. These differences cause the cold water to sink to the bottom of the ocean and the warm water to rise. With the help of wind-driven surface currents, the dense water flows into the ocean basin, which drives the lighter water to the surface. This form of water circulation is global in nature and is known as the thermohaline circulation. These currents are also known as the ocean conveyor belt, because they provide a continuing recirculation of ocean water. One of the most important ocean currents is the Gulf Stream. This current originates as an upwelling of water in the Gulf of Mexico, exits through the Straits of Florida, and follows the eastern coastlines of the United States and Newfoundland before crossing the Atlantic Ocean. It then splits into two streams: one flows north along the coast of northern Europe and the other flows south off the coast of West Africa. The Gulf Stream brings warm air and moisture to the eastern coastlines of North America and to northern Europe, which moderates their climates. Without the Gulf Stream, the climate of northern Europe would resemble that of Greenland.

The air in Earth's atmosphere also continuously circulates around the globe and is driven by the rotation of Earth, the heat of the sun, and ocean evaporation. This type of air circulation represents a global ocean-atmospheric phenomenon. These air circulations are also involved in the generating of storm patterns that occur when cold and warm air currents meet. These storm patterns include tropical storms, winter storms, and hurricanes. One of the most well-known atmospheric systems is the El Niño-Southern Oscillation (ENSO). Its fluctuation from year to year in location and in intensity has a profound impact on the climatic weather conditions in both South and North America. The other important atmospheric system is the North Atlantic Oscillation, which regulates the strength and direction of the westerly winds and storms that traverse the North Atlantic.

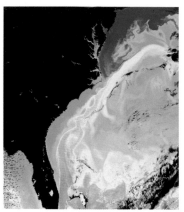

Gulf Stream

The Gulf Stream is orange and yellow in this representation of water temperatures in the Atlantic. *(Public Domain)*

II. THE GREENHOUSE EFFECT AND GLOBAL CLIMATE

II.1. How does the atmosphere cause the greenhouse effect?

You experience the greenhouse effect every time you get into your car on a hot summer day. In this situation, you notice that the temperature inside the car is significantly hotter than the temperature outside the car. The basic principle of the greenhouse effect is based on the semi-permeability of glass to UV light and heat (infrared radiation). On a hot summer day, your body feels the heat, because the heat is being absorbed by your clothing and your body. If, however, a surface is reflective, then the solar radiation is also reflected. In a car, the greenhouse effect is due to the property of the glass in the car window. Glass is permeable to UV light, which enters the car and transfers its energy to the internal surfaces of the car. This energy is then released by the seats and other objects in the car as heat. However, the glass of the car window is impermeable to the heat and therefore, traps the heat energy

A modern greenhouse

The greenhouse effect maintains internal temperature. *(GNU Free Documentation License)*

inside the car, resulting in an elevated temperature. The greenhouse effect also exists as a global phenomenon and is critical for life on Earth. Then, why is the greenhouse effect considered so negative in the discussion of global warming?

Earth has remarkably stable temperatures between day and night, with differences less than 10-15°C in most places around the world. In the tropical rainforests and along coastal regions, the daytime and nighttime temperatures vary by only a few degrees. In comparison, the surface temperature during a lunar day (moon) is 107°C, whereas the surface temperature during the lunar night is -153°C. This difference exists because the moon does not have an atmosphere to moderate its surface temperature. Both Earth and the moon receive energy from the sun in the form of radiation (in UV light, visible light, and heat). Earth absorbs 70% of this energy and reflects 30% back to space. Earth's temperature is in a steady state, because its atmosphere moderates the heat gained and the heat lost. Without the atmosphere, Earth's average temperature would be -19°C instead of 14°C. Earth's atmosphere provides a greenhouse shield that prevents heat from being rapidly lost during night time. It is the effectiveness of this greenhouse shield that determines the surface temperature of Earth.

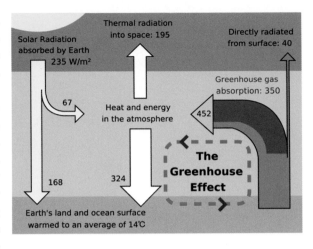

Earth's greenhouse effect
A representation of the exchanges of energy between outer space, Earth's atmosphere, and Earth's surface. *(GNU Free Documentation License)*

Earth's atmosphere is important in determining the climate. At sea level, the air contains approximately 78% nitrogen, 21% oxygen, 1% argon, 0.038% carbon dioxide, trace amounts of other gases (such as methane), and 1% water vapor. At higher altitudes, the composition varies slightly, but the concentration of air is reduced because of lower gravitational pull on the gas molecules. Neither nitrogen nor oxygen has any effect on infrared radiation, and because of this, these gases do not contribute to the greenhouse effect. Only carbon dioxide, water vapor, and methane are effective greenhouse gases. Of these gases, it is carbon dioxide that was mostly likely involved in creating the snowball Earth. Evidence has been found suggesting that a rapid absorption of large amounts of carbon dioxide by newly-exposed continental rocks dramatically decreased the atmospheric carbon dioxide. The reduction in this greenhouse gas caused the temperatures to drop and allowed for extensive ice accumulation. The temperatures were further decreased by the ice, which reflects solar energy back to space. This situation resulted in a runaway cooling over the entire globe, including the equator. The subsequent warming of Earth was most likely due to the release of greenhouse gases from volcanic activities. However, researchers have estimated that it took approximately 1,000 years for Earth to thaw.

Today's atmosphere is considered Earth's "third atmosphere," because evidence suggests that the composition of Earth's atmosphere has changed over the 4.56 billion years of Earth's history. When it was born, Earth most likely had an atmosphere of hydrogen and helium, because these two elements were the predominant elements in the early solar system. By about 4.4 billion years ago, Earth had cooled and had formed a crust that had widespread volcanic activities, which released steam, carbon dioxide, ammonia, and nitrogen. These gases formed Earth's second atmosphere. This atmosphere was over 100 times denser than the current atmosphere and lacked oxygen. Slowly, the carbon dioxide in this atmosphere dissolved in the oceans and was precipitated out as carbonates. In addition, the atmospheric ammonia was converted to nitrogen. By about 3.3 billion years ago, photosynthetic bacteria, which are similar to modern day cyanobacteria, started to release oxygen into the atmosphere through photosynthesis. The earliest oxygen that was released was absorbed by the sea and used to form oxides of metals such as iron, calcium, silica, and others. Gradually, however, oxygen started to accumulate in the atmosphere to the modern day 21%. In contrast, today's carbon dioxide is only 0.038%, a level that serves as an adequate pool for constructing carbohydrates by photosynthetic organisms.

II.2. *What is global warming?*

Global climates have undergone dynamic changes over Earth's long geologic history. Local climates result from these global climate changes. Therefore, to understand the short-term weather pattern in a particular region, researchers study global climatic variations. With the increasing computation power of modern computers, researchers have developed computer programs to analyze global climate patterns over a long time period. One way to obtain the necessary data is to extract cores from ice sheets that have been laid down over thousands of years in the poles. By analyzing the thickness of layers in the core, researchers have discovered that Earth's temperature exhibits fluctuations in a 20,000 year cycle. This natural temperature cycle correlates with the concentrations of carbon dioxide in the atmosphere, providing strong evidence that carbon dioxide is a greenhouse gas. From these observations it was concluded that Earth experiences natural cycles of greenhouse warming and that each cycle of warming is followed by a cycle of cooling that produces periods of glaciations.

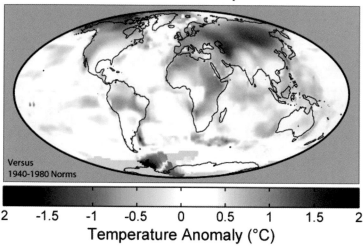

1995-2004 Mean Temperatures

Versus
1940-1980 Norms

Temperature Anomaly (°C)

Global warming map

Mean surface temperature changes from 1995 to 2004 in comparison to 1940 to 1980.
(GNU Free Documentation License)

Since the beginning of the 20th century, weather conditions, such as temperature, precipitation, and wind speed, have been recorded around the world. These observations have provided meteorologists and climatologists with a wealth of data to use in making short-term weather forecasts and long-term climate predications. Accurate short-term weather forecasts are necessary for warning populations, particularly in large urban areas, to avoid severe weather conditions. Over the past two decades, climatologists have also discovered that global temperature, which is taken as the average temperature on Earth, has increased since the beginning of the Industrial Revolution. It accelerated during the 1950s when the burning of fossil fuels reached a new height. Based on the climatic model, an increase in the atmospheric CO_2 level will lead to an increase in global temperature, due to its effect as a greenhouse gas. However, it has been discovered that the actual rise in global temperature has exceeded the level that was predicted by the climatic models when all the natural causes for global warming had been taken into account. This observation has suggested that the emission of CO_2 into the atmosphere by human activities has caused a change in both short-term weather conditions and in long-term climate patterns. This anthropogenic-induced warming has been named global warming.

It has been recognized that over the geologic history of Earth, the fluctuation of its surface temperature was the result of many contributing factors, such as the orbit and rotation of Earth, the fluctuation in solar energy, Earth's geologic activities, and the gaseous composition of Earth's atmosphere. These are natural cycles that are beyond human control. Scientists from different disciplines have also realized from the study of fossil records that living organisms, such as the ancestors of cyanobacteria, have also changed Earth's atmosphere and affected its climate. Almost all of these changes, however, have occurred slowly over a period of thousands or even millions of years. For example, sea levels have changed repeatedly over the past several million years, but the changes generally have taken place over several thousand years. In contrast, the current impact on global climate is occurring at a swift pace. Scientists predict that by raising the global temperature by as little as 0.5°C, the global sea level can rise as much as 3 ft. What does this change mean? If one takes New

York City as an example, one third of the city would be under water, dividing the island of Manhattan into two islands.

Since 1850, researchers have been carefully collecting temperature measurements around the world to create a record of global temperatures. There have been fluctuations in global temperatures in the past 150 years, but an upward trend is undeniable. Since 1850, the average annual global temperature has risen by nearly 0.7°C. During the same period, the atmospheric CO_2 concentration has risen from approximately 280 ppm (parts per million) to nearly 380 ppm, an increase of nearly 35%. This observation has led to great concerns among climatologists, because CO_2 is an important greenhouse gas. The climatologists have turned to climate models based on the known natural causes of global climate changes. When they introduced the projected CO_2 emission into the climate models, they were shocked by the possible alteration to Earth's surface temperature. Following this initial discovery, researchers around the world have used various climate models to analyze the impact of CO_2 and other greenhouse gases on global temperature. Similar results have been obtained from the many studies that have been conducted by different experts in the field. The general agreement is that if the current rate of CO_2 emission (also known as CO_2 forcing) continues, the increase in global temperature by 2100 will range from 2.2°C to 4.8°C. Human societies could be drastically altered by these increased temperatures.

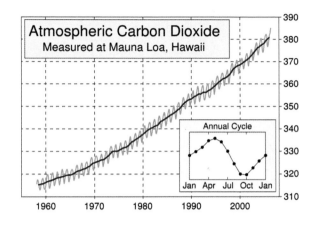

Atmospheric carbon dioxide

Small seasonal oscillations in an overall yearly upward trend.
(GNU Free Documentation License)

II.3. What other human activities affect global climate?

Human activities make important contributions to the weather. The strength of hurricanes, for example, can be affected by human activity. In the early 2000s, researchers around the world were studying the factors that affect the severity of hurricanes. One researcher accidentally discovered that hurricanes were generally more severe and had higher wind speeds and greater precipitation on weekends than on weekdays. Similarly, there was greater likelihood to have rainy weather over weekends than on weekdays. Further studies have linked these weather phenomena to air pollution, particularly in large urban areas. Air pollution is important in cloud formation because it releases small particulates into the atmosphere. These particulates form the nuclei for the condensation of water vapor in the atmosphere to form clouds. Researchers have identified a strong correlation between the increased levels of pollution during the week when human activities are the highest and the severity of the weather. Human activities can have a significant impact on even day-to-day weather.

Air travel is an important component of modern transportation, and each day, over several hundred airlines operate numerous flights around the world. Airlines are also significant polluters because of the particulates that are emitted in the exhaust of the planes. On a clear day, the sky is crisscrossed with contrails left by planes. The contrails are miniature clouds that are formed by the condensation of water vapor on the fuel particulates. Scientists suspect that the contrails could impact global weather, but they had been unable to test this idea because of the difficulties that would be caused by experimenting with commercial flights. However, an opportunity came unexpectedly after the September 11, 2001 attacks. After the attacks, the United States government, as well as the governments of many other countries, suspended commercial air traffic for three days. This was an excellent opportunity to study global temperatures in the absence of contrails. To the surprise of scientists, the daily temperature around the world over these three days was nearly 1°C higher than

Contrails

They are responsible for global dimming. *(Public Domain)*

the average historical temperature for the time of the year. This finding suggests that the contrails are lowering Earth's temperature. How does this observation fit into global warming? The answer to this question is most alarming.

The results on the studies of the contrails were surprising, because few scientists would have predicted that airplane contrails could have such a significant impact on global temperature. However, this should not have been surprising, because the impact of particulate pollutants in cloud formation is well known. In the 1960s, an Israeli scientist discovered the effect of pollutant-induced cloud formation during a study on irrigation and crop production. He discovered that since the beginning of the 20th century, industrial pollution has led to higher levels of cloud covering in certain parts of the world, blocking solar radiation from reaching Earth's surface in these areas. Interestingly, clouds do not contribute to the greenhouse effect; instead they serve as mirrors, reflecting solar radiation back into space. Over the past 50 years, pollution has increased the cloud covering and has reduced the amount of solar energy reaching Earth's surface. This phenomenon is known as global dimming. The decrease in solar penetration has had a significant impact on plant growth and on the surface temperature. Most researchers agree that solar dimming might have masked the effect of greenhouse gas-induced global warming. But, is this a good thing?

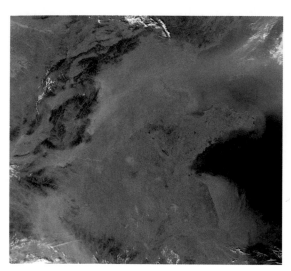

Pollution over China

Smoke and haze caused by dozens of fires burning on the surface. *(Public Domain)*

Researchers have realized that global dimming might have counterbalanced the impact of global warming in the past several decades. However, many countries have experienced the health hazards of air pollution and are making a strong effort to establish and enforce strong environmental laws to control transportation and industrial pollution. This effort in controlling pollution will also reduce cloud covering. Consequently, more solar radiation will reach Earth's surface, contributing to global warming. Researchers predict that as more industrialized nations begin to control pollution in their countries, global dimming will be significantly reduced. The dire prediction is that the global temperature rise could be as much as 8°C. If such a temperature change occurs, the global seawater level could rise as much 16 ft; most of Florida and Louisiana would be under water.

III. The Effects of Global Warming

III.1. What are the physical consequences?

The tilting of Earth's axis along its orbital plane leads to different distributions of solar radiation in different times of the year (i.e., the different seasons). In the North Pole, the ice cap is a large sheet of ice, whereas in the South Pole, ice accumulates on the Antarctic continent. The polar ice caps fluctuate from season to season, but the overall quantities of the ice and snow remain relatively constant. However, in the geologic time of thousands and millions of years, the ice caps have grown or

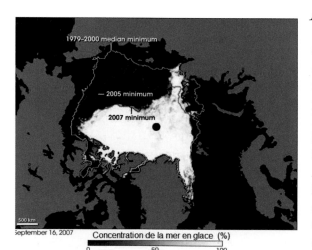

Shrinkage of the Arctic ice cap

Arctic shrinkage as of 2007 compared to the 2005 and the 1979-2000 averages. *(Public Domain)*

shrunk due to climate variations. Over the geological history of Earth, physical factors, such as the orbital and rotational cycle of Earth and geological activities, have had a significant impact on the ice caps. Researchers have strong evidence that during a significant portion of Earth's history, both ice caps have melted by warm climates. This observation is significant when considering that the polar ice caps and glaciers hold 2.4% of Earth's water (97% of surface water is located in the ocean and 0.6% is freshwater that is found in rivers, lakes, ponds, and underground caverns). Even though 2.4% is not very much, the sea level would rise as much as 50 ft if the glaciers and ice caps were melted. Global warming could lead to the melting of the polar ice caps and glaciers around the world. The impact of the water that would be released from the ice caps and glaciers on coastal regions would be devastating; many cities would be completely inundated.

Global warming will increase the atmospheric temperature. In turn, this higher atmospheric temperature will raise the energy of air currents and will create more violent storms and hurricanes. A trend of extreme weather has already been evident in the past several decades as the global temperature has gradually increased. Worldwide, the proportion of hurricanes reaching categories 4 and 5 has risen from 20% in the 1970s to 35% in the 1990s. Warmer air temperatures during the past 50 years have increased precipitation and have resulted in hurricanes that bring more rainfall, causing serious flooding and mudslides. Incidents of extreme weather, such as hurricane Katrina in 2005, have been particularly catastrophic for urban areas with large population densities. Global warming has also been implicated in the dramatic redistribution of rainfall around the world. Until about 20 years ago, East Africa received rain during summer rainy seasons. This rain was important to support the local agriculture. There had been occasional droughts, usually once every ten years. However, global warming has altered the rain clouds that normally come across the equator, moving them farther south. The consequences have been catastrophic for this region, resulting in famine and starvation. The unpredictability of the weather patterns in the past several years has created significant social and economic stress around the world.

Global warming is also likely to have serious effects on ocean currents and disrupt coastal climates. Earth's oceans have a profound impact on the global climate through the various ocean currents that bring moisture and heat to the coastal regions around the world. One of the most important ocean currents is the Gulf Stream that flows from the Gulf of Mexico along the eastern seaboard of the U.S. and Canada before heading into the Atlantic Ocean. The temperate climate in these regions is due to the warm ocean water that flows along the Gulf Stream. However, even more importantly, Northern Europe relies on the heat that the Gulf Stream brings to its coast to maintain a moderate climate. Countries, such as Norway, Sweden, and Finland, would have much more severe winters without the Gulf Stream. Furthermore, without this ocean current, they would be covered by permanent glaciers similar to that of Greenland. The Gulf Stream is generated by the thermohaline circulation that relies on the temperature differences and salinities of the sea water. Both of these properties can be affected by increases in global temperature. Climate models have repeatedly shown that the thermohaline circulation of the Gulf Stream is highly susceptible to global warming. Furthermore, these models demonstrate that the Gulf Stream could be altered in its flow or be completely shut down. Such changes would have serious climatic impacts on these coastal regions.

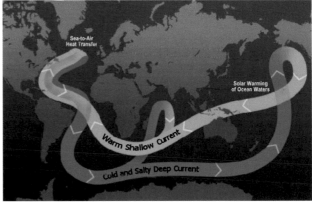

Thermohaline circulation

A global stream of ocean current driven by temperature differences between the surface and the deep ocean.
(Public Domain)

Even though global warming is part of the natural cycle of Earth's climate, climatologists are concerned about the current rate of climatic changes due to human activities. The rate of greenhouse gas emission through the burning of fossil fuels is many times faster than the natural cycle of carbon dioxide accumulation. Scientists are concerned by the abruptness of these changes that have occurred in the last 150 years after the dawn of industrialization. The seriousness of these changes have only been recently recognized, and current climate models suggest that an increase of 6°C in global temperature will bring catastrophic changes to the weather, the biological world, and the human society by 2100, less than 100 years from now. In its 2007 report, the United Nations Intergovernmental Panel on Climate Change (IPCC) issued the following statement: "Anthropogenic warming could lead to some impacts that are abrupt or irreversible, depending upon the rate and magnitude of the climate change." How will these changes affect the biological world and human society?

III.2. What is the global warming controversy?

In the past several years, global warming has been in the news because of fierce debates regarding the accuracy of the scientific conclusions on its cause, nature, and prediction. Many of the disputes are driven by political, social, and cultural agendas in deciding on what the best policies are for managing the problem. Scientific evidence has provided little doubt regarding the rising global temperature in association with an increase in CO_2 concentration in the atmosphere. The main disagreement among different groups is whether the increase in CO_2 concentration is the cause of global climate change or not. The proponents of the CO_2 greenhouse theory argue for a dramatic decrease in the use of fossil fuels and rapid development of alternate forms of energy. Their opponents argue that the unprecedented warming trend is within normal climatic variations, and therefore, no action is necessary. In the United States, the Democrats generally accept global warming. Even though the scientific community has offered full support for anthropogenic global warming, the general public remains uncertain of the evidence in support of this assessment.

For the general public, global warming is remote and difficult to understand. Most people find it difficult to understand how a change in a few degrees in global temperature could have a widespread impact on Earth's climate. Most individuals say: "A few degrees? So what? If I change my thermostat a few degrees, I live fine." Furthermore, without the scientific background on the geological history of Earth's global temperature, it is difficult for a layperson to contemplate how a few degrees difference in global temperature could have a severe climatic impact. This type of incredulity makes it difficult for someone to comprehend the potential adverse conditions that could be brought about by global warming. Another important factor of the public's disbelief of global warming is the financial and economic impact of accepting the scientists' predictions of future climate change. If the general public is willing to accept the seriousness of global warming as predicted by the scientific community, they must also be willing to accept the necessity to replace fossil fuels with alternate energies, such as solar energy, biofuel, and hydrogen fuel. Many of these energy alternates are under-developed and costly, making them economically infeasible at the present time.

The evidence for global warming is based on the rise in global temperature during the past 150 years after the discovery and widespread use of fossil fuels. The release of greenhouse gases that result from the burning of fossil fuels is correlated with the rise in global temperature. However, since there is no experimental approach to test the direct effect of carbon dioxide on global temperature, the scientific evidence is only circumstantial at the present time. However, based on past geological records of Earth's climate and observations of the impact of carbon dioxide on the climates of other planets, the scientific support of the role of carbon dioxide on Earth's temperature is strong. Although the rise in global temperature is an empirical observation and cannot be refuted, the cause of this rise is where the scientific argument fails. The link between greenhouse gas emission and the rise in global temperature faces stiff challenges. Since most of the conclusions about the correlation between greenhouse gas emission and global temperature are based on climatic modeling, the opponents to this idea claim that the modeling data were not properly interpreted and that there could be alternative explanations.

The counter-arguments for global warming abound. There is a rigorous debate in the scientific community and among the general public between those who accept and those who reject global warming and climate change. Although a majority of scientists have endorsed the relationship between greenhouse gases and anthropogenic global warming, there is a small group of scientists who question the validity of the conclusion that was drawn from Earth's geological history and climatic modeling. Such debates among scientists are part of the scientific process, as all of the major scientific theories have their supporters and dissenters. For many years, for example, the big bang theory and the theory of natural selection had been debated repeatedly in the scientific community. Only as more evidence continues to accumulate will the scientific theory be either strengthened or eventually abandoned. However, the debates on most scientific theories are generally restricted to scientists due to their highly specialized nature and technical sophistication, and the scientists rarely bring the issues to the general public. However, global warming poses a very different situation for the scientists who are involved in the research, causing them to bring the issue to the general public.

III.3. Why is global warming still hotly debated?

Global warming has become a social issue with many financial, economical, political, and ethical implications. For the general public, subscription to the idea of global warming takes on a moral perspective: leaving a habitable world for future generations. However, the executives and employees of the oil industries have a tendency to distrust the arguments for the relationship between anthropogenic greenhouse gas and global temperature increase. They point out that developing public and governmental polices based on these arguments is imprudent and damaging to the well-being of the national economy. It is not that they do not care about the consequences of global warming, but they are yet to be convinced that the scientific data is sufficiently robust for drawing this type of conclusion. Since there are many credible scientists who also hold this view, the oil industries provide them funding for their research. This creates the appearance that the scientists are doing the bidding of the oil companies, making their research findings less credible. The scientists who support the evidence that there is a strong correlation between anthropogenic greenhouse gas and global temperature rise feel that they have a responsibility to inform the public and to alter both governmental policies and individual behavior to avert a disastrous global climate change.

Per capita greenhouse gas emissions by country in 2000 (including land-use change)

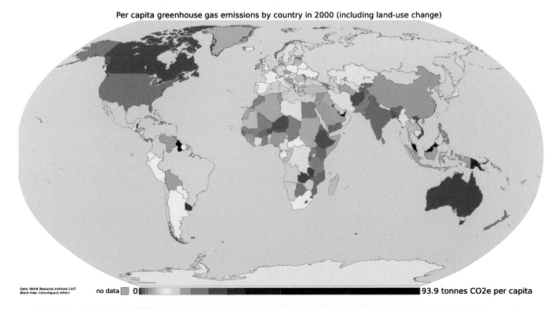

no data   0   93.9 tonnes CO2e per capita

Per capita greenhouse gas emission

By country for the year 2000.
(GNU Free Documentation License)

Public attention

A recent documentary and a movie on the issue of global warming.
(Education Fair Use)

Global warming has become the first global political issue, with many nations involved in the debate. The United States, with a population of 300 million people, is responsible for 20% of the global carbon dioxide emission in comparison to 18% in China with a population of 1.3 billion people and to 11.4% of the European Union with a population of 497 million people. On a per capita basis, the United States emits five times more carbon dioxide than China and three times more than the European Union. Fossil fuels are the bedrock of modern industrial societies, and the way of life of these countries are dependent upon this energy source. Switching the use of fossil fuels to a non-greenhouse gas-emitting energy source will pose a serious threat to the present life style and create instability in the current economic and political situations. However, the global warming issue requires worldwide dialogue and cooperation. For obvious reasons, the United States government is not embracing global warming from the political perspective, because it can cause serious disruptions to the economic well-being of its citizens. Similarly, developing countries such as China do not want to embrace the issue of global warming because of the need for fossil fuels for expanding its industrialization.

In the past several years, frequent news coverage has been devoted to global warming in response to films such as *An Inconvenient Truth* and the *11ᵗʰ Hour*, in addition to extensive television science programming on the topic. Based on worldwide surveys, the general public has shown clear concerns for the consequences of global warming and climate change. In one worldwide poll, 90% of the respondents considered climate change to be a serious problem. In another poll in the United States, 80% of the respondents perceived that global warming is probably occurring. However, in one U.S. poll, only 71% of the respondents conceded that human activity is a significant cause of climate change. When asking whether it is necessary to take major steps in the immediate future to address global warming, only 60% of respondents in a U.S. poll indicated yes. Another interesting result came from a British poll: 56% of the respondents believed scientists were still questioning climate change. Why are there such discrepancies in these survey results? The answers most likely lie in the difficulties that the general public has in understanding the scientific and social debates of global warming. Using focus groups, a Canadian study reported that the public has a poor understanding of the science behind global warming and climate change.

In the 2004 apocalyptic science-fiction film *The Day After Tomorrow*, Earth was depicted in the grip of an abrupt climate change with massive tornadoes decimating the city of Los Angeles and fierce floods and ice storms overwhelming New York City. This abrupt climate change was depicted as the result of global warming that led to the melting of the polar ice caps. According to the story, the increase in global temperature disrupted Earth's natural cycle and caused it to enter into an ice age. The film expressed the worst fears of climatologists in that irreversible global climate change could occur over several hundred years rather than over several hundred thousand years. Some climate models suggest that such abrupt changes might occur as early as the end of the 21ˢᵗ century. According to these climate models, dramatic changes in the use of fossil fuels are essential. However, models are only as good as the conditions that are used to construct the models. There will be always arguments that not all the conditions are known and consequently, the models are incorrect. It is clear that the general public is deeply concerned by climate change in their generation as well as for the future generations. However, they are not convinced that they should pay the economic and social cost until there is stronger scientific evidence that anthropogenic gases are responsible for global warming.

Chapter 26

Origins

What is the origin of life and the universe?

The Creation of Adam (1512)
Michelangelo created the most famous Fresco in the Sistine Chapel.
(Public Domain)

CHAPTER. 26 ORIGINS

Creation of the Earth

"A medieval missionary tells that he has found the point where heaven and Earth meet..." *(Public Domain)*

Some important questions that have yet to be fully answered by today's scientists concern the origins of life and the physical universe. There are thousands of creation stories around the world because every culture has its own creation story that is intertwined with its religion and philosophy. Most people living in the U.S., for example, are familiar with the Judeo-Christian creation story of Adam and Eve. However, other religions have creation stories that are vastly different. But, who tells the right story? Is there a creation story that is based on modern science? How do we know if the story that is told by modern science is the right one? To help answer these questions (and others), it is useful to understand how scientific theory is developed.

I. SCIENTIFIC THEORIES

I.1. *What is a theory?*

Theory is vital for our existence, and every person creates an elaborate set of individualized theories to guide them through daily life. Without this ability to create and utilize theory, life would be impossible. This is exemplified by those individuals who have experienced damage to their frontal lobe, the site where theory is created. These individuals can no longer function independently because their frontal lobe has lost its ability to develop theory. Almost daily, our brain forms theories, a process that is innate to our intellectual capacity. Most of us are completely unaware of this vital function of our brain. But, what is a theory? Why is forming theory important to human survival? How do we construct and use theories? One way in which to answer these questions is to use a common example: dieting. By personal experience, we know that the consuming of an excessive amount of food over a period of time leads to weight gain. Also, a loss of appetite due to sickness results in weight loss. Therefore, we can form a theory that food consumption is correlated with body weight. This theory has applicational value, and individuals can use this theory to make predictions and to direct their actions. If, for example, an individual wants to lose weight, then less food consumption would be their course of action.

Theory is also vital for a society, and the adoption of a set of theories by a society leads to the formation of culture and tradition. Some of these theories are extremely powerful and can result in a society carrying out some of the most extraordinary and unimaginable acts. One such example is the story of the sun god in the Aztec creation myth. The Aztecs and the other ancient Central American cultures had a theory that they must offer human sacrifices every 52 years for the sun to continue to shine. They believed that if they failed to appease the sun god, life would perish because the sun would disappear. Over centuries, the Aztec warriors captured prisoners to be sacrificed by the priests on the tops of pyramids. The most monumental sacrificial act took place in 1487 with the re-consecration of the Great Pyramid of Tenochtitlan. Prisoners were captured from neighboring states in Mexico and in Central America and were sacrificed on top of the pyramid. Their hearts were hacked out of their chests before they were beheaded and thrown down the pyramid. During a period of four days, as many as 80,000 prisoners were sacrificed in one of the greatest massacres in recorded history. For the Aztecs, a revengful sun god was the theory that drove them to carry out these gruesome acts.

The Aztec Sun Stone

The sun god is depicted in the middle holding a human heart in both hands. *(Creative Commons Attribution)*

Human society also functions because of social theory or ideology. Throughout history, social theories have been important in determining the economic structure and social fabric of a society. These theories are as powerful as the cultural theories that shaped many ancient societies. Communism, for example, is a social theory which states that the best society is based on a classless, stateless society and is one that follows the principles of common ownership as the means of production. Communism is a social ideology that was advanced by the 19th-century philosopher, Karl Marx. The impact of communism in the 20th century on the former Soviet Union, China, and many other countries is far reaching. As a social theory, communism created a divided world, which led to the Cold War during most of the post WW II era. Communism originated from the observations that during the Industrial Revolution, capitalism had developed a small class of powerful industrialists. In communism, it is believed that a capitalist society is inherently unjust and that the oppression of the working class has created a flawed society.

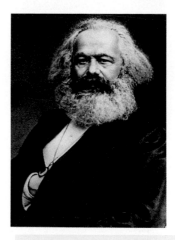

Karl Marx
The founder of communism.
(Public Domain)

Theory is important in every aspect of our lives. At the personal level, theories guide our daily actions and help us make choices. At the cultural level, theories are the foundation of traditions, although many individuals who adhere to these traditions are most likely unaware of the original theories that formed the traditions. At the societal level, theories are vital to guiding the operation of the societies. Our laws, social policies, political systems, and economic structures are based on these theories. All these theories are also based on individual intuition. In addition, these theories eventually permeate through the social organization and become adopted and modified to form the prevailing theories that guide both individual and societal actions. The sun god theory of the Aztecs led to the gruesome acts of human sacrifices, and the social theory of communism has led to incredible upheavals of societies. These theories, however, are different from the scientific theories, which have also led to unprecedented changes in human behavior. Everyone is likely to agree that the theories of the Aztec sun god or of communism are not scientific theories. What makes scientific theories different from these theories?

I.2. The making of a scientific theory

During the American Civil War, over 620,000 soldiers from the Union and Confederate armies died between 1861 and 1865. The Civil War was the deadliest war in American history. However, only 30% of the deaths were actually battlefield deaths. The remaining deaths occurred among the wounded and those in military camps behind the front lines. Many of the soldiers died in military hospitals from gangrene and other wound infections. The Civil War was the first major war in the history of the United States that used effective firearms and artillery. Because of this, many soldiers were wounded in their arms and legs by bullets and shrapnel. Since antibiotics had yet to be discovered, the military surgeons used amputation as a way to stop infections from spreading to other parts of the body. However, the surgeons did not sanitize either their instruments or their hands. To tend to large numbers of injured soldiers, surgeons moved from one patient to another with their amputation saws still tinted with blood from the previous patient. Consequently, the surgeons unwittingly spread infectious bacteria in the military hospitals. Only on rare occasions did these patients survive the infectious diseases that followed their surgery. These horrifying deaths raised many questions among the surgeons as well as among the scientists back home. It is often in these types of devastating situations that scientific theories are born.

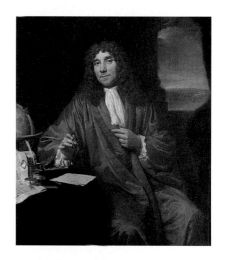

van Leeuwenhoek
First to observe bacteria. *(Public Domain)*

Just as the American Civil War experienced its first battle in 1861, a major breakthrough took place across the Atlantic Ocean in France. Louis Pasteur, a French microbiologist, was discovering the origin of microorganisms. Even though Antonie van Leeuwenhoek had discovered bacteria in 1676, there were disputes over the origin of bacteria until Louis Pasteur performed his careful and clever experiments. The prevailing idea at the time was that bacteria formed spontaneously from decaying animal flesh or from vegetation. Pasteur, however, proposed that bacteria are transmitted from organism to organism. To explain this, he proposed a new theory: the germ theory. He based this theory on observations he had while

Louis Pasteur
First to formulate the germ theory.
(Public Domain)

studying the causes of sour wine. He discovered that if the grapes were contaminated with unwanted bacteria, the wine was soured by the acid that was produced by these bacteria. He then developed a method to kill the bacteria by heating the fermentation mixture to a certain temperature (usually around 75ºC). This method is currently known as pasteurization and is used to eliminate infectious agents in milk. This discovery saved the French wine industry and made Pasteur a French national hero. Unbeknownst to all at the time, Pasteur's germ theory was to become one of the most important scientific theories of all time.

After Pasteur published his work in 1862, scientists around the world immediately recognized the significance of the germ theory. Many realized that this theory could be applied to many aspects of life from wine making to human diseases. Many scientists rushed to confirm the germ theory with their experiments. From these experiments, it was discovered that animals and humans were affected by similar infectious diseases and that bacteria were the disease-causing agents. During the next ten years, the causative bacterial agents of diphtheria, bacterial pneumonia, whooping cough, tuberculosis, bubonic plaque, gas gangrene, and leprosy were discovered by scientists around the world. This time was known as the Golden Age of Bacteriology because of the rapid progress that occurred in the field in just a few years. Immediately after the formulation of the germ theory, sterilization techniques were developed for surgical procedures to prevent the entry of bacteria into wounds. Joseph Lister in Scotland developed and promoted the idea of sterile surgery, and he successfully introduced the first antiseptic to sterilize surgical instruments and to clean wounds. His name has become forever associated with the mouthwash antiseptic, Listerine. The germ theory was also important because it provided an association between two previously unrelated events: wound infection and bacteria. If the germ theory had been known before the American Civil War, countless of lives could have been saved.

Listerine
Named after Joseph Lister. *(Public Domain)*

The development of the germ theory provides an example of two important properties of scientific theories. The first is that a scientific theory is an attempt to explain a natural phenomenon. One of the reasons why the germ theory was not discovered until nearly 200 years after the discovery of bacteria is the perception of how infectious diseases were transmitted. Until the beginning of the 19th century, infectious diseases were considered to be supernatural. In other words, they were acts of punishment that were inflicted by gods. If infectious diseases resulted from acts of supernatural beings, then humans could not possibly understand any aspect of these diseases. Therefore, it was pointless to study infectious diseases. These perceptions, however, were changed in the early 19th century, when the development of scientific methodologies suggested that it was possible to study and understand natural phenomena. Pasteur was among the first scientists to take on these challenges. The second property of a scientific theory is that it must be testable by experimentation. Natural phenomena are thought to obey the laws of nature, making them observable and understandable by anyone equipped with the appropriate instruments. These two properties give scientific theories their uniqueness in regards to the other types of theories.

Scientific theory differs from all other forms of theories, because of its predictive power. In the germ theory, for example, Pasteur and other bacteriologists predicted that for any infectious disease, infectious microorganisms could be found. It is through this predictive power that the bacteria that were causing infectious diseases were isolated and identified. The predictive power of the germ theory is also responsible for establishing the causative agents for modern diseases such as Lyme disease, AIDS,

Ebola, West Nile, and many others. The germ theory also predicted that if chemical agents were found that could kill the infectious agents, then it would be possible to develop treatments for infectious diseases. This prediction led to the search for antibiotics, and penicillin was discovered in 1928, less than 80 years after the germ theory was proposed. The germ theory, like all other scientific theories, provides an accurate description of nature that is based on careful observation, experimentation, and verification. None of the other forms of theory have these properties.

I.3. Modifications of a scientific theory

Scientific theories and other theories share one common aspect: they result from creative thoughts of the human mind. Many scientific theories have resulted from careful and extensive thought processes, but some scientific theories came from a sudden and unexpected insight. In other words, some scientific theories are obtained through logical thinking, whereas others come as a burst of inspiration. Furthermore, the first burst of insight that gives rise to a basic idea of a scientific insight could be illogical and bizarre. It is the subsequent refinement of the original idea through scientific methodology that separates the scientific theories from other forms of theories. However, the scientific methodology must fulfill certain steps, and the development of Pasteur's germ theory can be used to demonstrate these steps. Pasteur proposed that according to the germ theory, an infectious agent can be isolated from an animal that is afflicted by the disease. Furthermore, injecting this infectious agent into a healthy animal should cause the same disease. Lastly, the same infectious agent can be isolated from the infected animal. Therefore, to establish the correctness of the germ theory, these experimental steps had to be carefully performed, and the results had to confirm the prediction, otherwise the theory is invalid. Such experiments cannot be conducted to prove other types of theories, such the Aztec sun god theory.

When Pasteur first formulated the germ theory, he was unaware of the existence of viruses. Therefore, when it was discovered that viruses could transmit infectious diseases but could not be isolated using the same techniques that were used to isolate bacteria, the germ theory seemed false. It was not until several decades later and with the invention of the electron microscope that scientists isolated and described viruses. Even though the germ theory had been originally developed to explain the diseases caused by bacteria, it needed to be modified to include viruses. The germ theory faced another challenge with the discovery that some infectious agents are even simpler than viruses; they are protein molecules known as prions. One example of a disease that is caused by a prion is mad cow disease. Prions are often transmitted between individuals by the consumption of infected brain tissues. The first human example of these diseases was discovered among the natives in New Guinea who practice ritualistic cannibalism.

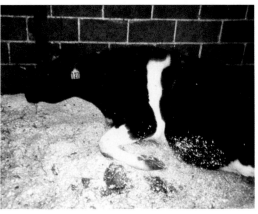

Mad cow disease
Typical symptoms of this neurological disease.
(Public Domain)

The Aztec sun god theory and other religious proclamations are different from scientific theories, because they cannot be disputed by evidence. The main reason for this is their supernatural nature. Anything that is considered supernatural is beyond human reasoning and knowledge. Furthermore, a person who believes that something is true based on a spiritual experience that only he or she had cannot have that experience verified by others. Consequently, the experience can neither be confirmed nor denied. This type of theory is considered to be nonfalsifiable; this is

What is science?

Any theory that cannot be falsified is not a scientific theory. *(Public Domain)*

the most important difference between a scientific theory and a nonscientific theory. Intelligent design is a good example of a nonfalsifiable theory, because in the premise of the theory, it states that some aspects of life are designed by an "intelligent" or supernatural being. Since it is not possible to examine the intention and logic of a supernatural being, intelligent design is similar to the Aztec sun god theory in that it cannot be falsified. Any theory that cannot be falsified is not a scientific theory.

Scientific theories form a complex network to build a grander scientific theory that provides a greater explanatory power of natural phenomena. Therefore, each individual scientific theory must be reliable, accurate, and fulfill the criteria for a scientific theory. The germ theory is an excellent example to demonstrate how various theories can be interlinked to provide a better understanding of infectious diseases. From the germ theory came the understanding of the immunological theories of host defense. These theories provide an appreciation of how the bacteria interact with the host immunological mechanisms. From this knowledge, it became possible to predict the outcome of an infectious disease. Also, because of this knowledge, Pasteur and other bacteriologists developed vaccines that stimulate the immune response to protect an individual against more deadly infections in the future. From these observations, it is clear that the germ theory has been validated partly because it is part of a bigger theoretic framework. The success of a scientific theory is through its continuing modifications and integrations with other scientific theories. Nonscientific theories do not share this important property, and they are generally limited and isolated.

II. THE ORIGIN OF THE UNIVERSE

Two of the greatest scientific theories of all time addressed the most profound and significant questions of the human mind: the origin of the universe and the origin of life. For most of human history, these questions were addressed mainly by the priests and shamans who provided mythical supernatural stories. For many years, these questions seemed to be beyond the ability of humans to fathom, because they were too grand and complex. However, through the scientific process, two grand theories on the origins of both the universe and life were constructed that were based on many smaller theories that had preceded them. These two theories linked other theories together and created a remarkable synthesis. One of these theories, the big bang theory, provides an explanation of the origin of the universe.

II.1. *The heliocentric model*

The Great Pyramids of Giza

They were built as astronomical observatories. (*Creative Commons Attribution*)

Human ingenuity can be traced back to the great architectural monuments that were built around the world dating back to the great ancient civilizations of the Egyptians, Greeks, Chinese, and Mayans. These colossal projects include the Great Pyramids of Giza and other structures, some of which were designed as astronomical observatories. Many of these ancient cultures kept meticulous records of the movements of the planets and stars. Using this information, the designers of these ancient monuments precisely orientated these buildings in relation to the rising sun. It is now clear that these monuments were built to recognize the importance of the seasonal changes in bringing life-giving water to nourish the crops. In the Nile Delta, the prediction of the annual flood water was linked to the passing of the seasons, and in the jungles of South America, the arrival of the annual rainy season was also linked to seasonal changes. The ability to accurately predict these important seasonal changes created the need for the understanding of the natural cycles of the year. In every part of the world, this knowledge became critical for the survival of the people. Those who possessed this knowledge became the holders of magical power. Therefore, for thousands of years, human ingenuity in their architecture can be traced to the need and desire to understand the physical world.

For generations, star gazing has been a popular pastime until the advent of city lights and television. City lights cause light pollution, blocking out the star lights, and television keeps people indoors. However, throughout history, the night sky has been the greatest show on Earth and has provided entertainment for countless generations. Early star gazers recognized that the night sky is not static; it undergoes constant changes. However, there are observable patterns, and these patterns undergo gradual, regular, and cyclical changes. These changes were carefully and meticulously recorded over a long period of time by different cultures. These early astronomers discovered that the night sky provides a valuable way to mark the change of seasons. In many cases, this information was used to predict seasonal changes. There are over several thousand stars that are visible to the human eye, and early astronomers had divided these stars into constellations. With their consistent, but mysterious, movements over the night sky, these stars became deities that oversaw human affairs from far above. For thousands of years, the night sky was awe-inspiring for the ancient humans, and their origin and nature were mysterious and fascinating.

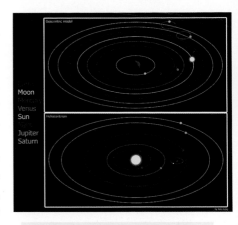

Comparision between the two models

Geocentric versus heliocentric.
(Public Domain)

For any observers on Earth, it is difficult to understand that Earth is in motion, revolving along its axis and traveling through space around the sun at a speed of 107,218 km/h. For an inhabitant on Earth, the planet is as solid as it could be. In fact, it was difficult for many to understand that the Earth is round. However, as far back as ancient Egypt, some astronomers realized that Earth is spherical, and they even calculated the circumference of Earth to be approximately 24,000 miles. This knowledge, however, was lost to Western civilization during the Dark Ages and was not rediscovered until the Renaissance. The ancient Greeks and Egyptians had perceived Earth to be the center of the universe and had established an elaborate model to explain the changing positions of the stars. Ptolemy, an ancient mathematician, geographer, astronomer, and astrologer, developed the most detailed and sophisticated model to account for the movements of all stars around Earth. He envisioned that Earth was in the center of the universe and that the sun, moon, and stars were encased in layers of crystal spheres that revolved around Earth. Despite some major discrepancies, his model was accurate enough to predict the movements of most stars. Until the 16th century, Ptolemy's model, known as the geocentric model, was well-accepted by the religious and political establishments.

The refutation of the geocentric model came from an unusual place: a Catholic cleric named Nicolaus Copernicus. His name is now synonymous with the beginning of the scientific revolution. Copernicus was a polymath of the Renaissance period and had expertise in mathematics, medicine, astronomy, theology, politics, and economics. Throughout his life, he had served under various political and religious leaders of the time. Copernicus, however, was particularly interested in the discrepancies of the geocentric model. He had also been fascinated by the minor inaccuracies in the calendar of time, which had caused difficulties in accurately setting the dates for important religious events, such as Easter. He began to examine the alternatives to the geocentric model and discovered that by placing the sun in the middle of the solar system and by having Earth orbit the sun, all of the observed discrepancies were resolved. Copernicus dared not publish his findings, knowing that it would be considered heresy by the Catholic Church, which held the doctrine that Earth was created by God to be the center of the universe. His work was eventually published a year after his death in 1543. Not surprisingly, the publication caused an immediate upheaval. His theory of the sun-centered, or heliocentric, model would be tested by Galileo, who used the newly-invented telescope and would be proven correct.

II.2. Beyond the Milky Way galaxy

Copernicus's heliocentric theory is considered one of the greatest scientific theories in human history. The heliocentric theory resolved many problems that had been previously associated with the geocentric theory. One of the first scientists

Galileo
The first experimentalist.
(Public Domain)

Edwin Hubble
He discovered the dimension of the universe. *(Public Domain)*

Mount Wilson Telescope
Used by Edwin Hubble in his observations.

who adopted the heliocentric theory was Galileo Galilei, an Italian mathematician, physicist, and astronomer. The theory provided Galileo with a framework by which to search for new information to support this model. To this end, Galileo improved the newly-invented telescope to observe the night sky. Among his first discoveries were the four moons (Io, Europa, Ganymede, and Callisto) of Jupiter. He carefully plotted the orbits of the moons and discovered that instead of orbiting Earth, they orbited Jupiter. This observation provided the first definitive proof that Earth was not the center of the universe. In addition, this observation finally refuted the geocentric theory that had lasted for over 1500 years. However, Galileo was soon in trouble with the Catholic Church because his view on the heliocentric model was considered to be heresy. He was fortunate not to have been burned at the stake for his views. Instead, he was sentenced to house arrest for the rest of his life. What happened to Galileo is an excellent example of how a prevailing scientific theory can be refuted by new evidence but not be accepted because of religious doctrine. However, ultimately reality triumphed, and within the next fifty years, the solar system was discovered and the orbits of the planets were described.

The heliocentric model of the solar system described the physical relationship between the planets and the sun. In this model, it was determined that the sun was not in the service of Earth as depicted by some ancient mythologies, such as the Aztec sun god theory. In other words, the senseless human sacrifices that had been performed by the Aztecs had been based on a flawed theory. This example gives a clear demonstration of the importance of theories, and how theories can drive humans to perform unimaginable cruelties and horrific acts. Galileo and other astronomers strove to further refine the heliocentric model by surveying the sky with their telescopes. In time, they focused on a patch of diffuse white light that was arching across the night sky and determined that this faint white light had been emitted by individual stars. After determining the relative positions of the visible stars, astronomers discovered that Earth's sun is only one of the billions of stars in the Milky Way. These types of observations have led to the recognition that Earth's sun is not in the center of the universe. Our solar system resides in a vast neighborhood of stars that make up the visible universe. Copernicus's heliocentric theory has changed our view of Earth in the physical world.

In the beginning of the 20th century, it was believed that the physical universe was composed of only the stars in the Milky Way. The number of these stars had also been estimated to be 200 to 400 billion. After many years of measuring and cataloging the stars, astronomers believed that the Milky Way constituted the total of the universe. However, this view was challenged when Edwin Hubble, an American astronomer, started to use the world's most powerful telescope in the early 1900s to observe distant stars. Using highly precise calibrations, he was surprised to discover that these distant stars were located outside the Milky Way and that they were actually collections of stars that were similar to the Milky Way. He named these star collections galaxies. Today, it is known that there are over 20 billion galaxies in the universe, each forming a huge cluster of stars.

After the discovery of galaxies, astronomers began to study how galaxies behave in relation to each other. To accomplish this, Hubble measured the light spectrum of the galaxies and discovered a phenomenon known as red shift. He found that if a light source was moving away from an observer, the color appeared red. This phenomenon is similar to the sound of a whistling train. The pitch of the whistle is lower when the train it is moving away from an observer, whereas the pitch of the whistle is higher when it is moving toward the observer. Using this principle, Hubble observed that all the light that is emitted by the galaxies appears red, suggesting that the galaxies are moving away from each other. This led him to conclude that the universe is expanding. Hubble's findings, however, were in conflict with the prevailing view that the universe is static and that it has been here for eternity. Another question arose from Hubble's observations: If the universe is expanding, then did it have a beginning? This idea has created the most exciting search in the history of astronomy: the search for the origin of the universe.

II.3. Creation of the universe

Issac Newton
He proposed a "mechanical universe." *(Public Domain)*

Despite his incredible achievements, Issac Newton once wrote: "If I have seen a little further it is by standing on the shoulders of Giants." Newton is one of the greatest scientists of all time because he understood the importance of work that had been done by scientists before him. He understood the weaknesses and strengths of these works and was able to find grand syntheses through pure intuition and insightful thinking. He then designed exceptionally clever experiments to test these syntheses. As a result of his experiments, Newton formulated his laws of motion, which provide explanations of how physical objects interact with each other. His laws describe the motion of everyday objects as well as that of planets. Also, his law of gravitation allows for the accurate prediction of falling objects under the pull of Earth's gravity, as well as for planets' orbits around the sun. Using Newton's laws of motion and gravitation, astronomers can make predictions for the precise location of any planet in its orbit. Using the same principles, space engineers have sent space crafts to explore the far corners of the solar system with pinpoint accuracy. Newton was the first scientist to demonstrate that the physical world can be described and predicted by theories, and because of this, he was among the first to demonstrate the extraordinary power of scientific theories.

Newton's laws described a predictable universe, but he did not try to uncover the force that governs the universe. Albert Einstein, a physicist, decided to explore the relationships between energy and mass in an attempt to find out how the universe works. From his study, he developed the most famous equation of all time: $E=mc^2$ (E as energy, m as mass, and c as the speed of light). This equation suggests that the mass and energy that is contained in the universe causes it to continually expand. Einstein, however, favored a static universe, and because of this, he introduced a constant in his equation, called the cosmological constant, to offset the energy that pushes the universe apart. When Einstein met Hubble during one of his visits to Mount Wilson, he admitted that the cosmological constant was the worst blunder of his scientific career. Despite this admission, however, he and most other astronomers discounted the possibility of an expanding universe in favor of a continuing and static universe. Proponents of the expanding universe had also suggested that if the universe is expanding, then there must have been a beginning. One of the opponents of the expanding universe theory derogatorily referred to it as the "big bang" theory. Interestingly, the name stuck. Up till about 1960, the two camps fought with each other, and it appeared the static theory was gaining more favor. However, neither theory had solid supportive evidence.

During the 1950s, the big bang theorists postulated that the universe began with a massive explosion from an unimaginably dense mass that was smaller than a pearl. This super-dense material exploded, forming hydrogen atoms, which eventually coalesced to form stars and then galaxies. Through elaborate calculations, one astrophysicist had postulated that large amounts of energy had been released from the original explosion and that the remnants of this energy had infiltrated the entire universe in the form of microwaves. If this energy could be detected, then the big bang theory could be proven correct. In the 1960s, two physicists, who were working for Bell Lab and who were unaware of this theory, built a large microwave receiver to study radio communication. When they turned on the microwave receiver, they received background signals regardless of where they turned their receiver. In other words, the microwave signals came from every corner of the universe. Inadvertently,

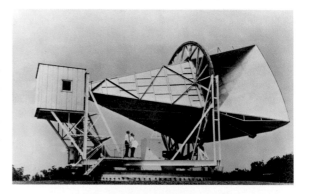

Microwave receiver
This led to the discovery of the cosmic microwave background. *(Public Domain)*

Cosmic microwave background

It is the remnant of the big bang. *(Public Domain)*

they had discovered the remnants of the big bang. Because of this observation, astronomers no longer had any doubt that the universe indeed began with a huge explosion.

After the discovery of the microwave signals, which is currently known as cosmic microwave background radiation, several probes were sent by NASA to survey the cosmic microwave background in the entire universe. From these results, researchers have reconstructed the events that occurred a billionth of a second after the explosion had occurred 13.7 billion years ago. Immediately after the initial explosion, the universe underwent a rapid expansion, known as hyperinflation. Ordinary matter, such hydrogen atoms, was formed soon after. The hydrogen atoms then coalesced to form stars, which clustered together to form galaxies, including the Milky Way galaxy. About 4.57 billion years ago, a star was formed from the remnants of an exploding supernova to become the sun of our solar system. Some of the remaining materials aggregated to form planets, including Earth.

The big bang theory is a powerful theory that was built from many other theories that had been developed over hundreds of years. It is now thought to be one of the grandest of all scientist theories. It is likely that the big bang theory will undergo refinements as more evidence becomes available. However, the basic premise of the theory is likely to remain.

III. BIOLOGICAL EVOLUTION

Another grand scientific theory is the theory that explains the enormous diversity in the biological world. This is the theory of biological evolution.

III.1. Explaining biological diversity

The Fall of Man
Adam and Eve. *(Public Domain)*

Biological diversity is around us, from our individual variations to the different biological organisms that surround us. Plants, animals, and microorganisms have carved out their special niches in the environment that they share with other living organisms. In the tropical rainforests, which have a warm and moist climate, there are many different living organisms that occupy various ecological niches of the environment. For example, there are over several thousand species of orchids living in the tropical rainforests around the world. Each of these species has evolved to occupy various ecological niches in the lush tropical environment. Furthermore, with each species of orchids using highly specialized insect pollinators, there is at least the same number of insect species. Even though the tropical rainforests occupy less than 10% of the land mass on Earth, they contain more than 60% of all species. Nevertheless, the competition in the tropical rainforests is fierce for both plants and animals, and each species has developed unique adaptations to survive. When explorers first entered the tropical rainforests, they were overwhelmed by the extraordinary diversity of life. They were amazed by the supreme adaptations that had been accomplished by the biological organisms. With over 1.5 million species of living organisms that have been cataloged and another estimated 30 million species that have yet to be identified, biological diversity is both puzzling and awe-inspiring.

During a human lifespan, life appears unchanging. This unchanging nature of life forms was confusing because it was difficult to understand how so many different types of organisms could have been created. The ancient Greeks, such as Aristotle, were the first to contemplate the origin of biological diversity from a naturalistic perspective. The Greeks proposed that living organisms can be arranged on a hierarchical "Ladder of Life" (*scala naturae*), with simple organisms occupying the lower steps, higher organisms occupying the higher steps, and humans situated at the top of the ladder. They believed that this classification formed the Great Chain of Being. In this system, humans were considered the most perfect life form. However, the Greeks never made clear the origin of this Ladder of Life. After Judeo-Christian theology gained power after the 1st century AD, the Ladder of Life was combined with the biblical account of creation. Other major religions, such as Islam, Hinduism, and Buddhism, also have similar accounts of the creation of biological diversity.

During the 19th century, the view on biological diversity began to change as a greater understanding of biological species started to emerge. The first evidence came from the breeding of domesticated animals and plants. One of the most interesting examples came from the selective breeding of certain parts of the wild mustard plant to give rise to some common vegetables: cauliflower from the flower cluster, cabbage and Brussels sprout from the lateral bud, broccoli from the flower stem, kale from the leaves, and kohlrabi from the stem. Selective breeding provided strong evidence that by selecting individual variations within a population, it was possible to dramatically change the characteristics of a biological species. Furthermore, during the 19th century, naturalists found many examples of different species that have extremely similar morphological characteristics. In contrast, it was also observed that some individuals of the same species can have very different appearances. Based on these observations, biologists began to realize that biological species are not fixed. It was possible for one species to split off and form two different species or for one species to become an entirely new species. However, it was unknown how this transformation took place.

Charles Darwin was not the first to recognize biological evolution. However, he was the first scientist to describe the theory of natural selection to explain biological evolution. Darwin had worked on his theory for nearly 20 years after his famous around the world journey on the HMS *Beagle*. Darwin was reluctant to publish his theory to explain evolution until 1858, when he received a letter from another naturalist, Alfred Russel Wallace, who had described in his letter an almost identical theory. Darwin arranged for their papers to be jointly presented at a scientific meeting that year. In 1859, Darwin published his book *On the Origin of Species*. In this book, Darwin outlined how natural selection is the driving force for evolution. This theory was able to provide a complete explanation for the creation of biological diversity, despite its exceptional simplicity. Darwin's book was quickly embraced by naturalists and biologists, and his theory of natural selection has become the bedrock of biology.

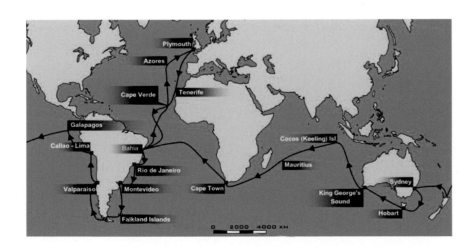

Voyage of the HMS *Beagle*
Darwin formulated his theory of natural selection on this journey.
(Public Domain)

III.2. Mechanism of evolution

Alfred Russel Wallace

The co-discoverer of the theory of natural selection. *(Public Domain)*

It is important to distinguish between the theory of natural selection and the phenomenon of evolution, which is supported by strong and unequivocal evidence. Evolution is a phenomenon in which living organisms undergo changes. These changes are evident in individual variations, extinctions of biological species, development of antibiotic resistant strains, selective breeding, and numerous other examples. Natural selection is a theory that explains the mechanism through which evolution occurs. Darwin did not discover evolution, which has been known since antiquity, but he offered an explanation of how evolution can take place. The beauty of the theory of natural selection is its simplicity. To formulate his theory, Darwin made several assumptions that were based on evidence he had collected and outlined in his book. His first assumption was that living organisms always produce more offspring than can possibly survive. His second assumption was that there are individual variations, and his third assumption was that these variations can be passed from generation to generation. His fourth assumption was that the individuals that had the variations most suitable for the environment would leave more offspring. The final conclusion was that the characteristics of a species can undergo changes in response to environmental changes. He called his theory, natural selection.

The theory of natural selection was obvious to many 19th century biologists, because most of them had already accepted the evidence that Earth is much older than the 6,000 years that was accepted by the Victorian theologians. Instead, the biologists believed Earth was at least several hundred million or even several billion years old. This was important because the theory of natural selection suggests that with the long geologic time of Earth, it is possible for simple organisms to evolve into complex organisms, even into the human species. Another implication of the theory of natural selection was that all living organisms are descendents of a common ancestor. Therefore, according to the theory of natural selection, the human and the chimp species share a common ancestor, because there are many similarities between humans and chimps. Darwin took it one step further by proposing that the cradle of the human species is in Africa, the same place where the modern chimps live. Because of these implications, the theory of natural selection raised strong protests from the religious leaders. Their main problem with the theory was that it took away the idea that humans are creations of God. Furthermore, this theory suggested that life on Earth rose naturally rather than being the result of divine creation.

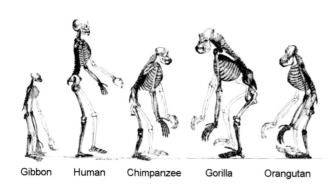

Gibbon   Human   Chimpanzee   Gorilla   Orangutan

Ape skeletons

The hominoids are descendants of a common ancestor. *(Public Domain)*

When Darwin first published his theory, the strongest evidence in support of his idea was the large degree of variations within the plants and animals that had been domesticated. Through intentional breeding, certain traits can be selected, and after only 20 generations of selective breeding, a "pure" breed results. The other evidence in support of Darwin's theory is the fossil records, which provided evidence that over millions of years, biological organisms have changed from one form to another. These records indicate that new species replaced old species in adaptation to new environmental conditions. For example, according to Darwin's theory, humans and chimpanzees must be the descendents of a common ancestor because of the morphological similarities between the two species. The evolution of these two species was the result of natural selection by the different environments that these two species had lived in. However, because of the rarity of fossil formation, fossils of the transitional forms were not easily found. It was not until the discovery of the Neanderthals and Lucy that the human transitional forms could be described. Because of the discovery of more fossils each year, the evidence for evolution has now become incontrovertible.

Furthermore, with the advances in genetics and molecular biology, the biological mechanism of natural selection is also becoming better understood.

Modern advances in biology would not have occurred without the theory of natural selection. Similarly, the enormous advances in astronomy would not have occurred without Copernicus's theory of the solar system. Both theories acted like a spotlight and shone where researchers should continue their search. Because of the theory of natural selection, the field of genetics was developed to address Darwin's assumptions that traits are passed from generation to generation. This led to the discovery of genes and eventually, to the structure of DNA. Another assumption of the theory is that there are many variations among members of a species. This led to the search for the molecular basis of variation and eventually, to the discovery of mutation as the molecular basis of biological change. From all this evidence, it has become irrefutable that natural selection is the biological mechanism by which new species are formed in response to environmental changes. Furthermore, it is now understood that the process of natural selection is not purposeful, because the process of mutation is random.

III.3. Consequences of the theory

In a 1973 essay, the Russian evolutionary biologist Theodosius Dobzhansky wrote: "Nothing in biology makes sense except in the light of evolution." This is a statement that every modern biologist agrees with, because evolution and the theory of natural selection provide a framework by which to understand biological diversity. Through evolution, biologists can build a family tree of life that provides ancestral relationships to link together all living organisms in the biological family. Plants and fungi are no longer separate from animals, because they are linked together by a common ancestor. Bacteria and viruses are also part of this large biological family. Because of natural selection, researchers have reconstructed how life evolved as far back as the formation of the first life on Earth. With the theory of natural selection, biologists can also make accurate predictions of how past environments affected the formation of new species and how future environments will affect existing species. This knowledge is vital for assessing the human impact on ecosystems, such as tropical rainforests, the coral reefs, and other natural habitats.

For centuries, when a child was born with a fatal condition such as cystic fibrosis, sickle cell disease, Tay-Sachs disease, or Down syndrome, the family had no explanation other than attributing the condition to a supernatural cause. The occurrences of these diseases appeared to be completely random and inexplicable. However, the theory of natural selection explains that these conditions are the consequences of variations that were caused by random mutations. Because of these assumptions, researchers have identified the mutations of genetic diseases, leading to the diagnosis, prevention, and treatment of genetic disorders. Another important impact of the theory of natural selection is an understanding of the development of antibiotic resistance. When a bacterial population is subjected to a selective pressure, such as the presence of an antibiotic, the theory of natural selection predicts that because of random variations, some members of the species will possess a mutation that makes them resistant to the antibiotic. These individuals survive and pass the traits to their offspring. Within a very short time period, an entire population of resistant bacteria emerges. This understanding has led to great advances in managing the use of antibiotics.

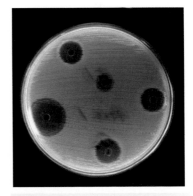

Evolution and antibiotic resistance
Natural selection and the use of antibiotics. *(Public Domain)*

The theory of natural selection has also had an immense impact on the social structure of human society. One of the most important impacts was on the understanding of human sexual differences. Throughout history, women have suffered from sexual discrimination and were considered the inferior sex because of their physical differences from men. The theory of natural selection has provided a

Human variations

Natural selection acts on the human population. *(Public Domain)*

deeper understanding of the sexual differences through the perspective of sexual selection, which is based on the difference in the biological roles of the sexes. Indisputably, these understandings have led to greater equality in many modern societies. Similarly, the theory of natural selection has provided scientific explanations for the biological differences that exist between ethnic groups in different parts of the world. Variations such as skin color, physiques, and facial features have now been shown to be the result of the environment acting through the process of natural selection. Furthermore, through the theory of natural selection, human physiology and behavior can be understood from the perspective of the hunter-gatherer world, a time when human ancestors lived in very different environments than the modern, technologically-driven societies. The theory of natural selection also predicts that the pace of cultural and technological evolution is faster than the pace of biological evolution. Therefore, the theory of natural selection already has and will continue to have a significant impact on human societies.

When Darwin was working on the theory of natural selection, he realized the impact his theory would have on the Victorian society, which had been founded on the Judeo-Christian theology of special creation. The theory of natural selection states that life occurs through random processes and not through any special creation. The existence of the human species is a natural process of evolution and did not have a purposeful design. The theory of natural selection was initially rejected by the scientific community as many new scientific theories are when they are first introduced. With increasing evidence over the past 150 years, the theory of natural selection has been repeatedly tested. It has now met all the criteria for a robust scientific theory, and, at this point, the theory of natural selection has provided the best explanation for the diversity of life on Earth. However, the theory of natural selection is still being tested and refined, and it serves as a theoretical foundation for developing applications in medicine, agriculture, and biotechnology. Together with the big bang theory, the theory of natural selection is one of the most important theories in the modern age. Both theories will continue to shape our science, technology, philosophy, and religion.

Chapter 27

Beyond

Are technologically-advanced civilizations rare in the universe?

The Eagle Nebula
Also known as the "Pillars of Creation" where star formation occurs.
(Public Domain)

CHAPTER. 27 BEYOND

There is a great deal of fascination about UFOs and aliens. In a 2002 nation-wide poll, as many as 48% of those surveyed believed that aliens have visited Earth. In the same poll, 58% thought UFOs were real spacecraft that have been sighted numerous times around the world. About 70% believed governments have intentionally covered up information regarding UFOs. However, there is no scientific evidence of the existence of any life forms other than life on Earth. From a scientific standpoint, UFOs exist only in science fiction. Nevertheless, searching for extraterrestrial life is a legitimate scientific question, and over the past 50 years, a scientific discipline, known as astrobiology, has emerged with the purpose to search for extraterrestrial life.

I. DO TECHNOLOGICALLY ADVANCED CIVILIZATIONS EXIST BEYOND EARTH?

In science fiction stories and Hollywood movies, aliens are often portrayed as intelligent beings from technologically-advanced civilizations. In the movie *ET*, a boy befriended an alien, who was stranded on Earth. Eventually, the alien made contact with its companions and was rescued by their spaceship. In another popular science fiction film, *Independence Day*, a group of hostile aliens attacks major cities on Earth with a fleet of massive spacecrafts. In both movies, the aliens were depicted to possess advanced technologies in space travel and communication. Because of the vastness of the Milk Way galaxy, some scientists have suggested that the likelihood for the existence of technologically-advanced civilizations is high. However, what is the scientific evidence for their existence?

I.1. *What are the ways to search for technologically-advanced civilizations?*

In the 1997 science fiction film *Contact*, a young astronomer uses radio telescopes to listen for signals that have been sent from other star systems in the Milky Way galaxy. The idea of listening to signals from outer space is based on radio communication. This technology is currently used in all forms of electronic communication from cell phones to televisions. In addition, radio communication is used for interplanetary communication between Earth and spacecrafts that are sent to explore other planets in the solar system. Using radio communication, astronauts can remain in constant contact with mission control. Radio communication also allows spaceships to send back pictures of distant planets. Because of its usefulness, it is likely that technologically-advanced civilizations would also use radio communication. Detecting such communication would be strong evidence for their existence.

In recent years, powerful antennae, known as radio telescopes, were invented to receive radio signals that have been generated thousands of light years away. Astronomers discovered that stars can also be observed by radio telescopes, because stars release radio waves. Many radio telescopes have been built, including the Green Bank telescope in Green Bank, West Virginia. This radio telescope is the world's largest fully steerable radio telescope and is also the world's largest land-based movable structure. The other famous radio telescope is the VLA (Very Large Array) radio telescope, which is composed of 27 independent antennae, working together as a single unit. With each antenna having a dish of 82 ft in diameter and weighing 230 tons, they make an impressive display of modern technology. Because of these powerful instruments, radio astronomy was developed and has been used to discover pulsars and radio galaxies. In recent years, radio telescopes have been used to search for radio communications of technologically-advanced civilizations.

Hollywood movies

Extraterrestrial intelligence is popular among the general public as seen in these movies. *(Educational Fair Use)*

Since radio waves are abundant in Earth's atmosphere and in outer space, it is difficult to separate terrestrial from extraterrestrial radio wave signals. However, using multiple reference radio telescopes around the world, researchers have been able to discern earthbound signals from extraterrestrial signals. Another challenge has been to magnify the signals that have originated in star systems that are light years away without increasing the background signals. However, the greatest challenge has been to identify those extraterrestrial signals that are emitted from advanced technological civilizations. To solve this, astronomers have developed computer programs that discriminate and analyze "intelligent" radio wave signals amidst the background radio waves. Recognizing what is an "intelligent" signal is difficult, because it is possible that what are intelligent signals to other civilizations might be meaningless to human listeners. Nevertheless, the search for "intelligent" signals from technologically-advanced civilizations is ongoing.

Green Bank radio telescope
World's largest fully steerable radio telescope and also the world's largest land-based movable structure. *(Public Domain)*

In the 1960s, a group of astronomers proposed to use radio telescopes to conduct a systematic search for technologically-advanced civilizations in the Milky Way galaxy. They formed the organization known as SETI (Search for Extra-Terrestrial Intelligence). Their goal is to detect radio transmissions from technologically-advanced civilizations that might exist on distant planets. SETI uses radio telescopes to monitor radio wave transmissions. To help analyze signals that are obtained from radio telescopes, SETI launched the SETI@home project. Any individual can download a software package and use their personal computer to perform signal analyses on behalf of SETI. Over 5 million computer users in more than 200 countries have signed up and have collectively contributed over 19 billion hours of computer processing time. Over the last 40 years, SETI has received both governmental and private funding. In recent years, however, almost all of SETI's funding has been provided by private contributions, including funding for the new Allen Telescope Array in California. When completed, this array is expected to consist of 350 antennae and will form the most powerful radio telescope ever built.

In the science fiction movie *Contact*, one character states that the discovery of extraterrestrial intelligence by listening for contact via radio telescopes would be the greatest possible human achievement "for the history of history". However, after more than 40 years of "listening," SETI's search for "intelligent" radio transmission from outer space remains negative. This lack of success has been puzzling for SETI researchers, because the size and age of the universe strongly suggest that many technologically- advanced civilizations must exist. The Italian physicist Enrico Fermi perceived this lack of evidence as a paradox. This paradox could be explained by three possible explanations. First, the initial assumption of the abundance of technologically-advanced intelligent civilizations is incorrect. Second, the current observations are incomplete in the search. Third, the search methodologies are flawed, and the search indicators are incorrect. This inability to find evidence for technologically-advanced civilizations in a universe filled with stars and galaxies is known as the Fermi paradox.

Very Large Array (VLA)
27 independent antennae form a single radio telescope. *(Public Domain)*

I.2. *Do technologically-advanced civilizations really exist?*

The belief of many SETI scientists that technologically-advanced civilizations must exist beyond Earth is based on the mediocrity principle. Prior to the discovery of the solar system by Copernicus in the 16th century, Earth was considered unique and humans the result of special creation. In the last 450 years, however, scientists have discovered that humans are products of evolution on a small planet in a mediocre star system in the Milky Way galaxy that has 200 billion other stars. This galaxy is among 40 billion other galaxies in the observable universe. With such large numbers of stars and planets in the universe, it seems logical that the evolution of other technologically-advanced civilizations must have occurred many times on other planets. The idea that under the right conditions, life will evolve from simple to complex and eventually emerge as a technologically-advanced civilization is known as the mediocrity principle. In fact, some scientists estimate that up to 1% of the planets with life are likely to develop intelligent life and technologically-advanced civilizations.

In early 1960s, scientists held several meetings in an attempt to estimate the number of technologically-advanced civilizations in the Milky Way galaxy. One such meeting, known as the Green Bank meeting in 1961, brought together leading astronomers, physicists, biologists, social scientists, and industry leaders to discuss the possibilities of detecting intelligent life in the Milky Way galaxy. Prior to the meeting, Frank Drake, an astronomer, formulated an equation to estimate the number of detectable technologically- advanced civilizations in the Milky Way galaxy. Even though Drake only intended to use his equation as a way to focus the discussion of the meeting, the equation became one of the most famous equations in astrobiology. It came to be known as the Drake equation, and it has been used to calculate the number of technologically-advanced civilizations in the Milky Way galaxy as well as in the universe as a whole.

Frank Drake devised his equation using a set of variables that are important in determining the number of detectable technologically-advanced civilizations. In his equation N is the number of such civilizations. The equation contains seven variables for the calculation of N.

$$N = R* \times f_p \times n_e \times f_l \times f_i \times f_c \times L$$

The first variable is $R*$, which is the average rate of star formation in the Milky Way galaxy. The current estimate is 7 stars per year. The next variable is f_p, which is the estimate of the number of stars that have planets. The current estimation is that approximately 50% of stars are likely to have planets. The third variable is n_e, which is an estimation of the average number of planets that can potentially support life. Based on the understanding of the solar system, it is likely that two planets in each star system are capable to support life. Recent studies of other star systems in the Milky Way galaxy have confirmed these numbers.

The other variables in the Drake equation are more difficult to determine, and their values can only be speculated. For example, the fourth variable in the equation is f_l, which is the fraction of the planets that can potentially support life that actually develop life. Scientists estimate that this could occur on one third (0.33) of these planets. However, because the mechanism by which life originates remains unknown, there is no way to confirm this number. Until a better understanding of the origin of life on Earth is obtained, this variable will remain undeterminable. The fifth variable is f_i, which is the fraction of planets with life that can develop intelligent life. This factor is also impossible to determine, because the condition for the evolution of intelligent life is not known. The current estimation is that 1% of life on these planets will become intelligent life.

The last two variables in the Drake equation pose the greatest challenge. The sixth variable, f_c, estimates the number of intelligent civilizations that can develop technological abilities to communicate with radio waves across interstellar space in the same manner as modern human society. Currently, scientists speculate that 1% of intelligent civilizations have developed these capabilities of interplanetary communication. The seventh variable, L, is the most interesting and reflective of the human condition. In addition to creating advanced communication technologies, humans have also developed military technologies, such as nuclear bombs, that can annihilate modern society and even the human species. L is the variable that estimates the longevity of a technologically-advanced civilization before it self destructs or is destroyed by a natural disaster. The current estimate for L is 10,000 years.

Milky Way galaxy
Earth's home galaxy, with over 200 billion stars. *(Public Domain)*

When Frank Drake first derived his equation, most of the variables were unknown or poorly understood. The value of N that was based on the early estimations ranged from 1 to 100,000 detectable technologically-advanced civilizations in the Milky Way galaxy. Currently, most scientists accept the following values for the variables.

$R* = 7/\text{year}, f_p = 0.5, n_e = 2, f_l = 0.33, f_i = 0.01, f_c = 0.01$, and $L = 10000$ years

Using these numbers, the solution of N for the Drake equation is:

$N = 7 \times 0.5 \times 2 \times 0.33 \times 0.01 \times 0.01 \times 10000 = 2.31$

Based on this calculation, amidst 200 billion stars and possibly trillions of planets, the Milky Way galaxy could host only two technologically-advanced civilizations, including the human civilization. If this is the case, then the principle of mediocrity is wrong, and the Fermi paradox is valid.

I.3. Why technologically-advanced civilizatons might be rare?

The absence of other detectable technologically-advanced civilizations has led to the idea that the evolution of such civilizations is rare. This conclusion is also based on the understanding of human evolution and the development of human technology. Because of this understanding, many scientists have suggested that serendipity is important in the development of a technologically-advanced civilization. Many have concluded that the evolution of the human species and the development of modern technology resulted from a set of unlikely events. Human intelligence did not occur until 4.6 billion years after the formation of the solar system, and it is highly likely that during this long time period, the evolutionary processes could have taken different directions leading to entirely different results. Serendipity, rather than inevitability, appears to have been important in the evolution of technologically-advanced human civilization.

There is one event in Earth's history that many scientists consider to be crucial in the evolution of modern humans. This event is the Cretaceous extinction which occurred 65 million years ago. In Earth's crust beneath the Yucatan Peninsula in Mexico, the Chicxulub crater bears the evidence of an impact of a 6-mile-wide asteroid that hit Earth 65.5 million years ago. Prior to this impact, dinosaurs were the dominant large land animals for over 150 million years. Mammals were small and inconspicuous, occupying only small ecological niches. This serendipitous event allowed mammals to occupy the vacated ecological niches and replace dinosaurs as the dominant large land animals. Without this event, the great apes would have never evolved, and humans would not have walked the Earth. Instead, the dinosaurs would still be the dominant large land animals on Earth. During the biological history of Earth, there have been many geological events that have caused episodes of mass extinction.

Asteroid 253 Mathilde
Measuring about 50 km across.
(Public Domain)

Humans probably would not have evolved from the common ancestors of the chimpanzees if the events that caused the climatic changes in Africa had not occurred. When the tropical African jungles were converted into savannas, humans needed to adapt to survive. To adapt to these environmental changes, human ancestors evolved bipedalism. In addition, the human brain enlarged to meet the needs for making simple stone tools and for developing more complex behavior and greater cooperation within social groups. Over a period of five million years, as many as 20 different human species had evolved and had become extinct. The modern human species, *Homo sapiens*, was the last to evolve in East Africa 250,000 years ago. They endured harsh environmental conditions of drought and food shortage as a result of climatic change. Because of these conditions, humans were at the brink of extinction about 120,000 years ago. Fortunately, a small band of several thousand individuals survived and gave rise to modern humanity. About 40,000 years ago, these human ancestors left Africa to populate the rest of the world, including the territories occupied by *Homo neanderthalensis*, a different species of humans. Modern humans prevailed, and the Neanderthals became extinct. However, if conditions had been different, it is highly likely that it would have been the modern humans who became extinct. Therefore, it is through a series of serendipitous circumstances that modern humans have survived.

The advancement of human technology is the result of cultural evolution, which is equally serendipitous. The beginning of human technology was marked by the construction of the Egyptian pyramids, particularly the Great Pyramid of Giza nearly 4,500 years ago. The methods of construction were only known to the ancient Egyptians, indicating that technology does not occur for every group of humans. Similarly, when Christopher Columbus and the Spaniards arrived in the Americas, they found that the native population still used stone implements, whereas Asians and Europeans had used metal-refining technologies for over several thousand years. Even today, there is wide gulf between different parts of the world in the utilization of technologies. In some isolated parts of the world, some populations still adhere to a hunter-gatherer life style. They live in the lush environment of the tropical rain forest, and their survival does not require technology. Therefore, the development of technology is not an inevitable path of human progress.

It took 4.6 billion years for technologically-advanced humans on Earth to evolve. This suggests that technologically-advanced civilizations might be rare in the Milky Way galaxy, because many stars have shorter life spans. The vast distance between stars in the Milky Way galaxy further reduces the probability for technologically-advanced civilizations to communicate with each other. Furthermore, even though the physical laws are the same throughout the universe, the communication modes that might be employed by different technologically-advanced civilizations could be incompatible. Human technology might not be able to detect the communication signals sent by other civilizations. In addition, such civilizations might also occur at very different times from that of human civilization. Consequently, many scientists conclude that the likelihood in detecting technologically-advanced civilizations is infinitely small. However, the possibilities of detecting other life forms, particularly simple life forms, in the solar system and in other star systems are considered to be high.

Egyptian pyramids
For thousands of years, they were the largest structure on Earth.
(Public Domain)

II. COULD SIMPLE LIFE FORMS EXIST BEYOND EARTH?

Even though technologically-advanced civilizations are unlikely to exist, most astrobiologists hypothesize the existence of simple life forms in the solar system and on planets of other star systems in the Milky Way galaxy. Supporting evidence for this idea includes the existence of simple organisms on Earth that can survive and thrive in conditions so extreme that no other organisms can tolerate. Even though the familiar, hospitable Earth environment is absent in the solar system, the extreme conditions that support some life forms have been found on other places in the solar system. Consequently, most astrobiologists have focused their search for extraterrestrial life in the parts of the solar system, such as Mars, Europa, and Titan, where such conditions exist. Exploration of these locations in the solar system has just begun, and the findings could change the understanding of life on Earth.

II.1. What are the extreme life forms on Earth?

Until recently, the environmental conditions that are suitable for life on Earth were thought to be limited to Earth's surface (or just below the surface). Availability of water, abundant sunlight, moderate temperature (between 10°C and 30°C), appropriate pressure (1 atmospheric pressure), appropriate atmospheric mixture (20% oxygen and other gases), and stable climatic conditions are essential for life to survive and thrive. However, researchers have discovered that some biological organisms can thrive in environments that are very different from the environment that exists on Earth's surface. One such environment includes the ocean bottom where the pressure is several thousand times higher than the atmosphere at Earth's surface. Other unusual environments include temperatures near or above 100°C, complete absence of sunlight, underneath or within thick layers of ice, and near-absence of water. These types of environments are known as extreme environments, and the organisms that thrive in them are known as extremophiles.

Most extremophiles are simple microorganisms that share many similarities with other microorganisms that live in the environment on Earth's surface. However, they have evolved special adaptive features that allow them to survive and grow in the extreme environments. Depending on their habitats, extremophiles have evolved biological molecules (proteins, nucleic acids, carbohydrates, and lipids) that allow them to sustain high pressure, low temperature, or any other unusual conditions. Despite these differences, extremophiles share the same genetic code and same biochemical processes of all other living organisms on Earth. Furthermore, studies of the extremophiles further demonstrate the powerful process of natural selection in the evolution of diverse life on Earth from a common ancestor. However, despite their hardiness, there is one condition that all extremophiles need to survive: the presence of water. In the absence of water, there is no life.

One group of extremophiles was discovered in the hot springs of Yellowstone National Park in Wyoming. Researchers identified more than fifty species of simple organisms in the hot springs at temperatures as high as 80°C. These organisms not only thrive in these temperatures, but had actually evolved to require the high temperatures to survive. These organisms are prokaryotic organisms (without cell nucleus), but they are not the same as bacteria. They were given their own classification as archaebacteria, which represents one of the three branches of life on Earth. Nearly all archaebacteria are extremophiles that live in extreme environments, which include high pressure (pizeophiles), extremely low-water environment (xerophiles), high acidity (acidophiles), high alkalinity (alkaliphiles), and low temperature (psychrophiles). During the past several decades, extremophiles were discovered in some of the most unexpected places on Earth.

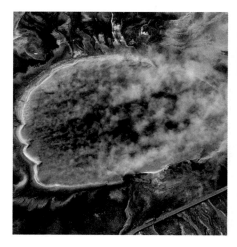

Hot spring in Yellowstone Park

The Grand Prismatic Spring is home for extremophiles. *(Public Domain)*

One of the most remarkable extremophile was discovered 8,000 ft below the surface of the ocean in the cracks along the ocean floor. The cracks allow for the formation of deep sea hydrothermal vents that are created by superheated water coming through fissures on the ocean floor. Along these hydrothermal vents are structures known as black smokers, which are chimney-like structures that are coated with archaebacteria. These archaebacteria are known as hyperthermophiles, because they thrive in a temperature of 90°C and under pressure that is 250 times that of the surface atmosphere. They obtain their energy from hydrogen sulfide that is released from the molten larva beneath the ocean floor. They derive this energy in a process known as chemosynthesis. These simple microorganisms form the basis of food chains that form a complex ecosystem. Tube worms (similar to earthworms) form a mutualistic relationship with these archaebacteria by providing them with oxygen and by receiving nutrients from them. Other complex organisms that are found in this ecosystem include clams, snails, and shrimp. All these organisms have adapted to live in this extreme environment.

The discovery of extremophiles provides evidence that life can thrive in conditions that were previously considered not possible. The deep sea hydrothermal vent ecosystems demonstrate that life can thrive in the absence of energy from the sun by utilizing energy from Earth's center. Therefore, many scientists have proposed that life on Earth might have originated from the ocean bottom rather than on the surface of the planet. This idea is further supported by the knowledge that during the first several hundred million years after its formation, Earth's surface was an inhospitable place.   Without a protective atmosphere, UV-radiation blanketed Earth's surface killing any new life that might have been formed.   Furthermore, repeated meteorite bombardments caused violent geological and climatic changes.   However, deep in the bottom of the ocean, life found a stable environment in which to develop and evolve.   Many scientists speculate that this type of unusual environment is most likely to harbor life in other parts of the solar system.

II.2. Why is Mars a likely place for life to exist?

Every since its discovery in antiquity, Mars has been considered a possible place for life other than Earth in the solar system.   Mars' orbit is located within the circumstellar habitable zone, a region that is of appropriate distance from the sun for the existence of liquid water.   Over the years, surveys of Mars' surface topography by orbiting satellites have revealed clear evidence of river canyons, lake beds, and ocean floors that were once filled with water.   Analyses of Martian rocks by the Mars Exploration rovers, Spirit and Opportunity, have provided clear evidence of the formation of sedimentary rocks in an once-aqueous environment.   However, the present day Mars is dry and arid with no sign of liquid water.   The only possible site of liquid water is beneath the Martian polar ice caps.   Recently, NASA dispatched the Phoenix Lander, which landed on Mars in 2007, to look for water under the polar ice cap.   The data that have sent back to Earth have provided some evidence for liquid water under the polar ice, raising the possibilities of the existence of archaebacteria-like organisms underneath.

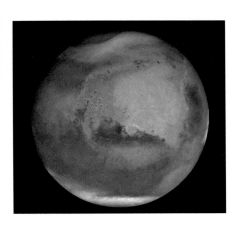

Martian polar ice caps

These ice accumulations suggest the presence of liquid water in the Martian past. *(Public Domain)*

Martian topography and sedimentary rocks suggest that liquid water was once abundant on Mars.   Scientists suggest that liquid water disappeared between 500 million years to 1 billion years after the formation of the planet.   They also propose that the loss of the Martian atmosphere was responsible for the loss of liquid water on the surface of the planet.   Similar to Earth's atmosphere, the Martian atmosphere is vital in maintaining a constant surface temperature through its greenhouse effect. Without its atmosphere, the Martian surface experiences wide temperature variations between day and night.   This phenomenon is also observed in Earth's deserts, where surface liquid water quickly evaporates.   It has been estimated that during its early planetary history, the Martian atmosphere was similar to that on Earth.   However, the current atmosphere of Mars is only 1% of the atmospheric mass of Earth.

Recent research has indicated that the solar wind was responsible for the destruction of the Martian atmosphere.   Solar wind is a stream of charged particles, primarily electrons and protons, which are emitted by the sun.   These are highly energetic subatomic particles that react with atmospheric elements, causing them to escape the Martian gravity.   On Earth, the atmosphere is protected by its magnetosphere, a strongly magnetized region that surrounds Earth and acts like a shield against the incoming solar wind.   The magnetosphere deflects the solar wind and protects the Earth's atmosphere from its damaging effects.   During the first 500 million years of its existence, Mars possessed a magnetosphere, which protected its atmosphere against the solar wind.   However, as the Martian core cooled and ceased to rotate, its magnetosphere disappeared, causing its atmosphere to be stripped away by the solar wind.

Martian landscape

Rocky terrain that is devoid of water and life. *(Public Domain)*

Mars is the most explored planet in the solar system.   Since the 1960s, over several dozen orbiters, landers, and rovers have been sent to Mars by the Soviet Union, the United States, Europe, and Japan.   During the first 30 years of Mars exploration, nearly 50% of the missions failed to achieve their objectives.   Later missions have achieved a much higher success rate because technology has improved in the past decades.   Currently, three orbiting satellites examine Mars topography and geological features from the sky, and three robotic machines from NASA (the Spirit Rover, the Opportunity rover, and the Phoenix lander), carry out observations and experiments on the ground. In addition, there will be a fourth robotic machine, known as the Mars Science Laboratory (MSL), which will be launched in September 2009 for landing on Mars in August 2010. The MSL will be much larger than the Mars rovers and the Phoenix lander. It will be about the size of an SUV. The MSL will perform chemical and physical analyses on Martian soil and on the atmosphere to look for the telltale signs of life. Positive results could lead to the sending of a manned Mars mission to conduct a more thorough search for Martian life.

Most scientists believe that life once existed on Mars due to the now abundant evidence of the presence of liquid water in its past. However, the current Martian surface is arid and dry, and without liquid water, it is a lifeless place. The only possible places for the existence of life are the subterranean lakes that are located below the polar ice caps. This possibility was considered because of the discovery of a large lake on Earth, known as Lake Vostok, which is located beneath the Antarctic ice. The heat that is generated by geological activities beneath the Earth's crust keeps the water from freezing. There is evidence that archaebacteria (psychrophiles), as well as other living organisms, survive and thrive in this environment. However, digging through the Martian polar ice caps is beyond current robotic technology

Martian rock fragments
Show characteristics of being formed in the presence of water. *(Public Domain)*

II.3. Could simple life exist elsewhere in the Solar System?

The solar system is not a hospitable place for life, because in most places liquid water cannot exist. Among the other terrestrial planets, Mercury and Venus are too hot to support liquid water. Both planets have mean temperatures that are above the boiling point of water. Even though Venus is farther away from the sun than Mercury, its mean surface temperature is 461°C (Mercury is 169°C) due to its thick carbon dioxide atmosphere and heavy clouds of sulfur dioxide. Both gases create a serious case of greenhouse warming. The gas giants, including Jupiter, Saturn, Uranus, and Neptune, are too cold to support liquid water on its surface. Jupiter's mean surface temperature is -108°C, and the mean surface temperature of the other planets decreases further because they are even further away from the sun. Neptune, the eighth and farthest planet from the sun, has a mean surface temperature of -201°C.

In 1977, a pair of unmanned spacecrafts, Voyager 1 and Voyager 2, was launched to explore Jupiter, Saturn, Uranus and Neptune. It was the first time for astronomers to closely examine these planets and their moons. In 1989, Galileo, another unmanned spacecraft, was launched to investigate Jupiter and its moons. In 1997, the unmanned spacecraft Cassini-Huygens was launched to study Saturn and its moon. These spacecrafts have vastly increased our understanding of Jupiter, Saturn, and their moons. Even though there is no sign of liquid water on Jupiter, Saturn, Uranus, and Neptune, the spacecrafts have sent back images of two of the moons of Jupiter and Saturn that contain evidence of the presence of vast amounts of liquid water on or beneath their surfaces. With the existence of liquid water on these moons, scientists speculate that life might be present. These two moons are Europa, which is a moon of Jupiter, and Titan, which is a moon of Saturn.

Europa is the 6th largest moon (next in size to Earth's moon) in the solar system and the fourth largest moon of Jupiter (one of the four moons discovered by Galileo in 1610). It has a smooth surface, an appearance which is distinctive in comparison to other moons in the solar system. Europa is covered with a thick layer of ice that lies over a liquid ocean. The thickness of the surface and the ocean is estimated to be 62 miles and is believed to contain more water than all the oceans on Earth. The energy for maintaining the liquid water comes from a process known as tidal flexing, which is the gravitational force exerted by Jupiter on the core of Europa. This generates heat energy as result of the internal geological activities of the core. Scientists speculate

Galilean moons of Jupiter
From the top, they are Io, Europa, Ganymede, and Callisto. *(Public Domain)*

that this energy also could be harnessed by archaebacteria-like organisms that are similar to those found in the hydrothermal vents on Earth's ocean floor. Currently, Europa holds the greatest promise to finding life in the solar system.

Titan is one of Saturn's moons and is the second largest moon (next to Ganymede of Jupiter) in the solar system. It is 50% larger than Earth's moon and is larger in volume than Mercury. Titan is one of the most geologically-active moons and has massive volcanic eruptions because of tidal flexing caused by Saturn's gravity. Titan is the only moon in the solar system that has a stable atmosphere consisting of mainly nitrogen and clouds of water, methane, and ethane. It also has Earth-like climates with wind, rain, and storms. On the surface, Titan has a liquid ocean of water and ammonia that is surrounded by shorelines and sand dunes. Titan's environment is very similar to the early environment of Earth and has a rich hydrocarbon atmosphere that is highly favorable for the evolution of simple life. Despite its vast distance from Earth, scientists believe that archaebacteria-like life forms might exist in this environment.

Exoplanets or extrasolar planets are planets that exist beyond the solar system and are orbiting other stars. Ever since the mid-19th century, astronomers had assumed that these planets existed but none were observed until the 1990s. With new detection technology, exoplanets have been regularly found, and over 300 exoplanets have been detected and confirmed thus far. The early exoplanets that were detected were Jupiter-like planets (massive gas giants). Because of improvements in detection technology, smaller, terrestrial Earth-like planets have now been discovered. At approximately 20 light years from Earth, scientists have recently discovered an Earth-like planet known as Gliese 581 d. This planet is considered to be the best example of a terrestrial exoplanet that orbits in an appropriate distance from a central star to harbor liquid water. As observation technology improves, more knowledge will be gained regarding exoplanets. Perhaps if human civilization endures another 10,000 years, direct human exploration of life on these planets might become a reality.

III. Is Earth unique in the development of life?

From the exploration of the solar system, scientists have recognized that environments that are capable for supporting life are uncommon in the solar system. Earth is the only planet in the solar system that has the right conditions for the evolution of life. Recent research suggests that Earth occupies a unique position in the solar system and that the solar system is ideally positioned in the Milky Way galaxy to support the development of life. Scientists call this the Goldilocks phenomenon, based on the well-known children's story *Goldilocks and the Three Bears*. Astronomers have used the Goldilocks phenomenon to describe Earth's planetary properties to be just right, not too hot, too cold, too small, or too big. Furthermore, scientists suggest that the Goldilocks phenomenon of Earth is rare in the universe and that the evolution of intelligent life is unique.

III.1. What makes the Solar System right for life?

The solar system resides in the Milky Way galaxy, which is one of the 40 billion galaxies in the observable universe. Earth's sun is one of the stars among the 200 billion stars found in the Milky Way galaxy. The galaxy was formed shortly after the formation of the universe about 13.6 billion years ago, whereas the solar system was formed much later around 4.6 billion years ago. The Milky Way galaxy is classified as a barred spiral galaxy. The spiral arms of the galaxy orbit a galactic center that has been hypothesized to be a supermassive black hole. The galactic center is the site of stellar activities and results in the birth of new stars. There are possibly four

Liquid water on Europa
The possible presence of liquid water. *(Public Domain)*

Titan
Image obtained by Cassini spacecraft showing surface details and atmosphere. *(Public Domain)*

spiral arms that stretch from the galactic center. The spiral arms are also the sites of active stellar activities because of supernova explosions from the death of stars. The remnants of the supernovae form interstellar dust clouds known as nebulae, which are the sites of new star formation. Earth's sun is a second generation star that was formed in a nebula.

To support life, it is important for a sun to be a second generation star that is located in one of the spiral arms far away from the galactic center. The stars that are formed near the galactic center are first generation stars that contain exclusively hydrogen and helium. Most of them do not have planets, and for those with planets, the planets are gas giants that many times larger than Jupiter. These first generation stars are short lived, usually living one to two billion years, and they die in supernova explosions. Heavy elements, such as carbon, oxygen, and nitrogen, are formed in supernovae. The secondary stars and their planets (such as Earth) that are formed from the nebulae of the dead stars are rich in heavy elements, creating conditions for the evolution of life. Therefore, only star systems, such as the solar system, which are formed in the nebulae of dead stars, are suitable for life.

The location and orbit of the solar system in the Milky Way galaxy were discovered to be important for the evolution of life. The solar system is in a relatively safe distance from potentially dangerous supernovae, pulsars, neutron stars, and black holes that are abundant in the galaxy. In addition, the orbit of the solar system around the galactic center is nearly circular (one orbit in every 250 million years), preventing it from coming too close to the powerful and destructive giant stars and black holes that are found in the center of the galactic core. The orbital speed of the solar system also prevents it from crossing the spiral arms, which have a high concentration of dangerous supernovae and neutron stars. The solar system has approximately the same orbital speed as the spiral arms, allowing it to stay in the same position relative to the spiral arms. These two galactic properties of the solar system keep the solar system out of harms way and provide a stable environment for the evolution of life on Earth.

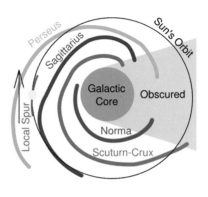

Sun's orbit

The sun orbits the galactic core in a circular orbit. *(Public Domain)*

Astronomers have discovered that for life to evolve in a star system, the central star must be of an appropriate size and composition. The sun in the solar system appears to be the right size for energy output and life-span. Large stars are short-lived, with a life-span of millions rather than billions of years before exploding as supernovae. This time period is most likely not long enough for life to evolve. Large stars also emit much higher levels of ultraviolet radiation, which is damaging to surface life forms. Smaller stars, known as red dwarfs, have a mass of less than one half that of the sun and are also unsuitable to support life. They are smaller than the sun and produce insufficient light energy to support photosynthesis as it occurs on Earth. Nearly 80% of the stars in the Milky Way galaxy are red dwarfs. The sun belongs to a class of stars known as G type stars, which are not common. Only 5% of the stars in the Milky Way galaxy are G type stars.

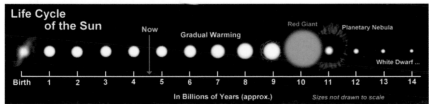

Life span of the sun

The sun is the type of star that can support life. *(Public Domain)*

The galactic habitable zone is a region of the Milky Way galaxy where the conditions are conducive for the development of life. Within the Milky Way galaxy there are many different interstellar conditions with most regions of the galaxy being unsuitable for the development of life. For life to develop, the star system must be in regions of the galaxy that contain heavy elements that are formed by supernovae. However, the star systems must also be far enough away from the galactic core and the spiral arms to avoid outbursts of radiation from supernovae and black holes. The understanding of the characteristics of the galactic habitable zone will benefit the search for exoplanets that are likely to harbor life. The search for these planets can be focused on star systems that are located in the galactic habitable zone. As technology improves, this knowledge will also be valuable in examining the existence of habitable zones in other galaxies.

III.2. *What are the conditions that make Earth suitable for life?*

The path of development from the formation of Earth to the evolution of intelligent life covers nearly the entire 4.56 billion years of Earth's history. The conditions on Earth have changed over this period and have allowed for the evolution of simple life to complex life. Many factors contributed to the development of life, but the most important factor is the orbital position of Earth in the solar system. Earth's orbit is in the ideal position for the existence of liquid water. At either one million miles closer or farther from the sun, liquid water would not exist on Earth. There is only a narrow region in the solar system where the sun's energy output is just right to maintain the conditions for liquid water. This region is known as the circumstellar habitable zone. The orbits of Venus and Mars are also in the circumstellar habitable zone, but their planetary conditions fail to support liquid water. In addition to being a medium for life to develop and thrive, liquid water is also important in modulating Earth's climate because of its capacity to absorb heat.

The Terrestrial planets
From top: Mercury, Venus, Earth, and Mars. *(Public Domain)*

The size of Earth is important for the existence of liquid water. Mars is a good example of how smaller planets have difficulties supporting liquid water. Mars once had liquid water on its surface, which was protected by an atmosphere similar to Earth's atmosphere. Mars lost its protective atmosphere when it lost its magnetosphere. Because of its much smaller size (11% of Earth's mass), Mars core cooled and stopped its rotation, leading to the disappearance of its magnetosphere. Without the protection of the magnetosphere from the solar wind, Mars' surface water disappeared with the disappearance of the atmosphere. Due to a larger mass, Earth's core remains active, producing a protective magnetosphere that exists till today. Earth's active core also creates geological activities that slowly and continuously reshape Earth's surface in the form of plate tectonic movements.

Recent studies have revealed that conditions on Earth would likely be very different if there had been no moon, and life might not have developed on Earth. The moon is the fifth largest natural satellite in the solar system, and it is extremely unusual for a planet with the size of the Earth to have such a large moon. Most moons in the solar system are captured through gravity by the host planets, but it is very unlikely for a small planet to capture a large moon. Earth's moon was formed from the impact of a Mars-sized body, known as Theia. The impact created the moon, tilted Earth's axis of rotation (creating Earth's seasons), and accelerated Earth's speed of rotation. Because it is a large satellite in relation to Earth, the moon acts as a gyroscope and stabilizes Earth's axial tilt, preventing extreme seasonal variations. Without the moon, life on Earth would not have the stable environment that has existed for billions of years and that is needed for life to evolve.

Meteor crater
Created about 50,000 years ago by a meteorite about 50 meters (160 ft) across. *(Public Domain)*

During the early history of the solar system, meteorites, asteroids, and comets continuously bombarded planets and moons, leaving large craters on their surfaces. These bombardments had devastating effects on Earth's life, and the extinction of the dinosaurs at the end of the Cretaceous period bears witness to these attacks. However, Earth appears to be protected from this bombardment despite the presence of these objects in interplanetary space. One answer to this observation is the Jupiter effect, which suggests that Jupiter protects Earth. Between Jupiter and Mars is the asteroid belt, which contains millions of asteroids. Due to its massive size (318 times as massive as Earth), the gravitational force of Jupiter maintains these object in the asteroid belt, preventing them from plunging into the inner planets. Earth is still bombarded by small meteorites regularly. However, with the gravitational protection that is provided by Jupiter, Earth has been immune from large asteroid attacks.

The presence of liquid water, active geological activities, stable climatic conditions, seasonal variations, and lack of asteroid bombardment are all contributing factors for the development and evolution of life on Earth. Living organisms were able to survive and evolve over long stable periods that often lasted millions of years. However, the evolution from simple life to complex life was abrupt and erratic. The first evidence of life appears to have existed about 3.6 billion years ago. These were simple unicellular organisms that were the direct ancestors of the archaebateria. About 3.2 billion years ago, photosynthetic microorganisms appeared on Earth's surface and started to transform the atmosphere. Over the next 2.5 billion years, these simple microorganisms gradually increased the concentration of oxygen in the atmosphere to the current 20%, leading to the evolution of complex life that began 540 million years ago. The emergence of technologically-advanced human civilizations only took place during the last 100 years. Perhaps for these reasons, many scientists have started to reconsider the principle of mediocrity.

III.3. Is Earth rare?

Proponents of the principle of mediocrity argue that Earth is an unremarkable planet orbiting an average star in a common place galaxy among billions of galaxies in the universe, which could be one of many universes that are in existence. Therefore, life should be abundant in the Milky Way galaxy as well as in the universe. Thus far, studies of the properties of Earth and of other planets in the solar system indicate that Earth might be rare and uniquely suitable for the development of life. In a book *Rare Earth: Why Complex Life is Uncommon in the Universe* (2000), two scientists (Peter Ward and Donald Brownlee) argue that the evolution of complex multicellular life on Earth was the result of a highly unlikely combination of galactic, stellar, and planetary events and circumstances. Their idea became known as the rare earth hypothesis, which is in contrast to the principle of mediocrity, a principle that has received support from prominent scientists such as Frank Drake and Carl Sagan.

The proponents of the rare earth hypothesis still support the likelihood of the abundance of simple microbial life in the Milky Way galaxy and beyond, even though they argue against the abundance of complex life. Since the basic ingredients for life (carbon, oxygen, hydrogen, and nitrogen) are everywhere in the universe, once liquid water appears, life should evolve. Many scientists predict that all life forms in the universe is likely to be carbon based, because carbon is the most abundant element that can form four chemical bonds, a property that is important in constructing complex biological molecules. Many scientists also propose that DNA could be the molecules for transmitting genetic information for living organisms beyond Earth. Furthermore, natural selection is likely to be the biological mechanism for the evolution of living organisms on other planets as well. All the present evidence indicates a common chemical basis for life in the Milky Way galaxy and beyond. The likelihood for the existence of simple extraterrestrial life is very high.

Based on the theory of natural selection, the evolution of the human species is the direct result of environmental changes. However, due to the randomness of mutations, the evolution of the human species could have proceeded in many different directions. Therefore, if the evolution of the human species was to start again, the result could be very different. Instead of intelligent humans, Earth could be populated with intelligent raccoons. The evolution of human intelligence is the result of the selection of traits that contribute to reproductive fitness. Human intelligence and creativity are likely to be by-products of the traits that intended to promote reproductive success. It is possible that many of the traits for language

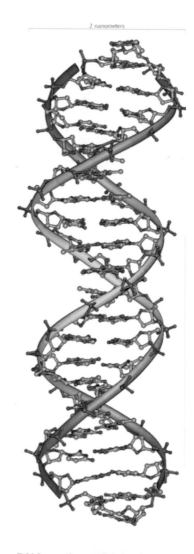

DNA as the universal molecule of life

It is likely that all life forms in the universe use DNA as genetic material. *(Public Domain)*

and creativity have no direct survival value. Furthermore, it might be fortuitous that these traits were important in the development of modern technology. The recent discovery and development of modern technology can be considered purely serendipitous and unintentional. Many scientists predict that the repetition of the same evolutionary and developmental path on a different planet with a different set of conditions is highly improbable.

Searching for extraterrestrial life has a high financial cost. To escape gravity is the primary cost of space exploration. Currently, it costs $10,000 to send 1 lb of material into orbit. A round trip for a human to the International Space Station carries a price tag of $30 million. Sending an astronaut to the moon costs $500 million and to Mars costs $10 billion. Using unmanned spacecrafts is the only financially viable means to explore the planets and moons of the solar system. However, technological breakthroughs are unpredictable, and what might seem infeasible now might become common in several decades. The cost of space travel might see dramatic reductions in the coming years. Furthermore, new telescopes are being constructed to be placed on Earth and deployed in space to discover Earth-like exoplanets in distant star systems. Despite the cost, human society continues to devote significant resources in the search for extraterrestrial life.

There are many reasons that searching for extraterrestrial life is among some of the highest priorities in modern science. Search for life beyond Earth will provide insights into the origin of life on Earth. The outcome of this search can answer questions such as whether life originated on Earth as a result of abiosynthesis or whether primitive life was brought to Earth by interstellar dust. The discovery of extraterrestrial life will rank among the most important discoveries in human history. The discovery of extraterrestrial life will also redefine human's place in the universe and will have profound impact on human culture, religion, and philosophy, leading to unprecedented social changes. This type of scientific research also represents the collective advancement of humanity in search for human's place in the universe. Furthermore, knowing whether there is life beyond Earth will meet the human need to seek the "purpose" and "meaning" of individual existence.

Space travel

High cost for escaping gravity. *(Public Domain)*

International Space Station

Human space exploration is in its infancy. *(Public Domain)*

Summary

Our current understanding of the universe is a remarkable intellectual achievement. Science has provided humans with the ability to look to the beginning of the universe 13.6 billion years ago and to the formation of Earth 4.6 billion years ago. Through technology, scientists have achieved the remarkable ability to send spacecrafts to the edge of the universe several billions miles from Earth and still be able to receive the signals that they send back. Our extraordinary technological achievements came in a time span of less than 100 years. It is difficult to predict or imagine the world 10,000 years or even 1,000 years from now. Will our descendents travel in spacecrafts at the speed of light and explore distant planets? Will they find technologically-advanced civilizations in the Milky Way galaxy? If this is the destiny of the future of the human species, it is important for governments around the world to promote shared prosperity and environmental sustainability at the global level. Otherwise, human society will end in self destruction, and none of these mysteries will ever be resolved.

Glossary

Biological and Scientific Terms

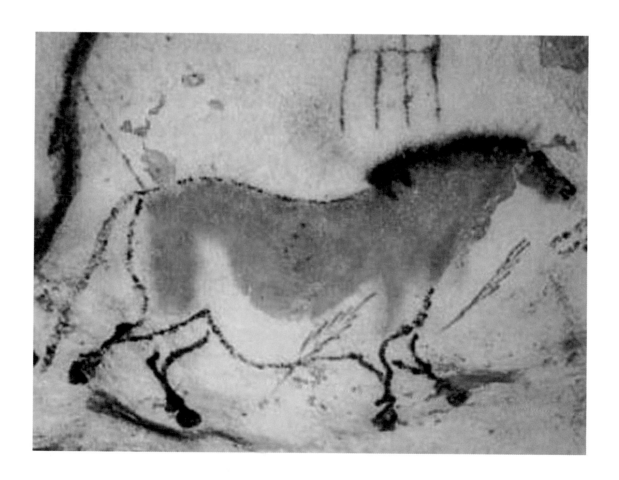

GLOSSARY

A

abiogenesis The scientific study of how life originally arose on Earth; most likely from nonliving organic matter.

abomasum The fourth stomach compartment of ruminants.

absence seizure A type of seizure that causes a brief (30 seconds or less) loss of consciousness.

acetylcholine A neurotransmitter that has several effects, including slowing the heart rate and making skeletal muscles contract.

acetylcholinesterase An enzyme that catalyzes the hydrolysis of acetylcholine.

acquired immune deficiency syndrome (AIDS) An infectious disease caused by HIV, a retrovirus.

actin A protein in muscle that interacts with myosin to cause muscle contraction.

adenine One of the nitrogenous bases in DNA and RNA that is used in storing and transporting genetic information.

aerobic respiration The process by which cells generate energy in the presence of oxygen.

allele Any of the alternate forms of a gene.

allergy A disorder of the immune system caused by abnormal sensitivities to substances in the environment.

alternative splicing The process by which a mRNA can be rearranged to form different mRNAs.

alveolus One of the millions of tiny sacs within the lungs where gas exchange occurs.

Alzheimer's disease A primary degenerative dementia.

amino acid Any one of the twenty subunits of proteins.

amoeba A single-celled organism that is a parasite of other organisms.

amphetamine A substance that has stimulating effects on the nervous system.

amygdala An almond-shaped structure in the brain that is part of the limbic system. It is primarily involved in the processing of the memory that is associated with emotional events.

amyloid A waxy substance that is formed in the brains of people with Alzheimer's disease.

anaerobic respiration The process by which cells generate energy without oxygen.

androgen A class of male hormone.

aneurysm A fluid-filled sac in the wall of an artery that can weaken the artery wall.

angiosperm A flowering plant, which forms seeds inside a protective chamber called an ovary.

anisogamy A form of sexual reproduction that involves gametes of different sizes.

anterograde amnesia A type of memory loss where new events are not transferred to long-term memory.

anther The part of the stamen of a flower that bears the pollen.

anthropocentrism The concept that humans are the central concern and that only humans can judge all things.

anthropomorphism The attribution of human characteristics to animals or to other nonhuman beings, such as objects or supernatural phenomena.

antiepileptic drug A medication that is used to treat epilepsy.

antigen A foreign substance, usually a protein, that stimulates lymphocytes to proliferate and secrete specific antibodies that bind to the foreign substance.

aphasia The loss of the ability to speak and/or to understand language.

apoptosis A form of programmed cell death in multicellular organisms.

arbovirus A large group of viruses that are spread by invertebrate animals (arthropods), most commonly blood-sucking insects.

archaebacteria A group of bacteria that can survive in environments similar to those found on early Earth, such as hot springs, sea vents that release sulfide gases, and around volcanoes.

arthritis The inflammation of joints.

asexual reproduction Reproduction that occurs without the formation of gametes. Asexual reproduction produces offspring that are genetically identical to the parents.

asteroid A small, celestial body that drifts in the solar system in orbit around the sun.

asthma An allergic reaction in the lungs, characterized by spasms in the airways.

astrobiology The study of the origin and evolution of life in the universe.

atmosphere The mixture of gases that surrounds Earth and is held in place by Earth's gravity.

atom The smallest unit of matter that retains the properties of an element.

ATP (adenosine triphosphate) A molecule that is found in all living organisms and is used as the main, immediate source of usable energy. ATP is formed by the metabolism of foodstuffs by the cell's mitochondria.

autism A brain developmental disorder that is characterized by impairments in social interactions and language.

autoimmune disease An immunological disorder in which the immune system reacts against the body's own molecules.

autosomal dominant inheritance A condition that arises from the presence of a dominant allele on an autosome. This allele is always expressed, even in the heterozygote.

autosomal recessive inheritance A condition that arises from the presence of a recessive allele on an autosome. This allele is only expressed in the homoygote.

autosome Any chromosome other than a sex chromosome.

avian influenza (bird flu) An infectious disease of wild and domestic birds that is caused by influenza viruses.

axon An extension of a nerve cell that transmits impulses outward from the cell body of a neuron.

B

bacteria Unicellular prokaryotes, which are usually surrounded by a thick cell wall. Most absorb their food from the surroundings, but some use photosynthesis.

bacteriophage A virus that infects bacterial cells.

basal ganglia A mass of grey matter that exists in the white matter close to the base of each cerebral hemisphere of the brain. The basal ganglia function to regulate the body's voluntary movements.

beta cell A type of cell in the pancreas that makes and releases insulin.

big bang theory A scientific theory that states that the universe arose from a dense, small piece of matter at about 13.7 billion years ago.

biodegradation The process by which substances are broken down by other living organisms.

biodiversity All of the variety of life; usually refers to the variety of species that make up a community.

biofilm A structured community of microorganisms that exist within a self-developed matrix which is adherent to a surface.

biomass The dry weight of organic material in an ecosystem.

biotechnology The use of living organisms (often microbes) to perform useful tasks.

bipedal An animal that has two legs or feet.

bipolar disorder A mental illness in which a person's mood alternates between extreme mania and depression, also known as manic depression.

blastocyst A mammalian embryo consisting of a hollow ball of cells that implants in the wall of the womb.

blind sight The ability to respond appropriately to visual stimuli without having the feeling of actually seeing the stimuli.

body mass index A statistical measure of the weight of a person based on their height.

bottleneck effect Genetic drift resulting from a drastic reduction in population size.

bower A shady, leafy shelter or recess that is used by certain types of birds to court mates.

brachiopod A phylum of marine animals that are sessile and two-shelled.

brainstem The lower part of the brain that is continuous with the spinal cord. It consists of the midbrain, pons, and medulla.

BRCA mutation Changes in a gene that results in breast cancer.

Broca's area The part of the brain that is involved in speech production.

bronchiole A thin breathing tube that branches from a bronchus within a lung.

bronchus One of a pair of breathing tubes that branch from the trachea into the lungs.

C

cancer Unrestrained and invasive cell growth that results in a tumor or tumors.

cancer cell A cell that divides continuously and inappropriately.

Capgras syndrome A rare disorder in which a person holds a delusional belief that a close family member has been replaced by an identical-looking imposter.

carbohydrate A class of biological molecules consisting of simple sugars (monosaccharides), two-monomer sugars (disaccharides), and other multi-unit sugars (polysaccharides).

carbon cycle The biogeochemical cycle by which carbon is exchanged between the biosphere, hydrosphere, and atmosphere of Earth.

carbon fixation The process by which carbon dioxide is converted into organic compounds by plants.

carbon monoxide A poisonous gas that is colorless, odorless, and tasteless.

carcinogen Any agent that causes cancer.

carrier An individual who is heterozygous for an inherited disorder and who does not have the symptoms of that disorder.

carrying capacity The number of individuals that an environment can maintain.

cell A basic unit of living matter that is separated from the environment by a plasma membrane.

cell body The part of a cell that contains the nucleus.

cell membrane A lipid bilayer, which is coated with proteins and which forms the outer layer of a cell.

cell wall A rigid layer surrounding a cell that is located outside of the plasma membrane. It provides support and protection and can be found in bacteria, fungi, plants, and algae.

cellulase An enzyme that breaks down cellulose.

cellulose A large polysaccharide that is composed of many glucose monomers and that provides structural support for plant cell walls.

cerebellum The part of the brain located directly behind the front part of the cerebral cortex. It consists of two hemispheres connected by a thin central region and serves to control and coordinate muscular activity and maintain balance.

cerebral cortex The wrinkled, gray outer layer of the front parts of the brain's cerebral hemispheres. Its functions include the perception of sensations, learning, reasoning, and memory.

chemosynthesis The conversion of carbon molecules and nutrients into organic molecules.

chloroplast An organelle found in plants and in other organisms capable of photosynthesis. A chloroplast absorbs sunlight and uses it to form organic food molecules.

chlorophyll The pigment in plants that captures the light energy required for photosynthesis.

cholera A infectious disease that causes extreme and often fatal diarrhea.

chromatin Long, coiled fibers of DNA with attached proteins. This is the form used by chromosomes when a eukaryotic cell is not dividing.

chromosome A threadlike, gene-carrying structure found in the nucleus of all eukaryotic cells.

cilia Thin, tail-like projections extending from the cell body.

circadian rhythm A 24-hour cycle in the biochemical, physiological, and behavioral processes of living organisms.

cloaca The terminal region of the gut in many animals including reptiles, amphibians, birds, many fish, and some invertebrates.

clone Any organism that is genetically identical to its parent.

cocaine An addictive drug that functions as a stimulant.

codon A three-nucleotide sequence in mRNA that specifies a particular amino acid or polypeptide termination signal

cold seep An area of the ocean floor where hydrogen sulfide, methane, and other hydrocarbon-rich fluid leaks out.

collagen A protein that is found in bone, skin, tendons, and cartilage.

colony collapse disorder A condition where the worker bees suddenly disappear from a honey bee colony.

coma A prolonged state of deep unconsciousness.

commensalism A relationship between two organisms where one receives benefits and the other is not particularly harmed or helped.

cone cell A cone-shaped cell, which is sensitive to light and color in the retina.

congenital adrenal hyperplasia A disease that results from a defect in the synthesis of cortisol by the adrenal glands. The defects result in an excess or in a deficient production of sex hormones, which then affects the development of the primary and secondary sex characteristics.

coral reef A structure made from the skeletons of corals.

corpus callosum A structure in the mammalian brain that connects the left and right cerebral hemispheres.

cortisol A hormone produced by the adrenal cortex that is involved in the response to stress.

Cretaceous A geologic timescale that ranges from the end of the Jurassic Period, from about 146 to 136 million years ago, to the beginning of the Paleocene epoch of the Tertiary Period, from 65 to 64 million years ago.

cross fertilization The fusion of sperm and egg that are derived from two different individuals.

crossing over The exchange of DNA segments between areas of homologous chromosomes during meiosis.

cyanobacteria A phylum of bacteria that obtain their energy through photosynthesis. These bacteria are often referred to as blue-green algae.

cystic fibrosis A genetic disease that occurs when two copies of a recessive allele is present. It is characterized by an excessive secretion of mucus.

cytokine Proteins that are extensively used in the communication between cells.

cytoplasm The area inside a cell between the plasma membrane and the nucleus.

cytosine One of the nitrogenous bases in DNA and RNA that is used in storing and transporting genetic information.

D

decomposers Organisms that consume dead organisms.

delusion A belief that is false, fanciful, or derived from a deception.

dendrite A branched extension of a nerve cell that receives electrical signals from other neurons and conducts those signals to the cell body.

deoxyribonucleic acid (DNA) The genetic material that organisms inherit from their parents.

diabetes mellitus An autoimmune disease in which body cells cannot effectively absorb glucose from the blood.

diploid cell A cell that contains two homologous sets of chromosomes.

dizygotic twin (fraternal twin) Twins that are derived from two separately fertilized eggs.

DNA fingerprinting A method of identification that compares fragments of DNA. It is also known as DNA typing.

DNA sequencing A method of determining the order of nucleotides in a segment of DNA.

dominant allele The allele that is fully expressed in the heterozygote.

dopamine A neurotransmitter that functions in many areas of the brain.

doppler effect A perceived change in the frequency of a wave as the distance between the source of the wave and the observer changes. A common example is the perception that a sound of a siren changes when the vehicle producing the siren approaches and then passes an observer.

Down syndrome A genetic disorder that results from the presence of three chromosome number 21. It has many characteristics, including specific facial features, short stature, and learning difficulties.

Drake equation The representation of an attempt to estimate the number of extraterrestrial civilizations in the Milky Way galaxy with which Earth might someday come in contact with.

drive The motivation behind actions or desires.

Duchenne muscular dystrophy A human genetic disease caused by a sex-linked recessive allele. It is characterized by progressive muscle weakening and loss of muscle tissue.

dyslexia A language learning disability that is characterized by difficulties in reading and spelling.

E

egg cell A female reproductive cell.

electroencephalogram A record of the electrical activity of the brain.

electrolysis The passing of electricity through a substance to break down the substance into its components.

electron microscope A high-powered microscope that uses beams of electrons focused by an electron lens to create a magnified image.

element A substance that cannot be broken down to other substances by ordinary chemical means.

embryo The early developmental stage of an organism that is produced from a fertilized egg.

encephalitis Brain inflammation that is usually caused by a viral infection.

endocytosis The movement of materials into the cytoplasm of a cell by membranous vesicles or vacuoles.

endorphin A substance in the brain that acts as a natural painkiller. Endorphins bind to the same cell receptors that bind to morphine.

endosymbiosis The process by which one organism lives inside the body of another organism.

energy The capacity to perform work.

enzyme A protein that serves as a biological catalyst, changing the rate of a chemical reaction without itself being changed into a different molecule in the process.

ephedrine A drug that behaves similar to epinephrine (adrenalin). It is commonly used as a nasal decongest, and its side effects include rapid heartbeat, tremor, dry mouth, and anxiety.

epigenetics A change in gene expression that occurs without a change in the corresponding DNA sequences.

epilepsy A medical disorder of the brain involving episodes of abnormal electrical discharges within the brain.

epinephrine (adrenaline) A hormone secreted by the adrenal gland during times of emotional stress or excitement. It functions to stimulate the heart, constrict small blood vessels, raise blood pressure, and elevate blood glucose levels.

episodic learning The learning that occurs during an emotional experience.

estrogen A steroid hormone secreted by the gonads. It functions to maintain the female reproductive system and to promote the development of female body features.

eukaryotic cell A type of cell that has a membrane-enclosed nucleus and other membrane-enclosed organelles. All organisms, except bacteria, are composed of eukaryotic cells.

eumelanin A protein that is found in hair and skin that causes black, yellow, and brown coloration.

eusocial A high level of social organization that includes reproductive division of labor, overlapping of the generations, and cooperative care of the young.

evolution All the changes that transform life on Earth, leading to the diversity of organisms. Evolution results from genetic change and the consequent phenotypic change in a population or species over many generations.

exon The region of DNA within a gene that is transcribed into mRNA.

exoplanet A planet not in the solar system that is orbiting a star.

extracellular matrix The part of a tissue that is not part of the cells of the tissue.

extremophile An organism that can thrive in conditions that exceed the optimal conditions for growth of most organisms.

F

Fallopian tube A pair of slender tubes through which the egg moves from the ovaries to the uterus. It is also the site of fertilization.

fat A large lipid molecule that function as an energy-storage molecule.

fertilization The union of the nucleus of a sperm cell with the nucleus of an egg cell, a process that results in the formation of a zygote.

fetus A developing human from the ninth week of gestation until birth.

fixed action pattern A complex behavior pattern that once started, cannot be changed and must run to completion.

flagellum A long, whip-like projection that functions to propel cells and organisms

fossil A preserved remnant or impression of an organism.

fragile X syndrome A cause of sex-linked mental retardation. It is characterized by maccroorchidism, hypotonia, and autism.

frontal cortex The front area of the brain. It is important in many functions, including impulse control, judgment, language, memory, problem solving, planning, and coordinating.

fungus A heterotrophic eukaryote that digests its food externally and absorbs the resulting small nutrient molecules. Common examples include the molds, mushrooms, and yeasts.

G

gamete A haploid reproductive cell (sperm or egg).

gastrula The phase of embryonic development that follows the blastula phase. During this phase, the three embryonic germ layers (endoderm, ectoderm, and mesoderm) are formed.

gene A basic unit of hereditary information consisting of a specific nucleotide sequence in DNA (or RNA).

gene cloning The production of multiple copies of a gene.

gene expression The process whereby genetic information flows from genes to proteins.

genetic code The set of rules that govern the correspondence between nucleotide triplets (codons) in mRNA and amino acids in a protein.

genetic disorder The harmful effect produced when a detrimental allele occurs in a human population.

genetic engineering The isolation, manipulation, and reintroduction of DNA into cells or organisms.

genetic recombination The production, by crossing over, of chromosomes with gene combinations that are different from those in the original chromosomes.

genetics The science of heredity.

genome A complete set of an organism's genes.

genus In classification, the taxonomic category above species.

germ theory A theory that states that microorganisms are the cause of many diseases.

gestation The state of carrying the developing young within the female reproductive tract.

global dimming A decrease in the amount of sunlight that reaches the earth.

glucagon A peptide hormone secreted by islet cells in the pancreas. It functions to raise the level of glucose in the blood.

glucose The most common sugar used by most organisms.

gonad An organ that produces reproductive cells.

greenhouse effect The warming of the atmosphere by excess carbon dioxide.

grey matter A major component of the central nervous system. It consists of nerve cell bodies, capillaries, and some nerve extensions.

guanine A nitrogenous based that is used in storing and transporting genetic information.

H

hallucination A sensory perception that is experienced in the absence of a stimulus. Hallucinations can occur in many sensory modalities including visual, auditory, olfactory, tactile, or gustatory.

haploid cell A cell containing a single set of chromosomes.

heliocentric model The theory stating that the sun is in the center of the solar system.

hemagglutinin A glycoprotein found on the surface of the influenza virus. It functions to bind the virus to a host cell.

hemoglobin An iron-containing protein in red blood cells that binds to oxygen and transports it to body tissues.

hemophilia A human genetic disease caused by a sex-linked recessive allele. It is characterized by excessive bleeding following an injury.

hermaphroditism A condition in which an individual has both female and male gonads and functions as both a male and a female in sexual reproduction by producing both sperm and eggs.

heroin An illegal drug that mimics the endorphins in function.

heterozygous The condition of having two different alleles for a given gene.

hippocampus A part of the brain that is found within the temporal lobe. It is part of the limbic system and is important in forming memory.

HIV (Human immunodeficiency virus) The retrovirus that attacks the human immune system and causes AIDS.

HLA gene Encodes for a protein that is important for the function of the immune system.

homozygous The condition of having two identical alleles for a given gene.

hormone A regulatory chemical that travels in the blood from its production site, usually an endocrine gland, to other sites, which then respond to the regulatory signal.

Huntington's disease A human genetic disease that is caused by a dominant allele. It is characterized by uncontrollable body movements and degeneration of the nervous system.

hydrogen cyanide A poison that interrupts aerobic respiration.

hydrolysis A chemical process in which molecules are broken down by water.

hyperthermia An unusually high body temperature.

hyperthermophile Organisms that can grow and reproduce at extremely hot temperatures.

hypertrichosis A medical condition where one has excessive body hair.

hypoglycemia An abnormally low level of glucose in the blood.

hypothermia An unusually low body temperature.

I

immune system The organ system that protects the body by recognizing and attacking specific kinds of pathogens and cancer cells.

implantation The attachment of the blastocyst to the wall of the uterus.

imprinting The learning that occurs only at a particular life stage.

inflammation A condition that causes redness, swelling, pain, and heat.

infrared radiation A portion of the invisible electromagnetic spectrum consisting of wavelengths the size between light and radio waves.

insectivorous An organism that has a diet consisting chiefly of insects and of similar small creatures.

insulin A protein hormone, secreted by islet cells in the pancreas, that lowers blood glucose level.

intersexual selection Males compete for mates by charming or exciting the females.

intracytoplasmic sperm injection An *in vitro* fertilization procedure in which a single sperm is injected directly into an egg.

intrasexual selection Males compete with each other for mates through display or physical contests.

intron A section of RNA that is spliced out of the mRNA before the mRNA is used for translation.

in vitro fertilization Uniting sperm and egg in a laboratory container, followed by the placement of a resulting embryo into an uterus.

isogamy A form of sexual reproduction involving gametes of the same size.

J

Junk DNA Portions of the DNA for which no function has yet been identified. About 97% of the human genome has been designated as "junk."

K

k selection Species invest more heavily in fewer offspring so that each one has a better chance of surviving.

kin selection The concept that altruism evolved because it increased the number of copies of a gene common to a genetically-related group of organisms; a hypothesis about the ultimate cause of altruism.

Klinefelter syndrome A condition that is caused by the presence of 2 X chromosomes and one Y chromosome.

L

larva An immature individual that is structurally and often ecologically very different from an adult.

life cycle The entire sequence of stages in the life of an organism.

life expectancy The longevity of an individual under a specific set of environmental conditions.

life span The length of time that a member of a species can expect to live.

limbic system An area of the brain that is involved in emotion, motivation, and memories that are associated with emotions.

lipid An organic compound consisting mainly of carbon and hydrogen atoms. Common lipids include fats, waxes, phospholipids, and steroids.

long-term potentiation An increase in the strength of a synapse that can last for days, months, or years.

lysosome A digestive organelle in eukaryotic cells that contains hydrolytic enzymes, which are used to digest food and to breakdown wastes.

M

magnetosphere A highly magnetized region that surrounds and is captured by an astronomical object such as a planet.

major histocompatibility gene Encodes for a protein that is important for the function of the immune system.

mantle The thick shell of dense rock surrounding the liquid metallic outer core and lies directly beneath the Earth's thin crust.

marsupial An animal that use a pouch on the mother's abdomen to raise the young. These animals do not use a placenta to develop their young but give birth to immature young.

meiosis In a sexually reproducing organism, the division of a single diploid nucleus into four haploid daughter nuclei. Meiosis results in haploid gametes.

melanocortin A hormone that is produced by the pituitary gland and functions to stimulate the melanocytes to produce pigment.

melanocyte A cell that produces pigment.

messenger RNA (mRNA) The type of ribonucleic acid that encodes genetic information from DNA and conveys it to ribosomes, where the information is translated into amino acid sequences.

metabolic disorder Any number of medical conditions that result from an interference with the production of energy. Many of these disorders are genetic disorders.

metabolism All of chemical changes within cells.

metamorphosis The transformation of a larva into an adult.

meteor A rock from space that has entered Earth's atmosphere.

meteoroid A rock in space, often the remnant of a comet.

meteorite A meteor that has fallen to Earth.

methamphetamine An addictive drug that causes euphoria and excitement by acting directly on the brain's reward mechanism.

microcephaly The condition of having a small head or having a small space for the brain within the skull. This condition is often associated with learning problems.

midbrain The middle part of the three main divisions of the brain.

minimally conscious state A condition that occurs after severe brain injury where a patient exhibits occasional behavior that is purposeful.

mitochondrion An organelle in eukaryotic cells where cellular respiration occurs and where ATP is made.

mitosis The division of a single nucleus into two genetically identical daughter nuclei.

mneumonics The practice of improving or helping the memory.

monogamy A relationship in which both individuals have only one sexual parter.

monozygotic twin (identical twin) This occurs when a single egg is fertilized to form one zygote which then divides into two separate embryos.

morphine An opiate painkiller that acts directly on the central nervous system.

morula An embryo at an early stage of development consisting of approximately 12-32 cells.

motor cortex The regions of the cerebral cortex that are involved in the planning, control, and execution of voluntary motor function.

Mullerian duct Paired ducts in the embryo that form parts of the sexual organs.

Mullerian inhibitory factor A glycoprotein that inhibits the development of the Mullerian ducts in a male embryo.

multicellular Organisms that consist of more than one cell and that have differentiated cells that perform specialized functions.

mutagen A chemical or physical agent that interacts with DNA and causes a mutation.

mutualism A relationship between two organisms where both receive benefits.

mutation A change in the nucleotide sequence of DNA.

myosin A muscle protein that interacts with actin to cause muscle contraction.

N

narcolepsy A neurological condition that causes excessive daytime sleepiness.

natural selection Differential success in reproduction by different phenotypes.

nebula An interstellar cloud of dust that serves to form new stars.

nematocyst Cells that have been designed to capture prey and to defend an organism. These cells are responsible for the stings of jellyfish.

neuraminidase An enzyme on the surface of the influenza virus that functions to release the virus from its host cell.

neurofibrillary tangle Protein aggregates that are found in the neurons of Alzheimer's patients.

neurotransmitter A chemical that is used by neurons to relay, amplify and modulate electrical signals.

neutron An electrically neutral particle found in the nucleus of an atom.

niche The role of organisms within their natural environment that determines their relationships with other organisms.

nitrogenous base An organic base that contains the element nitrogen.

nondisjunction The failure of chromosomal pairs to appropriately separate during meiosis.

norepinephrine A neurotransmitter that is involved in the flight or fight response. It is also involved in regulating the regions of the brain that are involved in attention and impulsivity.

nuclear fission The process in which the nucleus of an atom is split into two or more smaller nuclei.

nuclear fusion The process in which multiple nuclei are joined together to form a heavier nucleus.

nucleic acid A large molecule that is composed of nucleotide chains. Common nucleic acids include DNA and RNA.

nucleoprotein A protein that is structurally associated with a strand of DNA or RNA.

nucleosome A short length of DNA that is wrapped around proteins.

nucleosynthesis The formation of new atomic nuclei from preexisting nuclei.

nucleotide An organic monomer consisting of a five-carbon sugar bonded to a nitrogenous base and a phosphate group. Nucleotides are the building blocks of nucleic acids.

nucleus The genetic control center of a eukaryotic cell.

nucleus accumbens The brain region that is involved in reward, pleasure, and addiction.

O

occipital lobe The visual processing center of the brain.

omasum The third compartment of the stomach of a cow or other ruminant. It is located between the abomasum and the reticulum, and its inner surface has folds that break up food.

oocyte A cell in the outer layer of the ovary that gives rise to an egg cell.

operational sex ratio The ratio of sexually-competing males to sexually-receptive females.

opium A narcotic drug that is obtained from the unripe seed pods of the opium poppy.

organ A structure consisting of several tissues working together to perform specific functions.

organelle A structure with a specialized function within a cell.

organism An individual living entity, such as a bacterium, fungus, plant, or animal.

orthomyxovirus A family of RNA viruses that infect vertebrates. A common member of this family is the influenza virus.

ovary The female gonad, which produces egg cells and reproductive hormones.

oviduct The tube that conveys egg cells from the ovary during ovulation.

ovule A structure found in seed plants that develops into a seed after fertilization.

ovum An unfertilized egg or female gamete.

oxidation The loss of electrons from a substance involved in certain types of chemical reactions.

oxytocin A hormone that is involved in social recognition and bonding.

ozone layer The layer of the upper atmosphere that protects life on Earth from the harmful ultraviolet rays in sunlight.

P

paleontology The study of life in prehistoric times.

pancreas A large gland that is located near the stomach. It functions to secrete digestive enzymes into the small intestine and to secrete hormones, such as insulin and glucagon, which are involved in regulating the blood glucose level.

pandemic A widespread epidemic that affects people in many different countries.

paraphasia The loss of the ability to speak correctly. One often substitutes one word for another and inappropriately changes words and sentences.

parasitism A relationship between two organisms where one benefits and the other is harmed.

parasomnia A wide variety of sleep disorders.

Parkinson's disease A degenerative disorder of the central nervous system that impairs motor skills and speech.

parthenogenesis A form of asexual reproduction where development occurs without fertilization by a male.

patrilocal A society in which females leave their families and join the families of their mates.

pedomorphism A condition where the adults of a species retain some characteristics previously seen only in the juveniles of the species.

peptide Two or more amino acids linked by a peptide bond.

periodic table A tabular method of displaying all the chemical elements.

persistent vegetative state A permanent condition of someone who has severe brain damage, but who also has some awakefulness without any detectable awareness.

petal A modified leaf of a flowering plant. Petals are often the colorful parts of a flower that attracts insects and other pollinators.

phagocytosis A process by which a cell engulfs a particle with its cell membrane.

phantom limb The sensation that a missing or an amputated limb is still attached to the body and is normally functioning.

phenylethylamine A neurotransmitter involved in the feelings of love. It has also been found in chocolate.

phenylketonuria An autosomal recessive disorder caused by a deficiency in the enzyme phenylalanine hydroxylase.

pheomelanin A protein in skin and hair that causes pink and red coloration.

pheromone A chemical, or a set of chemicals, produced by an organism that transmits a message to other members of the same species.

phospholipid A type of lipid molecule containing phosphorus and two fatty acids. Phospholipids are an important component of biological membranes.

photosynthesis The process by which plants and some bacteria use light energy to make sugars and other organic food molecules from carbon dioxide and water.

pineal gland A gland in the brain that produces melatonin.

placenta The organ that provides nutrients and oxygen to the embryo and disposes of the embryo's metabolic wastes.

plasma membrane The thin layer of lipids and proteins that separates the cytoplasm of cells from the environment.

plate tectonics Forces within Earth that cause movements of the crust, resulting in continental drift, volcanoes, and earthquakes.

pluripotent stem cell A cell that can create all other cell types.

pneumonia An inflammation of the lungs that is caused by bacteria, viruses, or fungi.

pollen A substance produced by flowering plants that contains the male reproductive cells. It is carried to plants by wind and insects.

pollination The transfer of pollen grains to the female structure of a plant resulting in fertilization.

pollinium A cohering mass of pollen grains that is transported as a whole during pollination.

polyandry A relationship in which the female individual has multiple sexual partners at one time.

polygyny A relationship in which the male individual has multiple sexual partners at one time.

polypeptide A chain of amino acids linked by peptide bonds.

polysaccharide A carbohydrate polymer consisting of many monosaccharides (simple sugars) linked together.

population A group of interacting individuals belonging to one species and living in the same geographic area.

predation The consuming of other organisms.

predator A consumer in a biological community.

prey An organism consumed by a predator.

primary sexual characteristics The parts of the body which are involved in sexual reproduction.

progesterone A steroid hormone secreted by the ovary. It is important in maintaining the uterine lining during pregnancy.

prokaryotic cell A type of cell lacking a membrane-enclosed nucleus and other membrane-enclosed organelles.

protandry A condition where an organism begins life as a male but then changes into a female.

protein A long chain of amino acids, linked by peptide bonds.

protogyny A condition where an organisms begins life as a female but then changes into a male.

psilocin A chemical produced by some mushrooms that can cause hallucinations.

psychrophile Organisms that can grow and reproduce in extremely cold temperatures.

pulsar A rotating neutron star that emits radio waves.

Q

quadrupedal An animal with four limbs and feet which are all used for walking.

R

r selection A species that produces many offspring, many of which are unlikely to survive.

radiation Energy that is emitted in the form of particles by substances whose atoms are not stable and are spontaneously decaying.

radiometric dating A technique used to date materials that is based on the rate of decay of naturally-occurring isotopes.

receptor A molecule or site that is in a cell or on a cell surface that binds to a specific molecule.

recessive allele An allele whose effects are masked in heterozygotes by the presence of a dominant allele.

recombinant DNA A DNA molecule having genes derived from two or more sources.

recombinant DNA technology Techniques used for synthesizing recombinant DNA and transferring it into cells, where it can be replicated and expressed.

red blood cell A cell containing hemoglobin, which transports oxygen.

reproductive cloning The process of creating an identical copy of an organism for the purpose of reproduction.

reticulum The second stomach compartment of ruminants.

retina The light-sensitive membrane in the back of the eye that receives an image from the lens and sends it to the brain.

retrograde amnesia A type of memory loss where previous events cannot be recalled.

rhodopsin A light-sensitive pigment found in the rod cells of the retina.

ribonucleic acid (RNA) A type of nucleic acid consisting of nucleotide monomers with a ribose sugar and nitrogenous bases.

ribosomal RNA The type of ribonucleic acid that, together with proteins, makes up ribosomes.

ribosome A cell organelle consisting of RNA and protein organized into two subunits and functioning as the site of protein synthesis in the cytoplasm.

rod cell A rod-shaped receptor in the retina of the eye that is sensitive to dim light but not to color.

S

schizophrenia A psychiatric condition that is characterized by disorders in perception, expressions of reality, and by significant social and occupational dysfunction. People with this condition have disorganized thinking and experience delusions and hallucinations.

scolex The head of a worm that is used to attach it to the intestine of a host.

secondary sexual characteristics Traits that distinguish the sexes but that are not part of the reproductive system.

self-fertilization The fusion of a sperm and an egg that are produced by the same individual organism.

semantic learning The learning that occurs through the attachment of meaning to words.

serotonin A neurotransmitter that is involved in several functions, including the regulation of body temperature, mood, sleep, sexuality, and appetite.

sex chromosome A chromosome that determines whether an individual is male or female.

sexual dimorphism The difference in form between the different sexes of the same species.

sexual reproduction The creation of offspring by the fusion of two haploid sex cells (gametes), forming a diploid zygote.

sickle cell anemia A recessive disease caused by a single amino acid substitution in the hemoglobin molecule. Under certain conditions, the sickle cell hemoglobin molecules clump together and distort the shape of the red blood cell.

sign stimuli Simple visual clues that usually bring about a fixed action pattern response in a different organism of the same species.

somatosensory cortex The regions of the brain that respond to sensory stimuli coming from the skin and internal organs and the perception of these stimuli.

speciation A process in which two populations achieve reproductive isolation.

species All of the organisms in a population that are capable of interbreeding.

sperm A male gamete.

SRY gene The sex determining gene on the Y chromosome.

stamen The male, pollen-bearing part of a flower.

stem cells (embryonic) Cells derived from the inner cell mass of a blastocyst that retain the capacity of differentiating into any cell type.

steroid A natural or synthetic lipid substance that contains four carbon rings.

stigma The part of a flower's female reproductive organ that receives the male pollen grains.

stroke A sudden blockage or rupture of a blood vessel in the brain.

style An extension of a flower's ovary that supports the stigma.

substantia nigra The part of the midbrain that is affected in Parkinson's disease.

supernova An explosion of a large star in the later stages of stellar evolution.

synaptic cleft The area between neurons where neurotransmitters are released.

T

Tay-sachs disease A fatal genetic disorder that results in the accumulation of gangliosides in neurons.

temporal lobe The area of the brain that is located on the side of each of the cerebral hemispheres. It is involved in many functions including auditory processing, speech, high-level visual processing, and memory.

teratogen An agent that alters the normal development of a fetus.

testosterone A hormone that stimulates an embryo to develop into a male and promotes male body features.

thalamus An area of the brain that relays sensory information to the cerebral cortex.

therapeutic cloning The process of creating an identical copy of an organism for the purpose of developing a therapy for a specific condition.

thymine A nitrogenous base that is used in storing and transporting genetic information.

transcription The first stage of gene expression in which a mRNA molecule is synthesized from a sequence of DNA.

transsexualism A condition where a person identifies with the sex that is different from the one in which they were born with.

translation The synthesis of a polypeptide using the genetic information encoded in a mRNA molecule.

translocation A rearrangement of parts of nonhomologous chromosomes.

transposon A segment of DNA that can move to a new position either on the same chromosome or on another chromosome.

trimester In human development, a 3-month-long period in pregnancy.

tuberculosis An infectious disease that affects the lungs.

Turner syndrome Several chromosomal abnormalities, of which the most common is the presence of a single X chromosome.

U

unicellular An organism consisting of a single cell.

uterus A female organ where fertilized eggs become implanted.

V

vasopressin A pituitary hormone that affects pair-bonding.

virus A noncellular particle that consists of a protein coat surrounding a strand of genetic material.

vitreous humor The fluid component of the area that fills the main cavity of the eye between the lens and the retina.

W

Wernicke's area The part of the brain that is involved in the understanding of speech.

white matter A major component of the nervous system that consists of myelinated axons.

wild-type gene The typical form of a gene as it occurs in nature.

Wolffian duct A paired structure in an embryo that gives rise to certain male reproductive structures.

X

xylem The woody supportive plant tissue that carries water and other components from the roots through the stem and leaves.

XYY syndrome A hereditary condition involving the presence of an extra Y chromosome.

Z

zygote The diploid cell resulting from the fusion of male and female gametes (fertilization).

INDEX